Ecology, utilization, and management of marine fisheries

 Tsimpsean Indian trolling for chinook salmon in a yellow cedar dugout at Metlakatla in southeastern Alaska. (Photo taken in 1909 by John N. Cobb, founder [in 1919] and first dean of the Fisheries School of the University of Washington, Seattle.)

Ecology, utilization, and management of marine fisheries

George A. Rounsefell

Professor of Marine Biology, Marine Environmental Sciences
Consortium, Dauphin Island Sea Lab, Dauphin Island, Alabama;
Professor of Marine Science, University of Alabama,
Tuscaloosa and Birmingham, Alabama

WITH 186 ILLUSTRATIONS

The C. V. Mosby Company
SAINT LOUIS   1975

Library of Congress Cataloging in Publication Data

Rounsefell, George Armytage, 1905-
  Ecology, utilization, and management of marine fisheries.

  Bibliography: p.
  Includes index.
  1. Fishery management. 2. Fisheries. 3. Marine fishes. I. Title.
SH328.R68   333.9′5   74-28328
ISBN   0-8016-4203-5

CB/CB/B   9   8   7   6   5   4   3   2   1

dedicated to
Ernest Seton Thompson
great field naturalist of pioneer North America
who first urged me to study biology

✒ Preface

During the two decades following publication of the first textbook on fishery science by Rounsefell and Everhart in 1953, man has journeyed to the moon and to the bottom of the deepest ocean trenches. Tremendous advances in many fields of science and technology have produced an impressive list of text and reference books on specialized topics in fisheries and related fields, such as ichthyology, mariculture, oceanography, marine biology, fishing vessels, limnology, management practices, population dynamics, fishery law, economics, coastal management, and marsh ecology, plus a host of symposiums covering a wide range of topics.

A text suitable more than 20 years ago is no longer adequate; need for a how-to-do-it manual has vanished in view of the aforementioned specialized material. It is timely and necessary to pull together all the threads. Even in this endeavor I depart somewhat from my own thesis in that I do not include purely freshwater topics except where they add to our understanding of the marine milieu.

This is definitely not a revision. The material is new and, although given in logical sequence, is in sections to aid the presentation in any order desired by the instructor.

I stress the importance of the environment and its effect on the abundance, distribution, and life history adaptations of various commercial species. My approach is philosophical rather than pragmatic. A student can be taught absolutes, but if they change, the student is lost. Students must understand how and why certain phenomena occur; they need to be taught to think, not to slavishly follow the ideas of some professor who after years of teaching may have become dogmatic in approach.

Within recent years, man has altered the marine environment more than in all past history. Witness the atomic detonation at Amchitka, the serious discussion of a sea-level Central American canal, the planning of offshore islands for airports, power plants, and deep draught ships, and the multiplication of artificial reefs. I discuss these projects and their possible environmental effects. Some glaring examples, such as the filling in for real estate of the formerly beautiful Boca Ciega Bay and the degradation of San Francisco Bay, are self-evident. Some of the effects are more subtle, such as those accompanying changes in the freshwater input to an estuary, the dumping of urban refuse on the continental shelf, the dissecting of a bay with spoil banks, and the destruction of productive salt marshes.

I estimate the food potential of the world oceans to give proper perspective to ensuing discussions on populations and the need for management measures.

This text is not only for the fishery student and for the great host of environmental biologists in related disciplines who lack the time to peruse the plethora of material on the subject, but also for the fisherman, the fishery or coastal zone administrator, and the interested layman. To facilitate reading, a glossary of technical terms is appended.

I especially wish to gratefully acknowledge the encouragement, advice, and help of several colleagues. The late Dr. E. Carl Sensenig, while chairman of the Advisory Board of the Institute of Marine Science (now Marine Science Programs) of the University of Alabama, Tuscaloosa and Birmingham, strongly encouraged me to prepare this text and I deeply regret he could not see its completion. Dr. Robert Shipp kindly reviewed and commented on most of the text. Chapters on the physical environment were read by Dr. William Schroeder; those on invertebrates by Dr. Barry Vittor; and other chapters were read by Mr. Alexander Dragovich, Dr. George Crozier, Mr. Roland McPhearson, and Dr. David Dean. Mr. Thomas Walker prepared several of the halftones.

GEORGE A. ROUNSEFELL

❦ Contents

ix

APPENDICES

✄ Introduction

Sverdrup et al. (1942) arrogate to the term "oceanography" everything that transpires in the sea.

Oceanography embraces *all studies pertaining to the sea* and integrates the knowledge gained in the marine sciences that deal with such subjects as the ocean boundaries and bottom topography, the physics and chemistry of seawater, the types of currents, and *the many phases of marine biology** (italics mine).

More recently it has become fashionable to propose a narrow definition of "fishery science," and then to append a second definition of "fishery oceanography," or "fishery hydrography," to the older literature. Such a stance compels us also to consider any number of terms, e.g., fishery engineering, fishery law, and fishery economics, as entities separate and apart from fishery science. It also seems to imply that fishery workers have only suddenly stumbled on the notion that some of the data collected by "oceanographers" could be useful in fishery work.

I consider fishery science to embrace that aggregation of knowledge useful in wresting from the aquatic environment any living substance desired by mankind when this is accomplished in accordance with sound conservation principles.

---

*From Sverdrup, H. U., M. Johnson, and R. H. Fleming. 1942. The oceans. Prentice-Hall, Inc., New York. 1087 pp.

Fisheries is not a science in itself (neither is oceanography), but rather it is the application to the marine milieu of most of the basic sciences and some of the humanities. The primary objective is the development and utilization of the living resources of the seas on a perpetuating basis. This requires a broad understanding of both the fauna and their environment. The term "fishery" is used in its broadest sense. The seafarer finds no incongruity in a whale fishery, a sponge fishery, a pearl oyster fishery, or an abalone fishery. Because we are dealing with marine products, we can include the harvesting of algae and the artificial rearing of marine forms.

As we enter the closing decades of the 20th century, mankind has succeeded in fulfilling Malthus' prophecy. While the world waits to see whether we can avert famine through population control, man has outgrown his terrestrial home and its food-producing capabilities. He must perforce turn to the sea to buy a little more time to prove whether he can indeed forge a social structure that can endure without the Four Horsemen—Pestilence, War, Famine, and Death.

For centuries men have harvested the bounty of the sea. As long ago as the 17th and 18th centuries, with the crude gear then available, men sadly decimated many especially vulnerable species. The marine mammals suffered most. The huge Steller sea cow of the Bering Sea, discovered in 1741, was exterminated by 1768. The sea otter, once abundant from California to the Aleutians, was almost exterminated. I recall the thrill of my first sighting of sea otters playing in the kelp beds off Shuyak Island in 1925—proof that they still survived. The great herds of fur seals shrank to a few thousand. The Greenland right whale and the Atlantic gray whale disappeared. Several species of marine fishes owe their continued existence to the lack of profit in fishing for scattered individuals. Notwithstanding the plight of a few especially vulnerable species, it is only within the present century with the development of highly efficient gear that man has truly realized that there is no such thing as an inexhaustible resource.

There is little use to belabor the now hackneyed expression "maximum sustainable yield." Choosing to ignore economics, many biologists once placed on a pedestal as their ultimate goal the attainment from any species of the maximum poundage of substance. This feckless worship brought them into conflict with reality. Today it is realized that without profitable exploitation there can be no lasting fishery. The use of sufficient effort to obtain the maximum poundage rarely represents the point of maximum profit; in fact, the additional effort usually destroys any chance for profit.

Even the decision as to the amount of effort required to produce the "maximum" profit is fraught with peril. This is most obvious when two or more nations are fishing the same stock of fish. Unless their costs per pound landed are equal, they differ in the most desirable intensity of fishing. Even with equal landing costs one must also consider the relative economic benefit each nation can derive from the use they make of the raw product; a protein-hungry nation may decide it can afford to subsidize fishing indefinitely at an apparent financial loss rather than feed cereals to livestock.

It is impossible to treat in detail what is contained in thousands of volumes. I have been forced to concentrate on the major fisheries and gloss over minor groups. In

so doing I have tended to select, where available, North American species and North American fisheries. Life history examples are given for some major types of organisms.

I shall not apologize for the chapters describing the marine environment. The oceanographer may skim these, but the information contained therein is absolutely essential to a thorough understanding of fishery problems; for those lacking an adequate oceanographic background it will save days of winnowing through numerous tomes.

Fishing gear and fishing vessels are described in great detail in many recent publications. Our limited coverage acquaints the student with the principal types of fishing gear, the species each is used for, and their advantages and disadvantages insofar as they affect conservation measures. My treatment of fishing gear also stresses the effect of the behavior of the species sought in determining the most efficient methods of harvesting.

The impact of the outboard motor, farm ponds, and reservoir construction turned fishing into a hobby for millions. As early as 1949 over 1,100,000 farm ponds covered some 530,000 acres. Since then the construction of many additional multipurpose reservoirs has caused further snowballing of angling enthusiasm and participation. As the majority of our largest cities are within easy driving distance of the seacoast (or the Great Lakes), much of this aroused interest has turned toward marine sport fishing. In many localities the provision of boats, lodging, tackle, bait, and guides is a major commercial enterprise, often outstripping what is normally referred to as commercial fishing. This sport fishery actually takes a very significant portion of the total catch of certain species. This includes those nonschooling species frequenting the surf, rocky shores, or shoal estuaries, e.g., the surfperches, the striped bass, the tautog, and many of the weakfishes. Also of major importance are such seldom-eaten fishes as the tarpon, sharks, and billfishes. Salmon are the featured sport fish of the Northwest.

The deterioration of water quality in our

coastal embayments threatens the very existence of some fisheries and sharply curtails others. Although the techniques for studying pollution and its effects cannot be detailed in a text of this scope, I have endeavored to explain how some forms of pollution affect marine resources and some of the problems that arise. Within the last decade the problems of maintaining a habitat suitable for healthy and resilient populations have become acute as the multiple use of coastal waters and attendant engineering projects have increased sharply. The threatened loss of nursery areas for juvenile forms and of adult habitats for sessile forms is a source of great apprehension. Another long-standing man-made problem in habitat alteration is the blocking of anadromous species from free access to the areas required for spawning, for the growth of juveniles, and for the return unharmed of the young to the sea.

A small beginning has been made toward increasing the yield of the seas by methods of agriculture centuries old. One such measure is fertilization of the waters, either through induced upwelling (still in a strictly experimental stage) or through the addition of organic or inorganic fertilizers to enclosed or semienclosed bodies of water. Another method of proved success has been the use of the entire water column for the rearing of mussels, oysters, and other mollusks. Perhaps the most promising trend for the future is the increasing emphasis on the development of efficient genetic strains of organisms.

Whether the world production of marine products will ever reach its potential depends very largely on whether the agencies that manage the fisheries are permitted to exercise their best judgment based on carefully gathered facts. In international waters adequate conservation measures are seldom promulgated and less often enforced. A common property resource is difficult enough for one agency to administer but next to impossible when several countries are involved. The most outrageous example was the stupid and selfish destruction of the Antarctic whale herds despite the existence of the International Whaling Commission.

HISTORICAL BACKGROUND

The recorded history of fishery exploitation extends back until it is lost in legend and shrouded by the mists of time. I am rather certain that the first species to be utilized by man in most areas were the mollusks, the anadromous species, and those schooling species that followed the shore where they could be trapped by the ebbing tide. Erhard Rostlund (1952) showed that the North American aborigines captured and consumed surprisingly large quantities of fish.

A favorite method for capture of the anadromous species was the use of a weir across a stream. Remnants of such a weir for taking Atlantic salmon and perhaps alewives were found in the Charles River in the heart of Boston. Natives of the Northwest used the same technique, which was continued by the Russians. Moser (1899) shows numerous pictures of these "zapors," which were made by felling a large spruce or hemlock across a stream against which stakes were leaned to obstruct the salmon, which, in their attempt to pass the barrier, were led upstream through long tunnels of branches into fish-tight enclosures. I have examined such barriers at Karta Bay in southeastern Alaska. So dependent were the natives of the interior of British Columbia on dried salmon for their winter food supply that an unusually poor run of sockeye salmon in the Fraser River meant starvation in scores of native villages (McLean, 1932). Natives dwelling near the coast were more fortunate. Not only were there more species of salmon ascending the smaller streams, but they also had runs of smelt, lampreys, alewives, and shad. These latter species were usually taken with dip nets of webbing cleverly woven from the inner bark of cedar trees, from rawhide, or from the stems of certain plants.

The Indians of the Northwest rendered oil from the spring-running eulachon, a true smelt, and stored the rich oil (solid at ordinary temperatures) in floats of giant kelp before the arrival of the ubiquitous 5-gallon kerosene cans. Alexander Mac-Kenzie discovered the coast of British Columbia in 1793 by descending the Bella Coola River along the trade route for eulachon oil between the coastal and interior natives (Hart and McHugh, 1944).

Coastal natives in some areas depended heavily on oysters, clams, abalones, and mussels. That the natives gathered in large numbers to consume these delicacies is attested to by the numerous shell mounds of prehistoric vintage adjacent to oyster beds and clam flats. These shell mounds dot the salt marshes of the northern Gulf coast, conspicuous by their giant oak trees apparently thriving in the calcareous soil of the mounds, which are set apart from the acid soils of the surrounding pine barrens. Shell mounds and midden heaps were not confined to the Gulf. I recall delving into one I discovered on Ismailof Island in 1926. It is adjacent to Halibut Cove Lagoon in Cook Inlet, an annual wintering area for hibernating schools of Pacific herring. Bone spear points suggested the natives also took seals and perhaps the white beluga whales I saw pursuing the herring, even following them through a narrow channel into the lagoon itself.

The natives also captured strictly marine fishes. Thus the Northwest Indians with their large seagoing dugouts of yellow cedar took halibut on wood-and-bone hooks. They devised the reef net (described in Chapter 7) for taking salmon in salt water and the unique herring rake. They also placed boughs in the water to collect the adherent ova of spawning herring. This gourmet item is now the basis of a profitable fishery in Alaska.

There is some dispute concerning who first exploited the Grand Banks. De Loture (1949) mentions Basque, Breton, Norman, and Portuguese vessels; there may have been others. Before the Pilgrims landed in New England, these fishermen from western Europe were salting and drying codfish along the coast, chiefly in easily defended positions such as Monhegan and Saint-Pierre Islands or headlands along the Newfoundland coast.

In the early centuries of the exploitation of these new fisheries by Europeans there was little effort toward conservation. While the American colonists were destroying the Atlantic salmon runs and hunting the gray and right whales to extinction in the Atlantic, the Russians were doing the same to the Steller sea cow and the sea otter.

Need for the intelligent development and utilization of marine fisheries occurred long before the requisite knowledge was available. So-called fishery science is not one of the basic disciplines but rather the practical application of the sciences to solving fishery problems. These numerous roots cause some difficulty and confusion in tracing the early development of this applied science. During the early development we must wander farther afield than in later years when the picture begins to focus.

Since the first roots were in marine biology, perhaps we should start with Edward Forbes (pronounced "4 B's"), the Manxman who dredged with crude hemp ropes in the Aegean Sea about 1840. As marine life continued to become scarcer with increasing depth, he reached the interesting conclusion that life is nonexistent below 300 fm.

The first great milestone toward understanding the sea was the *Challenger* Expedition. The *Challenger* was a steam vessel manned by a Navy captain and crew and a staff of scientists, including zoologists, chemists, and geologists. The vessel spent 3 years at sea, returning in 1876 after a journey of nearly 70,000 miles, taking soundings and dredge and net collections at hundreds of stations. The results of the expedition were published continuously until completed in 1895 in 40 quarto volumes with hand-colored plates. The editor, Sir John Murray, interpreted the new and important discoveries on bottom sediments. Man had finally glimpsed the enormity and complexity of the seas.

The U. S. Fish Commission was formed in 1870 under the able direction of Spencer

F. Baird, who had been secretary of the Smithsonian Institution. Intrigued by the fact that salmon and trout could be successfully reared from the fertilized egg, their first efforts stressed fish culture. When their first steam vessel, the *Fish Hawk,* was commissioned, it was outfitted as a floating marine fish hatchery. Three generations later we fully appreciate the futility of this effort. With all our modern technology, many of the problems they blithely ignored are still not satisfactorily solved.

During this period knowledge was slowly accumulating. The ability to mark, release, and later recapture individual fish to determine salient points in their life histories was first demonstrated by Charles G. Atkins on Atlantic salmon kelts at the East Orland (Craig Brook) hatchery of the U. S. Fish Commission from 1872 to 1874.

The first real attempt to relate abundance to fishing effort was made by T. Wemyss Fulton of the Fisheries Board for Scotland, who, in the 1890's, compared the catches of steam trawlers to actual fishing effort in terms of hours of steaming. Freidrich Heincke of Germany in 1898 published a racial study of European herring populations utilizing meristic, numeric, and morphometric characteristics. Considering the stage of development of statistical methods, it was a notable effort. During this period C. G. J. Petersen worked on the ecology of plaice and developed the Petersen disk tag, which was superior to any fish tags then in existence.

The International Council for the Study of the Sea, formed in 1901 to promote research in marine sciences, was joined by practically every European nation bordering the Atlantic. Although very successful in promoting research in fisheries and oceanography, it has failed rather miserably in promoting cooperation in the adoption of meaningful conservation measures.

In the early 1900's William Garstang in England decided from studies of the growth of plaice living in different population densities that there was no need to worry about the depletion of fish populations because increased growth rates would compensate for any diminution in numbers. This attractive theory has failed to stand the test of time.

Perhaps the beginnings of modern fishery science can be dated from 1914 when Johan Hjort of Norway published *Fluctuations in the Great Fisheries of Northern Europe,* a truly monumental work. Einar Lea, his fellow countryman, meanwhile revealed much of the life history of the Atlanto-Scandian herring populations, especially the effect on the fisheries of great fluctuations in population size caused by dominant year classes.

In the United States during this time fishery work was dominated by the students of David Starr Jordan, first president of Stanford University. The first volume of *The Fishes of North and Middle America* by Jordan and his associate Barton Warren Evermann came out in 1898. This huge four-volume monograph was the greatest ichthyologic work of its time. Many of Jordan's students deviated from pure ichthyology into the fields of life history, ecology, and population structure and dynamics, laying the necessary groundwork for future progress.

Based chiefly on the studies of Charles Henry Gilbert and Willis H. Rich in the United States and Richard Rathbun and Wilbert A. Clemens in Canada, Jordan, together with Edward E. Prince of Canada, started the movement in 1918 that finally culminated in the now famous treaty to restore the salmon populations of the Fraser River. He was retired when I met him in the 1920's, but his followers already dominated fishery work in the West. Norman Bishop Scofield, one of Jordan's students, guided fishery work in California throughout the formative years when it became the foremost state in the research and development of marine fisheries. Among other students of Jordan who aided in this work I should mention John Otterbein Snyder who published extensively on the life histories of the salmons and trouts of the Pacific coast; Edwin C. Starks who worked on the osteology of fishes; and Frank W. Weymouth who, with his students Harvey C. McMillin and Seton H. Thompson, made notable contributions to the knowledge of the effect of environmental factors on the growth of bivalves. In 1930 Weymouth, with his student Milton J. Lindner, started the intensive shrimp investigations in the Gulf of Mexico that are culminating in a great advance in mariculture.

Another student of Jordan, Will F. Thompson, studied the declining abundance of halibut in British Columbia before directing the fishery research laboratory in California in the early 1920's. In 1925 he assumed direction of the newly formed International Fisheries Commission (now the International Halibut Commission) that had been vigorously sponsored by John Pease Babcock of British Columbia and Miller Freeman of Washington. After a few years of research the Commission espoused the quota system of regulation to restore the abundance of halibut. Although outwardly successful, this method caused many economic difficulties. The basic interpretation of the research on halibut has been strongly attacked by Martin Burkenroad, and the concepts require reexamination.

Publicity concerning the restoration of the abundance of halibut stocks assured Thompson's selection in the 1930's as the first director of the new International Pacific Salmon Fisheries Commission to implement the treaty first pursued by Jordan and Prince in 1918. His chief achievement in this endeavor was his promotion of the design and construction of fishways to permit sockeye salmon to ascend the Fraser River through Hell's Gate Canyon at all stages of river flow. Later he directed the Fisheries Research Institute of the University of Washington, an institute financed largely by the salmon packers to gather scientific facts to counter the conservation regulations of the Department of the Interior prior to Alaska's achievement of statehood. Unfortunately the Institute has been very remiss in the publication of their scientific results—the same sin

of which they had accused the Department of the Interior. Thompson's controversial career produced strong adherents but many dissenters, and the resulting breach is as yet unhealed.

Before leaving the salmon investigations I must mention Wilbert A. Clemens who converted the small summer biological station at Departure Bay, British Columbia, into one of the world's most modern fishery research stations. From 1925 into the 1930's, R. Earle Foerster and William E. Ricker at Cultus Lake in the Fraser River drainage laid the basis for an understanding of the freshwater life history of the sockeye salmon. Similar basic studies were being made on pink salmon by Frederick A. Davidson at Olive Cove and Little Port Walter in southeastern Alaska and by Andrew L. Pritchard at McClinton Creek in the Queen Charlotte Islands of British Columbia.

In the eastern United States during the earlier years of this century there was on the whole less work on the management of fisheries than on the West Coast, but there was more emphasis on life histories, physiology, and the marine environment. This was probably the result of (1) the greater importance of mollusks and crustaceans to the Atlantic fisheries and (2) the somewhat closer ties of eastern fishery workers to the academic community.

One of the outstanding pioneers on the Atlantic coast was Henry B. Bigelow of Harvard University who in 1925 published (with William W. Welch) a monograph entitled *Fishes of the Gulf of Maine*. In the following 2 years he published monographs on the plankton and on the physical oceanography of the Gulf of Maine. His work did much to indicate the close relationship between biological oceanography and fisheries.

Charles J. Fish, while director of the U. S. Fishery Laboratory at Woods Hole, published a monograph in 1925 on the plankton of the Woods Hole region. Later he worked at the Buffalo Museum and demonstrated the applicability of marine hydrographic instruments and techniques to

Showing the sliding screens and smolt counting and marking pens used at the outlet of Cultus Lake by Foerster and Ricker in their famous study of the life history of the sockeye salmon.

the study of inland seas. He returned to the University of Rhode Island and promoted the formation of the modern Narragansett Bay laboratory of the university. During this latter period he invited me to Rhode Island where we spent a week together examining Rhode Island streams for their possible suitability for restoration of the Atlantic salmon.

Paul S. Galtsoff served as a medical officer in the czar's army in World War I. He was then made director of the marine laboratory at Sevastopol. Forced to flee to Turkey, he learned English before coming to the United States where he earned his doctoral degree at Columbia University. Galtsoff pioneered in extensive studies of oyster physiology and ecology on all coasts of the United States. He also studied pearl oysters in Panama, Hawaii, and Venezuela, the devastating sponge disease in Florida,

oyster parasites, the Florida red tide, and estuarine pollution from pulp mill wastes and oil spills. He coordinated and edited the monograph *Gulf of Mexico: Its Origin, Waters, and Marine Life*. His section of the monograph (there were over 55 contributors) is a classic for which he prepared by teaching himself Spanish so he could read the voluminous material as originally published. He learned the language so well that he was able to deliver an address in Spanish at the Universidad de Oriente in Cuba. His numerous publications culminated in the comprehensive monograph *The American Oyster*.

Galtsoff was an inspiration to numerous assistants and associates. Walter Chipman worked with him on oyster and pollution problems and then directed the atomic laboratory at Beaufort, North Carolina, where numerous experiments were performed on the uptake and loss of radioisotopes by living organisms. Philip Butler became director of the Gulf Breeze laboratory in Florida. In addition to his excellent work on oysters, he became an authority on the distribution in the environment of various biocides and developed techniques for detecting the long-range effects of sublethal concentrations of biocides on marine organisms.

Victor L. Loosanoff, like Galtsoff, was in the czar's army. He was a Cossack officer and after the war he and some companions fought their way across Siberia to Harbin, Manchuria. By way of Japan he came to Seattle and earned his way through the University of Washington by halibut fishing. He soon became director of the shellfish laboratory at Milford, Connecticut, and took his doctorate at Yale University. Loosanoff and his staff developed methods for the artificial hatching and feeding of larval oysters, methods that have been so successful that oyster hatcheries are now a commercial reality.

Other early oyster biologists include Thurlow Nelson of Rutgers University who worked on oyster ecology and physiology in Delaware Bay; John Mackin who became an authority on oyster diseases; and Henry Federighi who showed that the oyster drill, *Urosalpinx cinerea,* cannot tolerate the lower range of estuarine salinities.

As we approach closer to the present I find it more difficult to trace any clear pattern of teacher and pupil or even of closely knit associations. However, in reciting this history of marine fishery science I have attempted to avoid the mention of individuals still professionally active, and I have also confined my remarks on recent authors to those studying on this continent. I will conclude by naming a few individuals in various areas. This is certain to be a hit-or-miss affair; only time is the final judge of a contribution.

Starting with eastern Canada, Archibald Huntsman gained wide recognition for his work on Atlantic salmon, but he will be best remembered for the high standards of excellence he demanded of the biologists working for the Fisheries Research Board. Among early salmon biologists I must mention H. C. White and his careful life history studies on the Apple River, Nova Scotia. David L. Belding also studied the Atlantic salmon, but I remember him for his excellent early papers on the alewife and clam fisheries of Massachusetts. Vadim-D. Vladykov of Quebec has published on a variety of subjects—sturgeon, salmon, trout, eels, capelin, and haddock—but perhaps his most interesting papers are on the white beluga whale.

Oscar Elton Sette studied sardines at the California fishery laboratory on Terminal Island under the tutelage of Will F. Thompson. Then he worked at Cambridge, Massachusetts, on the fluctuations in the mackerel fisheries, about which he published several papers. Later he returned to Stanford University and was chiefly instrumental in devising methods for relating biological and oceanographic data to practical fishery problems.

William C. Herrington and I commenced fishery work in 1924 at the California fishery laboratory on Terminal Island. In 1925 he joined the International Halibut Commission, publishing an excellent paper on halibut growth and migration based on extensive marking experiments. In 1930 he became director of the U. S. fishery laboratory at Cambridge, Massachusetts, to study the decline in haddock stocks. His chief contribution was a careful assessment of the use of savings gear mesh in otter trawls to permit the escape of small haddock. He espoused the protection of small haddock by the use of savings gear as the only regulation necessary to conserve the haddock populations. This measure, while very useful, is difficult to enforce and has proved insufficient in the face of mounting fishing pressure.

Robert A. Nesbit worked on middle Atlantic coast fisheries, publishing the results of an extensive investigation of the weakfish.

In the 1920's he devised the internal tag, which is very successful on fishes with too weak a bone structure for conventional external tags. His chief contribution was the espousal of the concept of limited entry into a fishery as the only means of maintaining a profitable fishery in a publicly owned resource. Although his idea has been tried in Maryland and elsewhere and usually rejected, it is again receiving attention as other methods are failing.

William C. Kendall published monographs on the smelts (1927) and on the salmons and trouts of New England (1914, 1918, 1935) that are redolent of the detail and perception of the naturalist, seldom emulated in our modern bustle.

Working at Beaufort, North Carolina (and in the National Museum in Washington), Samuel F. Hildebrand and his close associate Isaac Ginsburg published extensively on the systematics of commercial fishes. Hildebrand also published several papers on foreign fishes, including those of Panama and Peru. One of his chief contributions with Louella E. Cable (1930, 1938) was the detailed study of many larval fishes of the mid-Atlantic coast.

John C. Pearson published on a variety of fishery subjects, including the life history of the blue crab in Chesapeake Bay (1948) and the larval development of penaeid shrimps (1939), but he is perhaps best remembered for delineating the estuarine–continental shelf dependency of the sciaenid fishes of the Texas coast (1928).

William W. Anderson worked with Milton Lindner on the penaeid shrimps of the Gulf and south Atlantic, especially on the early tagging experiments; he also published on the life history of the mullet. His chief contribution was the thorough and extensive biological-oceanographic studies of the continental shelf waters of the south Atlantic coast.

F. G. Walton Smith, born a British subject, worked in the West Indies and then came to the United States. He founded and developed the marine laboratory of the University of Miami into one of the foremost fishery-biological laboratories of the world, especially for marine studies of subtropical waters.

Gordon Gunter worked with Lindner on shrimp in the early 1930's. Later he directed the marine laboratory of the University of Texas at Port Aransas. Although he published extensively on almost every phase of Gulf coast fisheries, I consider his chief accomplishment the founding and development of the Gulf Coast Research Laboratory at Ocean Springs, Mississippi.

Milner B. Schaefer, always Benny to his friends, commenced his research career as a biologist for the state of Washington. He worked on tuna in Hawaii and later directed the Inter-American Tropical Tuna Commission, which he molded into perhaps the foremost international fishery research organization. His last post was director of the marine resources division of the University of California at La Jolla. He made notable contributions to the theory of fishery dynamics and to the techniques of fishery management.

I first knew Wilbert McLeod Chapman as a graduate student at the University of Washington. Although "Wib" published several excellent research papers early in his career, he will be remembered chiefly as the strongest supporter of oceanic and international fishery research and cooperation. He insisted on a thorough study by the federal government of the tuna resources of the Pacific based on Hawaii and saw to it that the reports were published as fast as the research projects were completed. His strong advocacy of narrow territorial seas accorded with the wishes of the American tuna and shrimp fishery organizations. (He held private positions during his career with the San Diego tuna boat fishermen's organization and later as director of the Van Camp research organization.) However, this policy has boomeranged as foreign fishing fleets invade the eastern Bering Sea, the New England fishing banks, the deeper portions of the continental shelves off Washington and Oregon, the large banks in the Gulf of

Alaska, and the wide continental shelf off the middle and south Atlantic states. Allowing our foreign fishery policies to be run almost wholly by the larger tuna corporations for over two decades has resulted in our present position as a second-rate fishing nation.

Suggested readings

de Loture, R. 1949. History of the great fishery of Newfoundland. (Translated from French by Clyde C. Taylor in 1957.) U. S. Fish Wildl. Serv., Spec. Sci. Rep. Fish. **213**:1-147.

Galtsoff, P. S. 1962. The story of the Bureau of Commercial Fisheries Biological Laboratory, Woods Hole, Massachusetts. U. S. Fish Wildl. Serv., Circ. **145**:1-121.

Hart, J. L., and J. L. McHugh. 1944. The smelts (Osmeridae) of British Columbia. Fish. Res. Bd. Canada, Bull. **64**:1-27.

Hedgpeth, J. W. 1964. Man and the sea. (Series of lectures given over KPFA, Berkeley, Calif., April 7-13, 1964.) Pacific Marine Station, Dillon Beach, Calif.

McLean, J. 1932. Notes of a twenty-five years' service in the Hudson's Bay Territory. The Champlain Society, Toronto.

Moser, J. F. 1899. The salmon and salmon fisheries of Alaska. Bull. U. S. Fish Comm. **18**: 1-178.

Rostlund, E. 1952. Freshwater fish and fishing in native North America. Univ. Calif. Publ. Geography **9**:1-313.

part one

❧ The marine environment

chapter 1

✒ The physical environment

OCEAN BASINS AND THEIR CIRCULATION

To understand the distribution and abundance of marine organisms one must envisage the shape and character of the ocean basins and their adjacent seas. How these basins were formed and how they are changing are subjects for geological and physical oceanographers; we are interested in the waters themselves and the underlying substrate because of their effects on living organisms.

The one World Ocean centers around Antarctica and has three branches, the Pacific, Atlantic, and Indian Oceans, radiating in three directions like the spokes of a wheel (Fig. 1-1). Except for the so-called Southern Ocean surrounding Antarctica, the only water connections between oceans are the narrow inter-island channels connecting the Pacific and Indian Oceans north of Australia and the shallow (90 m) Bering Strait between the Pacific and the Atlantic.

The waters of these basins, constantly in motion, are acted on by winds, by the Coriolis force resulting from the spinning of the earth, and by tidal forces caused by solar and lunar gravitational pulls.

In addition to horizontal movement (advection), there is vertical movement (convection) caused by the sinking and rising of water masses of different densities. In general water tends to sink at high latitudes because of increasing density, both from the decrease in temperature and from the increased salt content caused by the freezing of the top layers to form sea ice, which retains but a portion of the original salts. At low latitudes the increase in temperature lowers density; in the tropics this may be augmented by heavy rains. The result, in the simplest terms, is the flow of cold dense water at great depths from the poles toward the equator and the flow of warm, less dense surface layers from the equator toward the poles.

This idealized picture of circulation is broken by continental masses and by bands of prevailing winds that are deflected by the Coriolis force. These bands of winds follow rather definite patterns that, with the sun, shift north and south during the year.

The Polar easterlies originate in the Polar High and blow from the east around both poles down to about 60° to 70° latitude. Here they encounter the prevailing

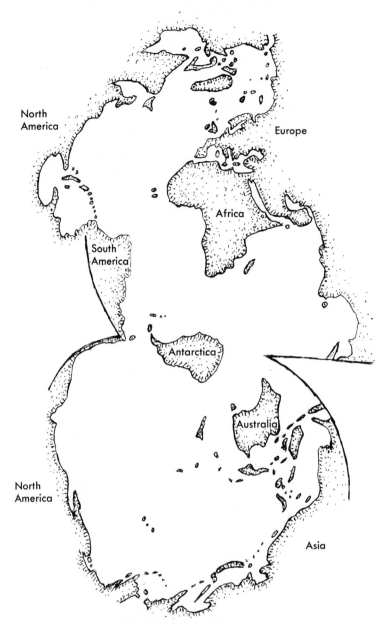

Fig. 1-1. The World Ocean. A South Pole projection.

westerlies, causing the stormy Polar Front at the Polar Low.

The prevailing westerlies (from the southwest in the northern hemisphere and the northwest in the southern hemisphere) originate in the Subtropical High, or Horse Latitudes (about 35° latitude). They are the cause of the easterly surface drift encircling Antarctica.

Originating on the opposite side of the same Subtropical High, the Trade Winds (from the northeast in the northern hemisphere and the southeast in the southern hemisphere) blow toward the equator. Near

Fig. 1-2. Surface currents of the Atlantic Ocean.

AgC	Agulhas Current	Warm	GS	Gulf Stream (called the	Warm
AnC	Antilles Current	Warm		Florida Current between	
BgC	Benguela Current	Cool		Florida and Cuba)	
BzC	Brazil Current	Warm	IC	Irminger Current	Warm
CnC	Canary Current	Cool	LC	Labrador Current	Frigid
CrC	Caribbean Current	Warm	NAD	North Atlantic Drift	Warm
EGC	East Greenland Current	Frigid	NC	Norway Current	Cool
ECC	Equatorial Countercurrent	Warm	NEC	North Equatorial Current	Warm
FC	Falkland Current	Cold	SEC	South Equatorial Current	Warm
GaC	Guiana Current	Warm	WWD	West Wind Drift	Cold
GeC	Guinea Current	Warm			

the equator, where they meet, is the Equatorial Low, with a belt of calm and variable winds known to sailors as the Doldrums.

These prevailing winds and the Coriolis force cause great circular currents in both the Atlantic and Pacific Oceans. In the North Atlantic and North Pacific these currents run in a clockwise direction; in the South Atlantic and South Pacific they are counterclockwise. The Indian Ocean does not reach a sufficiently high northern

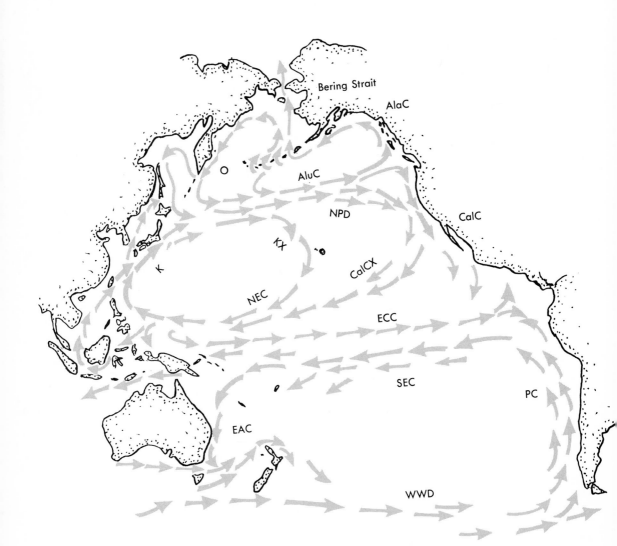

Fig. 1-3. Surface currents of the Pacific Ocean.

AlaC	Alaska Current	Cool	KX	Kuroshio Extension	Warm
AluC	Aleutian Current	Cool	NEC	North Equatorial Current	Warm
CalC	California Current	Cool	NPD	North Pacific Drift	Warm
CalCX	California Current	Warm	O	Oyashio	Cold
	Extension		PC	Peru (Humboldt) Current	Cool
EAC	East Australia Current	Warm	SEC	South Equatorial Current	Warm
ECC	Equatorial Countercurrent	Warm	WWD	West Wind Drift	Cold
K	Kuroshio	Warm			

latitude to form a constant clockwise current; the prevailing currents vary seasonally with the monsoon winds.

The principal surface ocean currents are shown in Figs. 1-2 to 1-5. The shape of the continental masses causes some differences between the circulation patterns of the Atlantic and Pacific. However, they have some common features. The warm Gulf Stream may be compared to the Kuroshio and the cold Labrador Current to the Oyashio. The South Atlantic system

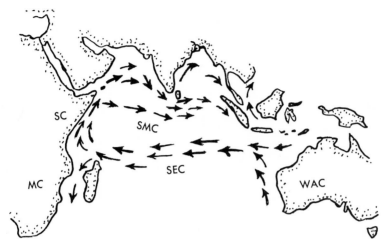

Fig. 1-4. Surface currents of the Indian Ocean during the northern summer monsoon (southwest monsoon, August to September).

MC	Mozambique Current	Warm	SMC	Southwest monsoon	Cool
SC	Somali Current	Cool		Current	
SEC	South Equatorial Current	Warm	WAC	West Australia Current	Warm

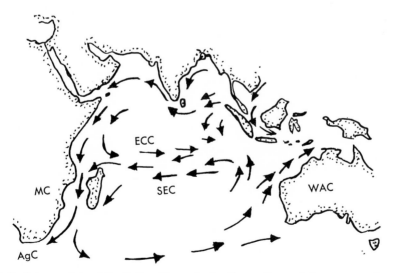

Fig. 1-5. Surface currents of the Indian Ocean during the northern winter monsoon (northwest monsoon, February to March).

AgC	Agulhas Current	Warm	SEC	South Equatorial Current	Warm
ECC	Equatorial Countercurrent	Warm	WAC	West Australia Current	Cool
MC	Mozambique Current	Warm			

resembles a mirror image of the North Atlantic, with the warm Brazil Current substituted for the Gulf Stream and the cold Falkland Current for the Labrador Current. In the central areas of these two oceans there is, in each hemisphere, a great gyre of water with little central movement, i.e., a giant eddy. The most famous is the Sargasso Sea of the North Atlantic. In the southern hemisphere the boundaries of these gyres are not very distinct because of the lack of continental obstruction at high latitudes.

Except for a relatively shallow layer of warm water between the Arctic and Antarctic surface waters, the remainder of the ocean is cold (Fig. 1-6). Because of the strong density differences between this warm surface layer and the deeper waters, the surface circulation is usually quite separate.

The depth of the warm water layer (the lower boundary is usually considered to be at about the 8° C isotherm) varies. Along the western boundaries of the oceanic gyres, e.g., in the Gulf Stream, it may extend to 1000 m. It is characteristically much shallower in the tropics, especially along the equator, deepest in the midlatitudes, and comes to the surface at 50° to 60° S lat. and about 40° to 50° N lat. Vertical stability is relatively strong near the tropics but weaker in the midlatitudes. Toward the poles the cold layers reach the surface. Here, because of the low temperatures, waters tend to increase in density and sink until they reach a layer of the same density, whereupon they spread laterally. The chief cold water masses are the Antarctic and Arctic Bottom Water and the Antarctic and Arctic Intermediate Water.

By far the largest volume of Polar Bottom Water is formed around Antarctica, chiefly in the Weddell Sea. A smaller amount is formed between Greenland and Spitzbergen in the Greenland Sea (Fig. 1-7). This Arctic Bottom Water, formed sporadically during exceptionally cold winters, occasionally spills over the shallow (about

500 m) Iceland-Faroe ridge into the eastern Atlantic basin; more infrequently it spills over the Greenland-Iceland ridge into the western Atlantic basin. It moves southward along the deepest parts of the Atlantic toward the equator and beyond.

The Atlantic Ocean thus contains two important sources of Bottom Water, the Pacific but one. Because of the ridge along the eastern boundary of the Scotia Sea between South America and Antarctica and the general easterly drift of the currents around Antarctica, this Bottom Water must circle Antarctica before reaching the Pacific Ocean. On the way around Antarctica it becomes slightly warmer from mixing with overlying layers, increasing from about −0.9° C in the Weddell Sea to −0.4° C southwest of Australia and to +0.4° C in the Drake Passage at the southern tip of South America.

The Antarctic Bottom Water spreads slowly northward along the bottom in the Atlantic, Indian, and Pacific Oceans. Having perhaps the greatest density of any recognized water mass, it is impeded in its progress by the midoceanic ridges, which divide the ocean basins into eastern and western troughs, which in turn are broken into basins by the lateral faults.

The other chief cold deep water layers, the Arctic and Antarctic Intermediate Waters, are formed just on the polar side of the Polar Fronts. Intermediate Water is formed all around Antarctica, but in the northern hemisphere it is formed only in the Irminger and Labrador Seas in the Atlantic and just south of the Kurile Islands in the Pacific. In the Atlantic the Antarctic water can be traced across the equator to 25° N lat., but in the Pacific the Arctic and Antarctic Intermediate Waters do not appear to cross the equator.

In addition to *cold* deep waters, the Atlantic and Indian Oceans receive from the Mediterranean and from the Red Sea highly saline warmer waters of intermediate density. The Mediterranean water flows out of the Strait of Gibraltar along the bottom

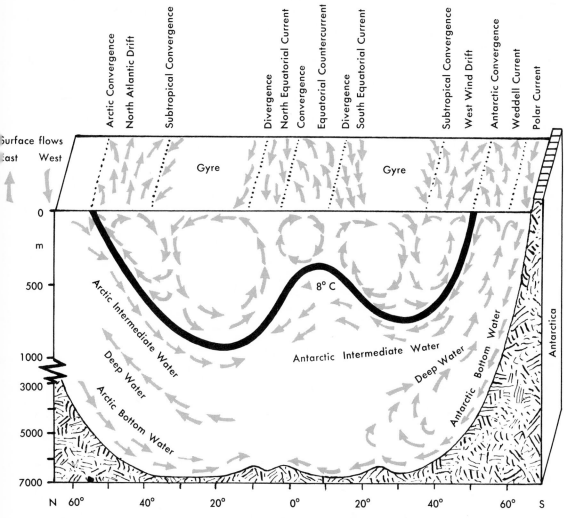

Fig. 1-6. Surface currents and water mass movements along approximately the 30° meridian in the Atlantic Ocean between 65° N lat. and 65° S lat. The heavy curve is the 8° C isotherm separating the warm and cold water spheres.

and sinks to about 1000 m as it gradually mixes and cools. It is the source of the Upper Deep Water of the Atlantic that intrudes between the Antarctic Intermediate Water and the Bottom Water. This Mediterranean water at Gibraltar has salinities of about 38 to 39 °/$_{00}$ and a temperature of about 13° C, but it quickly becomes lower in salinity and temperature as it mixes. It comes from water of intermediate depth formed in the Levantine Basin of the eastern Mediterranean from surface water that

has sunk as an indirect result of excessive evaporation. Minor sources of warm, highly saline water are the Persian Gulf and the northern basin of the Gulf of California.

Perhaps the greatest interest in the deep water layers arises from their mission of carrying life-giving oxygen throughout the ocean. Unfortunately where oxygen is plentiful nutrients are usually low because of the oxidation of organic substances. Thus the Atlantic with its large sources of Deep Bottom Water is high in oxygen but

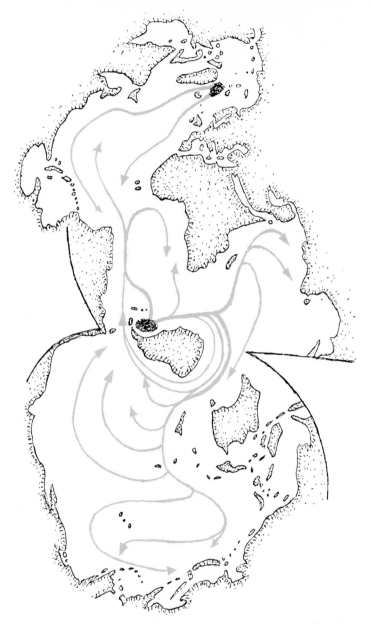

Fig. 1-7. Movements of Arctic Bottom Water from east of Greenland and of Antarctic Bottom Water from the Weddell Sea as it spreads along the ocean floor following the deepest channels.

relatively poor in nutrients. The reverse is true for the Pacific where, because of the much smaller relative quantities of Bottom Water, oxygen becomes increasingly low as one travels northward from Antarctica, and anaerobic conditions occasionally exist.

The thermocline between the warm and cold water spheres usually agrees with an oxygen minimum. A second and more pronounced thermocline appears in all three oceans between about 20° to 25° N lat. and 20° to 25° S lat. This shallower thermocline varies from about 20 to over 250 m below the surface. It appears to coincide usually with the salinity maximum. This thermocline is shallowest toward the equator and also toward the east as the Trade Winds drive lighter water against the western shores.

There is a close relationship between thermoclines and the oxygen minimums as the lowest level occurs in the layers of minimal advection of oxygen, which are closely related to the layers of least horizontal water movement (Wyrtki, 1962). The larger low oxygen water masses occur in the subtropics in the eastern areas of the oceans where advection is very weak at intermediate levels and ascending movements prevail.

THE SEAS
General classification

The water masses of the seas often differ from those of the oceans proper. The degree and type of difference depend on (1) the width and depth of their connection with the oceans, for this governs the amount and the water strata involved in water exchange, (2) the presence or absence of significant volumes of water deeper than the exchange level, (3) the relative importance of evaporation versus freshwater input, and (4) climatic and latitudinal factors favoring or retarding their circulation.

The classification we have adopted for seas is shown in Table 1-1. The groups chosen to serve as basic types are as follows:

1. Seas with wide oceanic connections, often called bordering seas, marginal seas, or pelagic seas. These can be conveniently grouped as follows:
   a. Deep pelagic seas
   b. Shallow pelagic seas
2. Seas with restricted oceanic connections. Such seas can be conveniently classified according to the relative effects of evaporation versus precipitation:
   a. Negative or endorheic seas
   b. Positive or exorheic seas
3. Seas without an oceanic connection or interior seas. These, like category 2, can be conveniently classified according to whether the area is endorheic or exorheic:

   a. Saline interior seas
   b. Freshwater interior seas

Areas such as the Philippine Sea are termed seas as a convenience in describing an area of the ocean. Such contiguous pelagic seas have been treated in Table 1-1 as part of the ocean they border. It should be noted that there is no criterion for defining an interior sea. In the legislation creating the Sea Grant Program, however, the United States Congress specifically classified all of the states bordering the Great Lakes as coastal states and therefore entitled to share in the benefits of the Sea Grant Program.

Circulation

Seas with more than one opening, especially if the openings are widely spaced or moderately deep, tend to maintain a vigorous circulation. With a single opening a critical factor is the depth of the opening in relation to the depth at which the adjacent ocean or sea contains stratified layers. If the sea contains a large basin below the sill depth of the opening, the waters of this basin tend to reflect the salinity and temperature of the outside water layer just above the sill depth.

If there is very little vertical circulation within the basin, the contained waters tend to stagnate below the sill depth in the deeper portions of the basin. Fortunately in many seas with shallow sills there is sufficient vertical circulation to prevent or ameliorate stagnation.

Vertical circulation occurs in seas with a negative water balance through the sinking of surface waters. As evaporation increases their salinity, the surface waters, when chilled, sink to their new density level. This results in dense water spilling over the edge of the sill and replacement water flowing in at the surface.

BOTTOM CONFIGURATION OF OCEAN BASINS

Although the geological history of the ocean basins is not strictly germane, their

Table 1-1. Environmental data on oceans and seas

	Volume (10^3 km³)	Depth		Area (10^3 km²)	Deepest sill (m)	Cryptodepression (m)	Type
		Mean (m)	Maximum (m)				
Arctic Sea	—	—	5,180	12,405	500		Deep pelagic
White Sea (inner)	—	—	340	ca 67	20		Exorheic
Barents Sea[1]	271	200	500	1,360			Shoal pelagic
Baffin Bay	158	—	2,300	ca 225	600		Deep pelagic
Hudson Bay and approaches	158	128	229	1,232			Exorheic
Gulf of St. Lawrence	30	127	549	238			Shoal pelagic
North Sea	54	94	665	575			Shoal pelagic
Baltic Sea	23	55	463	422	18		Exorheic
Irish Sea and English Channel	10	58	263	178			Shoal pelagic
Mediterranean Sea[2]	3,781	—	5,092[3]	2,505	320		Endorheic
Sea of Marmara	18[4]	—	1,182	—	70		Exorheic
Black Sea	537	1,197[5]	2,244	423	40		Exorheic
Sea af Azov	0.3	8	14	38	5		Exorheic
Caribbean Sea	—	—	7,200	2,640[6]	ca 2,000		Deep pelagic
Gulf of Mexico	—	—	4,077	1,593	1,600		Deep pelagic
Gulf and Caribbean	937.3[7]	2,174[7]	—	—			
Atlantic Ocean proper	319,260	3,852	—	82,884			Oceanic
Atlantic subtotal				16,863			Deep pelagic
				2,351			Shoal pelagic
				2,505			Endorheic
				2,182			Exorheic
				82,884			Oceanic
Bering Sea	3,259	1,437	4,273	2,268			Deep pelagic
Okhotsk Sea[8]	1,228	777	3,374	1,580	2,318		Deep pelagic
Japan Sea	1,713	1,752	3,712[7]	978			Deep pelagic
East China Sea	263	349	2,377[7]	752			Deep pelagic
Yellow Sea	19	25	103	487			Shoal pelagic
South China Sea			5,016	3,400			Deep pelagic
Gulf of Thailand	14	46	83	306	58		Exorheic
East Indies archipelagic seas	?	?	6,504	3,026			Deep pelagic
Total Gulf of California	132	813	—	—			
Gulf of California (outer)			3,700	ca 108			Deep pelagic
Gulf of California (inner)			1,500	ca 54	200		Endorheic
Bass Strait	5	70	—	75			Shoal pelagic
Pacific Ocean proper	707,856	4,285	—	165,206			Oceanic
Pacific subtotal				12,112			Deep pelagic
				562			Shoal pelagic
				54			Endorheic

						Classification
					306	Exorheic
					165,206	Oceanic
North Australia Sea[9]	ca 721	—	—	1,800	1,411	Deep pelagic
Andaman Sea	694	870	4,180	1,800	798	Deep pelagic
Red Sea	215	491	2,300[10]	125	438	Endorheic
Persian Gulf	6	25	186	80	239	Endorheic
Indian Ocean proper	291,030	3,964	—	—	73,443	Oceanic
Indian subtotal				306	2,209	Deep pelagic
					677	Endorheic
				165,206	73,433	Oceanic
Caspian Sea	79.3	182	946	972	436.4	Interior, endorheic
Aral Sea	1.0	16	68	—	62.0	Interior, endorheic
Lake Balkash	0.1	6	27	—	17.6	Interior, endorheic
Great Lakes of North America	24.6	101	307	151	245.3	Interior, exorheic
Great Slave Lake	1.6	62	614	464	25.4	Interior, exorheic
Great Bear Lake	?	>120	400	>18	30.6	Interior, exorheic
Lake Winnipeg	3.1	13	19	—	24.5	Interior, exorheic
Lake Baikal	23.0	730	1,741	1,279	31.5	Interior, exorheic
Lake Ladoga	0.9	52	250	245	18.7	Interior, exorheic
Lake Tanganyika	18.9	572	1,470	647	34.0	Interior, exorheic
Lake Victoria	2.7	40	79	—	68.8	Interior, exorheic
Lake Nyasa	8.4	273	706	242	30.8	Interior, exorheic
Interior subtotal					516.0	Interior, endorheic
					509.6	Interior, exorheic
GRAND TOTAL					31,184	Deep pelagic seas
					2,913	Shoal pelagic seas
					3,236	Endorheic seas
					2,488	Exorheic seas
					516	Interior endorheic seas
					510	Interior exorheic seas
					321,533	Oceanic waters
Total all seas	362,380 × 10³ km²					
Total all land	146,817 × 10³ km²					
Percent of seas	71.108					
Percent of land	28.892					
Ratio sea/land	2.454					

[1] Demel and Rutkowicz, 1958.
[2] Includes Sea of Marmara.
[3] Ryan, 1966.
[4] Ullyott and Pektaş, 1952.
[5] Includes Sea of Azov.
[6] Gordon, 1966.
[7] Stocks, 1938.
[8] Petelin, 1966.
[9] Timor Sea, Arafura Sea, and Gulf of Carpenteria.
[10] Neumann and Pierson, 1966.

present bottom shape and type of substrate play an important role in determining their suitability for various organisms.

The continental margin consists of the continental shelf, the usual abrupt change to the steep continental slope, and the continental rise, which usually contains materials from the slope. The abyssal plain is normally flat but may have hills and rises. The midoceanic ridge follows approximately the center line between continents. It has a rift valley down its center that oceanographers now believe is the point at which the continents have drifted and are drifting apart (Menard, 1969).

This type of continental margin is varied, especially in the Pacific, by the presence or absence of a narrow continental shelf outside of which is a deep trench or trough. The ocean margin of the trough is often the location of an island arc.

In addition to the mountains of the midoceanic ridges, there are numerous isolated peaks that may also occur along a line. If they rise above the surface, they form a chain of islands. Those with sharp peaks are called seamounts. However, many, called guyots, are flat-topped. Seamounts and guyots are most numerous in the central and northern Pacific.

A striking feature of the bottom is the fracture zones. These may be 100 km wide and several hundred kilometers long. These zones are usually mountainous and separate basins of different depths. They cross the midoceanic ridges in many places, and where they cross there is normally an extensive horizontal displacement of the ridge.

Another interesting feature is the submarine canyons, some of which are as wide and deep as the Grand Canyon. Some appear to be submarine extensions of river valleys, but others cut deeply into the edge of wide continental shelves remote from any streams. It is known that occasionally sediments move down these canyons as strong turbidity currents, causing them to continue eroding.

OCEAN SEDIMENTS (Fig. 1-8)

Ocean sediments are classified as terrigenous or pelagic, according to their origin. Terrigenous deposits are carried down by rivers or torn from the shore. They may also contain skeletons of shallow water organisms. When turbid river waters become mixed with saline water, the material in suspension quickly sinks to the bottom. Thus terrigenous sediments usually stop at about 100 fm (183 m) at the so-called mud line; beyond this point there is a gradual transition to deep water or pelagic sediments. Terrigenous deposits are sometimes carried offshore by turbidity currents flowing down submarine canyons.

Pelagic sediments consist of red clay and oozes augmented with wind-blown sand, particles from floating pumice, and such oddities as sharks' teeth and the otoliths of whales. These oddities are often coated with manganese. The oozes consist largely of the skeletal remains of pelagic organisms that have sunk to the bottom and are either siliceous or calcareous, according to the organism that is predominant. They can be classified as follows:

1. Calcareous oozes contain over 30% calcium carbonate.
   a. *Globigerina* ooze contains the shells of pelagic Foraminifera, especially those of organisms belonging to the genus *Globigerina*. Calcium carbonate content may run as high as 60% to 70% and occasionally to 90%. These deposits are second in extent only to the red clays and are especially abundant in tropical and subtropical waters. The distribution is controlled somewhat by depth; red clays are dominant in the deeper and colder water. This is because calcium carbonate can by dissolved by free carbon dioxide. Carbon dioxide increasingly disassociates with depth and dissolves the calcareous shells either during or after sinking so that the remains, without calcium carbonate, join in the formation of the red clay. This type of ooze is abundant at 1500 to 3000 m but becomes scarce at 4000 m.
   b. Pteropod ooze is merely a variety of calcareous ooze in which the dominant remains are not Foraminifera but ptero-

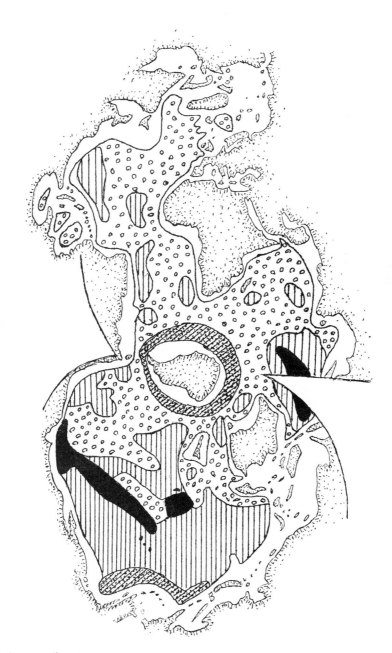

Fig. 1-8. Ocean sediments.

Terrigenous sediments . . . . . . .White
Pelagic sediments
   Red clay . . . . .Vertical rules
   Calcareous oozes . . . . .Open circles
   Siliceous oozes
      Diatom ooze . . . . .Dark with diagonal rules
      Radiolarian ooze . . . . . . .Black

pods, small pelagic mollusks. Pteropods are not abundant in very cold waters, as these pelagic mollusks prefer tropical and subtropical waters. The deposits are much less extensive than those of the Foraminifera.

2. Siliceous oozes, as the name implies, contain less calcium carbonate and more silica. They are most abundant in areas where calcium carbonate production is lower or in depths and areas in which a large proportion of the calcium carbonate is dissolved. Siliceous oozes are of two types—those formed by the frustules of diatoms and those containing the skeletons of radiolarian protozoa.

   a. Diatom ooze is most abundant all around Antarctica south of the Antarctic Convergence and in the northern portion of the North Pacific.

   b. Radiolarian ooze occurs chiefly in a band around the tropics but is most abundant in the Pacific because there the calcareous oozes are dissolved at a lesser depth due to the lower oxygen concentrations that permit higher concentrations of free carbon dioxide.

The red clays cover the largest area of the ocean bottoms, especially at the greater depths. By far the greatest area of red clay is in the Pacific. The bulk of the material is ferric hydroxide, with some manganese oxide. There is usually a small percentage of calcium carbonate and a smaller percentage of silica.

THE CONTINENTAL SHELF

The continental shelf is defined variously as lying above the 200 m contour, above the 100 fm contour, and above the point where the gradual incline of the shelf changes abruptly to the steeper slant of the continental slope. Estimates of the average width vary from 30 to 44 miles (48 to 71 km), with a range of 0 to 800 miles (1288 km); the greatest width is off the Siberian coast. The point where the gradually shelving bottom abruptly changes slope may vary from 20 m to as much as 500 m in depth.

The area of the oceans and their connecting seas is estimated at 362 million km². Estimates of the area of the shelf vary around 27 million km². If one includes in the shelf the total area of seas with sills less than 100 fm in depth, the area of the oceans proper below the shelves is reduced to about 331 million km². The area cut off from the oceans by the 100 fm contour, about 31 million km², is thus 21.1% as large as the land surface (147 million km²).

Shelves vary so considerably that we may note a few general types. Glaciated shelves found off glaciated coasts may be rather rugged with hills and valleys. The extensive banks off New England extending to Newfoundland are of this type, containing a large proportion of boulders and rubble deposited as glacial moraines. The bottom of the Barents Sea is a glaciated extension of the European continent; much of it is covered with glacial deposits. This, perhaps the widest continental shelf, extends from Norway to Spitzbergen and Novaya Zemlya and averages about 200 m in depth but contains channels of up to 400 m running from the Arctic Sea and from the Norwegian Sea into the shelf. The deepest (up to 500 m) is the Bear Island Channel, which parallels the Norwegian coast south of Bear Island.

In sharp contrast to conditions on the New England–Maritimes banks, great areas of the Barents Sea bottom deposits are covered with a thin layer of ferric and manganese oxides (in the form of hydrates). In the same areas the oxygen content is very low. Similar conditions obtain in the Gulf of Bothnia.

River shelves occur off the mouths of large rivers, especially along shelving coasts, as along northern Siberia and in the Bering Sea and the Yellow Sea.

Off coasts bordered by high young mountains the shelf tends to be narrow and steep. Usually the edge is fairly deep. In contrast, the shelves formed by coral reefs are shallow, the depth at the edge being about 20 m, because reef-forming corals can exist only in shoal water.

WATER EXCHANGE IN BASINS

The importance of circulation in basins was briefly mentioned in the discussion of seas. There are certain factors that govern the type and amount of water that is exchanged between the basin and the water above or beyond the sill depth of the basin. The attributes of the water that characterizes the basin depend on the relative amount and character of this exchange (Fig. 1-9).

The Black Sea is the classic example of a large sea in which freshwater input greatly exceeds evaporation. The result is a constant outflow of low salinity water through the Bosporus. The sill is shallow (40 m) compared to the mean depth of nearly 1200 m. Authorities differ on the water budget of the Black Sea, but all agree that very little of the 36 $^0/_{00}$ layer of salt water in the Sea of Marmara enters the Black Sea. The surface salinity is 17 to 20 $^0/_{00}$ but increases to 21 to 23 $^0/_{00}$ at 150

to 200 m. Below 50 m, oxygen decreases until there is none at 150 to 200 m; here hydrogen sulfide appears. Thus the shallow sill combined with intense stratification results in a stagnant basin; the Black Sea bears a close resemblance to a meromictic lake.

Many have postulated that the complete renewal of the deep waters (below about 30 m) in the Black Sea occurs in a period of 2500 years. This estimate, however, is based on the quantity of highly saline water flowing through the Dardanelles into the Sea of Marmara. The estuarine type of circulation in the Bosporus and Dardanelles accentuated by the rugged and uneven channels and fast currents—which cause great turbulence—is such that the inflowing denser water is mixed with the undersurface of the overlying water and carried back out. Turkish oceanographers found no bottom water entering the Black Sea under

Fig. 1-9. Mobile Bay Earth Resources Technology Satellite data buoy (ERTS-A) used by the Marine Environmental Sciences Consortium at the Dauphin Island Sea Lab, Alabama, in cooperation with the Marshall Space Flight Center (NASA) at Huntsville, Alabama. Buoy continuously monitors and transmits physical environmental parameters to Sea Lab and ERTS satellite. (Photo by Thomas Walker.)

normal conditions. A large scale model of the Bosporus by Ullyott at Robert College in Istanbul illustrates clearly, in operation, the typical estuarine pattern of enhanced outflow and the positive relationship between volume of outflow and volume of inflow of the lower layer of denser water, which seldom overflows the entrance sill into the Black Sea. The waters of the Black Sea below about 150 to 200 m are devoid of oxygen and rich in hydrogen sulfide.

According to Izhevskii (1961), several Russian authors claim that the upper layers of the Black Sea are enriched by upwelling from below the photosynthetic zone caused both by winds and by convection during the cold winters. He also cites Vodyanitskii (1954) as ascribing upwelling chiefly to the constant cyclonic currents running along the Black Sea coasts. This is shown by the domelike form of the water masses, the domes being in the center of the western and eastern portions of the sea (Neumann, 1942).

The Baltic Sea resembles the Black Sea in the outflow of low salinity water over a shallow (18 m) sill. The surface salinity in the Baltic Sea (about 7 $^0/_{00}$ in the center) is much lower than in the Black Sea; the bottom salinity is a few parts higher. With an average depth of only 55 m and weaker stratification, there is far less tendency toward stagnation than in the Black Sea. Stagnation does occur in some of the deeper basins, those below 80 to 100 m. Every few years at sporadic intervals when river flow is low, more North Sea water enters the Baltic Sea. Having greater density, it forces the stagnant water out of the deeper basins.

The Norwegian fjords present an interesting case showing the importance of depth and length of the sill. Sverdrup et al. (1942), using data from Fleming and Revelle (1939), sum up the major differences between stagnant and nonstagnant fjords. They compared fjords of similar size (7 km long) and found that those with a long shallow sill (4.2 m) were stagnant,

whereas those with a short and slighter deeper sill (10.8 m) maintained periodic or continuous water exchange. It is noted, however, that the authors indicate in their illustration that fresh water entered the heads of the stagnant fjords, whereas no fresh water is indicated for the nonstagnant fjords. As a case in point, a small (3 km long) fjord known as Halibut Cove Lagoon in Cook Inlet, Alaska (Rounsefell, 1930), has a sill less than a meter deep at low tide, nearly a mile in length (1.6 km), and narrow (25 m). The depths inside range from 25 to 45 fm (46 to 76 m). The fjord has very steep shores and no freshwater source, yet the fjord for many years was the wintering location for a stock of large herring that were fished near the bottom with gill nets.

These fjord examples suggest that the chief effect on the circulation of the added surplus of fresh water into a basin is the hindrance to convection caused by the resulting stratification. If an abrupt pycnocline is formed below sill depth, then the exchange of basin water with water outside of the basin may occur only at irregular intervals. In very small or shallow basins in which the volume of the tidal prism bears a high ratio to the basin volume, the turbulence resulting from tidal flow may result in vertical mixing sufficient to prevent stagnation.

The Gulf of Georgia, similar to the Black and Baltic Seas, has an excess of freshwater runoff. The sill depths, however, are somewhat deeper (274 m in Haro Strait). Waldichuk (1957) states that *if no tides existed* the following would occur.

With the seasonal change in the inflowing deep water from Juan de Fuca Strait, at least a certain amount of the water in the Strait of Georgia below sill level could be replaced by the dense water intruding during the summer months. Some mixing and dilution below sill level would occur throughout the year by turbulent outflow of surface water. This mixing would be quite small if no tides existed. Fresh water flowing out near the surface would tend to stabilize the water column against mixing by winds from the surface. In general, the conditions would tend to approach those which

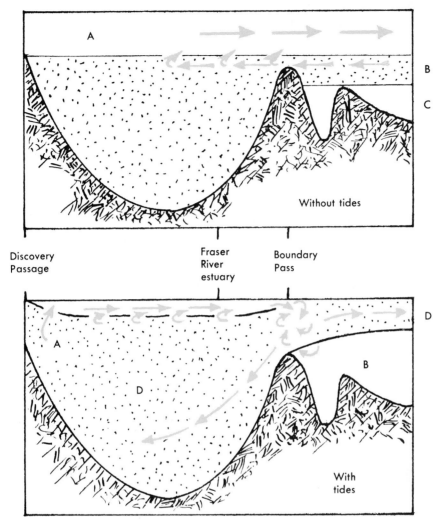

Fig. 1-10. Schematic illustration of Gulf of Georgia–Strait of Juan de Fuca system. Upper diagram illustrates probable conditions if there were no tides. Lower diagram illustrates existing conditions with tidal mixing at sills. *A,* Upper brackish layer. *B,* Intermediate Strait of Juan de Fuca water. *C,* Deep Strait of Juan de Fuca water. *D,* Mixture of *A* and *B.* Discovery Passage is located at north end of Gulf of Georgia; Fraser River estuary intervenes between Discovery Passage and Boundary Pass, which is between Gulf of Georgia and Strait of Juan de Fuca. (Modified from Waldichuk, M. 1957. J. Fish. Res. Bd. Canada **14:**321-486.)

exist in certain of the Norwegian fjords or in the Black Sea. They could not be as extreme, however, because the sill depth is much greater in the Strait of Georgia than it is in the European examples. A turnover might occur more frequently and be less damaging to life forms than in the case of a catastrophic turnover in Norwegian fjords.

In contrast to the hypothetical condition just described. . . . Tidal mixing occurs in the channels of the San Juan Archipelago at all times stir-ring the freshwater from the Strait of Georgia into the deep water intruding from Juan de Fuca Strait. . . .*

The hypothetical situation and the actual case that exists because of the strong tides

*From Waldichuk, M. 1957. Physical oceanography of the Strait of Georgia, British Columbia. J. Fish. Res. Bd. Canada **14:**321-486.

(mean tidal range of 3.6 m) are depicted in Fig. 1-10.

The Sea of Azov merits mention as an extreme and rather unique example of a sea with a very positive water balance. Connected with the Black Sea by the Strait of Kerch, the average depth is only 8 m, with 14 m as the maximum. The total volume of 300 km³ bears an annual ratio to the incoming waters of the Don River that varies from 25:1 to 6:1; the average annual river discharge is 26 km³. Despite the shoal water, Izhevskii (1961) states that phenomena associated with benthic oxygen deficiency lethal to all life occasionally develop in the central portions of the sea, adding that benthic oxygen deficiency recurs every summer.

In basins with a negative water balance the depth of the sill is also of great importance in determining the nutrient content of the waters. The Mediterranean Sea is the classic example. The entrance sill is 320 m; another sill at 324 m between Sicily and Tunis divides the sea into eastern and western basins. Convection occurs chiefly in the eastern basin close to Asia Minor, where evaporation is very high. When the resulting high salinity water is slightly chilled, it sinks to intermediate depths and flows westward across the Sicily-Tunis sill and spills into the Atlantic over the sill in the Strait of Gibraltar. The deeper waters of the Mediterranean are formed in winter along the northern coasts in areas where intermediate water is lacking, permitting convection currents to reach the bottom. The water that spills out of the Mediterranean is replaced by an inflow of surface water from the Atlantic. This downward circulation keeps the deeper waters of the Mediterranean oxygenated, but the nutrient level is extremely low because the inflowing Atlantic water originates in the surface layers from which the nutrients are already depleted.

In considering flow in and out of a basin not only the depth but also the total cross section must be considered. An example often cited is the Gulf of Kara-Bogaz on the Caspian Sea. The long shallow entrance so restricts water exchange that the salinity in the gulf is many times higher than in the Caspian Sea. A somewhat similar arid area situation exists on the Texas coast. The Laguna Madre has such shallow connections with the Gulf of Mexico that over a long period of years massive mortalities of fish occurred at irregular intervals from hypersalinity. Since construction of the Intracoastal Canal through the Laguna, this condition has been somewhat alleviated.

There are several basins in which the water balance is more or less neutral. Their circulation depends somewhat on vertical exchange occurring within the basins themselves. Thus in the Arctic Sea, surface waters freeze and the underlying water sinks to form Arctic Bottom Water, which occasionally spills out into the Atlantic. In Baffin Bay also, winter freezing causes surface layers to sink and spill over the sill into Davis Strait.

One feature of basins in zones of positive or neutral water balance is that the water in the basin below sill level reflects the salinity and temperature either of the surface layers that sank to fill the basin or, when convection is lacking, the salinity and temperature of the water strata of the connecting body of water at the sill level. The Caribbean Sea and Gulf of Mexico deep waters are thus warmer than waters at corresponding depths in the Atlantic. Conversely, below sill level the waters of Baffin Bay are colder and lower in salinity than those of Davis Strait.

Suggested readings

Cromwell, T. 1953. Circulation in a meridional plane in the central equatorial Pacific. J. Mar. Res. **12:**196-213.

Defant, A. 1961. Physical oceanography, vol. 1. Pergamon Press, Inc., New York. 727 pp.

Dietrich, G. 1957. General oceanography. (Translated from German in 1963.) John Wiley & Sons, Inc., New York. 588 pp.

Hachey, H. B. 1961. Oceanography and Canadian Atlantic waters. Fish. Res. Bd. Canada, Bull. **134:**1-120.

Herlinveaux, R. H. 1962. Oceanography of Saanich Inlet in Vancouver Island, British Columbia. J. Fish. Res. Bd. Canada **19**:1-37.

Hutchinson, G. E. 1957. A treatise on limnology. I. Geography, physics, and chemistry, John Wiley & Sons, Inc., New York. 1015 pp.

Izhevskii, G. K. 1961. Oceanological principles as related to the fishery productivity of the seas. (Translated from Russian in 1964.) IPST Cat. No. 917, OTS 63-11120. Office of Technical Services, U. S. Department of Commerce, Springfield, Va. 185 pp.

King, C. A. M. 1962. An introduction to oceanography. McGraw-Hill Book Co., New York. 337 pp.

Menard, H. W. 1969. The deep-ocean floor. Sci. Amer. **221**:127-142.

Murray, J. 1913. The oceans. Henry Holt, New York. 256 pp.

Murray, J., and J. Hjort. 1912. The depths of the ocean. Macmillan International, Ltd., London. 821 pp.

Neumann, G., and W. F. Pierson, Jr. 1966. Principles of physical oceanography. Prentice-Hall, Inc., New York. 545 pp.

Pickard, G. L. 1963. Descriptive physical oceanography. Pergamon Press, Inc., New York. 200 pp.

Sverdrup, H. U., M. Johnson, and R. H. Fleming. 1942. The oceans. Prentice-Hall, Inc., New York. 1087 pp.

Ullyott, P. 1953. Conditions of flow in the Bosphorus. Univ. Istanbul, Hydrobiol. Res. Inst., Ser. B. **1**:199-215.

Waldichuk, M. 1957. Physical oceanography of the Strait of Georgia, British Columbia. J. Fish. Res. Bd. Canada **14**:321-486.

chapter 2

❦ The primary biological environment

PHOTIC ZONE AND NUTRIENT SUPPLY

The yield of the seas depends ultimately on primary productivity. The amount of primary productivity in any area (laying aside momentarily the contribution of nutrients from land drainage) depends on the quantities of basic nutrients available in the surface and near-surface layers. These nutrients must lie in the photic zone above the compensation point, at which point the production by photosynthesis balances the energy required for respiration and basic metabolism.

The depth of the photic zone varies greatly from area to area. In areas of high turbidity it may be only a few centimeters. In the deep oceans, away from the influence of land drainage and in areas of low productivity, it may extend as deep as 600 m.

Obviously sustained high productivity depends on the continuous introduction of basic nutrients into the photosynthetic zone. The extremely low productivity in many oceanic gyres, e.g., the Sargasso Sea, is caused by the paucity of vertical circulation in these vast surface eddies. Despite a deep compensation point in the clear waters, nutrients are usually insufficient to induce normal productivity.

As surface organisms die, they sink below the photic zone, gradually decaying. Their sinking is slowed by the increasing density and higher viscosity of the water. This occurs especially at pycnoclines, as where a warmer surface layer encounters a sharp thermocline. Oxygen lowers the nutrient content of the water by oxidizing organic substances, which occurs in approximately the same way as respiration metabolism—consuming oxygen and releasing carbon dioxide. Therefore the highest concentrations of available nutrients are usually found somewhat deeper than the oxygen minimum.

This store of accumulated nutrients below the photic zone can only be brought into the photic zone under certain conditions.

1. Divergence. Two currents tend to flow apart, thus creating a zone that is filled by water from below.

2. Alongshore winds. Winds blowing parallel to the shore with the shore on the left (facing downwind) in the northern hemisphere and to the right in the southern

hemisphere push the surface water offshore, creating a zone that is filled by water ascending from below. This is because (in the northern hemisphere) the Coriolis force causes water under wind stress to flow at an angle to the right of the direction of the wind.

3. Convergence. Where two water masses flow together, one or the other (or both) tend to sink, which may cause water to rise elsewhere to fill the void. Thus the Antarctic circumpolar water mass is formed by upwelling to the south of the Antarctic Convergence.

4. Cooling of surface waters. As surface waters moving poleward are cooled, they sink to their density level and must be replaced by less dense water from below. This process is of most importance in the Arctic Sea.

5. Turbulence. Where strong horizontal currents of different temperature and density clash, strong turbulence results in mixing. This increases the density of the mixed water, resulting in cabelling, or sinking. This in turn brings some deeper water to the surface. This is most pronounced in collisions of warm and cold currents such as the Gulf Stream with the Labrador Current, the Kuroshio with the Oyashio, and the Brazil Current with the Falkland Current.

6. Eddies. Strong swift currents often create eddies along their boundaries. Cyclonic (counterclockwise) eddies in the northern hemisphere (reverse for the southern) maintain in their center a lower sea surface. This low pressure area is continuously being filled from below.

7. In the lee of a land mass jutting into a current. This is well illustrated by the upwelling just south of where Cabo Frio juts into the Brazil Current. The same applies to islands in a current; they often induce upwelling in their lee.

8. Where currents pass over a shoal or a seamount.

9. Where water mass movements create domes or ridges of lower temperature. In tropical areas with a shallow thermocline such a thermal dome may not reach the surface but yet be in the photic zone.

The principal areas of upwelling are shown in Fig. 2-1. Coastal upwelling is most pronounced on the western shores of continents in the Trade Wind belt. This is not entirely true in the Indian Ocean, in which the seasonal monsoon winds cause the locations of upwelling to vary drastically with the seasons. The greatest upwelling in the Indian Ocean occurs on the Somali and Arabian coasts. The monsoon winds also affect areas of the Pacific, causing some upwelling along the coasts of Thailand and South Vietnam.

Although there is some upwelling all along the boundaries of the Equatorial Countercurrent with the North and South Equatorial Currents, the principal offshore upwelling of this type occurs near the equator along a stretch of about 6000 km in the Pacific.

Around Antarctica is a broad ring of rising deep water, especially in the Atlantic Ocean sector. This is caused both by the sinking of shelf water on the edges of the continent to form the deep Antarctic Bottom Water and the sinking of outward flowing surface water at the Antarctic Convergence to form the Antarctic Intermediate Water. This leaves a void between the two sinking layers that is filled by water ascending from deep layers.

A large share of this Deep Water originates in the faraway North Atlantic, thereby aiding in restoring the water balance between the northern and southern hemispheres, the imbalance of which is caused by diversion of a large share of the South Equatorial Current into the North Atlantic. During its long slow journey from the north below the photic zone this deep water has accumulated a large store of nutrients. This ascending mass of nutrient-rich water causes the tremendous plankton blooms that nourish the huge populations of euphausiids, the "krill" that feed the Antarctic stocks of baleen whales.

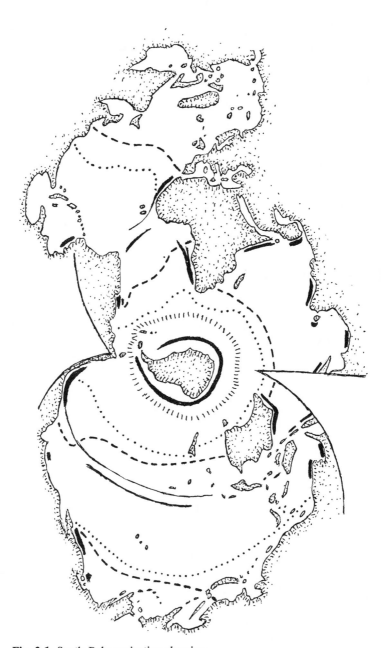

Fig. 2-1. South Pole projection showing:
Principal areas of upwelling. . . . . Black
Antarctic convergence . . . . Hachured line
20° C isotherm
   In July . . . . Dashed line
   In January. . . . . Dotted line

The effect of this upwelling on surface water temperatures is apparent (Fig. 2-1) if one notes the positions of the 20° C isotherms as they approach the coast in areas of upwelling. Since measurements all indicate that the water moving to the surface in upwelling areas comes from layers not exceeding 200 to 300 m in depth and as little as 40 m with strong vertical stability, it is apparent that these layers must themselves be replenished from even deeper water sources in order to complete the water cycle from the poles to the equator and back.

Upwelling water rises very slowly; Cushing (1969) suggests a normal rate of about 1 m/day. As a result, the surface currents may carry the upwelled water far offshore before the nutrients are largely utilized.

In summary, the areas of nutrient-rich oceanic waters (disregarding areas enriched by land drainage) owe their nutrient supply to the movement of water from beneath the photic zone toward the surface. This is accomplished in three main ways: (1) upwelling caused by wind-driven currents moving apart or away from a land mass, (2) sinking of surface waters as they approach cool higher latitudes, causing displacement by deeper water, and (3) intense mixing and cabelling where strong surface currents meet, causing deeper water to be brought to the surface. The effects of land drainage are discussed later.

UTILIZATION OF BASIC NUTRIENTS

The base of the food chain in the seas is phytoplankton. The many groups present range in size from as small as 1 μ up to 1 mm. Most numerous are the minute coccolithophores, the diatoms, and the dinoflagellates. Usually less numerous are silicoflagellates, green algae, blue-green algae, and other diverse groups, some only slightly known. The blue-green algae of the genus *Oscillatoria* (also called *Skujaella* or *Trichodesmium*) may be very numerous at times in warm seas, e.g., the Red Sea, and, similar to some of the freshwater blue-green algae, may

be able to fix elemental nitrogen. I have seen the surface of the Gulf of Mexico discolored for many miles by windrows of *Oscillatoria,* and airplane pilots flying between New Orleans and Tampa have often mistaken the reddish discoloration for the dreaded red tide. Earlier workers on the red tide even speculated about the concentration of nutrients released by the death of vast quantities of wind-aggregated *Oscillatoria* as a possible causative agent in the overblooming of *Gymnodinium breve.* Many of the dinoflagellates share with the planktonic blue-green algae the ability to thrive abundantly in warm, nutrient-poor seas.

In the presence of certain inorganic nutrients plus carbon dioxide and water, these tiny plants (or plantlike animals such as dinoflagellates) are able to capture a portion of the energy of light to synthesize carbon compounds. They require some form of nitrogen (not gas) and phosphorus. Diatoms require silica for their tests. The requirements in the form of trace elements and vitamins are only dimly understood, but copper, iron, manganese, cobalt, vanadium, iodine, etc. may be needed by different forms (O'Kelley, 1968). Pequenat et al. (1969) have calculated that zinc is not a limiting factor in the marine environment.

It has been found that some dinoflagellates cannot be reared in pure culture without the addition of vitamins, which may be supplied by bacteria in unialgal cultures. Fortunately, unlike the situation on land, trace elements are quite ubiquitous in the sea, although their levels may be very low at times. Of course these plants liberate oxygen as a by-product of photosynthesis, thus providing the additional oxygen required for their respiration.

The chief limiting nutrients appear to be nitrogen (in the form of nitrates, nitrites, or ammonia) and phosphorus. The ratio of nitrates to phosphates in seawater normally approaches 15 atoms of nitrogen to 1 atom of phosphorus. However, even in the presence of these nutrients, the presence or lack of other substances can slow or inhibit growth. Thus some algae grow better following the blooms of another species, but the opposite may also be true (Lucas, 1949).

Like other nonconservative elements in seawater, silicon fluctuates in concentration. Silicates are used in the tests of diatoms and in the skeletons of radiolarians. As a consequence, surface waters exhibit a marked seasonal curve of silicate concentration. High in the winter and very early spring, the silicates are rapidly depleted by the spring plankton blooms, reaching a low point by midsummer. After the diatom blooms have fallen off, the level of silicates begins to rise in late summer and early autumn. Whether or not silicates have a limiting effect on plankton blooms is not well established.

Contrary to the habit of diatoms, the dinoflagellates usually bloom in the autumn after the diatoms have already exhausted most of the available nutrients. The ability of dinoflagellates to bloom at low nutrient levels appears to depend on their concentration of the nutrients from the entire wind-stirred portion of the water column. This is directly related to their motility, which enables them to remain at or near the surface in the photosynthetic zone in areas of gentle downward vertical circulation caused by convergences such as occur at the mouths of estuaries, parallel to the shore during times when there are onshore winds, or in wind-created convection cells.

The relationship between the abundance of a dinoflagellate, *Gymnodinium breve,* and the concentration of silicates yielded indications of a negative correlation (Rounsefell and Dragovich, 1966). This should probably be interpreted as another indication of the fact that the dinoflagellates bloom chiefly at low nutrient levels and not during diatom blooms.

Bacteria also play an extremely important role in the nutrient cycle. Autotrophic bacteria, which are in the minority, manufacture substances through photosynthesis, whereas the chemotrophic forms obtain energy from the oxidation of such substances as ammonia, nitrite, methane, hydrogen, and hydrogen sulfide. The relative importance of chemotrophic bacteria in synthesizing organic material is not sufficiently understood, but the abundance of such bacteria and of the substances they utilize for energy would indicate that such synthesis is of appreciable magnitude.

One important function of bacteria is the conversion of dissolved organic substances into particulate matter that can then be utilized by animal forms. For instance, Zobell and Feltham (1938) estimated that in a shallow marine mud flat, bacteria daily produced 10 g (dry weight) of organic matter per cubic foot of mud.

Heterotrophic bacteria also break down larger plants (seaweeds, eelgrass, and various marsh grasses). This results in a food consisting of bacteria and decayed vegetation that is readily consumed by many invertebrates. This detritus is of great importance in estuarine situations.

While discussing the various forms that synthesize organic material by photo- or chemosynthesis, one cannot neglect the direct utilization of dissolved organic substances by invertebrates. The relative importance of thus sidestepping one trophic level is not yet fully understood. However, when speaking of the base of the food chain we cannot neglect the role of these organic entities.

Baylor and Sutcliffe (1963) bubbled air through filtered seawater to produce a foam in which dissolved organic matter forms particulate organic matter. They fed one group of brine shrimp, *Artemia salina,* with yeast, one with the suspension of organic particles, and a third lot (controls) with filtered seawater that had not been subjected to air bubbles. Those fed yeast grew slightly faster than those fed the particulate organic matter. The controls differed very significantly in growth from those fed the suspension, and all controls died by the eighth day of the experiment.

DISTRIBUTION OF BASIC NUTRIENTS

The calculated volume of the seas is about $1,378,000 \times 10^3$ km^3. If we assume that the average depth at which growth from photosynthesis outweighs losses from basic metabolism is 50 m, 18,119,000 km^3 of the seas is available in which to convert nutrients into new growth. This is about 1.3% of the volume of the seas.

If the annual production of living plant matter in the seas is in the neighborhood of 19 billion tons (Pike and Spilhaus, 1962), the average production is about 52.4 tons/km^2. This comes to 0.105 pounds (47.6 g)/m^2 of surface area. We must remember that this is chiefly one-celled plants. The loss to the next trophic level is about 80% to 90%. If we settle for 85%, we have only 16.4 g/m^2, consisting chiefly of zooplankton, still mostly inedible. This amounts to 6633 g (14.6 pounds)/acre.

It becomes rather obvious that *on the average* the seas have a very low productivity. In two cuttings, my neighbor averages 3262 pounds of hay per acre of a 20-acre field. Even if he loses 85% in feeding it, the gain of 589 pounds per acre is an entire order of magnitude greater than the 14.6 pounds produced by the seas.

To maintain fishable production in any area in a steady state there must be a continuous supply of nutrients to replace those synthesized into organic substances. Ignoring for the moment chemosynthetic production, synthesis takes place in the lighted surface layer. At any given moment the major share of the nutrient elements in this layer is tied up in the protoplasm of living organisms. Since the remaining supply of available nutrients is only sufficient to maintain growth for a short period of time, it is obvious that more nutrients must become available. From whence can these nutrients come? There are three possible sources in any particular area:

1. Drainage from the land. It was estimated by Clarke (1916) that the world's rivers annually carry into the oceans 2.7 billion metric tons of dissolved substances. These are extremely important to some fisheries.

2. Recycling of nutrients. The death of organisms, their decay, and the reuse (with some energy loss) of the organic substance is a cycle of great importance. However, when this is the sole important source of nutrients the whole system must proceed very slowly. This is exemplified by the spring flowering of diatoms followed by a great drop in production as the available nutrients are depleted.

3. The flow into the lighted surface area of water from deeper layers. Because these deeper waters lack light for photosynthesis, they tend to store nutrients, perhaps derived chiefly from the decay of organisms that have sunk below the euphotic zone. This type of nutrient renewal is the basis for many of the world's greatest fisheries. As long as the nutrient-rich water continues to enter an area, production continues unabated. In many areas this vertical water exchange is seasonal; production waxes and wanes with its volume.

MECHANICS OF NUTRIENT ENTRY INTO PHOTIC ZONE

Before discussing the relative fertility of various seas and oceanic areas, I wish to point out the primary causes of the great disparity that exists even between closely adjacent areas. From the foregoing discussion it is obvious that in the seas, as on land, continued growth depends on the continuous replacement of nutrients. On land the soil acts as a savings account so that the total nutrient supply cannot be as quickly or as thoroughly depleted as in the euphotic zone of the sea. Fig. 2-2 illustrates several of the more important types of surface water exchange (excluding smaller bodies of water).

Type A (Fig. 2-2) occurs in the Mediterranean, the Red Sea, the Persian Gulf, and the northern Gulf of California. The nutrient level in the Mediterranean is the worst of any large sea, and this is reflected in the

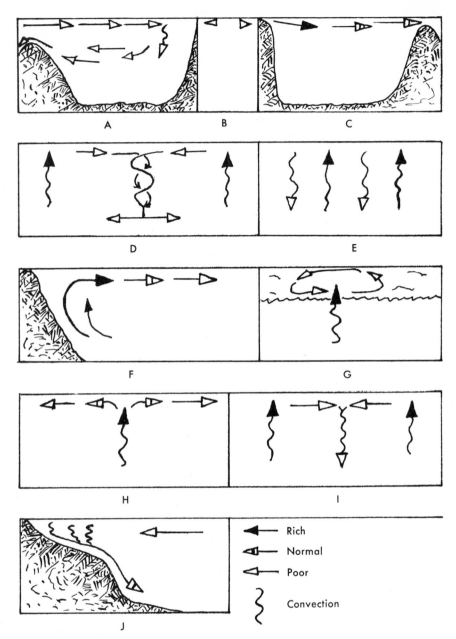

Fig. 2-2. Nutrient exchange in the euphotic zone. **A,** Surface inflow into an endorheic zone, e.g., the Mediterranean Sea. **B,** Oceanic gyre lacking currents or convection, e.g., the Sargasso Sea. **C,** Nutrient enrichment by rivers, e.g., the Black Sea. **D,** Cabelling where warm and cold surface currents meet, e.g., the Grank Banks. **E,** Sinking of surface waters by cooling, e.g., the Arctic Sea. **F,** Coastal upwelling from alongshore winds, e.g., California. **G,** Upwelling in depressed center of a cyclonic surface eddy, e.g., the eastern United States. **H,** Upwelling along a divergence where surface currents flow apart, e.g., Equatorial Divergence. **I,** Upwelling at some other point encouraged by sinking of surface water along a convergence where two surface currents meet, e.g., Equatorial Convergence. **J,** Cascading where winter cooling on the shelf induces sinking of shelf water, which flows along bottom and off shelf and is replaced with surface water lower in nutrients, e.g., the Irish Sea.

poverty of its fisheries. The cause is obvious; the incoming water from the surface layer of the North Atlantic is already depleted of nutrients.

Type B, indicating little or no surface water exchange, is typified by the Sargasso Sea, a deep lens of warm water normally extremely unproductive. Similar situations exist to a lesser degree in other great oceanic gyres.

Type C illustrates the replenishment of nutrients by rivers. The Black Sea, given as an example, is somewhat atypical since the entire basin below 150 to 200 m is stagnant because of the shallow sill. Other areas benefiting from river flow include the Sea of Azov, the Caspian Sea, the Yellow Sea, the Gulf of Mexico, the Gulf of Georgia, and innumerable estuaries. In addition to the nutrients brought into an area in the waters of the river itself, the fresh water may also cause enrichment in the euphotic zone by bringing deeper water to the surface. For instance, the fresh waters from the Fraser River discharge into the Strait of Georgia and, because of the positive water balance, flow out through the San Juan Archipelago. Thus Tully and Dodimead (1957) describe the strait as an arm of the sea into which a river discharges, forming a brackish upper zone that moves persistently seaward, entraining seawater en route.

Type D illustrates cabelling where strong warm and cold currents clash. Because of the nonlinear relationship between temperature and density, the mixed waters increase in density and sink to their new density level. This causes the upward convection of water that originates below the surface layers. This type of exchange is prominent where the Gulf Stream system meets the Labrador Current and where the Kuroshio runs head-on into the Oyashio.

Type E illustrates the thermohaline convection that occurs typically in high latitudes and most prominently in such extremely cold situations as Baffin Bay and the Norwegian, Labrador, Okhotsk, Bering, and Weddell Seas. The winter monsoon causes this type of mixing in the Japan, Yellow, and China Seas. It also occurs in warmer situations, especially when evaporation has so increased the density of surface water as to upset the vertical stability. This type of exchange is responsible for much of the productivity of the polar seas.

Type F illustrates wind-induced coastal upwelling. Such upwelling occurs chiefly in the Trade Wind belt on the western sides of the continents. The best examples occur off Peru, Angola, California, Morocco, and northwestern Australia. However, limited coastal upwelling occurs in a great many places, sometimes seasonally, especially in the Indian Ocean and in Indonesian areas that are subject to the monsoons.

Type G illustrates the rise of deeper water in the depression left in the center of a cyclonic (counterclockwise in the northern hemisphere and clockwise in the southern hemisphere) eddy. Such eddies often occur along the eastern seaboard of the United States.

Types H and I illustrate the convection of subsurface water to the surface where divergences or convergences occur. Such current boundaries may extend for hundreds of kilometers.

Type J shows winter cooling of a shallow shelf in which the cooling water cascades over the edge of the shelf, carrying with it what nutrients are available. The shelf water is replaced by surface water already depleted of nutrients.

To summarize the methods of entry of nutrients into the photic zone as shown in Fig. 2-2, the most important from a fisheries standpoint are F, H, and I, which are primarily oceanic phenomena, followed closely by method D.

Suggested readings

Barnes, H. 1957. Nutrient elements. In Hedgpeth, J., editor. Treatise on marine ecology and paleoecology, memoir 67, vol. 1, chap. 11. Geological Society of America, National Research Council, Washington, D. C. pp. 297-343.
Baylor, E. R., and W. H. Sutcliffe, Jr. 1963. Dis-

solved organic matter in sea water as a source of particulate food. Limnol. Oceanog. **8:**369-371.

Lucas, C. E. 1949. External metabolites and ecological adaptation. In Symposium of the Society for Experimental Biology. III. Selective toxicity and antibiotics. Academic Press, Inc., New York. pp. 336-356.

O'Kelley, J. C. 1968. Mineral nutrition of algae. Ann. Rev. Plant Physiol. **19:**89-112.

Pequenat, J., S. W. Fowler, and L. F. Small. 1969. Estimates of the zinc requirements of marine organisms. J. Fish. Res. Bd. Canada **26:**145-150.

Provasoli, L. 1958. Nutrition and ecology of protozoa and algae. Ann. Rev. Microbiol. **12:**279-308.

part two

🌿 Habitats and limiting factors

chapter 3

❧ Physical and chemical limiting factors

OXYGEN
Distribution and concentration

Surface waters, with their intimate contact with the atmosphere, seldom lack sufficient oxygen to sustain life. However, if oxygen is being utilized faster than it can be dissolved at the interface with the atmosphere, the level may fall below the lethal tolerance limits for most animal forms. This can occur in shoal waters under the following conditions:

1. Respiration of fish. This is especially apt to happen in streams overcrowded with spawning fish when there is no air movement to disturb the water surface so as to favor the exchange of gases (Davidson, 1933).
2. Respiration of plants during hours of darkness. This occurs in both fresh and marine waters when plants or autotrophic Protista are exceptionally abundant. Heavy overblooming of autotrophic organisms can also cause oxygen supersaturation during hours of sunlight, especially in calm weather. This also may kill fishes through the formation of gas emboli in the gill capillaries, causing suffocation.
3. Oxidation of organic substances. This can occur through pollution (discussed elsewhere) or naturally through the accumulation of organic material. Thus fish kills often occur in small bodies of water when the water becomes suddenly well mixed so that light accumulated organic sediments are dispersed through the water column.

Below the photosynthetic zone in the great ocean basins the oxygen level of each water mass depends chiefly on the following factors:

1. What the oxygen level of the water was at the surface before it sank. Because of the relationship between temperature and solubility, water sinking at high latitudes will normally contain more oxygen than water sinking in the tropics.
2. The proportion of the original oxygen lost either by the respiration of living organisms or by the oxidation of material sinking from the surface. This proportion depends on the quantity of material available for oxidation, the prevailing temperature, and the length of time the water has been in the dark.

This latter figure cannot be easily obtained. For example, in discussing the rapidity of the water exchange between the Atlantic Ocean and the Mediterranean Sea,

Sverdrup et al. (1942) state that ". . . the in- and outflow is sufficient to provide for a complete renewal of the Mediterranean water in about seventy-five years." A little calculation quickly shows that their figures for inflow, 1,750,000 m³/sec, would indeed completely fill the Mediterranean Sea in less than 75 years. The question is, after 75 years, how much of the water in the basin is water that was there 75 years ago? Certainly the warm saline water sinking during the winter in the Levantine Basin does not fill the bottom of the sea. Rather it flows westward more or less horizontally to Gibraltar. Although there is renewal of deeper water from sinking during severe winters in the Adriatic and Tyrrhenian Seas, the lower oxygen values, especially in the deeper portion of the eastern basin, would indicate that the deeper basin waters are more ancient than the quickly renewable surface waters. Landis (1970a) mentions a residence time somewhat less than 100 years for the deep Mediterranean water based on carbon-14 determinations.

With regard to the great ocean basins, Fig. 1-7 shows that the deepest waters of the ocean originate in the Atlantic Ocean sector of the World Ocean surrounding Antarctica and in the Arctic Sea just east of Greenland. Thus the Atlantic Ocean contains both large sources of cold aerated Bottom Water. The Pacific Ocean, containing a good half of all the water on the globe, has no direct source of Deep Bottom Water, which must travel completely around Antarctica to reach the Pacific. The great disparity between water volume and sources of aerated water in these two oceans is very apparent. The deeper waters of the Atlantic contain from 5 to 6 ppm of oxygen; the Pacific contains 4 to 4.5 ppm near Antarctica and about 3 ppm at 50° N lat. The oxygen minimum layer in the Atlantic is about 3 ppm, and in the Pacific it is about 0.5 ppm. In the Pacific the deep waters progressively decrease in oxygen from south to north. The deep waters of the western Pacific contain slightly more oxygen than the

eastern Pacific, suggesting that deep water from the southern hemisphere moves toward the North Pacific in a clockwise direction.

The oxygen content of the major portions of the ocean basins is sufficient to sustain life. Oxygen values are usually lowest below sharp changes in density, probably as a result of the oxidation of sinking material in which the rapidity of sinking is slowed by the density gradient. A deep oxygen minimum layer tends to occur at the junction of the warm- and cold-water spheres, and a second shallow oxygen minimum layer exists below the sharp thermocline in equatorial and tropical waters.

In some deep trenches and basins the oxygen level may fall too low to sustain life. This occurs, for instance, in the Cariaco Trench of the Caribbean and in the Sulu Basin. However, stagnation is most common in basins in which water exchange is restricted by shallow sills and an excess of outflowing fresh water such as the Black Sea, deeper portions of the Baltic Sea, and several smaller Norwegian fjords.

The rate at which oxygen is consumed in the deep oceans is very low. Thus Riley (1951) estimates that 90% of the organic matter produced in the euphotic zone is consumed in the upper 200 m, leaving but 10% to be oxidized in deeper layers. He calculated the amount of oxygen consumed per year at several depths in the Atlantic. At 2000 m it amounted to 0.0013 ml/l and at 4000 m to only 0.00013 ml/l. His estimate of minimum rates in the deeper waters indicates that oxidation there has been continuing for 10,000 years. Kulp (1953) made estimates of the age of deep water by carbon-14 dating of the carbonate from large water samples and obtained ages ranging from 450 to 1950 years. These estimates show that oxygen consumption in deep waters is exceedingly slow, which might be expected from the low temperatures, sparse fauna, and lack of dead organic matter.

The assumption that the various processes that determine oxygen values are in a steady state has been disputed by Worthington

(1954). His data showed a decline of 0.3 ml/l of oxygen in North Atlantic Deep Water in two to three decades, which is an annual consumption rate of 0.015 ml/l. His interpretation is that Bottom Water is formed only sporadically during especially cold cycles, the last of which occurred in the decade 1810 to 1820. This implies that deep water always tends to become anaerobic unless the rate of replacement averages higher than the rate of consumption.

In addition to the low oxygen levels found in stagnant basins, there are other areas in which oxygen may fall too low to sustain fishable populations. An example is given by the fisheries on the shelf that extends from the southern tip of India some 2200 km to Karachi, Pakistan. The low oxygen levels appear during the southwest monsoon when upwelling occurs along this stretch of coast. Banse (1968) states that upwelling water along the southwestern coast of India can be very low in oxygen; concentrations below 0.25 ml oxygen/l (less than 5% of saturation) are common on the shelf, and some stations were devoid of oxygen. He further states:

> The fact that off Bombay, as off Calicut, the oxygen content dropped to zero in near-bottom water suggests that there may possibly be a vast area on the outer shelf (and perhaps also on the middle shelf) approximately from Cochin to Karachi that is devoid of commercially exploitable concentrations of demersal fishes during the southwest monsoon. The fishes very likely disappear before the oxygen has completely vanished.*

Requirements

The oxygen requirements of aquatic organisms vary between species and between age groups or developmental stages of the same species. The oxygen requirement also depends on the organism's activity (which is partially a function of temperature) and whether the organism has had an opportunity to become physiologically adjusted.

_____

*From Banse, K. 1968. Hydrography of the Arabian Sea shelf of India and Pakistan and effects on demersal fishes. Deep-Sea Res. **15:**45-79.

The minimum oxygen requirements of 13 species of freshwater fishes (Rounsefell and Everhart, 1953) show tolerances ranging from immeasurable traces for the golden shiner, *Notemigonus crysoleucas,* to 2.2 ppm in the Atlantic salmon, *Salmo salar.* Experiments on young silver salmon, *Oncorhynchus kisutch,* by Davison et al. (1959) show that tolerance changed only slightly at temperatures between 12° and 20° C, but fell rapidly at temperatures above 20° C. They also found that fish held near the low tolerance level of 2 ppm lost weight; at 2.9 ppm they gained weight.

Warmwater fishes in general have a lower threshold of tolerance. Five small species of warmwater fishes, three Cyprinidae and two Poeciliidae, were found by Whitworth and Irwin (1961) to exist comfortably at an oxygen level of 1 ppm, and large numbers survived at oxygen levels of 0.45 ppm.

Experimental information on the oxygen tolerance of marine fishes is scanty. Hall (1929) studied oxygen consumption at various oxygen tensions for scup, *Stenotomus chrysops;* northern puffer, *Sphoeroides maculatus;* and toadfish, *Opsanus tau.* He concluded that the oxygen consumption is much higher in very active species than in the sluggish toadfish. His data for oxygen are given as "oxygen tension" without qualifications as to the existing barometric pressure or water vapor (see Ricker, 1934), so it is difficult to compare his results with those of the previously mentioned authors. However, his data show the toadfish surviving at 0 oxygen tension (stated as 0 to 1 mm Hg).

The oxygen level can be very important in the incubation of eggs. McNeil (1966) found, for instance, that low oxygen levels in stream gravels caused by low stream flow produced a 60% to 90% mortality of pink and chum salmon eggs in a southeastern Alaska stream.

In inland seas the concentration of oxygen in deeper waters varies from sea to sea. In the largest inland sea, the Caspian Sea, salinity toward the south end is 12 to 13 $^o/_{oo}$, dropping considerably toward the north end; on the eastern shore all bays with restricted water exchange have a very high salinity because of excessive evaporation. The vertical circulation is slight so that oxygen is scarce below 200 to 300 m and often 0 at the bottom, accompanied by bacterial generation of hydrogen sulfide.

In the adjacent Aral Sea the salinity is a little lower than in the Caspian Sea, but the composition is different; chlorides are lower than in average seawater, but sulfides are about four times higher.

Freshwater inland seas or lakes usually differ somewhat from the typical smaller lake with regard to circulation. In the temperate zone, thermal convection, deep stirring by winds, and wind-induced currents tend to prevent the seasonal formation of shallow thermoclines; in the larger of the Great Lakes, thermoclines, when they occasionally occur, are weak and evanescent. In tropical areas most lakes tend to be meromictic with deep, stable, stagnant layers; Lakes Tanganyika and Nyasa are typical.

Oxygen and nitrogen supersaturation of coastal waters

In Chapter 15 is described the deleterious effects on fishes of supersaturation of stream waters with atmospheric nitrogen. This occurs especially where falling water from a spillway plunges into a deep pool. Supersaturation with oxygen or with both oxygen and nitrogen can also occur in marine waters.

Oxygen supersaturation can result from photosynthesis. It can also occur, along with nitrogen supersaturation, when the sea surface is 100% saturated and there is a rapid change in temperature or barometric pressure. Thus if saturated water is warmed rapidly or if warm water is mixed with saturated cold water, supersaturation will occur and remain until the gases again reach equilibrium with the atmosphere.

In a 4-year study at Boothbay Harbor, Maine, Stickney (1968) concluded that when oxygen and nitrogen maintain the normal ratio at which they enter into solution from the atmosphere ($O_2 = 0.577N_2 - 0.22$), the supersaturation is caused by changes in some physical property of the water. When oxygen exceeds this ratio, the excess is that added by photosynthesis.

Stickney found it difficult to induce gas bubble conditions in herring at less than 200% saturation of pure oxygen. Nitrogen is dangerous at much lower concentrations; Ebel (1971) showed that nitrogen could kill juvenile chinook salmon at 127% saturation.

Under normal conditions Stickney suggests that natural gas levels in the environment are insufficient to be detrimental to organisms. However, when water is pumped from any depth into a fish or lobster pound or a shallow tank at atmospheric pressure, a nominal supersaturation becomes absolute. This can be further aggravated if the change in pressure is accompanied by a higher temperature.

SALINITY
General considerations

Salinity, as applied to seawater, is very exactly defined by Sverdrup et al. (1942). I paraphrase it as grams of solid material per kilogram of seawater when all carbonate is oxidized, bromine and iodine are replaced by chlorine, and all organic matter is oxidized. In true seawater the *proportions* of the major constituents are virtually constant regardless of source.

In rather dilute seawater, however, there may be significant deviations in these ionic ratios. Khlebovich (1968) stresses the "ecophysiological barrier" dividing marine and limnic fauna at a salinity of about 5 $^0/_{00}$. In his analysis he states that the calcium:chloride ratio rises steeply at about 5 $^0/_{00}$ in the waters of the Kara, White, Baltic, Azov, Black, and probably Caspian Seas, and in British Columbia. A perusal of the data offered by Clarke (1916) shows that these are areas in which the diluting river waters, the Danube, Vistula, etc., contain high ratios of calcium so that a rise in the calcium:chloride ratio with dilution should be expected. Kirsch (1956) found in Bute and Knight Inlets in British Columbia that, although the change in ionic ratios could be partially explained by dilution, the change exceeded such a dilution effect. He attributes this effect to cation exchange between the water and the suspended clays, the value of the resulting ionic ratio depending on the extent of dilution, the nature and concentration of the silt, and possibly the particle size distribution. Since the world's seawater salts contain on the average 1.15% calcium whereas lake and river waters average 20.39%, some rise in the proportion of calcium with dilution should be expected, and a physiologic barrier need not be postulated.

In inland seas there is a great diversity in the proportions of dissolved chemicals. Thus inland saline waters may have excessive proportions of carbonates, sulfates, chlorides, etc. The principal saline inland seas with which we are concerned, the Caspian and Aral Seas, differ from oceanic waters chiefly in their higher proportions of calcium, magnesium, and sulfates.

Two important differences between fresh water and seawater of major ecologic significance are the maximum densities and the freezing points. Whereas fresh water reaches its maximum density at a temperature of $3.94°$ C at one atmosphere, seawater of a salinity of 35.5 $°/_{00}$ reaches maximum density at $-3.8°$ C. While fresh water freezes at $0°$ C, seawater of 35.5 $°/_{00}$ commences to freeze at about $-1.96°$ C, under normal pressure. These two facts have a profound effect. Whereas the hypolimnia of freshwater lakes remain at $4°$ C or above, the deeper waters of the ocean basins are typically less than $0°$ C. The differences in vertical stability account for the usual shallow thermocline in fresh waters in contrast to the great depth of the mixed layer in oceanic waters.

The ability of organisms to tolerate changes in salinity is of the utmost importance to their distribution. Some organisms are *poikilosmotic;* i.e., they have no means of maintaining their internal fluids at a concentration different from that of the surrounding water. Others are *homoiosmotic* and endeavor to maintain the concentration of their internal fluids against external differences. Osmoregulation, or lack of regulation, is treated in detail in many physiology texts.

Regardless of the physiologic reasons for the tolerance or intolerance of levels or of changes in salinity, the degree of tolerance is of great importance to the seasonal and areal distribution of organisms. Stenohaline organisms, which can tolerate only a narrow range of salinity, cannot successfully invade the estuaries, for instance. Euryhaline organisms that attempt to maintain their own internal concentration expend a certain amount of energy. If the difference between internal and external concentrations becomes great, the animal may be under considerable stress. As a general rule marine forms can withstand lower salinities at higher temperatures. This may be influential in causing the adult forms of many species to migrate out of the estuaries during the winter. It has been suggested by Pearse and Gunter (1957) that this may account for the rich estuarine fauna of the tropics.

Gunter (1957) states that the young of many marine species are found in fresh waters. This is an established part of the life cycle of many marine fishes; the adults spawn in water of high salinity and the young invade the estuaries, often penetrating into wholly fresh water. Apparently as they grow larger (or older), their tolerance for low salinity is diminished. Nelson (1967) showed that this is the normal life pattern of the Atlantic croaker, *Micropogon undulatus,* and the spot, *Leiostomus xanthurus,* on the northern Gulf coast.

Many marine species cannot tolerate low salinities. Even in an estuarine situation the salinity gradient acts as a movable barrier to many species. To illustrate this point, the relative abundances of 29 species of fish taken by a small-mesh otter trawl in the Louisiana marshes during a 2-year period are shown in Fig. 3-1. The heavier density of *Mugil* and *Brevoortia* at low salinities is partially an artifact because the juveniles,

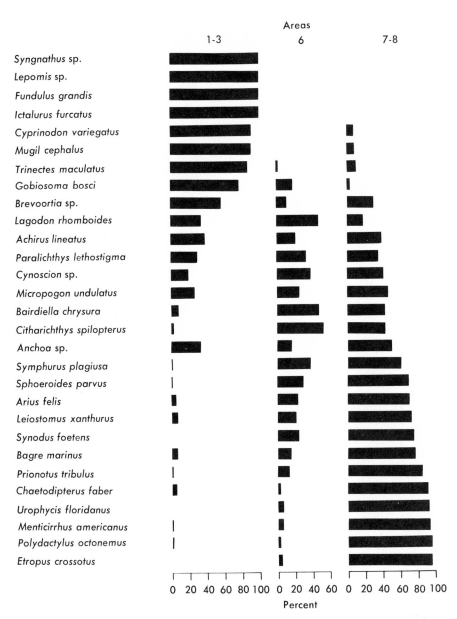

Fig. 3-1. Abundance of 29 species of fishes in three salinity ranges in Louisiana marshes over 2-year period.

		Salinities (monthly)	
Areas	Mean	Minimum	Maximum
1-3	3.48	1.28	6.46
6	11.61	6.96	13.86
7-8	15.97	9.50	21.66

abundant in this zone, were easily taken by the small trawl, whereas the fast-moving adults were seldom captured.

Despite these generalizations there are some groups of marine fishes in which one or more species has become acclimated to fresh water. Among the *Gadidae,* for instance, the freshwater ling or burbot, *Lota lota,* is circumpolar in distribution. The Atlantic tomcod, *Microgadus tomcod,* that inhabits coastal estuaries from Labrador to Virginia spawns indifferently during the winter in salt or brackish waters; I have observed them crowded into the wholly fresh water of Bangor Pool on the Penobscot River. One group is landlocked in Lake St. John, Quebec (Legendre and Lagueux, 1948). Wynne-Edwards (1952) also mentions the small cod (navaga or saffron), *Eleginus navaga* (or *E. gracilis*), entering the Mackenzie River and fresh waters in Alaska and eastern Siberia.

Among the temperate basses (family Percichthyidae), both the typically anadromous striped bass or rock, *Morone* (= *Roccus*) *saxatilis,* and the white perch, *Morone americana,* have wholly freshwater populations. Curiously, whereas the white perch is almost wholly in fresh water in the northern portion of its range, north of Cape Cod, where it is seldom found in seawater, the natural freshwater populations of the striped bass occur in the South, e.g., a fluvial population of striped bass occurs in the Alabama River.

Effect on reproduction

In much the same way that amphibians are tied to water for reproduction, a great many estuarine species, including the blue crab, *Callinectes sapidus,* cannot normally reproduce in the estuary but must seek waters of higher salinity to spawn (Sandoz and Rogers, 1944). This interdependence between the marine and estuarine environments is a rather delicate relationship, the strength of which varies from species to species, perhaps even from race to race of the same species. Kutkuhn (1966) shows

that 25 species of penaeid shrimp involved in world commerce can be arranged in descending order as to their dependence on the estuarine environment from a few that live wholly in the estuary to some such as the scarlet prawn, *Plesiopenaeus edwardsianus,* of the Gulf of Mexico and western Atlantic that develops and lives its entire life at depths of about 900 m.

It is obvious then that salinity plays a very considerable role in the distribution in both time and space of the various life history stages of many species. Thus Loosanoff and Davis (1963) found 7.5 $^0/_{00}$ to be the lowest salinity at which the American oyster, *Crassostrea virginica,* would develop normal gonads in Long Island Sound. In extensive experiments (Davis and Calabrese, 1964) with hard clams, *Mercenaria mercenaria,* and oysters, *C. virginica,* the larvae of the oyster developed normally at salinities ranging from 10 to 27 $^0/_{00}$, but survival was low, only 23%, at 7.5 $^0/_{00}$ salinity. Clam larvae did not survive in any numbers at salinities below 15 $^0/_{00}$. However, in both cases, the eggs required higher salinities than the larvae—17.5 $^0/_{00}$ for oysters (survival was low at 15 $^0/_{00}$) and 22.5 $^0/_{00}$ for clams. For both species the lower salinities were tolerated better at higher temperatures.

Some indication of the maximum salinity tolerated by larval oysters is shown by the tripling in the number of oysters per square meter in two central Texas oyster beds during the month of October after the higher salinities had dropped to about 35 $^0/_{00}$ (Copeland and Hoese, 1966).

The majority of the fishes of economic importance that spend any significant portion of their lives in the estuaries cannot reproduce at low salinities. Consequently they spawn either offshore or in the salt wedge invading the mouth or deeper channels of some estuaries. Such quasi-catadromous species include the red drum, *Sciaenops ocellata;* the black drum, *Pogonias cromis;* the mullet, *Mugil* sp.; the Atlantic croaker, *Micropogon undulatus;* the menhaden, *Bre-*

voortia sp.; the weakfishes, *Cynoscion* sp.; and the tarpon, *Megalops atlantica.*

Relationship to ultimate size

Apart from the fact that in many species only the young and therefore the smaller specimens are found in low salinities, there are other indications that individuals of stocks dwelling in low salinities are smaller than their counterparts living at high salinities. Among the sea herring, *Clupea harengus harengus* and *C. harengus pallasi,* those inhabiting the White and Baltic Seas and the inner passages of southeastern Alaska are smaller than their oceanic counterparts. Similarly, the races of the coho (silver) salmon, *Oncorhynchus kisutch,* that make their marine habitat the Gulf of Georgia are smaller than those races that venture into the open Pacific. Segerstråle (1957) states that the cod in the Baltic Sea show a marked reduction in size compared to those in higher salinity waters.

Perhaps the clearest illustration is afforded by the extreme case of the sockeye (red) salmon, *Oncorhynchus nerka.* In some lakes there are three populations—the seagoing anadromous population; the "residual" fish that are the young of the anadromous fish that did not go to sea either because of being entrapped in the lake by a fast-forming spring thermocline or because underpopulation of the young raised the threshold size for migration; and the adfluvial race of kokanees, sometimes dubbed *O. nerka kennerlyi* by the taxonomists.

The seagoing race is several times larger than the residuals, which in turn are usually slightly larger than the kokanees. However, when young kokanees have been forced to migrate to the sea, they return as large, or almost as large, as the regular anadromous stock. Similarly, along the New England seaboard those eastern brook charr, *Salvelinus fontinalis,* that spend a few months at sea return much larger than those individuals of the same population that chose to remain in the stream.

The comparatively smaller size attained by stocks of a species that live in waters of low salinity is usually explained on the basis of food supply. This may perhaps be defended when comparing the food in a typical north temperate lake to that available in the sea. It does not explain smaller size in a rich estuary or why occasionally kokanees do not grow large under favorable conditions of feeding.

Tolerance of freshwater fishes

In a study of 60 lakes in Saskatchewan (Rawson and Moore, 1944) it was found that the salinity tolerances of freshwater fishes varied widely. Very stenohaline species, the longnose dace, *Rhinichthys cataractae,* and the blacknose shiner, *Notropis heterolepis,* were not found in salinities over 0.6 $^o/_{oo}$. Seven species existed in lakes with 10 $^o/_{oo}$; only the ninespine stickleback survived at 20 $^o/_{oo}$. However, the introduction of several species (Rawson, 1946) showed that the whitefish, *Coregonus clupeaformis,* and the blue pike or walleye, *Stizostedion vitreum,* throve in large Redberry Lake (70 km^2) at a salinity of 15 $^o/_{oo}$. The whitefish grew twice as fast as those in Lake Winnipeg or the Great Lakes. These studies show that salinity of 15 $^o/_{oo}$ is approaching the tolerance limit for freshwater fish. This is close to the salinity osmotically equal to fish blood, about 14 to 15 $^o/_{oo}$. Jones (1964) cites Garrey (1916) as stating that freshwater fish will readily tolerate diluted seawater or similar "balanced" solutions of an osmotic pressure equal to that of their blood, but that higher concentrations are rapidly fatal.

Accelerated growth appears to be in keeping with other observations on the larger size of freshwater individuals of the same species in saline waters.

TEMPERATURE
Effect on growth and longevity

Temperature has a profound impact on all living organisms. Physiologic processes are accelerated with rising temperatures until an optimum is reached. This is illustrated by Fig. 3-2, which shows the acceleration of growth in young sockeye salmon with increased temperature up to a plateau, followed by a rapid decline with further increase in temperature. Physiologists have attempted to formulate rules for the interpretation of temperature effects on growth. These rules relate the speed of growth as a linear function of temperature that approximately doubles with each 10° C temperature increase. Obviously such rules are of little use except for small selected segments of the temperature range for each species. Each species tends to have its own range of favorable temperatures, and in many species found over wide areas, stocks inhabiting different areas have developed genetic differences in physiologic temperature accommodation.

An illustration of the differences in growth with temperature is afforded by consideration of the growth rates of the Pacific herring, *Clupea harengus pallasi,* from a number of localities (Fig. 3-3). The six races with the lowest growth rates are all from "inside" waters where space, food, and perhaps lower salinity probably overshadow any effect of temperature. Fig. 3-4 shows the length at age 6 years of the six faster growing "outside" races as plotted against the approximate nautical miles from San Diego. In explanation of this geographic cline, I have also plotted size against the approximate sea temperatures at a depth of 10 m. The San Diego temperature is speculative and will vary with upwelling; the other temperatures represent a 5-year summer average approximated from the isotherms shown by Dodimead et al. (1963).

The sea herring, a subarctic species, appears to have a rather low optimum temperature. As we proceed south, this optimum is gradually exceeded, as shown by the low abundance of herring south of Cape Flattery. This opinion is shared by Uda, who states:

> The decline of Asiatic and Alaskan salmon and herring fisheries in the past 50 years suggests to us the effect of Arctic and sub-Arctic warming on land and in the sea.*

That the optimum temperature for some species is exceedingly low is shown by the existence of fishes and invertebrates at great depths in the oceans. An outstanding example of the ability to survive and prosper at low temperatures is furnished by a member of the family Umbridae, the Alaska blackfish, *Dallia pectoralis* (Turner, 1886; Evermann and Goldsborough, 1907; Wynne-Edwards, 1952). This remarkable fish lives in great abundance in the shallow tundra bogs and ponds of northwest Alaska. The natives trap them by the thousands and let them freeze in the open air in baskets for dog and human food. On thawing they are as lively as before freezing.

Longevity as well as growth is affected by temperature. References are often made to

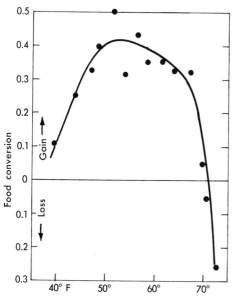

Fig. 3-2. Growth of young sockeye salmon in 2-week periods as shown by food conversion at different water temperatures. (From Rounsefell, G. A. 1958. U. S. Fish Wildl. Serv., Fish. Bull. **58:**83-169; based on data from Donaldson, L. R., and F. J. Foster. 1941. Trans. Amer. Fish. Soc. **70:**339-346.)

*Uda, M. 1961. Fisheries oceanography in Japan, especially on the principles of fish distribution, concentration, dispersal and fluctuation. Calif. Mar. Res. Comm. CalCOFI Rep. **8:**25-31.

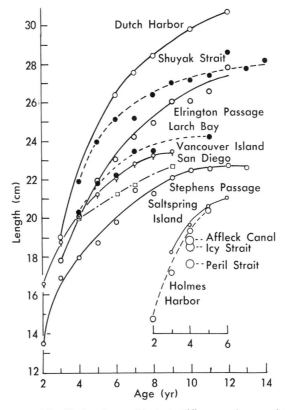

Fig. 3-3. Growth curves of Pacific herring to illustrate differences in growth by latitude and by presence in "inside" and "outside" waters.

Outside waters	
Dutch Harbor	Aleutian Islands
Shuyak Strait	Afognak Island
Elrington Passage	Prince William Sound
Larch Bay	Southeastern Alaska
West Coast	Vancouver Island
San Diego	California
Inside waters	
Stephens Passage	Southeastern Alaska
Affleck Canal	Southeastern Alaska
Icy Strait	Southeastern Alaska
Peril Strait	Southeastern Alaska
Saltspring Island	Gulf of Georgia
Holmes Harbor	Puget Sound

the smaller size of fishes in southern waters as compared to the same species in more northern waters. This does not mean that the southern stocks grow slower; quite the reverse, they usually grow faster, mature earlier, and die younger.

The Pacific razor clam, *Siliqua patula,* is fished from Pismo Beach, California, to Hallo Bay on Shelikof Strait, Alaska (Wey-mouth and McMillin, 1931). As shown in Fig. 3-5, the median length at the second annual ring decreases from 9 cm to just over 2 cm as one proceeds along the 2400 miles (3862 km) north from Pismo Beach to Hallo Bay. However, the age at which 5% of the 1-year-old clams still survive increases drastically. At Pismo Beach the 5% survival age is only 4.4 years with no clams over 5

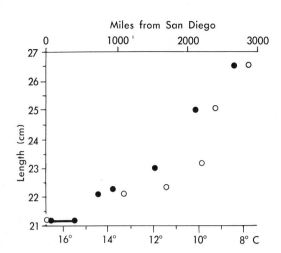

Fig. 3-4. Length of Pacific herring from "outside" waters at age 6 years in relation to temperature at 10 m (filled circles) and to miles from San Diego following trend of coast (open circles).

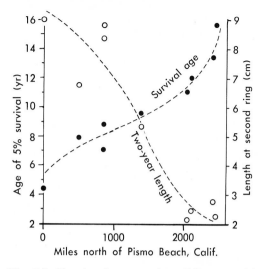

Fig. 3-5. Showing for razor clam *(Siliqua patula)* plot of distance northward from Pismo Beach, California, against length at second ring (open circles) and age at which 5% survive (filled circles).

years old; a few 9-year-old clams are taken in Washington, whereas in Alaska there are many 12- and 14-year-old clams, with some as old as 19 years of age.

Seasonal movements

Cold-blooded creatures seek to remain in their optimum temperature range insofar as it is compatible with their requirements for food, reproduction, and shelter. In order to accomplish this, many species must shift their habitat geographically or vertically with the seasons. Some, such as the bluefin tuna, perform long seasonal migrations, northward in the spring and southward in the fall; others move onshore in summer and offshore in winter; still others, chiefly benthic species, remain on the continental shelves in summer but move to the slopes in winter.

A good example of the latter movement (Fig. 3-6) occurs in the offshore trawl fishery of the state of Washington (Alverson, 1960) conducted by otter trawlers on the continental shelf and the continental slope at depths between 18 and 546 m and extending from north of the Columbia River to the northern end of Hecate Strait. The

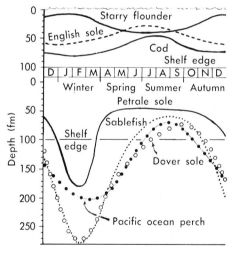

Fig. 3-6. Seasonal depths of significant catches of principal species in Washington–British Columbia otter trawl fishery, 1955 to 1957. (Modified from Alverson, D. L. 1960. Pac. Mar. Fish. Comm. Bull. **4**:1-66.)

Starry flounder	*Platichthys stellatus*
English "sole"	*Parophrys vetulus*
Pacific cod	*Gadus macrocephalus*
Petrale "sole"	*Eopsetta jordani*
Sablefish	*Anoplopoma fimbria*
Dover "sole"	*Microstomus pacificus*
Pacific ocean perch	*Sebastes alutus*

continental shelf is very narrow, only 56 km at the widest point; the largest area is contained in Hecate Strait. The different behavior of the four species of flounders is striking. The starry flounder, *Platichthys stellatus,* and the English sole (actually a flounder), *Parophrys vetulus,* are not found in commercial quantities in waters off the continental shelf. On the other hand, the petrale sole, *Eopsetta jordani,* and the Dover sole, *Microstomus pacificus,* show regular seasonal movements. The petrale sole moves offshore only during the coldest season of the year, but the Dover sole may be said to live offshore and move inshore during the warmest months.

The Pacific cod, *Gadus macrocephalus,* remains on the continental shelf but in most areas is about 55 m deeper in winter than in summer.

The sablefish or so-called black cod, *Anoplopoma fimbria,* remains in slope waters most of the year, spending only a few months on the deeper portion of the shelf.

The Pacific ocean perch, *Sebastes alutus,* is one of several species of rockfishes, family Scorpaenidae, abundant along the Pacific coast. They differ in their preferred habitats. Some species, e.g., the black rockfish, *S. melanops,* are taken in shoal waters, commonly among pilings (I have taken them on a light fly rod); fishermen often call them "black bass." *S. alutus* exhibits a very marked seasonal depth migration from slope to shelf. It is very abundant; during the developing years of the halibut fishery it was not marketable and because of its distended swim bladder died on reaching the surface. When halibut vessels were fishing an area, it was common to see for miles rows of large scarlet rockfish bobbing on the surface.

A fine example of the seasonal shift in vertical distribution is afforded by the pollock or saithe, *Pollachius virens,* in New England. During the summer months they school at the surface and can be taken with purse seines and even with dip nets, as they form dense boiling schools, but in the winter months they are taken on the bottom at depths of 80 to 90 fm (146 to 165 m) with otter trawls.

The haddock of Georges Bank invade the shoals at 5 to 20 fm (9 to 55 m) in spring and fall; in summer the shoals are too warm and in winter too cold. A further example is afforded by the estuarine-inhabiting genus *Cynoscion* of the Gulf of Mexico and the South Atlantic. These fishes are sensitive to cold, and along the Texas coast of the Gulf when the winter northerlies hit with a sudden drop in temperature, they retreat to deeper water, which is usually the dredged ship channels or areas from which large quantities of spoil have been removed, such as Offats Bayou in Galveston.

Sessile organisms suffer a disadvantage. Their lack of mobility often causes heavy losses of oysters in the intertidal zone during severe freezes.

Life history avoidance of lethal temperatures

Perhaps the best illustration of the dovetailing of life history with lethal temperature is shown by the Salmonidae. The lethal temperatures for the young of certain species of North American Salmonidae are shown in Fig. 3-7. The highest lethal temperature tolerances all occur in the young of the genus *Salmo*. The young of the three species on which data are available (the Atlantic salmon, *S. salar;* the rainbow trout, *S. gairdneri;* and the brown trout, *S. trutta*) spend some time in a warm fluvial environment, usually including one or more summers. The lake trout, *Cristivomer namaycush,* has the lowest temperature tolerance, but the young hatch in the spring in oligotrophic lakes where they can retreat during the hot summer to the cool hypolimnion below the thermocline. The young of the eastern brook charr, *Salvelinus fontinalis,* are midway between *Salmo* and *Cristivomer* in tolerance. They cannot tolerate midsummer temperatures in many streams, often including those inhabited by parr of *S. salar.*

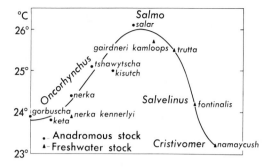

Fig. 3-7. Lethal temperatures for young Salmonidae. (From Rounsefell, G. A. 1958. U. S. Fish Wildl. Serv. Fish. Bull. **58**:83-169.)

In such situations young *S. fontinalis* seek cool spring-fed tributaries.

The lethal temperatures for young of *Oncorhynchus* cover a wide range. The two species with the highest tolerances are the chinook (king) and coho (silver) salmons, *O. tshawytscha* and *O. kisutch.* The young of *O. kisutch* and a large proportion of those of *O. tshawytscha* live in streams during the summer.

The young of pink and chum salmons, *O. gorbuscha* and *O. keta,* have the lowest temperature tolerance of any of the genus *Oncorhynchus,* yet they spawn in streams. The young emerge from the gravel of the redds early in the spring, however, and descend immediately to the sea, avoiding the high stream temperatures of summer.

The young of the sockeye salmon, *O. nerka,* usually dwell from 1 to 5 years in fresh water. However, being lacustrine anadromous rather than fluvial anadromous, the young, on emerging from the redds, seek a nursery lake in which to grow. In the southern portion of its range, only lakes temperature stratified in summer support runs of *O. nerka.*

Effect on reproduction

Most organisms can grow at temperatures both lower and higher than those required for reproduction. Temperatures critical to reproduction may vary with the reproductive stage. Thus many fishes require cool water for the maturation of the gonads. For some

invertebrates the critical temperatures for cleavage of the egg is lower than the temperature required by the larvae.

Incubation of largemouth bass eggs spawned at 70° F (21° C) at eight temperatures from 50° to 85° F (10° to 29° C) (Kelley, 1968) showed a high survival of all lots acclimated at the rate of 0.5° F (0.28° C) per hour but a high mortality of nonacclimated eggs outside of the range from 55° to 75° F (13° to 24° C). This supports the view that the critical factor was not the temperature of incubation but most probably a critical period in which the embryo is sensitive to rapid changes in temperature.

In experiments with oysters, Butler (1965) found that when Chesapeake Bay oysters were transplanted to Santa Rosa Sound, Florida, they soon became acclimated and started spawning at a temperature 5° C higher than they had commenced spawning in Chesapeake Bay. Their spawning pattern closely simulated that of the native Santa Rosa Sound oysters. They also spawned over a period of 5 months instead of their former 3½ months (Fig. 3-8).

From 10 years of records in Santa Rosa Sound, Butler has deduced that spawning is initiated following a 5° C temperature rise within a 30-day period. This indicates that spawning is not initiated by any hereditary response to a specific threshold temperature, but is regulated primarily by changing temperature levels. However, the reverse is not true, in that when southern forms are transplanted to northern waters they very often fail to spawn. This cannot be ascribed wholly to a lack of a sufficiently fast rise in temperature in northern waters, but must therefore indicate that both a temperature change and a temperature threshold are involved.

As a whole, in organisms whose range extends over a wide latitude with a wide temperature differential, the dates of spawning show a latitudinal cline. This is true of the Pacific herring, *Clupea harengus pallasi* (Table 3-1), whose single spawning season ranges from December at San Diego, Cali-

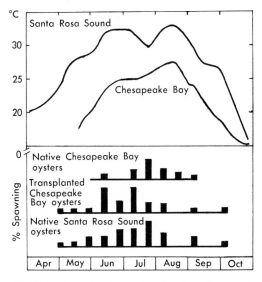

Fig. 3-8. Reproductive cycle of native Chesapeake Bay oysters compared to that of Chesapeake Bay oysters after growing 2 years in Santa Rosa Sound, Florida, and to that of native Santa Rosa Sound oysters. Horizontal bars indicate duration of spawning and vertical bars mark percent of spawning in each sample (20% to 90%). (Modified from Butler, P. A. 1965. Reaction of estuarine mollusks to some environmental factors. Biological problems in water pollution, third seminar, 1962. Publ. No. 999-WP-25. U. S. Public Health Service, Washington, D. C. pp. 92-104.)

Table 3-1. Pacific herring spawning[1]

Locality	Date
San Diego	Middle to end of Dec.
Monterey Bay	Jan. 20 to March 1
San Francisco	Jan. 9 to March 22
Tomales Bay	Jan. 9 to March 1
Oregon	Feb. thru March
Willapa Bay	Feb. 12-26
Grays Harbor	Feb.
Puget Sound[2]	Feb. 1 to April 7
North of Puget Sound	Jan. 20 to May 10
British Columbia	Feb. thru April
Southeast Alaska ("outside")	March 10 to April 15
Southeast Alaska ("inside")	April 1 to May 25
Prince William Sound	April 1 to May 15
Cook Inlet	April 20 to May 15
Kodiak-Afognak Islands	May 20 to June 10
St. Michael	June

[1]Rounsefell, 1930; Miller and Schmidtke, 1956; Scattergood et al., 1959; Chapman et al., 1941; Fraser, 1916; and Nelson, 1887.
[2]Omitting head of Puget Sound localities.

fornia, to June at St. Michael, near Nome, Alaska. It will be noted that in addition to the latitudinal cline, there appears to be a tendency for later spawning by herring inhabiting "inside" waters. This may be caused either by later warming of "inside" waters or later spring maturation because of the more severe winter conditions. We found spawning in June by a small population of herring living in Gut Bay on the inside of Baranof Island in southeastern Alaska; Gut Bay is a very deep fjord surrounded by snow-covered peaks with a shallow entrance channel about 60 yards (55 m) wide. Similarly, Outram (1955) reported herring spawning as late as July 2 and 3 in Burke Channel, a fjord in northern British Columbia.

The temperature at which fish spawn varies with the species and with populations of the same species. Thus among the Pacific salmons, the five species do not all spawn at the same season; there is a regular seasonal progression in the runs (Rounsefell and Kelez, 1938). In the Puget Sound area the modes of the runs are about a month apart (Fig. 3-9); kings, sockeyes, pinks, cohos, and chums spawn in that order.

The king salmon run covers the longest period but levels off much earlier than that of any of the other species; 40% of the run is over by June 30, whereas no other species has reached 2% of its run by that date. The sockeye mode is in the week ending August 3 and is practically over by August 25. It is followed by the modes of the pink salmon, the coho salmon, and the chum salmon, each about a month apart. Obviously some species are spawning during a rising temperature, others during a falling temperature.

Effect on survival of young

The prevailing temperature both prior and subsequent to the time of hatching can

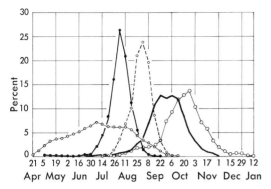

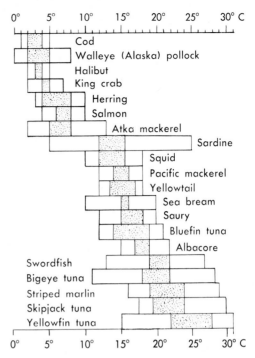

Fig. 3-9. Seasonal occurrence by 7-day periods of five species of Pacific salmon taken by traps as they migrated through Puget Sound and San Juan Islands toward natal streams to spawn. Modes from left to right are chinook (king) salmon (*Oncorhynchus tshawytscha*), sockeye salmon (*O. nerka*), pink salmon (*O. gorbuscha*), coho or silver salmon (*O. kisutch*), and chum salmon (*O. keta*).

Fig. 3-10. Water temperatures in which important offshore fishes were taken by Japanese. Modal (optimum) temperature is shown by stippled area; white includes 98% of catches. (Modified from Uda, M. 1961. Calif. Mar. Res. Comm. CalCOFI Rep. **8:**25-31.)

profoundly affect the proportion of young that survive. Field observations cannot always pinpoint the time at which the effect occurs. For instance, the survival of year classes of Pacific herring from Prince William Sound (Rounsefell, 1930) was found to be higher in years of warmer temperatures from March to June, inclusive, a period extending from a month or more previous to spawning to a month or 6 weeks after hatching of the eggs. That perhaps the correlation may not have been caused directly by temperature but indirectly through the effect of temperature on the food supply of the larvae is suggested by the faster growth of the more successful year classes.

Annual variations in temperature also affect survival through differences in growth rate. In many species, cannibalism and predation are enhanced when the young grow slowly; when growth is fast the organisms reach a size large enough to avoid heavy predation in a much shorter time. In rearing lobsters at Boothbay Harbor, cannibalism was so high because of the slow growth in the cold water of early spring that two measures were necessary: (1) the adult lobsters were held in submerged live cars in the

colder subsurface water to delay hatching of the eggs and (2) the seawater in the hatchery was heated.

Relationship to distribution

Marine fishes are sensitive to very minor changes in temperature. Bull (1952) was able to demonstrate their sensitivity to 0.03° C.

The distribution of the important offshore species taken in the Japanese fisheries, according to the temperatures where caught, is shown in Fig. 3-10. The stippled area represents the modal (optimum) temperature range, and the white indicates the temperature range covering 98% of the catches. Those species with a narrow temperature range are stenothermal, and those found in a wide range are eurythermal. The three truly benthic species—cod, halibut, and king crab—are obviously stenothermal.

Table 3-2. Distribution of three Gulf of Mexico bank fishes according to temperature where caught*

Species	Temperature of abundance (°C)			Temperature range (°C)	
	Mean	*Low*	*High*	*Low*	*High*
Gulf red snapper	20.6	16.7	24.4	13	28
Lane snapper	24.0	20.0	27.8	16	29
Red grouper					
Northern Gulf	18.9	17.2	20.0	16	29
Southern Gulf	24.7	23.9	26.1	20	28

*Data from Rivas, L. R. 1970. Comm. Fish. Rev. **32**:41-44; and Rivas, L. R. 1970a. Comm. Fish. Rev. **32**:24-30.

The break between the subarctic and subtropical species is very distinct, the upper limit of the optimum temperature shifting abruptly from 8° C to a lower limit of 12° C. Perhaps it should be noted that 8° C is the generally accepted isotherm separating the warmwater area of the oceans from the subarctic waters and from the deeper underlying waters.

As expected there is no very distinct break between subtropical and tropical species, but instead a gradual shift in optimum range occurs. The most interesting aspect is the wide range of temperatures tolerated by most of the species within the warmwater sphere. The albacore is an exception, covering only the narrow range from 15° to 22° C. It occupies a range about midway between the subtropical and tropical species. Although it is found in water as warm as that inhabited by the albacore, the bluefin tuna is more subtropical than tropical in range.

Uda's observations are corroborated by the albacore fishery in California. Most of the albacore are taken in the range of 62° to 66° F (16.7° to 18.9° C), corresponding closely with Uda's graph (Fig. 3-10). Rivas (1970, 1970a) gives somewhat comparable data for three important Gulf of Mexico bank fishes (Table 3-2).

CRITICAL SPACE
General considerations

All populations are limited in their abundance by one or more factors. For some species the actual amount of suitable habitat available at some stage of their life history may be the chief factor in determining the upper limit of their abundance. For most offshore-dwelling species with planktonic eggs and larvae, space is seldom the most critical factor. Space is most often critical in connection with reproduction and the rearing of young, although the amount of suitable substrate may also be of paramount importance to adults of some benthic or sessile species.

Spawning space

The limitation of abundance by the available spawning space is most evident in adfluvial, anadromous, estuarine, and coastal species in which reproduction is tied to physiographic and hydrologic features of freshwater and nearshore habitats. Even a few lacustrine species are involved. For instance, the lake trout, *Cristivomer namaycush,* spawns over coarse beds of rubble that are relatively free of sediments. In some lakes such areas are extremely limited. Where such areas are nonexistent, lake trout cannot reproduce successfully.

For anadromous species the size of the stock originating from any particular natal stream may depend chiefly on suitable spawning area. For species in which the young, on hatching, descend almost immediately to the sea, e.g., pink and chum salmon and smelt, *Osmerus eperlanus,* the upper limit of each stream population is determined by the number of young that can be produced in the particular spawning area. That this is a very real limiting factor has been shown by the rapid build-up of pink salmon runs in a few generations to where the number of adults arriving at the spawning beds is too large for the capacity of the area. This usually results in the death of many adults without spawning, the digging up of the earlier spawned eggs by the later spawners, and such overcrowding of eggs in the gravel that the majority die. This reduces the population to a very low level, and the cycle commences over again.

Even strictly marine species may be limited in abundance by spawning space. Thus two Pacific coast fishes, the grunion of southern California, *Leuresthes tenuis,* and the silver smelt, *Hypomesus pretiosus,* spawn only on surf-swept sand beaches. Even here they differ. The silver smelt spawns the adherent eggs on coarse sand beaches during day tides far enough down the beach so that they are constantly washed by the water. The grunion spawns on fine sand beaches during high night tides, the adults allowing themselves to be washed onto the beach where the eggs are buried and fertilized between waves. Spawning occurs just after high tide, and the pods of eggs are left in the hot dry sand until washed out by the next fortnightly series of high tides. Such peculiar behavior patterns not only limit the possible abundance of the species, they also leave the fish highly susceptible to capture by man as the beaches become crowded with humans.

In the same manner the fur seal herds were once tremendously abundant, but their upper limit was fixed by the area suitable for rookeries on their rocky islands as well as by competition among the nursing females for the limited supply of fish close enough to the rookeries to permit them to make their catch and return to their pups before they starved.

Space for younger organisms

The very young and juvenile stages of many organisms occupy a largely different habitat than the adults. Thus for those ad-fluvial and anadromous fishes of which the young usually dwell for some time in the streams (*Salmo salar, S. salar sebago, S. gairdneri, Oncorhynchus kisutch,* and *O. tshawytscha*), the size and fertility of the stream sets a definite upper limit to the numbers of young that can be recruited to the adult population.

Lacustrine anadromous fishes are also limited by the carrying capacity of the lakes in which the young are reared. This applies both to the alewife, *Alosa pseudoharengus,* and the sockeye salmon, *O. nerka.* Carrying capacity in this case, however, differs somewhat from the usual concept as only the young are involved. A brood may exhaust the available food, but if the supply lasts until the time of seaward migration, it is sufficient, as most of the growth occurs in the sea.

The same reasoning applies to many estuarine-dependent species in which the young invade the marshes and peripheral shallows but make the greater part of their growth in deeper waters. Most of these estuarine-dependent species in the Gulf of Mexico region spawn offshore in fully saline water; the young then enter the estuaries during the season of abundant food. These quasi-catadromous species include the menhadens, *Brevoortia* sp.; the chief commercial shrimps, *Penaeus setiferus, P. aztecus,* and *P. duorarum;* several of the sciaenids, e.g., *Sciaenops ocellata, Pogonias cromis, Micropogon undulatus,* and *Cynoscion* sp.; and the blue crab, *Callinectes sapidus.*

WAVE ACTION AND TIDAL HEIGHT

Waves affect the suitability of the shore as a habitat for many juvenile forms. Waveswept beaches are often devoid of sheltering vegetation; sand, if present, may shift about, which is injurious to attached organisms. If the bottom is chiefly mud and silt, waves can cause high turbidity, reducing photosynthesis. In contrast to sheltered shores, the shores exposed to wave action lack the concentration of particulate organic matter desirable in a nursery area.

This difference is easily noted by comparing the dense population of juvenile forms on the sheltered side of the barrier islands that fringe the Gulf coast, even in situations where salinity and temperature are equally favorable, to that along the exposed outside shores.

The huge waves generated by gales and hurricanes sometimes play havoc with clams, cockles, and such attached gastropods as abalones or periwinkles. Rubble crushes

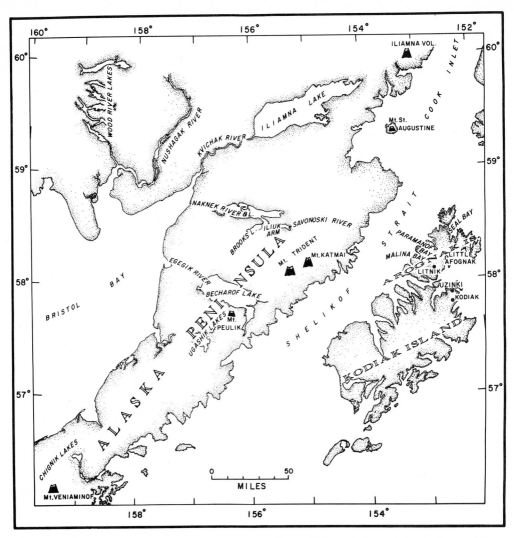

Fig. 3-11. Volcanoes and western Alaska areas. (From Eicher, G. J., and G. A. Rounsefell. 1957. Limnol. Oceanog. **2:**70-76.)

their shells as it rolls violently about, attached forms are torn loose, and clams may be either buried under deep sand or cast up in a windrow along the shore.

Storms, especially tropical ones, are often accompanied by extremely high tides. Butler (1965) discusses the very heavy sets of oysters, barnacles, and mussels immediately following such storms.

In 1950 a severe tropical storm near Pensacola, Florida, brought 7 inches of rain and a storm tide of 5.5 feet. In the week following the storm the set of oysters in-

creased from 1.1 to 73.0 spat/cm^2, the set of mussels from 0.1 to 3.2/cm^2, and that of barnacles from 0.3 to 170.6/cm^2. Butler mentions similar heavy sets in other areas following extreme tides, and the lack of increased setting following a heavy storm without an accompanying high tide. He attributes the tremendous increase in setting to the greater survival of larvae because of the increased phytoplankton production that results from trace elements or nutrients leached from the adjacent marshes.

VOLCANIC ACTIVITY

A string of volcanoes extends south-westward down the western side of Cook Inlet and along the Alaska Peninsula, continuing down the Aleutian Islands. Many of these are still smoking. Mt. St. Augustine erupted in 1883, Mt. Veniaminof in 1892, and Mt. Katmai in 1912, with a lighter eruption in 1913. Minor sporadic activity has occurred since. These Alaska volcanoes eject, instead of lava, great quantities of ash that is carried by the wind for distances of up to 300 miles, with heavy deposits for up to 100 miles (Fig. 3-11).

Following the eruption of Mt. Katmai in June 1912, ash and pumice fell on Brooks Lake and the Iliuk Arm of Naknek Lake to a depth of 10 to 20 inches; most of the ash was carried eastward across Afognak Island and northern Kodiak Island. Ten inches of ash was measured at Kodiak. Griggs (1920) showed the ash to contain 0.36% phosphorus, 0.47% magnesium, and 3.80% calcium.

Through study of the growth of spruce trees from Brooks Lake for the period 1855 to 1951 (Eicher and Rounsefell, 1957), it was discovered that after a steady decline in growth until 1914, the trees commenced to grow rapidly and were still growing well in 1951 (Fig. 3-12). The salmon smolts from the affected area (sampled in 1939) also grew faster than in neighboring lakes. Naknek and Brooks Lakes showed heavier concentrations of nitrite nitrogen, silica, and calcium carbonate than Kvichak or Wood Lakes to the north or Ugashik and Egegik Lakes to the south.

The negative effect was twofold: spawning salmon were killed in the streams of Afognak Island during 1912 and to a lesser degree in 1913, and many of the salmon parr from previous spawnings that remained in the lakes and streams also died. Thus the returns from the spawnings of 1911 to 1915 were small. However, from the spawnings of these small numbers (1916 to 1920), as large numbers as before the eruption returned, a remarkably fast recovery.

These data are scanty, but they suggest

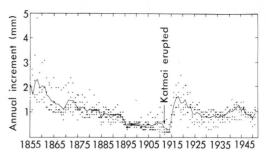

Fig. 3-12. Annual growth increments of five spruce trees from Brooks Lake, 1855 to 1951, showing the marked long-term effect of ashfall on soil fertility. (From Eicher, G. J., and G. A. Rounsefell. 1957. Limnol. Oceanog. **2:**70-76.)

that sporadic volcanic activity may have played a significant role in maintaining the lake fertility required to produce the millions of salmon smolts needed to sustain the large salmon runs of western Alaska.

CURRENTS

The direction and speed of surface and subsurface currents have a great effect on the survival of many marine species, the larvae and young of which are components of the plankton. This is especially important for demersal species in which the young must, at the proper stage, descend to the bottom.

On Georges Bank, one of the most productive North Atlantic fishing grounds, Colton and Temple (1961) list three flatfishes, six roundfishes, the herring, and the sea scallop as being the important commercial species with planktonic larvae. Except for the adhesive eggs of the herring, the eggs drift in the upper layers for a considerable time, although all 11 species are bottom spawners. The species and spawning seasons are as shown in Table 3-3.

The nontidal currents are such that a majority of the eggs and larvae during most seasons of the year would be carried off the bank and be lost to the fishery. Nevertheless, such enormous numbers are involved that enough young usually survive to maintain the fishery. Year by year differences in the survival of young indicate, however, that the variation in the nontidal cur-

Table 3-3. Spawning seasons of major commercial fishes found on Georges Bank

Species		Spawning season
Common name	*Scientific name*	
Pollock (saithe)	*Pollachius virens*	Dec.-Feb.
Atlantic cod	*Gadus morhua*	Jan.-March
Gray sole	*Glyptocephalus cynoglossus*	Jan.-April
Haddock	*Melanogrammus aeglefinus*	Feb.-April
American plaice	*Hippoglossoides platessoides*	March-May
Cusk	*Brosme brosme*	April-May
Silver hake	*Merluccius bilinearis*	May-July
Yellowtail flounder	*Limanda ferruginea*	May-July
Red hake	*Urophycis chuss*	June-Sept.
Herring	*Clupea harengus*	Sept.-Oct.
Sea scallop	*Placopecten magellanicus*	Sept.-Oct.

rent, which is strongly affected by prevailing winds, is a principal factor in determining annual survival.

Suggested readings

Alverson, D. L. 1960. A study of annual and seasonal bathymetric catch patterns for commercially important groundfishes of the Pacific northwest coast of North America. Pac. Mar. Fish. Comm. Bull. **4:**1-66.

Butler, P. A. 1965. Reaction of estuarine mollusks to some environmental factors. Biological problems in water pollution, third seminar, 1962. Publ. No. 999-WP-25. U. S. Public Health Service, Washington, D. C. pp. 92-104.

Colton, J. B., Jr., and R. F. Temple. 1961. The enigma of Georges Bank spawning. Limnol. Oceanog. **6:**280-291.

Davidson, F. A. 1933. Temporary high carbon dioxide content in an Alaskan stream at sunset. Ecology **14:**238-240.

Donaldson, L. R., and F. J. Foster. 1941. Experimental study of the effect of various water temperatures on the growth, food utilization, and mortality rates of fingerling sockeye salmon. Trans. Amer. Fish. Soc. **70:**339-346.

Eicher, G. J., and G. A. Rounsefell. 1957. Effects of lake fertilization by volcanic activity on abundance of salmon. Limnol. Oceanog. **2:** 70-76.

Griggs, R. F. 1920. The recovery of vegetation at Kodiak. Ohio State Univ. Bull. **24:**1-57.

Gunter, G. 1957. Predominance of the young among marine fishes found in fresh water. Copeia, No. 1. pp. 13-16.

Khlebovich, V. V. 1968. Some peculiar features of the hydrochemical regime and the fauna of mesohaline waters. Mar. Biol. **2:**47-49.

Kirsch, M. 1956. Ionic ratios of some of the major components in river-diluted sea water in Bute and Knight Inlets, British Columbia. J. Fish. Res. Bd. Canada **13:**273-289.

Kutkuhn, J. H. 1966. The role of estuaries in the development and perpetuation of commercial shrimp resources. In A symposium on estuarine fisheries. Amer. Fish. Soc. Spec. Publ. No. 3. pp. 16-36.

Leppakoski, E. 1969. Transitory return of the benthic fauna of the Bornholm Basin after extermination by oxygen insufficiency. Cah. Biol. Mar. **10:**162-172.

Nelson, W. R. 1967. Studies on the croaker, (Micropogon undulatus, Linnaeus) and the spot, (Leiostomus xanthurus, Lacepede) in Mobile Bay, Alabama. J. Mar. Sci. Alabama **1:**4-92.

Rawson, D. S., and J. E. Moore. 1944. The saline lakes of Saskatchewan. Can. J. Res., Sec. D. **22:**141-201.

Richards, F. A. 1957. Oxygen in the ocean. In Hedgpeth, J., editor, Treatise on marine ecology and paleoecology, memoir 67, vol. 1, chap. 9. Geological Society of America, National Research Council, Washington, D. C. pp. 185-238.

Riley, G. A. 1951. Oxygen, phosphate and nitrate in the Atlantic Ocean. Bingham Oceanog. Coll. Bull. **13:**1-26.

Rounsefell, G. A., and W. H. Everhart. 1953. Fishery science. John Wiley & Sons, Inc., New York. 444 pp.

Rounsefell, G. A., and G. B. Kelez. 1938. The salmon and salmon fisheries of Swiftsure Bank, Puget Sound, and the Fraser River. Bull. U. S. Bur. Fish. **49:**693-823.

Simmons, E. G. 1957. An ecological survey of the upper Laguna Madre of Texas. Publ. Inst. Mar. Sci., Texas **4:**156-200.

Stickney, A. P. 1968. Supersaturation of atmospheric gases in the coastal waters of the Gulf of Maine. U. S. Fish Wildl. Serv., Fish. Bull. **67**:117-123.

Uda, M. 1961. Fisheries oceanography in Japan, especially on the principles of fish distribution, concentration, dispersal and fluctuation. Calif. Mar. Res. Comm. CalCOFI Rep. **8**:25-31.

Weymouth, F. W., and H. C. McMillin. The relative growth and mortality of the Pacific razor clam (Siliqua patula, Dixon), and their bearing on the commercial fishery. Doc. 1099. U. S. Bur. Fish. Bull. **46**:543-567.

Worthington, L. V. 1954. A preliminary note on the time scale in North Atlantic circulation. Deep-Sea Res. **1**:244-251.

Zein-Eldin, Z. P., and D. V. Aldrich. 1965. Growth and survival of post-larval Penaeus aztecus under controlled conditions of temperature and salinity. Biol. Bull. Woods Hole **129**: 199-216.

chapter 4

❧ Biological limiting factors

OVERBLOOMING OF PLANKTON

The overblooming of planktonic organisms can cause mass mortalities of both fish and invertebrates either by lowering the dissolved oxygen concentration or by their formation of toxic materials; occasionally both causes may be operative. Overblooming occurs in many parts of the world, in some places annually and in others sporadically.

Lowering of the oxygen content to critical levels (such as often occurs in freshwater ponds) usually happens during periods of calm weather; this especially occurs in the very early morning after respiration without compensating photosynthesis has exhausted the oxygen. Sometimes an enormous bloom of phytoplankton will die and sink in shallow water and the decay of this organic mass will rob the overlying water of its oxygen.

Although more rare, fish kills are sometimes caused by heavy blooms that produce a supersaturation of oxygen in the surface waters. This occurred in Galveston Bay, Texas, where numbers of spotted sea trout, *Cynoscion nebulosis,* were killed by suffocation from gas embolism in the gill capillaries (Renfro, 1963).

Heavy blooms occur most frequently in tropical and subtropical waters. They are usually noted by discoloration, which may be caused by diatoms, swarms of copepods, ciliates, or chromogenic bacteria. The great majority are caused by dinoflagellates, which vary in color from nearly transparent to pale green, yellow, amber, and bright red. Many are luminescent. Some are armored (possess a cuticle) and others are naked.

Blooms occur in such widely separated areas as India, Somaliland, Angola and Namibia, the Bay of Izmir on the eastern side of the Aegean Sea, Peru, Chile, Japan, California, the Red Sea, the Gulf of California (once called the Vermilion Sea), and the Gulf of Mexico. In more temperate waters the blooms are not usually as noticeable, but occasionally they cause paralytic shellfish poisoning from southeastern Alaska to southern California and in eastern Canada (Brongersma-Sanders, 1957; Rounsefell and Nelson, 1966).

Dinoflagellates may be oceanic, neritic, or estuarine in their habitat. They have one peculiarity that was noted by Graham and Bronikovsky (1944) in studying oceanic species: they seem to thrive best when nutrients are at a low level.

Although most fish kills by dinoflagellates have been of very limited scope, the Florida red tide, *Gymnodinium breve,* has caused kills of great numbers of fish and invertebrates along the Gulf coasts of Texas, northeastern Mexico, and southern Florida. The organism is neritic, seldom blooming far inside the bays or very far offshore. Studies of extensive field data (Rounsefell and Dragovich, 1966) show that the blooms commence chiefly in the fall after the cessation of the diatom bloom. It appears that there are always sufficient nutrients available along the west coast of Florida for a bloom. However, heavy blooms occur within a salinity range of 28 to 35 $^0/_{00}$ and a temperature range of 16° to 30° C. The organisms become concentrated in convergences, which occur chiefly (1) around the mouths of the passes between the barrier islands where the estuarine waters meet the higher salinity waters of the open Gulf, (2) parallel to the shore with an onshore wind, and (3) in wind-created convection cells. Thus they are favored by a gentle downward vertical current in which their mobility enables them to remain in one spot while straining the nutrients from the whole water column. Strong winds disperse the blooms and cold weather kills them. There are strong indications that blooms are favored by the river water dilution of the Gulf water, so that it is postulated that the rivers contain one (or more) growth-promoting substances.

FOOD AT CRITICAL LIFE HISTORY STAGES

In the very early stages many organisms depend for survival on the immediate availability of suitable food in sufficient quantity. Thus it has been shown for some marine species with a high fecundity, e.g., the commercial penaeid shrimps of the Gulf of Mexico, that there is no apparent relationship between the size of the spawning stock and the number of postlarval shrimp entering the estuaries. The success or failure of the year class is determined during the period when the larvae are undergoing growth and metamorphosis while drifting as plankton.

PREDATION

Without predation most organisms would quickly fill their available habitat. In a few cases where predation has been absent or very light, populations have filled their environment with the disastrous consequences that occur whenever space or food become critical. Thus just as overpopulation of deer causes starvation in severe winters as they denude their winter range, overpopulations of spawning salmon can result in almost total spawning failure.

In general predators are of two types—density dependent and density independent. The density-dependent predators tend to wax and wane in abundance with the availability of the prey that is their chief article of diet. The density-independent predators have alternate sources of sustenance.

Usually the density-dependent predator has greater longevity than its prey and also a slower rate of increase. As a prey species increases, the predator population increases, taking a heavier and heavier toll. As the prey finally commence to decrease, the predators take an even larger proportion of the remainder. However, the predators must now decrease drastically. The total result is a more or less cyclic rhythm of both prey and predator with the predator lagging behind.

The density-independent predator plays a different role. A good illustration is predation by bears on runs of spawning salmon (Shuman, 1950). The bears take about the same number of salmon each season whether salmon are abundant or scarce. When runs are large, the toll is of little significance and may be actually beneficial during runs that are too large. When runs are small, however, the density-independent predator may take a damaging percentage of the run. In 1947 at Karluk, Alaska, bears took 94,000 salmon out of a run of 485,000 (19.4%).

Predation is a normal activity, and most species are subject to predation at practically every stage of their life history. Most predators are themselves prey for species of a higher trophic level. However, the trophic levels in the sea are not always clearly de-

fined. Thus a sea herring feeding on copepods or pteropods is at the second (consumer) trophic level. However, the same
herring may also consume diatoms, which
would constitute consumption at the first
trophic level. A herring will at times consume large quantities of sand lances *(Amno-
dytes),* which indicates consumption at the
third trophic level. It would appear virtually
impossible to follow simple trophic levels
for any species with such a complex food
web.

Nevertheless, it is obvious that near the
base of the food chain we find those organisms that feed directly on phytoplankton
or on the smaller zooplankton. This great
group of organisms includes the pelecypod
mollusks, the majority of the smaller schooling fishes, and the baleen whales.

The majority of the larger fishes prey on
smaller fishes, but many also prey on the
larger zooplankton and on benthic invertebrates. Since a considerable loss of energy
occurs between each trophic level, the biomass must decrease sharply between each
succeeding level.

INTRASPECIFIC COMPETITION

Analysis of the sockeye runs to Karluk
Lake (Rounsefell, 1958) showed that the
5-year cycles in abundance that persisted
throughout the earlier years of the fishery
were caused primarily by competition (probably cannibalism) by the 3- and 4-year-old
young sockeye in the lake inflicted on the
fry in their first year. This negative regression (r = 0.70) for conditions 2½ years
previously would yield a positive 5-year
cycle in the runs.

INTERSPECIFIC COMPETITION

Aside from the predator-prey relationship, the presence of one species may have
a significant influence on the abundance of
another. Again this relationship is most
readily apparent in anadromous species
among which the severe limitation on suitable spawning area means that a later
spawning species such as the pink salmon,

Oncorhynchus gorbuscha, sometimes causes
extensive damage to an earlier spawning species such as *O. nerka* by digging up their
previously buried eggs. Thus over a 70-year
period at Karluk, the returns per spawner
of sockeye spawning in the odd-numbered
years (in which pink salmon runs were very
small) were consistently and significantly
greater than the returns from sockeye spawning in the even-numbered years (Rounsefell,
1958).

In strictly marine species such competition is more difficult to demonstrate. Oyster
setting, for instance, may be impeded by the
settling of great numbers of barnacles on the
cultch, leaving little space for the oyster
larvae to occupy. The white shrimp,
Penaeus setiferus, and the brown shrimp,
P. aztecus, occupy the same shallow peripheral marsh areas, but here the extent of
competition, if it exists, is difficult to assess,
since the brown shrimp postlarvae enter the
estuaries in late winter and early spring
and most of the white shrimp postlarvae enter about 6 to 8 weeks later.

An interesting case of competition involves the abalone, *Haliotis* spp., and the sea
urchin, *Strongylocentrotus purpuratus* and *S.
franciscanus* (Cox, 1962). They both feed
on algae, but the sea urchins will sometimes
invade an area in great numbers and clean
the rocks so bare of algae that the abalones
are forced to leave. In many localities the
abalones subsist chiefly on drifting debris
from kelps, including the giant kelp. The sea
urchins also graze heavily on kelps, and in
some areas the sea urchins have destroyed
large areas of kelp beds. This is especially
true where the seawater has been enriched
by sewer discharges.

The sea otter's favorite food is sea urchins, so where sea otters are numerous
they tend to hold the sea urchins in check.
Unfortunately sea otters are also partial to
abalones and are skilled at gathering them,
either by seizing them while most of the
foot is relaxed and the shell raised at one
end to permit the capture of drifting algae,
or when this fails, by smashing through the

shell with a large rock, scooping out the intestines, and waiting until the dying abalone relaxes its grip on the rock.

Suggested readings

Cox, K. W. 1962. California abalones, family Haliotidae. Calif. Fish Game, Fish Bull. **118:** 1-133.

Ray, S. M., and W. B. Wilson. 1957. Effects of unialgal and bacteria-free cultures of Gymnodinium brevis on fish, and notes on related studies with bacteria. U. S. Fish Wildl. Serv. Fish. Bull. **57:**469-496.

Renfro, W. C. 1963. Gas-bubble mortality of fishes in Galveston Bay, Texas. Trans. Amer. Fish. Soc. **92:**320-322.

Rounsefell, G. A. 1958. Factors causing decline in sockeye salmon of Karluk River, Alaska. U. S. Fish Wildl. Serv., Fish. Bull. **58:**83-169.

Rounsefell, G. A., and A. Dragovich. 1966. Correlation between oceanographic factors and abundance of the Florida red tide (Gymnodinium breve Davis), 1954-61. Bull. Mar. Sci., Gulf Carib. **16:**404-422.

Rounsefell, G. A., and W. R. Nelson. 1966. Red-tide research summarized to 1964 including an annotated bibliography. U. S. Fish Wildl. Serv., Spec. Sci. Rep. Fish. **535:**1-85.

chapter 5

✿ Habitats and distribution

Relating a fish to its environment is made difficult both by the plasticity of many species and by the fact that many fishes occupy two or more environments either seasonally or during stages of their life history. To simplify matters I will first describe each environment. It must be remembered that many species occupy both fresh and marine waters.

STREAMS

The freshwater habitat starts with a flowing stream (or spring). Stream habitats can be classified roughly according to type of bottom, turbidity, temperature, and gradient. These are normally interrelated. A stream with a soft bottom of clay or silt will usually be turbid. The speed is determined by the gradient. The temperature of the water at any season varies with altitude, the general climate of the particular area, and the amount of shade.

One method of classifying stream habitats is solely by the gradient. For European streams, Huet (1959) proposes a division into four main types based chiefly on altitude and current speed (related to gradient). These can be summarized as shown in Table 5-1.

Huet refers to the increasing temperature,

width, and reduced current speed proceeding downstream as important factors, since they tend to eliminate poor swimmers and fish requiring high temperatures for reproduction from the upper reaches of the streams.

The scheme proposed by Huet, while applicable in most north temperate conditions such as are encountered in European streams, is not universal in its application. This is well exemplified by large northward-flowing streams such as the Mackenzie River, which is cold in its lower reaches. Even in more southerly rivers such as the Fraser the lower reaches contain generous populations of trout. The Mississippi-Missouri River system fits more closely into his categories. Therefore it would appear that temperature is more effective than gradient in determining species distribution in streams. However, since temperatures are usually lower at higher altitudes and since higher altitudes usually result in steeper gradients, the two attributes are not easily separable.

The implied suggestion of Huet that current speed is of overriding importance cannot be fully substantiated. Thus in the Machias River in Maine I have seen schools of suckers, *Catostomus,* quickly ascending through turbulent, swift rapids that were difficult even for a salmon. It must also be

Table 5-1. Classification of European streams according to altitude and current speed

Type	Slope (%)	Fish fauna
1	8-4.5	Trout, also grayling
2	5-2.5	Grayling, also trout, running water cyprinids, and predators
3	3.5-0.75	Chiefly running water cyprinids, other cyprinids, some trout, and predators
4	1.5-0.25	Chiefly still-water cyprinids, other cyprinids, and predators

remembered that the different stocks of a species may have developed different capabilities. Thus in Massachusetts the alewife, *Alosa pseudoharengus,* requires fishways it may ascend without exerting great effort and without leaving the water. However, in the Damariscotta River in Maine the alewives ascend a masonry fishway consisting of small pools separated by falls. I measured several of these falls and noted that the alewives were sometimes forced to leap 2 feet (0.61 m) through the air to reach the next pool.

Temperature

The faunal portion of a stream community is governed more by the average temperature than by the extremes. Therefore whether a stream is classified as a cool stream that is suitable for trout or salmon will depend chiefly on the height and duration of the maximum summer temperature. Some species have a life history geared to cope with such temporarily unfavorable conditions. For instance, Pacific salmon in warm streams tend to spawn in the autumn after the stream has cooled. The young salmon then are hatched in the late winter and can leave the stream before summer returns. This applies to pink and chum salmons (*Oncorhynchus gorbuscha* and *O. keta*). The sockeye *(O. nerka)* has evolved a

slightly different, but somewhat similar life history strategy. In the Karluk system, for instance, the early-running salmon spawn in the smaller streams entering the lake (during June and July); later arrivals tend to spawn more heavily in the cooler lake itself, chiefly on bars off the mouths of entering streams. The very late arrivals (October and November) spawn in large numbers in the Karluk River below the lake, which by this late date is sufficiently cool.

In the Quinault system on the outer Washington coast the blueback (a race of small sockeye) salmon enter the river in late winter and early spring before the stream becomes too warm. They proceed into Quinault Lake and remain there while their gonads mature in the cool hypolimnion. In the autumn they enter the now cool lake tributaries to spawn. The young drop downstream in the spring and into the cool lake before the onset of summer.

In the Ozette Lake system, north of the Quinault along the outer coast, attempts many years ago to hold adult sockeye in pens in the main river while their gonads were maturing failed miserably. The early-running sockeye must have cool water for gonad maturation.

Stream temperature may confine fishes requiring cool waters to the higher altitudes, since all but a few northward-flowing (in the northern hemisphere) streams are warmer in their lower reaches. Thus the eastern charr (brook trout), *Salvelinus fontinalis,* is confined in the South to the upper portions of streams in the Appalachians. Proceeding northward, portions of the brook trout populations in the streams of New England and the Maritimes spend a few months at sea. Farther north in Hudson Bay, entire brook trout populations may be anadromous.

In Baja California many streams originate in the cool midpeninsular mountains but after flowing into the bordering deserts become very hot; some disappear except during excessive flood conditions. The upper reaches of the Santo Domingo River in the Sierra San Pedro Mártir contain *Salmo gairdneri nelsoni,* an isolated subspecies or race of the steelhead or rainbow trout.

On the other side of the coin, some anadromous species are limited by low stream temperatures. Thus both the cutthroat and steelhead trouts, *Salmo clarki* and *S. gairdneri,* are limited in their northward range, the cutthroat not occurring north of southeastern Alaska and the steelhead being absent from the two coldest rivers in Bristol Bay, the Egegik and Ugashik.

For anadromous species in general, streams are used in one or more of three ways: (1) as an avenue of migration to and from a lake (e.g., the alewife or river herring, *Alosa pseudoharengus*), (2) as a spawning bed (e.g., *Oncorhynchus gorbuscha* and the smelt, *Osmerus eperlanus*), and (3) as both a spawning area and a nursery area (e.g., the silver salmon, *Oncorhynchus kisutch,* and the spring-running races of the king salmon, *O. tshawytscha*). The same uses apply to adfluvial species and the adfluvial populations of anadromous species introduced into larger interior freshwater seas such as the Great Lakes.

Spawning

Concerning the use of a stream as a spawning bed, the previously mentioned smelt often spawn in very early spring in small brooks that are practically or entirely dry later in the season. This fact, the seasonal use of a habitat when conditions are optimum for some specific activity of a species, can be extremely important in assessing the value of any particular water area to the abundance of a species.

The type of stream bottom and the related gradient are important to anadromous species but especially to those that bury their eggs in the bottom and depend on seepage through the substrate for an adequate oxygen supply to the buried ova. This applies to most of the Salmonidae and to the lampreys. Too fine a substrate may suffocate the ova, but large rubble may be too difficult for smaller species to move in constructing a redd.

Species that cast fast-developing ova without burial (e.g., American shad, *Alosa sapidissima,* or striped bass, *Morone saxatilis*) spawn successfully in relatively sluggish, soft-bottomed portions of streams that are entirely unsuitable for redd construction.

Some species, usually considered to be marine, utilize stream mouths for spawning. The tomcod, *Microgadus tomcod,* spawns indifferently in shoal fresh, brackish, or salt water (I have seen them congregate for spawning in the wholly fresh water below Bangor Dam on the Penobscot), and its eggs have been hatched artificially in fresh water. In this regard the tomcod is as anadromous as those populations of pink salmon (and some chum salmon) that spawn on the flats of the intertidal zone below impassable falls in southeastern Alaska and in Prince William Sound. Species (or populations) with this habit I classify as quasi-anadromous.

Use by catadromous species

The use of streams by catadromous species may be threefold: (1) as an avenue of up- and downstream migration to and from a pond or lake, (2) as a nursery area, and (3) as a feeding area for adults (although adults more normally make their growth in still waters).

Although the common eel, *Anguilla,* is always held up as the example of a catadromous species, many eels (chiefly males) remain in the estuaries. The others ascend both swift and sluggish streams, and many (perhaps most) enter ponds and lakes where they supposedly remain until they are adults, migrating downstream to the sea just before the onset of maturity. This general account is less clear-cut in actuality.

Perhaps because eels are chiefly nocturnal, their presence in streams is not always suspected. In Little Falls Stream on the Moosehorn Refuge in Maine the use of an electric shocker produced many eels up to a foot in length, and they attacked Atlantic salmon parr held in pens in a swift-flowing section of the stream. I have observed large adult eels ferociously devouring young alewives descending the fishway below Damariscotta Lake.

Although the several geographical species (or races) of *Anguilla* are the only strictly catadromous species commonly cited, there are a number of species in which at least a portion of the population fulfills the definition of "catadromous" fully as well as portions of the eel populations. The menhadens, *Brevoortia*, spawn offshore in high salinity waters; the very young enter estuaries and seemingly prefer the lowest salinities, even wholly fresh water.

This use by the young of the areas where streams debouch into embayments is so similar to the life pattern followed by many individuals of the "classic" example of a catadromous species that I use the term "quasi-catadromous" to describe this life history pattern.

INTERIOR SEAS
General considerations

Interior seas, by our definition, are large bodies of water without an oceanic connection. Those in exorheic areas contain fresh waters, and those in endorheic areas contain saline waters. The Caspian Sea is an anomaly. It receives the large discharge of the Volga River flowing from an exorheic area, but the basin itself lies in an endorheic area, so the basin has no discharge. Tides of a few centimeters have been demonstrated in the larger inland seas, but their effect on short-term water levels at any particular point is minimal, as they are overshadowed by seiches and by wind effects.

Saline interior seas

The three inland bodies of saline water that we consider large enough to classify as seas are the Caspian Sea, the Sea of Aral, and Lake Balkhash. In the Caspian Sea surface salinity varies from 12 to 13 $^o/_{oo}$ in the southern basin to 5 to 10 $^o/_{oo}$ in the central basin and to even lower values in the shallow northern basin into which the Volga empties. There is little oxygen below 200 to 300 m, and near the bottom it may drop to 0, accompanied by the production of hydrogen sulfide but in less quantity than in the Black Sea. The fauna are low in number of species, as is usual in a relict sea. Some are marine species from the Sarmantic and Pontic Seas of the Tertiary period, some are more recent marine additions from the Mediterranean and Arctic Seas, and some are from fresh waters.

Classifying the fishes present according to type of habitat presents some difficulty. The sturgeons are obviously fluvial anadromous, and the clupeoid, *Caspialosa*, is pelagic; the northern end of the Caspian Sea contains many freshwater forms that have adapted to the low salinity and could be classified under the broad term "lacustrine."

The Sea of Aral is slightly lower in salinity than the Caspian Sea, having a salinity of 10 $^o/_{oo}$, but over 31% of the salts are sulfate. The fauna are low in number, and the fishes are derived from fresh waters.

Freshwater interior seas

Freshwater interior seas occur from the Arctic (Great Bear and Great Slave Lakes) to the tropics of Africa. The type of fauna is highly dependent on the degree of circulation, on which the oxygen concentration depends. In oligotrophic north temperate lakes, fish can live at considerable depths; the burbot or ling, *Lota lota,* a gadoid fish, is a benthic species. The species with a low temperature tolerance, e.g., the lake trout, *Cristivomer namaycush,* inhabit the hypolimnion during warmer months and could be termed profundal. The majority of lake-dwelling species tend to live near the surface. Those that live near the surface away from the shores are termed pelagic. There is no suitable term to describe the numerous species that inhabit the lake shallows and shorelines, but they can be conveniently described as littoral. Among lake dwellers there are some species that ascend streams to spawn, and these we refer to as adfluvial.

BRACKISH WATERS

A zone of mixing occurs where the rivers and streams enter the seas. Many ecologists have proposed terms for this mixed water based on the salinity in parts per thousand, but there are as many systems as there are authors. Actually the salinity in many places may vary over a wide range within a very few hours depending on tides, winds, and stream flow. Stenohaline forms avoid these areas, but truly estuarine species tolerate a considerable change with no apparent discomfort. Sessile species such as oysters and mussels must be adapted to such rapid changes. If the salinity should drop below their tolerance level, they can close their shells and survive for considerable periods, providing the temperature is sufficiently low. Many of the species found in estuaries are euryhaline marine species that can live indifferently in full salinity or in considerable dilution.

In large bodies of low salinity water such as the Baltic, Black, and Caspian Seas, the conditions are far more stable than in the typical estuary. Hence there are both marine and freshwater components of the fauna that have become adapted to these less variable conditions. Under such conditions the subdivision of the areas according to the prevailing salinity might make more sense. The simplest and perhaps most defensible classification according to salinity was developed by Remane (1958) (Table 5-2).

Table 5-2. Classification of seas according to salinity

Salinity (°/oo)	Area designation
Down to 15	Marine region
8-15	Brackish marine
3-8	Typical brackish
Below 3	Brackish limnic

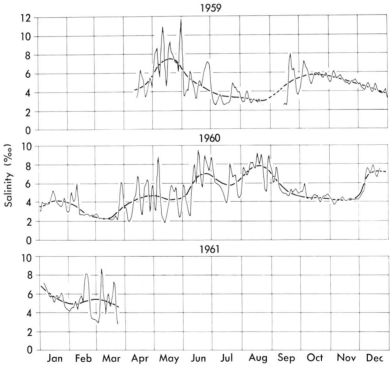

Fig. 5-1. Salinity in Louisiana marshes over 2-year period at Hopedale, showing erratic and sudden large fluctuations in salinity typical of many estuarine areas. (From Rounsefell, G. A. 1964. U. S. Fish Wildl. Serv., Fish. Bull. **63:**373-393.)

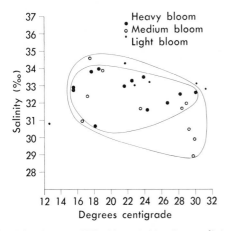

Fig. 5-2. Blooms of Florida red tide, *Gymnodinium breve,* occurring over a 7-year period and illustrating relationship between salinity tolerance and temperature. (From Rounsefell, G. A., and A. Dragovich. 1966. Bull. Mar. Sci., Gulf. Carib. **16:** 404-422.)

The categories given in Table 5-2 can be compared with the data shown in Fig. 5-1, in which the average salinities in the three estuarine areas over a 2-year period were 3.5, 11.6, and 16.0 $^0/_{00}$. However, the ranges of salinity in these areas were wide. Their extent is shown in Fig. 5-1 (Rounsefell, 1964); the day-by-day variations in salinity at the base station were extreme, and over the 2-year period there was no consistent seasonal pattern. Under such variable and unpredictable conditions it is clear that no rigid scheme of classification is warranted. It would appear rather that salinity should be regarded as a sliding scale, with each species having its own acceptable and preferred range. This range of salinity, moreover, will vary with the prevailing temperature, marine forms usually withstanding lower salinities at higher temperatures. This is illustrated in Fig. 5-2, which shows the tolerance of lower salinities at higher temperatures by the Florida red tide, *Gymnodinium breve.*

Khlebovich (1968) states that there is in many seas an "eco-physiological barrier" occurring at a salinity of about 5 $^0/_{00}$ because of the change in the ionic ratio between calcium and chloride as seawater is diluted with many river waters. Kirsch (1956) attributed this affect more to cation exchange with suspended sediments.

In classifying organisms as estuarine, one of the chief criteria should be the ability of the animal to withstand fairly rapid changes in salinity. Temperatures, although covering a wide seasonal range, do not normally fluctuate widely from day to day. This implies that animals living in the larger low salinity seas should not be classified as estuarine. In such seas a scheme such as that proposed by Remane (1958) might be useful if the one chosen defined points of division between salinity categories that held real meaning.

Since the estuarine habitat excludes the larger seas of low salinity, we are without terms to describe those fairly stable low salinity seas with oceanic connections on the basis of salinity alone. The migration in and out of the Black Sea of such oceanic fishes as the bluefin tuna and the bonito from the higher than oceanic salinities of the Mediterranean and the Sea of Marmara to the surface salinities of the Black Sea, ranging between about 17 to 20 $^0/_{00}$, suggests that only stenohaline marine species with a tolerance for a narrow range of high salinity are barred from such waters. This is further corroborated by the capture of organisms belonging to such genera as *Urophycis, Menticirrhus,* and *Polydactylus* in the high estuarine salinities prevailing along the western side of Breton Sound in the Gulf of Mexico.

NERITIC AND OCEANIC AREAS

The term "neritic" is used in the sense of "nonoceanic" and is meant to include the waters from the surface to the bottom that lie on or above the continental shelf, excluding only those areas of unstable and fluctuating salinities that we previously defined as estuarine habitats. The area of the shelf is estimated to be about 27 million km². The neritic areas, after subtraction of the estuarine environment but including the more stable brackish water areas that lie over the shelf, are somewhat less. Although this neritic area is small in comparison to the area of the waters overlying the deeper ocean, it is the scene of the greater share of the world's fisheries and thus ranks high in importance.

Obviously the neritic areas cannot be logically subdivided on the basis of salinity. For the bottom feeders the substrate is of great importance and may outweigh considerations of depth. Thus the rocky shores of the northeastern Pacific, the glaciated shelf from New England to the Grand Banks, the sand-mud bottoms of the northern Gulf and southern Atlantic states, and the coral reefs of the tropics represent widely differing conditions.

The picture is further complicated by the seasonal movements of many of the demersal species. Thus it may be noted in Fig. 3-6 (p. 53) that in the northeastern Pacific the starry flounder, *Platichthys stellatus,* the English sole, *Parophrys vetulus,* and the cod, *Gadus macrocephalus,* although showing some depth change with season, remained on the shelf. However, the petrale sole, *Eopsetta jordani;* the Dover sole, *Microstomus pacificus;* the sablefish (black cod), *Anoplopoma fimbria;* and the Pacific ocean perch (red rockfish), *Sebastes alutus,* were caught in abundance both on the shelf

and on the continental slope at depths as great as 200 fm (366 m) or more.

The relative abundance by depth of capture of the principal demersal species taken by otter trawl on Georges Bank over a period of 7 years (1932 to 1938) is shown in Fig. 5-3 (Rounsefell, 1957). The shallow zone (0 to 30 fm [0 to 55 m]) was the center of abundance for the blackback (winter) flounder, *Pseudopleuronectes americanus,* the lemon sole (merely a larger race of the blackback), and the yellowtail flounder, *Limanda ferruginea.* According to Bigelow and Schroeder (1953), winter flounders are abundant in very shoal bays and are seldom taken below 50 fm (91 m); the deepest record is of one taken at 70 fm (128 m). The yellowtail is very scarce at 40 to 50 fm (73 to 91 m).

The deep zone (61 to 125 fm [112 to 229 m]) was the center of abundance for ocean perch (redfish), *Sebastes marinus;* cusk, *Brosme brosme;* gray sole (witch), *Glyptocephalus cynoglossus;* pollock, *Pollachius virens;* white hake, *Urophycis tenuis;* and American plaice (dab), *Hippoglossoides platessoides.* However, this is misleading because the pollock frequents deep water in the fall and winter months but schools at the surface in the summer.

Cod, *Gadus morhua;* haddock, *Melanogrammus aeglefinus;* Atlantic halibut, *Hippoglossus hippoglossus;* and wolffish, *Anarhichas lupus,* are taken at all three depths.

The bathymetric patterns shown in Figs. 3-6 (p. 53) and 5-3 do not hold true at different latitudes or in different water masses. Alverson (1960) refers to reports by Moiseev (1953) that true cod, *Gadus macrocephalus,* in the Sea of Okhotsk and the western Bering Sea are abundant in deeper waters and may be found in commercial numbers at depths of up to 150 fm (274 m) during the winter. Moiseev also reports that another group of cod moves into shallow depths (8 to 27 fm [15 to 49 m]) during the winter along the southern Kurile Islands and adjacent to Hokkaidō and Honshū Islands, but returns to relatively deep water

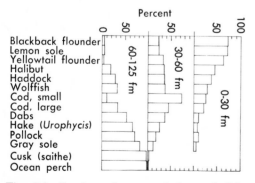

Fig. 5-3. Depth preferences of demersal fishes taken by otter trawl on Georges Bank during 1932 to 1938 as shown by their relative abundance by depth of capture. (Modified from Rounsefell, G. A. 1957. U. S. Fish Wildl. Serv., Fish. Bull. **57:**265-278.)

(55 to 135 fm [102 to 247 m]) during the summer.

Similarly, the ocean perch is rarely taken at less than 60 fm (110 m) on Georges Bank, but I have taken them on haddock line trawls at depths of less than 20 fm (55 m) at Mt. Desert Island and observed them at the surface at Eastport, Maine. Also, the lobster, *Homarus americanus,* becomes less and less abundant adjacent to the coast as one proceeds south from New England, yet large lobsters are caught by otter trawlers in deep water off the Virginia capes.

Clearly habitat can seldom be defined in terms of a single variable, whether it be salinity, depth, temperature, or perhaps additional variables. Thus fishes that are strongly thigmotropic may be relatively scarce over a smooth bottom, but they may congregate near boulders, outcroppings, or coral heads. This seems to be true of the cusk, *Brosme brosme,* which is described by Bigelow and Schroeder as:

. . . being found chiefly on hard ground, especially where the sea floor is rough with rocks or boulders; on gravelly or pebbly grounds; occasionally on mud with hake, but seldom on smooth clean sand. In Norwegian waters they often lurk among gorgonian corals. . . .*

The snappers, *Lutjanus* spp., in the Gulf of Mexico prefer rocky ledges and corals, often gathering around sunken hulls.

So many ecologic habitats exist in the neritic zone that appear to intergrade with one another that only broad categories can be clearly recognized. There are some species such as the tomcod, *Microgadus tomcod;* the tautog, *Tautoga onitis;* the Atlantic silverside, *Menidia menidia;* and the northern pipefish, *Syngnathus fuscus,* that are confined almost wholly to the narrow belt within a mile or so of the shore. These can be designated as shore species.

Those demersal species such as the winter flounder (blackback or lemon sole), *Pseu-*

dopleuronectes americanus, that rarely stray off the shelf can conveniently be dubbed epibenthic (shelf) species. This applies also to some of the invertebrates such as the scallops and some of the clams. Those that seasonally inhabit both the shelf and the slope could be classified as benthic shelf-edge species. For these benthic species, however, the term "mesobenthic" has been used and should be retained. The depth to which the term applies has not been defined, but I would suggest that 700 m would cover the depth range of the great majority of these species. This is more than the greatest depth encountered on any shelf proper, e.g., about 500 m is the limit of the deeper channels on the shelf of the Barents Sea.

The reality of the shelf-edge habitat is shown by the tilefish, *Lopholatilus chamaeleonticeps,* which occupies an extremely narrow depth range, according to Bigelow and Schroeder, who state:

. . . none ever being taken shoaler than about 45 fathoms, and very few much deeper than 100 fathoms. . . . The thermal range to which the tilefish is exposed, normally, is very narrow also, for the temperature of the bottom water along the zone inhabited regularly by it varies only between about 47° and about 53°, in most years, summer or winter.*

They blame the tremendous mass mortality of the tilefish that occurred in 1882 to a chilling of the waters that also exterminated the special invertebrate fauna that inhabited the same zone.

A few species live on the slope entirely below the shelf, e.g., the Atlantic chimaera, *Hydrolagus affinis,* which is taken on the slope to as deep as 2500 m. These purely slope species have most often been called archibenthic. This term, until more is known of the slope fauna, might be applied down to about 4000 m. Below this depth the term "abyssobenthic" can be used as a convenience. We do not defend this depth division with any degree of conviction.

---

*Bigelow, H. B., and W. C. Schroeder. 1953. Fishes of the Gulf of Maine. U. S. Fish Wildl. Serv., Fish. Bull. **53**:1-577.

*Bigelow, H. B., and W. C. Schroeder. 1953. Fishes of the Gulf of Maine. U. S. Fish Wildl. Serv., Fish. Bull. **53**:1-577.

For those species that neither tarry near the shore nor live on or near the bottom, classification of their habitat poses certain problems. Temperature and depth are obvious factors, but so are turbidity, currents, and food. The species that dwell in the water column above the shelf, other than those that never leave the nearshore zone (already classified as shore species), can be classified as neritic pelagic species. In areas with a very narrow shelf the shore and the neritic pelagic zones may be synonymous, but in areas with wide shelves the neritic pelagic zone may extend far offshore.

It has been customary to classify the habitats in the open ocean by depth strata. This, however, does not differentiate between the surface species (often termed epipelagic) that remain over oceanic areas and those surface species that wander indifferently over both neritic and oceanic areas. To meet this difficulty we propose to use the term "pelagic" to embrace both the neritic pelagic and the oceanic pelagic zones. Thus the marine surface (epipelagic) species come under one of three headings:

Neritic pelagic   Over shelf areas
Oceanic pelagic   Over oceanic areas
Holopelagic   Over shelf and oceanic areas

These three terms apply to strictly surface and very near surface species, e.g., scombroids, clupeoids, and the ocean sunfish. These are species that live in the photic zone, usually in the upper few meters of the water column.

Among the holopelagic species there is a rather distinct boundary between the subarctic and subtropical fishes. This is broadly hinted at by the break in species taken in quantity above and below about 10° C. (See Fig. 3-10, p. 57.) The actual boundary, according to Favorite (1969), between the North Pacific areas frequented by the holopelagic sockeye salmon, *Oncorhynchus nerka,* and those inhabited by the albacore, *Thunnus alalunga,* is determined only partially by surface temperatures, but chiefly by the presence or absence of a subsurface temperature minimum stratum. Although the surface temperatures at which both species are taken overlap, and salmon are taken at surface temperatures of up to 13° C, salmon are not found in the open Pacific south of 47° N lat. despite favorable surface temperatures.

The temperature minimum stratum (Figs. 5-4 and 5-5) is found between the depth to which winter-cooled water sinks in midocean and the surface layer warmed by the sun during spring and early summer. This temperature minimum stratum between the warmer surface layer (at the proper season) and the slightly warmer water below about 200 m is a relatively permanent feature of the northern North Pacific Ocean. At hun-

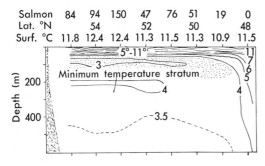

Fig. 5-4. Relationship between gill net catches of sockeye salmon during summer of 1956 in North Pacific and temperature minimum stratum occurring for nearly 500 miles along 155° W long. (Modified from Favorite, F. 1969. Comm. Fish. Rev. **31:**34-40.)

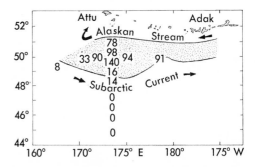

Fig. 5-5. Showing area of North Pacific covered by temperature minimum stratum and catches of sockeye salmon inside and outside area.

dreds of locations netted, only once were salmon and albacore taken in the same catch. In view of the rather distinct habitats involved here, I am breaking the oceanic pelagic zone at the boundary between the subarctic and subtropical areas into the cool pelagic and warm pelagic zones.

Below the epipelagic zones the term "mesopelagic" is generally used to identify the dimly lit zone extending from about the depth of the shelf edge to about 1000 m or slightly deeper (Bieri [1966] uses 700 m as the lower boundary); typical are the lantern-fishes, Myctophidae. Specimens of these mesopelagic forms are occasionally taken in shoal waters, but considering the much vaster collecting effort in shoal waters, this is not surprising.

CLASSIFICATION OF ORGANISMS BY HABITATS OCCUPIED

Fluvial. Species that dwell in moving freshwaters are called fluvial species. Since we are concerned primarily with marine fisheries, the interest in stream habitats stems chiefly from their use by anadromous, ad-fluvial, and catadromous species. Streams offer a multitude of microhabitats that we will not attempt to describe here.

Adfluvial. Adfluvial species dwell in smaller lakes or interior seas and ascend streams to spawn.

Lacustrine. Lacustrine species dwell in freshwater interior seas. For convenience these species can be referred to as littoral if they frequent the shores and shallows, e.g., the sticklebacks; as benthic if bottom dwelling, e.g., the burbot or ling, *Lota lota;* as pelagic if they inhabit the epilimnion or the surface layers in nonstratified seas, e.g., the landlocked alewife, *Alosa pseudoharengus,* in the Great Lakes; and as profundal if they dwell chiefly in the hypolimnion or mid-waters of interior freshwater seas, e.g., the togue or lake trout, *Cristivomer namaycush.*

Anadromous. Anadromous species spend a portion of their adult life in a marine or estuarine habitat and spawn in fresh water, or spend a portion of their adult life in a marine environment but spawn in estuarine waters.

FLUVIAL ANADROMOUS. Species that indifferently ascend streams with or without lakes, e.g., the chum salmon, *Oncorhynchus keta,* the sea lamprey, *Petromyzon marinus,* and the Atlantic sturgeon, *Acipenser oxyrhynchus,* are termed fluvial anadromous species.

LACUSTRINE ANADROMOUS. Ascending only (with a few exceptions) streams with lakes in which the young dwell for a time before descending to the sea, lacustrine anadromous species include the sockeye or red salmon, *Oncorhynchus nerka,* and the anadromous stocks of the alewife, *Alosa pseudoharengus.*

QUASI-ANADROMOUS. Quasi-anadromous species or certain stocks of some species leave a marine environment to spawn in an estuarine habitat. One example is certain populations of the pink salmon, *Oncorhynchus gorbuscha,* that spawn in the gravels of intertidal flats below impassable falls (Hanavan and Skud, 1954). Another example is the tomcod, *Microgadus tomcod.* This small gadoid fish, both euryhaline and eurythermal, dwells in shore and estuarine habitats and in many places spawns in the mouths of streams.

Catadromous. Species in which the young dwell and grow in streams and lakes and the adults spawn in a marine habitat are identified as catadromous species. This clear-cut definition is in fact violated by the classic example of a catadromous fish, the eel, *Anguilla* sp. Many individual eels, usually considered to be the males, remain in the estuaries until mature. The movement of some eels in and out between the streams and the estuaries is exploited in some of the smaller streams in Maine where eel weirs are built to catch both up- and downstream migrants.

Quasi-catadromous. The quasi-catadromous category includes a number of species that spawn in a marine environment, but the very young enter estuaries where they make rapid growth. Examples include the menhaden, *Brevoortia* sp.; the mullet, *Mugil cephalus;* the white and brown shrimps, *Penaeus setiferus* and *P. aztecus;* and the blue crab, *Callinectes sapidus.*

Estuarine. The estuarine classification includes euryhaline forms that both spawn and dwell in the estuaries. One species of sea trout, *Cynoscion nebulosis,* the spotted sea trout, is a piscine example. The American oyster, *Crassostrea virginica,* is an estuarine mollusk. Estuarine species can be conveniently called benthic estuarine or pelagic estuarine, depending on whether they inhabit the bottom or live in the water column.

Brackish. The brackish designation applies to species living in a stable brackish environment as contrasted to the fluctuating environment of an estuary. Examples of such brackish areas (salinity less than 15 $^0/_{00}$) are the Baltic, Caspian, and Aral Seas. The subcategories will be similar to those used for the marine habitats (salinity 15 $^0/_{00}$ and above).

Shore. The term "shore species" is applicable to marine species that never stray far from the shoreline. Some may live indifferently on either a neritic or estuarine shoreline. The smelt, *Osmerus eperlanus,* is an anadromous species that in the sea seldom strays more than a mile or two from land. Typical shore species are the killifish or mummichog, *Fundulus heteroclitus;* the silverside, *Menidia* sp.; the surf smelt, *Hypomesus pretiosus;* the jacksmelt, *Atherinopsis californiensis;* the California corbina, *Menticirrhus undulatus;* the shiner perch or shiner seaperch, *Cymatogaster aggregata* (Clemens and Wilby, 1961); the black rockfish, *Sebastes melanops;* and many of the smaller sculpins, Cottidae.

Marine benthic. Species that are designated as marine benthic normally dwell on or close to the bottom in either marine or stable brackish habitats.

EPIBENTHIC. Epibenthic refers to bottom species that inhabit the continental shelf. Some of these forms are euryhaline and at times invade estuaries and even stream mouths, e.g., in southeastern Alaska it is common to see the starry flounder, *Platichthys stellatus,* in the lower portions of streams. This classification applies to numerous fish and invertebrates, including the sea scallops and surf clams.

MESOBENTHIC. The mesobenthic category is difficult to define, but it comprises species that live on the deeper portions of the shelf and at times on the upper slope down to as much as 700 m. The tilefish, already mentioned, is a classic example; also included are some of the snappers, *Lutjanus;* the long-finned hake, *Phycis chesteri;* a few shrimps of the genus *Hymenopenaeus;* and many of the flatfishes, Pleuronectidae.

ARCHIBENTHIC. Species that are termed archibenthic live on the continental slope below the edge of the shelf down to 4000 m or to the 4° C isotherm. We have already mentioned the chimaera or ratfish of the Atlantic coast, *Hydrolagus affinis,* that, according to Bigelow and Schroeder (1953), has not been taken in less than 160 fm (293 m) and is found down to 1200 fm (2195 m). On the other hand, the Pacific coast chimaera, *Hydrolagus colliei,* although usually taken below 40 fm (73 m), often appears in shoal water, and the egg cases are laid there, often in the intertidal zone (Clemens and Wilby, 1961). The scarlet prawn of the Atlantic Ocean and Gulf of Mexico lives and develops in depths approaching 900 m (Kutkuhn, 1966). The deepsea angler, *Ceratias holboelli,* living, according to Bigelow and Schroeder (1953), between 200 and 750 fm (55 to 229 m) in depth, should be considered archibenthic.

The lower depth boundary of the archibenthic habitat will vary considerably in different areas if we consider the 4° C isotherm as a more realistic guide than mere depth. Murray and Hjort (1912) show that on the northern and southern slopes of the Wyville Thomson Ridge between the Shetland and Faroe Islands there is a very marked difference in the depth of the 4° C isotherm, about 1500 m on the southern slope and about 600 m on the northern slope, which is in the Norwegian Sea. In lower latitudes the depth of the 4° C isotherm approximates closer to 4000 m.

ABYSSOBENTHIC. Bottom organisms below about 4000 m or below the 4° C isotherm are termed abyssobenthic. Until more information is compiled this depth division is arbitrary.

Marine pelagic. Marine pelagic forms live off the bottom in either the marine or stable brackish habitats.

EPIPELAGIC. Epipelagic organisms live in the water column close to the surface in the photic zone.

Neritic pelagic. On the continental shelf it would be very difficult to make any distinction between the species that live very close to the surface and those that usually prefer to remain a little deeper, since most species change their depth somewhat in accordance with light, temperature, and water mass layers. Accordingly all continental shelf forms living in the water column off the bottom we designate as neritic pelagic species. By *off the bottom* we exclude species such as the round bankfishes that normally are sufficiently close to the bottom as to be readily captured by otter trawl. The ocean perch (redfish), *Sebastes marinus,* rises off the bottom at night but can be easily taken by otter trawl during the daylight hours, so for convenience we classify the ocean perch as a benthic species.

Oceanic pelagic. The term "oceanic pelagic" can be applied to those surface-living forms inhabiting the photic zone that normally remain over the slope and deep oceanic areas, seldom approaching land. Some are found chiefly in the oceanic gyres. Examples are the ocean sunfishes or headfishes, Molidae, and the sargassum fishes, *Histrio,* that live among floating seaweed *(Sargassum).*

Holopelagic. The term "holopelagic" can be applied to a whole host of surface-dwelling forms that are at home over both shelf and oceanic areas. These include most species of the migratory marine schooling fishes such as those of the Clupeidae, Engraulidae, and Scombridae families, with some exceptions.

• • •

As discussed earlier (Fig. 5-4), the oceanic pelagic and the holopelagic habitats can be subdivided at the subarctic-subtropical boundary into cold and warm habitats.

MESOPELAGIC. Mesopelagic applies to "off-the-bottom" forms living from the depth of the shelf edge or the lower limit of the photic zone down to about 1000 m. These species include the blacksmelts, *Bathylagus,* and the lanternfishes, Myctophidae family.

BATHYPELAGIC. The term "bathypelagic" has been used to describe forms living in the cold dark waters below about 1000 m to about 4000 m or to the 4° C isotherm.

ABYSSOPELAGIC. "Off-bottom" forms living below about 4000 m or below the 4° C isotherm are designated as abyssopelagic.

Benthopelagic. Forms that move seasonally from an epipelagic to a benthic habitat are known as benthopelagic species. Probably the best known example is the pollock, *Pollachius virens,* which is often taken by purse seines—one record was 60,000 fish in one set—although at other times it is taken by otter trawl down to 200 m. A more striking example is the sablefish, *Anoplopoma fimbria,* of the Pacific coast. Usually found near the bottom in depths of 200 down to 650 fm (366 to 1189 m), it is known to school at the surface where large numbers have been caught in Monterey Bay (Cox, 1948; Phleger et al., 1970).

Difficulties of habitat classification

All classifications such as the one just discussed, are necessarily somewhat arbitrary. Thus the lower boundary of the warm upper layers of the ocean is variously set at about the 8° or 10° C isotherm. This "thermosphere" varies in depth, being somewhat deeper along the western side of the oceans and shallower on the eastern side and in the tropics. It reaches the surface at about

50° S and 40° N lat.; however, this surface layer of warmer water is wider on the eastern shores of the oceans. Many of the forms living either in the deeper midwater or on the bottom in the colder waters beneath this warm water are restricted in their northern (or southern) range by the fact that their eggs, larvae, or juvenile stages must inhabit this overlying blanket of warmer water.

The depths placed on the habitats are admittedly arbitrary, because in subarctic and boreal regions where surface and deeper waters do not differ widely in temperature, forms that remain in deep water in the subtropics may often be found near the surface. Thus depth alone is not always a good criterion.

Some fishes are apparently quite eurythermal. Thus Bigelow and Schroeder (1953) state that the goosefish or angler, *Lophius americanus,* can be found from tidewater down to at least 365 fm (668 m). They are taken at temperatures as cold as 32° F (0° C) on the Newfoundland Banks and as high as 70° F (21° C) in shoal waters in North Carolina. Such widely ranging forms cannot be conveniently classified by a narrowly defined habitat.

Another example of ubiquitous distribution is afforded by the world traveler the bluefin tuna, *Thunnus thynnus.* It travels without any seeming restraint from Bimini in the Bahamas to Newfoundland, southern Labrador, and northern Norway. It moves in and out of the Black Sea from the high salinity of the Mediterranean to the 17 to 20 °/₀₀ of the Black Sea. It occurs over ocean depths and in shoal water. Many are caught annually in pound nets on Cape Cod, and I have seen them landed from the huge beach seines used on the shoal flats of the Gulf of Iskenderun. The bluefin is a fish of the warmer seas but tolerates lower temperatures than the skipjack tuna, *Euthynnus pelamis,* the yellowfin tuna, *Thunnus albacares,* or the striped marlin, *Tetrapterus audax,* as shown in Fig. 3-10 (p. 57), in which Uda shows 98% of the bluefin catch

off Japan taken in water at a temperature above 12° C. This corresponds closely to the 52° to 54° F temperature range that Bigelow and Schroeder (1953) state is the highest summer temperature in the Passamaquoddy Bay region. Here tuna have been taken only in the late summer of occasional years with higher than usual temperatures. Gibbs and Collette (1966) have shown that the Pacific and Atlantic bluefin tunas are subspecies, *Thunnus thynnus orientalis,* and *Thunnus thynnus thynnus,* respectively, but their habits and temperature tolerances appear to be similar.

The problem of classifying forms that live for some period in a fresh or marine habitat and reproduce in the opposite habitat seems rather simple, but in reality is not. In many north temperate streams individuals of the charrs may at times be adfluvial, fluvial, or anadromous, even in the same stream system. The relative proportions of a stock migrating to sea may also vary from season to season in accordance with climatic variations.

Since so much emphasis is placed on fishes that reproduce in fresh water but spend some time in an estuarine, brackish, or marine habitat, perhaps equal emphasis should be placed on the spawning habitats of nonfreshwater forms. Many fishes are tied

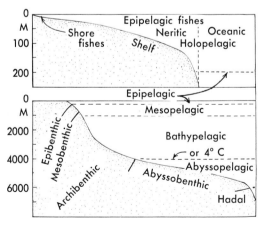

Fig. 5-6. Depicting wholly marine habitats in relation to depth and distribution in water column.

to very specific areas by their spawning requirements. The grunion, *Leuresthes tenuis*, spawns only near the high tide line in the intertidal zone of surf-swept fine sand beaches. Many of the epibenthic fishes have adhesive eggs that are deposited on hard substrate near the shore. The larvae of the oyster require hard objects or hard substrate on which to settle. The range of many marine fishes is limited because the adults must make a contranatant migration to their spawning area so that the young will be carried in a denatant direction by the currents to a suitable habitat.

A summary of the classification just presented follows. In addition, Fig. 5-6 depicts certain wholly marine habitats.

Fluvial
Adfluvial
Lacustrine
    Littoral lacustrine
    Benthic lacustrine
    Pelagic lacustrine
    Profundal lacustrine
Anadromous
    Fluvial anadromous
    Lacustrine anadromous
    Quasi-anadromous
Catadromous
Quasi-catadromous
Estuarine
Brackish (Use marine habitat subdesignations.)
Shore
Marine benthic
    Epibenthic
    Mesobenthic
    Archibenthic
    Abyssobenthic

Marine pelagic
    Epipelagic
        Neritic pelagic
        Oceanic pelagic
            Cold
            Warm
        Holopelagic
            Cold
            Warm
    Mesopelagic
    Bathypelagic
    Abyssopelagic
Benthopelagic

Suggested readings

Bigelow, H. B., and W. C. Schroeder. 1953. Fishes of the Gulf of Maine. U. S. Fish Wildl. Serv., Fish. Bull. **53**:1-577.

Clemens, W. A., and G. V. Wilby. 1961. Fishes of the Pacific coast of Canada, ed. 2. Fish. Res. Bd. Canada, Bull. **68**:1-443.

Hildebrand, S. F., and W. C. Schroeder. 1928. Fishes of Chesapeake Bay. Doc. 1024. Bull. U. S. Bur. Fish. **43**:1-366.

Huet, M. 1959. Profiles and biology of western European streams as related to fish management. Trans. Amer. Fish. Soc. **88**:155-163.

Rounsefell, G. A. 1957. A method of estimating abundance of groundfish on Georges Bank. U. S. Fish Wildl. Serv., Fish. Bull. **57**:265-278.

Rounsefell, G. A. 1958a. Anadromy in North American Salmonidae. U. S. Fish Wildl. Serv., Fish. Bull. **58**:171-185.

Rounsefell, G. A. 1964. Preconstruction study of the fisheries of the estuarine areas traversed by the Mississippi River–Gulf Outlet Project. U. S. Fish Wildl. Serv., Fish. Bull. **63**:373-393.

Thompson, W. F., and J. B. Thompson. 1919. The spawning of the grunion (Leuresthes tenuis). Calif. Fish Game Fish Bull. **3**:1-29.

part three

❦ Marine fisheries

chapter 6

World fisheries

PRODUCTION BY AREA, TEMPERATURE ZONE, AND SPECIES

A brief glimpse of the fisheries conducted in the various regions of the world is useful in developing a sense of the relative importance of different groups of fishes and of the fisheries conducted in each major area. The only readily accessible source of information that covers many large areas exists in the reports of the Food and Agriculture Organization. Therefore we commence this general look at the fisheries with a crude analysis of the world landings as given by the FAO *Yearbook of Fishery Statistics for 1968.*

In Table 6-1 are shown the world catches of marine fishes, crustaceans, and mollusks for which reasonable information on species is available; they are grouped by area of capture without regard to where landed or by whom caught. The areas used in the table are depicted in Figs. 6-1 and 6-2, which show the Atlantic, Pacific, and Indian Oceans.

The two largest producers are the Peruvian and northeastern Atlantic fisheries. The former is based on the anchoveta, *Engraulis ringens,* which is converted into fish meal. The latter is chiefly for food fishes.

Outside of Peru, the largest catches are made by Japan and the U.S.S.R. The Japanese tuna fleets fish wherever tuna are abundant, and their tuna catches cannot be accurately allocated to their locality of capture. Both the Japanese and Russian fleets fish in the eastern Bering Sea for various bankfishes and crabs. The Russian stern trawlers account for portions of the catches of hake off the Patagonia region, South Africa, and Morocco, as well as portions of the catches of several species along the U. S. Atlantic and Pacific coasts.

There are too many species involved to be able to present detailed data on all of them. As a compromise Table 6-2 shows the catches of the principal species or species groups by temperature zones. These temperature zones are not as well defined as one could wish. Brazil lies chiefly in the tropics but extends south into cooler waters. Similarly, the long coastline of Chile extends from warm subtropical waters into the cool or cold zone. In addition, we have not attempted in most cases to show individual species in a closely knit genus. Bearing these constraints in mind, we nevertheless find the breakdown into zones of temperature very useful in grasping the worldwide

Text continued on p. 97.

85

Table 6-1. World landings by species groups for certain areas during 1968 (thousands of metr tons)

	Clupeoids	Gadoids	Scombroids	Carangoids	Misc. bankfishes	Flatfishes	Misc. neritic fishes
Cold							
Northeastern Atlantic	3,615	4,250	1,004	9	253	398	3
Northwestern Atlantic	532	413	17		101	137	
Siberia	470	41	51	65	96	105	15
Alaska	14	2,310			104	13	
Argentina	33	174	19	3	5	1	15
Cool							
British Columbia–Oregon	62	9			39	29	
Japan	730	111	1,887	544	288	355	219
Southeastern Europe	373	1,070	210	136	36	35	68
Caspian Sea	369						
U. S. Atlantic	385	184	15	10	35	53	155
Australia–New Zealand	6	2	13	7	18	3	2
Uruguay		3					5
South Africa	868	629	103	145	1	1	
Chile	1,103	128	28	33	6		2
Warm							
California	17		143	26	6	10	
Taiwan–Hong Kong	54		161	40	44	2	45
Mediterranean	420	17	51	18	9	9	55
Morocco	173	7	21	7	1	1	
North Gulf of Mexico	427		3	1	10	1	8
Peru	10,277	18	73	16	7	1	8
Namibia[1]	970	1	2			1	
Tropical							
Mexico to Venezuela	72		20	11	51		8
Ghana, Senegal, etc.	120		88	48	67	3	24
Brazil	118	6	13	20	16	1	52
Angola	95		11	137	3		9
Philippines	222		144	482	53	5	29
Malaysia and Thailand	43		264	45	23	1	8
Mexico to Ecuador	101		35	16			4
India	432	2	76	75	5	11	33

[1]South West Africa. Namibia is the official name but is not widely recognized.

lmons	Cartilaginous fishes	Misc. tropical fishes	Misc. unsorted fishes	Crustaceans	Shelled mollusks	Cephalopods	Various mollusks	Totals
10	57			99	156			9,854
3				29	11			1,243
39				40				922
139				69				2,649
	14			1	9	3		277
151	1		1	27	33			352
114	90		24	202	516	974	108	6,162
	40		11	43	202	104	16	2,344
								369
	6			90	414	1		1,348
	5		30	33	45			164
	1		1		1	1		12
			43	7	1			1,798
	1			32	42	3	2	1,380
3				9	2	12		228
	35	3	99	27	15	18	2	545
	8		17	18	14	31	26	693
	1					1	1	213
				100	192			742
	25				6			10,431
				9				983
	10	7	54	71	31	1		336
	5	3	9	4				371
	11	19	22	53	4	1		336
	1		38					294
	1	70	49	31		18		1,104
	17	7	676	65	55	3	115	1,322
	3	1	88	26	5			279
	31	144	131	103			2	1,045

Fig. 6-1. World landings of marine fishes in 1968 for Atlantic, Indian, and southeastern Pacific Oceans. Landings in each area are given in tens of thousands of metric tons. Black coastline shows areas in which statistics by species were either missing or too general to be useful. (From Food and Agriculture Organization. 1969. Yearbook of fishery statistics for 1968, vol. 26. 320 pp.)

Fig. 6-2. World landings of marine fishes in 1968 for the northern and western Pacific Ocean, including the East Indies. For further details see Fig. 6-1.

Table 6-2. Total 1968 world landings by species group and temperature zone (thousands of metric tons)

	Catch	Cold	Cool	Warm	Trop-ical	Tempera-ture rating[1]	Most abundant
Clupeoids and similar species							
Capelin[2]	629	629				300	Far north
Argentine anchovy	32	32				300	Argentina
Sea herring	3,791	3,597	193	1		295	North Atlantic and Pacific
Sprat	181	175	2	4		295	Northeastern Atlantic
Smelts[3]	20	19	1			287	North Atlantic, British Columbia–Oregon
Sand lance	355	200	155			250	Northern seas
Deepsea smelts[4]	19	6	13			232	Japan, northeastern Atlantic
Caspian herring[5]	428		369	59		231	Caspian and Black Seas
River herrings	57	3	53	1		205	Western North Atlantic
Chilean sardine	96		94	2		200	Peru Current
Japanese anchovy	430		421	9		198	Japan, Taiwan
European pilchard	510	1	268	241		153	Southeastern Europe, Morocco, Mediterranean
Cape anchovy	332		170	162		151	Benguela Current
Menhaden	709		285	423	1	140	U. S. Atlantic and Gulf of Mexico
South African pilchard	1,587		685	808	94	138	Benguela Current
North Atlantic anchovy	340		74	266		122	Mediterranean, southeastern Europe
Anchoveta	11,272		1,009	10,263		109	Peru Current
Mullets	92		20	31	41	78	Worldwide in warm seas
Round herring	130		35	7	88	59	Brazil, Japan
Other sardines	157		24	7	126	35	India, Japan to Malaysia, Mexico to Ecuador
Shads and milkfishes	121		1	21	99	19	Southeastern Asia, India
Atherinids[6]	41		1	3	37	16	Philippines, Mediterranean
Other *Sardinella* spp.	152		5	5	142	9	Northwestern Africa, Caribbean
Other anchovies	167			14	153	8	Central America, California, Philippines, India
Thread herring	60		1	1	58	6	Northwestern Africa, Southeast Asia, Caribbean
Oil sardine	304				304	0	India
Wolf herring	11				11	0	India
Various clupeoids	71		20	12	39	73	India to Japan, southwestern Africa, Brazil
TOTAL	22,095						

NOTE: Round herring are probably *Etrumeus microps* for Japan (catch of 35,000 metric tons) and Taiwan (catch of 7,000 metric tons), and *Sardinella aurita* and/or *S. anchovia* for Brazil (catch of 88,000 metric tons)—a confusion of round sardines *(Sardinella)* with round herring.

[1]A scale from 300 to 0 derived by weighing the percentage in each temperature zone by 3 for the cold zone, by 2 for the cool zone, by 1 for the warm zone, and by 0 for tropical waters. Thus a species rated 300 was caught wholly in the cold zone, and one rated 0 was taken only from tropical waters.

[2]Includes a few argentine.

[3]*Osmerus.*

[4]Argentines, excluding *Mallotus* and *Osmerus.*

[5]*Caspialosa.*

[6]Includes a few grunion, *Leuresthes tenuis;* a few eulachon, *Thaleichthys pacificus;* and a few surf (or silver) smelt, *Hypomesus pretiosus.*

Table 6-2. Total 1968 world landings by species group and temperature zone (thousands of metric tons)—cont'd

	Catch	Cold	Cool	Warm	Trop- ical	Tempera- ture rating	Most abundant
Gadoids							
Alaska pollock[7]	2,201	2,201				300	Alaska
Norway pout[8]	493	493				300	Northeastern Atlantic
Pacific hake	109	109				300	Alaska
Grenadiers	33	33				300	Northeastern Atlantic
Navaga cod	19	19				300	Northwestern Pacific
Blue ling	6	6				300	Northeastern Atlantic
Cusk	39	38	1			297	North Atlantic
Patagonian hake	183	174	3		6	297	Argentina
Cod	4,091	3,174	917			278	Northern seas
Haddock	424	379	45			289	North Atlantic
Pollock[9]	363	304	59			284	North Atlantic, southeastern Europe
Whiting[10]	229	179	49	1		278	Northeastern Atlantic, south- eastern Europe
European ling[11]	59	45	14			276	Northeastern Atlantic, south- eastern Europe
Pollack[12]	7	5	2			271	Northeastern Atlantic
White and red hakes[13]	33	5	28			215	Northwestern Atlantic, U. S. Atlantic
Silver hake[14]	98		98			200	U. S. Atlantic
European hake	143	10	116	17		195	Southeastern Europe, Mediter- ranean, northeastern At- lantic
Cape hakes	630		629	1		200	Southwestern Africa
Chilean hakes	128		128			200	Chile
Potassou[15]	27		25	2		193	Southeastern Europe, Mediter- ranean
Peruvian hake	18			18		100	Peru
Various gadoids	49	20	24	3	2	227	
TOTAL	9,382						
Scombroids							
Mackerel[16]	2,330	1,030	1,213	62	26	239	Japan, northeastern Atlantic, U. S. Atlantic, southeastern Europe, Mediter- ranean
Saury	222	51	171			223	Japan, northwestern Pacific
Swordfish	32	4	23	5		194	Japan, northwestern Atlantic, southeastern Europe
Bigeye tuna	112		96	15	1	186	Japan, Taiwan

[7] *Theragra chalcogramma,* a member of the Gadidae family.
[8] *Trisopterus esmarkii.*
[9] *Pollachius virens.*
[10] *Merlangus (Gadus) merlangus.*
[11] *Molva molva.*
[12] *Pollachius pollachius.*
[13] *Urophycis.*
[14] *Merluccius bilinearis.*
[15] *Micromesistius (=Gadus) potassou.*
[16] *Scomber.*

Continued.

Table 6-2. Total 1968 world landings by species group and temperature zone (thousands of metric tons)—cont'd

	Catch	Cold	Cool	Warm	Trop-ical	Tempera-ture rating	Most abundant
Scombroids—cont'd							
Bluefin tuna	86	3	68	12	3	184	Japan, southeastern Europe, California, Mediterranean, northwestern Atlantic
Snoek	33		29	2	2	182	Southwestern Africa, Chile
Frigate mackerel	29		25	2	2	178	Japan, all cool seas
Billfishes	69		54	14	1	176	Japan, Taiwan
Albacore	174	1	112	54	7	162	Japan, California, southeastern Europe
Skipjack	246		169	39	38	154	Japan, California to Ecuador, northwestern Africa
Yellowfin tuna	291		145	108	38	137	Japan, Taiwan, California, southeastern Europe, north-western Africa
Cutlass fish	176		84	19	73	107	Japan, Taiwan, Philippines, India
Spanish mackerels	98		46	8	44	102	Japan to India, Central America, Chile, U. S. Atlantic
Bonito	122	1	8	81	32	84	Peru, Philippines, Mediterranean
Indian mackerel[17]	314				314	0	Philippines to India
Seerfishes	30				30	0	Philippines to India
Various tunas	166		91	34	42	130	Philippines, India, Japan
TOTAL	4,563						
Carangoids							
Yellowtail[18]	52		52			200	Japan
Jack mackerel	897	74	619	63	141	169	Benguela Current, Japan-Taiwan, southeastern Europe, northwestern Pacific
Dolphins	16		11	3	2	155	Japan
Butterfishes	56		13	10	33	64	Southeast Asia, Central America to Brazil
Bluefish	35	1	3	5	26	41	Ghana, Brazil, Mediterranean, U. S. Atlantic
Scads	321		54	12	255	38	South Africa, Angola, Japan-Taiwan, southeastern Europe, northwestern Pacific, California, Mediterranean
Various carangoids	515	2	123	13	377	51	Philippines, Japan, India, Southeast Asia, Central America to Brazil
TOTAL	1,892						
Misc. bank fishes							
Redfishes[19]	298	298				300	Northeastern and northwestern Atlantic
Atka mackerel[20]	103	103				300	Alaska

[17]*Rastrelliger.*
[18]*Seriola.*
[19]*Sebastes marinus* and *S. mentella.*
[20]A greenling, Hexagrammidae family, *Pleurogrammus monopterygius.*

Table 6-2. Total 1968 world landings by species group and temperature zone (thousands of metric tons)—cont'd

	Catch	Cold	Cool	Warm	Trop- ical	Tempera- ture rating	Most abundant
Misc. bank fishes—cont'd							
Lumpfish	3	3				300	Northeastern Atlantic
Wolffish	39	39				299	Northeastern and northwestern Atlantic
Rockfishes[21]	286	86	193	7		227	Japan, northwestern and northeastern Pacific, British Columbia to California
Anglers	38	12	24	2		227	Southeastern Europe, north-eastern Atlantic, Mediterranean
Gurnards	49	12	27	10		203	Japan, northwestern Pacific, Taiwan, Australia–New Zealand, Mediterranean
Cusk eel	6	1	4	1		200	Chile, Argentina, Peru
Sandfish[22]	52		52			200	Japan
Congers	9	1	7	1		200	Southeastern Europe
Cultus (ling) cod[23]	7		7			200	British Columbia–Oregon
Sablefish	20	1	17	2		195	Alaska to California
Morays	45		32	9	4	162	Japan, Taiwan, India
Sea bass[24]	34	3	17	9	5	153	Worldwide in cool to warm seas
Lizard fish	86		25	24	37	74	Philippines to Japan
Snappers and groupers	122		15	14	93	37	Brazil to northern Gulf of Mexico, Southeast Asia to Taiwan, Australia–New Zealand
Grunts	83		3	1	79	9	Northwestern Africa, Brazil, Philippines
TOTAL	1,280						
Flatfishes							
Greenland halibut	69	69				300	North Atlantic
Plaice	253	248	5			298	North Atlantic
Gray sole[25]	21	18	3			286	Northwestern Atlantic, U. S. Atlantic, northeastern Atlantic
Common sole	44	35	6	3		282	Northeastern Atlantic, south-eastern Europe, Mediterranean
Yellowtail (dab)[26]	35	8	27			223	U. S. Atlantic, northeastern Atlantic
Flukes[27]	17		17			200	Japan, U. S. Atlantic
Halibut	64	25	39			239	North Pacific, North Atlantic
Other flounders	397	236	149	11	1	256	Chiefly North Atlantic, North Pacific

[21]Scorpaenidae family, except *Sebastes marinus* and *S. mentella*.
[22]Trichodontidae family.
[23]A greenling, Hexagrammidae family, *Ophiodon elongatus*.
[24]Includes a very few striped bass and white perch, *Morone*.
[25]*Glyptocephalus*.
[26]*Limanda*.
[27]*Paralichthys*.

Continued.

Table 6-2. Total 1968 world landings by species group and temperature zone (thousands of metric tons)—cont'd

	Catch	Cold	Cool	Warm	Trop-ical	Tempera-ture rating	Most abundant
Flatfishes—cont'd							
Turbot	8	5		3		226	Northeastern Atlantic, Black Sea
Other soles	41		27	2	12	137	Japan, India
Various flatfish	225	9	203	6	7	195	Japan
TOTAL	1,174						
Salmons							
Atlantic salmon	12	12				300	Northeastern and northwestern Atlantic
Sockeye salmon	68	46	22			268	Yukon to Columbia River, Siberia
Pink salmon	162	78	84			248	Alaska to Oregon, Japan, Siberia
Chum salmon	153	38	115			225	Japan, Oregon to Alaska, Siberia
Coho salmon	48	12	36			225	California to Alaska, Siberia
King salmon	18	6	9	3		213	California to Alaska
TOTAL	461						
Cartilaginous fishes							
Picked dogfish	25	25				300	Northeastern Atlantic
Porbeagle	2	2				300	Northeastern Atlantic
Chimaeras	7	1	6			209	U. S. Atlantic, Argentina, Australia–New Zealand
Skates and rays	99	23	46	16	14	177	Worldwide
Sharks (except porbeagle)	163	13	84	25	41	143	Worldwide
Other dogfish	70	8	9	29	24	103	Worldwide
TOTAL	366						
Misc. neritic fishes							
Sea breams[28]	312	2	238	53	19	172	U. S. Atlantic, southeastern Europe, Japan, Mediterranean, Ghana to Angola
Puffers and leather-jackets	11		9		2	164	Japan, U. S. Atlantic, Philippines
Sciaenids	374	30	175	35	134	127	Japan to India, Brazil, Argentina, northwestern Pacific, U. S. Atlantic, north Gulf of Mexico, Peru
Flying fishes	26		14	4	8	123	Japan, India, Taiwan, Brazil
Surmullets	36		10	22	4	115	Mediterranean, southeastern Europe, Taiwan, India
Garfish[29]	9	2	4	3		17	Southeastern Europe, Mediterranean, northeastern Europe
TOTAL	768						

[28]Sparidae family. The looseness and inaccuracy of the FAO grouping of species is indicated by their footnote to the U. S. Atlantic catch for this group of fishes, which states that it contains "buffalofish, grunts, hogfish, jewfish, mojarra, pigfish, sand perch, sea robin, mangrove snapper, vermilion snapper, tautog, tripletail and warsaw"!

[29]*Belone.*

Table 6-2. Total 1968 world landings by species group and temperature zone (thousands of metric tons)—cont'd

	Catch	Cold	Cool	Warm	Trop- ical	Tempera- ture rating	Most abundant
Misc. tropical fishes							
Sea catfish	52			3	49	6	India, Brazil to Mexico, Taiwan
Barracuda	8				8	1	All tropical areas
Slipmouth[30]	111				111	0	Philippines to India
Bombay duck[31]	82				82	0	India
TOTAL	253						
Misc. unsorted fishes	1,290		109	115	1,066	25	
Crustaceans							
Caridean shrimp[32]	47	47				300	Northeastern Atlantic
Deep water prawn[33]	29	29				300	Northeastern and northwestern Atlantic
Penaeid shrimps	412		98	84	230	68	Carolinas to Brazil, Japan to India, Mexico to Ecuador, Australia–New Zealand
Various shrimps	111	8	35	36	32	117	Alaska to Oregon, southeastern Europe, Mediterranean, Chile, Taiwan, India
True lobsters	36	20	15	1		253	Northeastern and northwestern Atlantic, U. S. Atlantic, southeastern Europe, Mediterranean
Norway lobsters	32	17	13	2		246	Northeastern Atlantic to Mediterranean
Squat lobsters[34]	18		18			200	Chile
Spiny lobsters	58		35	10	13	138	Australia–New Zealand, South Africa, Namibia, Gulf of Mexico to Brazil, Japan, California to Ecuador
Edible crab	8	8				300	Northeastern Atlantic
King crab	131	98	33			275	Alaska, Siberia, Japan
Dungeness crab	22	4	11	7		190	Alaska to California
Blue crab	85		61	14	10	160	U. S. Atlantic to Mexico
Other crabs	157		101	5	51	132	Japan, Southeast Asia, Brazil
Various crustaceans	41	7	15	3	16	132	
TOTAL	1,187						
Mollusks							
Mussels	284	137	127	19	1	241	Northeastern Atlantic, southeastern Europe, Mediterranean, Argentina, Chile, Peru
Cockles	38	14	22		2	227	Southeastern Europe, northeastern Atlantic

[30]Leiognathidae family.
[31]*Harpodon nehereus.*
[32]*Crangon vulgaris.*
[33]*Pandalus borealis.*
[34]Galatheidae family.

Continued.

Table 6-2. Total 1968 world landings by species group and temperature zone (thousands of metric tons)—cont'd

	Catch	Cold	Cool	Warm	Trop-ical	Tempera-ture rating	Most abundant
Mollusks—cont'd							
Scallops	99	11	88			211	U. S. Atlantic, Australia–New Zealand, southeastern Europe, northwestern Atlantic, Japan
Clams	384	3	363	14	4	196	Japan, U. S. Atlantic, Chile
Oysters	809	3	586	193	27	171	Japan, U. S. Atlantic, north Gulf of Mexico, southeastern Europe, British Columbia to Oregon, Mexico-Venezuela, Australia–New Zealand
Abalones	21		16	2	3	162	Australia–New Zealand, Japan, California to Mexico
Arkshells	58				58	0	Southeast Asia, Mexico to Venezuela
Conchs and whelks	20	2	17		1	200	Japan, Chile, U. S. Atlantic
Various shelled mollusks	43	6	36		1	210	Southeastern Europe, Japan
Squid	917	4	868	26	19	193	Japan, southeastern Europe, Philippines, California, Mediterranean, Morocco
Octopus	192		173	17	2	189	Japan, southeastern Europe, Mediterranean
Cuttlefish	61		39	19	3	159	Southeastern Europe, Mediterranean, Japan, Taiwan
Various mollusks	274	1	126	29	118	103	Japan, Thailand, southeastern Europe
TOTAL	3,200						

Summary

	Total	Cold	Cool	Warm	Tropical
Clupeoids and similar species	22,095	4,662	3,889	12,340	1,193
Gadoids	9,382	7,194	2,138	42	8
Scombroids	4,563	1,090	2,334	455	654
Carangoids	1,892	77	875	106	834
Misc. bank fishes	1,280	559	423	80	218
Flatfishes	1,174	653	476	25	20
Salmons	461	192	266	3	
Cartilaginous fishes	366	72	145	70	79
Misc. neritic fishes	768	34	450	117	167
Misc. tropical fishes	253			3	250
Misc. unsorted fishes	1,290		109	115	1,066
TOTAL fishes	43,524	14,533	11,129	13,362	4,489
Crustaceans	1,187	238	435	162	352
Shelled mollusks	1,756	176	1,255	228	97
Cephalopods	1,170	4	1,080	62	24
Various mollusks	274	1	126	29	118
TOTAL invertebrates	4,387	419	2,896	481	591
Total by species	47,911	14,952	14,025	13,849	5,074
Total without species designation	3,650				3,650
Estimate (China, etc.)	6,689			6,689	
GRAND TOTAL	58,250	14,952	14,025	20,538	8,724

distribution of the various groups of organisms.

ECONOMIC VALUE OF SPECIES AND SPECIES GROUPS

The picture of the worldwide distribution and relative abundance of different groups of fishes is somewhat distorted by the lack of an adequate breakdown of the catches by species for many tropical areas. Therefore in Table 6-3 most "catchall" categories such as "various carangoids" have been omitted even though they represent a fair portion of the catch in some areas.

Table 6-3 is intended to provide a grasp of the relative weight of the landings of different species. The value will vary widely. The great bulk of the clupeoids and their allies are converted into fish meal for poultry and stock feed. This includes most of the anchovies, pilchards, sardines, sardinellas, all of the menhaden and capelin, and the sand lance. A fair proportion of the catches of sea herring and sprat are consumed directly. A certain amount of herring and sardines are canned, and a fair amount of herring are salted.

The gadoid fishes are largely consumed directly—fresh or as frozen fillets or fish sticks. Much of the hake catch may eventually be converted into fish protein concentrate, as the soft-fleshed hake do not lend themselves readily to direct use.

The third most important group of fishes is the scombroids. Over half, 2742×10^3 metric tons, consists of mackerels—common mackerels, Spanish mackerels, and Indian mackerels. These are very important food fishes. The two common species of mackerels—*Scomber scombrus* and *S. japonicus*—are cool-water species that are most abundant around Japan and the northern Atlantic. Spanish and Indian mackerels are warmwater and tropical species whose abundance is most probably underestimated because of the dearth of species statistics in Indonesia and other tropical waters. The tunas, while producing only 1060×10^3 metric tons, are important as perhaps the world's most abundant high-priced canned fish product. The tunas are wide-ranging fishes, and a large share of the catches are made far offshore. Although the catches are attributed in the statistics to specific countries, the fish are not necessarily captured in the same area as the port of landing.

The fourth most important group comprises the jacks, scads, or carangoids. The jack mackerels, horse mackerels, or maasbankers, genus *Trachurus,* are the eighth most abundant group of fishes. These are pelagic fishes occurring in abundance in areas of strong mixing or upwelling such as the Benguela, California, and Canary Current systems and off Japan, but they are also abundant in the Sea of Marmara. The scads, genus *Decapterus* and others, occur chiefly in warm or tropical seas. The yellowtail, genus *Seriola,* is most abundant off Japan and is now raised extensively in pens. Formerly of some abundance in California, it is now regarded there as a sport fish.

The fifth group, listed as "miscellaneous bank fishes," includes a large group of demersal fishes of widely separated origins. The redfishes (Atlantic) and the rockfishes (Pacific) of the Scorpaenidae family together yielded 584,000 metric tons. The redfishes inhabit cold waters exclusively, but the rockfishes range around the Pacific from Japan and Siberia to California. The other cold-water species are the Atka mackerel of Alaska, a greenling (Hexagrammidae family), and the wolffish, *Anarhichas,* of the North Atlantic, which is usually sold as fresh or frozen fillets under the name "ocean catfish."

The chief groups of the "miscellaneous bank fishes" in tropical waters are the snappers, groupers, grunts, and lizard fishes. The listed landings of 291,000 metric tons are minimal because of the lack of adequate data for Southeast Asia.

The flatfishes are of much greater economic importance than the landings of 1174×10^3 metric tons would indicate, since they are almost totally consumed fresh or frozen at premium prices. The Greenland halibut and the plaice are found

Table 6-3. Species or groups ranked by catch and temperature rating categories (thousands of metric tons)

Species or group	Cold (260-300)	Cool (190-259)	Warm (100-189)	Tropical (0-99)
	Temperature rating			
Anchoveta, *Engraulis ringens*			11,272	
Cod, *Gadus morhua* and *G. macrocephalus*	4,091			
Sea herring, *Clupea harengus* and *C. pallasi*	3,791			
Mackerel, *Scomber scombrus* and *S. japonicus*		2,330		
Alaska pollock, *Theragra chalcogramma*	2,201			
South African pilchard			1,587	
Squids		917		
Jack mackerel			897	
Oysters			809	
Menhaden, *Brevoortia* spp.			709	
Cape hakes (stockfish), *Merluccius capensis*		630		
Capelin, *Mallotus* spp.	629			
European pilchard			510	
Norway pout, *Trisopterus esmarkii*	493			
Japanese anchovy		430		
Caspian herrings, *Caspialosa* spp.		428		
Haddock, *Melanogrammus aeglefinus*	424			
Penaeid shrimps				412
Misc. North Atlantic flounders		397		
Clams		384		
Sciaenids			374	
Pollock, *Pollachius virens*	363			
Sand lance, *Ammodytes* spp.		355		
North Atlantic anchovy, *Engraulis encrasicholus*			340	
Cape anchovy			332	
Scads			321	
Indian mackerel, *Rastrelliger*				314
Sea breams			312	
Oil sardine				304
Redfishes, *Sebastes marinus* and *S. mentella*	298			
Yellowfin tuna			291	
Rockfishes, *Sebastes,* except *S. marinus* and *S. mentella*		286		
Mussels		284		
Plaice, *Pleuronectes* and *Hippoglossoides*	253			
Skipjack			246	
European whiting, *Merlangus merlangus*	229			
Saury, *Cololabis* and *Scomberesox*		222		
Octopus			192	
Patagonian hake, *Merluccius hubbsi*	183			
Sprat, *Sprattus sprattus*	181			
Cutlass fish			176	
Albacore			174	
Sharks (except the porbeagle or mackerel shark)			163	
Pink salmon, *Oncorhynchus gorbuscha*		161		
Chum salmon, *Oncorhynchus keta*		153		
Sardinella spp. (except round herring, oil sardine, etc. separately listed)				152
European hake		143		
King crab	131			
Round herring				130
Chilean hake, *Merluccius gayi*		128		

Table 6-3. Species or groups ranked by catch and temperature rating categories (thousands of metric tons)—cont'd

	Temperature rating			
Species or group	Cold (260-300)	Cool (190-259)	Warm (100-189)	Tropical (0-99)
Bonito				122
Snappers and groupers				122
Shads and milkfishes				121
Bigeye tuna			112	
Slipmouth				111
North Pacific hake, *Merluccius productus*	109			
Atka mackerel, *Pleurogrammus monopterygius*	103			
Skates and rays			99	
Scallops		99		
Spanish mackerels			98	
Silver hake, *Merluccius bilinearis*		98		
Chilean sardine, *Sardinops sagax*		96		
Mullets				92
Lizard fish				86
Bluefin tuna			86	
Blue crab			85	
Grunts				83
Bombay duck				82
Dogfishes (except picked dogfish)			70	
Billfishes			69	
Greenland halibut, *Reinhardtius hippoglossoides*	69			
Sockeye salmon, *Oncorhynchus nerka*	68			
Halibut, *Hippoglossus*		64		
Butterfishes				64
Cuttlefishes			61	
Thread herring				50
European ling, *Molva molva*	59			
Spiny lobster			58	
River herrings		57		
Sea catfish				52
Yellowtail, *Seriola*		52		
Sandfish, Trichodontidae family		52		
Gurnards		49		
Coho salmon, *Oncorhynchus kisutch*		48		
Caridean shrimp, *Crangon vulgaris*	47			
Morays			45	
Common sole, *Solea solea*	44			
Atherinids				41
Wolffish, *Anarhichas lupus*	39			
Cusk, *Brosme brosme*	39			
Anglers		38		
Cockles		38		
True lobsters, *Homarus*		36		
Surmullets			36	
Yellowtail (dab), *Limanda*		35		
Bluefish				35
Sea bass			34	
White and red hakes, *Urophycis*		33		
Snoek			33	
Grenadiers, Macrouridae family	33			
Argentine anchovy	32			
Norway lobster		32		

Continued.

Table 6-3. Species or groups ranked by catch and temperature rating categories (thousands of metric tons)—cont'd

Species or group	Temperature rating			
	Cold (260-300)	Cool (190-259)	Warm (100-189)	Tropical (0-99)
Swordfish		32		
Seerfishes				30
Deepwater prawn, *Pandalus borealis*	29			
Frigate mackerel			29	
Potassou, *Micromesistius* (=*Gadus*) *potassou*		27		
Flying fishes			26	
Picked dogfish, *Squalus acanthias*	25			
Dungeness crab		22		
Gray sole, *Glyptocephalus*	21			
Abalones			21	
Sablefish		20		
Conchs and whelks		20		
Smelts, *Osmerus*	20			
Navaga (Arctic) cod, *Eleginus navaga*	19			
Deep sea smelts and argentines (except *Mallotus* and *Osmerus*)		19		
Peruvian hake			18	
King salmon, *Oncorhynchus tshawytscha*		18		
Squat lobsters, Galatheidae family		18		
Flukes, *Paralichthys*		17		
Dolphins			16	
Atlantic salmon, *Salmo salar*	12			
Puffers, leatherjackets			11	
Wolf herring				11
Garfish, *Belone*				9
Congers		9		
Turbot		8		
Edible crab	8			
Barracuda				8
Cultus (ling) cod, *Ophiodon elongatus*		7		
Chimaeras		7		
Pollack, *Pollachius pollachius*	7			
Blue ling, *Molva dypterygia*	6			
Cusk eel		6		
Lumpfish, *Cyclopterus lumpus*	3			
Porbeagle, *Lamna nasus*	2			

almost exclusively in cold waters, the plaice only in the North Atlantic. Only a very small fraction of the flatfishes are taken in warm or tropical waters. Furthermore, the tropical flatfishes are chiefly small-sized species such as the tonguefishes and most of the true soles (Soleidae family), whereas the largest flatfishes, the halibuts, are distinctly arctic and boreal.

Although the salmons contributed only 461,000 metric tons to the world catch, they are of great importance because of

their high value as a canned product. In the 1967 United States landings salmon constituted only 5.3% by weight, but were second only to shrimp in value, with 11.1%.

The cartilaginous fishes play only a minor role in world fisheries because the flesh of most species contains an excess of uric acid. The flesh of the porbeagle or mackerel shark, however, is readily accepted, and in the United States mackerel sharks have been sold at times as swordfish.

The "miscellaneous neritic fishes" is a

catchall category for some diverse neritic groups. Most important are the members of the Sciaenidae family. Not only did they yield 374,000 metric tons, but they also furnished many thousands of days of sport fishing. In fact in many localities the sport fish yield (unrecorded here) doubtless exceeded the commercial landings. Most of the members of this family live in estuaries or sheltered bays. They include the sea trouts, weakfishes, or squeteagues, *Cynoscion;* the kingfish or ground mullet, *Menticirrhus;* the Atlantic croaker, *Micropogon undulatus*; the redfish or channel bass, *Sciaenops ocellata;* the spot, *Leiostomus xanthurus;* the black drum, *Pogonias cromis;* and many others. Many of them are quasi-catadromous, the young entering the estuarine nursery areas while very young.

The second neritic group of importance is the sea breams. This group of shore and estuarine species presumably consists of members of the Sparidae family, which includes scup, sheepshead, and pinfishes.

The crustaceans are of much greater economic importance than their landed weight would indicate. Shrimp and spiny lobsters exported to the United States have long provided a source of foreign exchange to a number of underdeveloped countries. The king crab of the North Pacific is also a gourmet item, whether canned or quick frozen. The importance of these crustaceans can perhaps best be illustrated by noting that in 1967 in the United States shrimp, with only 7.6% of the landings, was first in value with 23.5% of the total. Crabs, with 7.9% of the landings (live weight), accounted for 7.6% of the annual value. Northern lobster, with 0.7% of the landings, contributed 5.1% of the value, and spiny lobsters, with only 0.1% of the catch, constituted 0.7% of the value.

The mollusks can conveniently be divided into cephalopods and shelled mollusks. The total cephalopod landings of 1170×10^3 metric tons were taken chiefly in Japan, southeastern Europe, and the Mediterranean. In these countries they are highly esteemed. Well-prepared squid is considered a delicacy, but in the United States the small landings of squid are used principally as fish bait.

On the other hand, most of the shelled mollusks are highly prized in all countries. For example, in the United States in 1967 oysters comprised only 1.5% (including the shell) of the catch by weight, but they were fifth in value, with 7.3%; clams, with 1.8% by weight, were seventh, with 4.7% of the value; and scallops, with 0.3% by weight, were eleventh, with 1.8% of the value.

As an indication of the disparity in value of various fishes, we show in Table 6-4 the value to the fisherman at dockside of the principal fishery items landed in the United States in 1967. The fish used for reduction, pet food, and other industrial purposes, despite their bulk, bring little income to the fishermen. For example, herring, alewives, menhaden, anchovies, and industrial fish amounted to 1634 million pounds but were worth only $21,854,000; i.e., 40.3% of the landings were worth only 5% of the value, at an average price of 1.3 cents/pound.

It is quite obvious that the success or failure of a fishery is highly dependent on four factors: (1) the price of the raw product, (2) the cost of harvesting the product, (3) the quantity of the raw product available on a consistent basis, and (4) the value that can be added to the raw product through processing or preservation.

To illustrate this point Table 6-5 shows the value and landings of marine fishery products by the 20 leading fishing nations in 1967. It should be noted that for a number of years Peru invariably has been listed as the foremost fishing nation. This comes about through considering only the third point of the previously listed criteria, i.e., the total volume of the catch. If we consider the other criteria, Peru slips back to number 14.

The use of total volume can be erroneous from the standpoints of both human nutrition and economics. Practically all of the Peruvian catch (98% anchovetas) is turned into fish meal, which in turn is used as poultry and stock feed. Thus from the stand-

Table 6-4. Values at dockside of principal 1967 U. S. fishery landings

	Cents/pound		Totals (thousands)		Cumulative totals (thousands)		
Item	Live	Other	Pounds	Dollars	Pounds	Dollars	Cents/pound
Mollusks							
Abalone[1]		97.4	888	865	888	865	97.4
Bay scallops[1]		96.0	1,097	1,053	1,985	1,918	96.6
Sea scallops[1]		75.8	10,243	7,767	12,228	9,685	79.2
Hard clams[1]		74.1	16,182	11,981	28,410	21,666	76.3
Razor clams[1]		59.2	304	180	28,714	21,846	76.1
Oysters[1]		53.8	59,957	32,241	88,671	54,087	61.0
Soft clams[1]		40.1	9,823	3,936	98,494	58,023	58.9
Surf clams[1]		9.7	45,054	4,352	143,548	62,375	43.5
Squid	2.8		23,492	663	167,040	63,038	37.7
Crustaceans							
Northern lobster	83.7		26,745	22,389	26,745	22,389	83.7
Dungeness crab[2]		65.5	10,177	6,654	36,922	29,043	78.7
Spiny lobster	64.2		4,868	3,125	41,790	32,168	77.0
Penaeid shrimp[3]		64.2	154,924	99,461	196,714	131,629	66.9
King crab[1]		58.5	25,543	14,943	222,257	146,572	65.9
Stone crab	49.2		971	478	223,228	147,050	65.9
Blue crab[5]		42.1	20,312	8,551	243,540	155,601	63.9
New England shrimp[3]		21.9	4,397	963	247,937	156,564	63.1
Pacific shrimp[3]		9.6	44,230	4,246	292,167	160,810	55.0
Salmons							
King salmon	36.6		26,181	9,594	26,181	9,594	36.6
Coho salmon	32.3		38,290	12,694	64,471	22,288	34.6
Sockeye salmon	24.4		66,013	16,093	130,484	38,381	29.4
Pink salmon	12.1		51,721	6,278	182,205	44,659	24.5
Chum salmon	11.2		34,459	3,874	216,664	48,533	22.4
Snappers and basses[6]							
Red snapper		36.9	11,648	4,299	11,648	4,299	36.9
Black sea bass		19.0	4,217	800	15,865	5,099	32.1
Striped bass		18.3	9,451	1,729	25,316	6,828	27.0
Groupers		16.0	6,886	1,102	32,202	7,930	24.6
Tunas[6]							
Albacore		21.9	43,530	9,526	43,530	9,526	21.9
Yellowfin		15.4	127,808	19,637	171,338	29,163	17.0
Bluefin		14.7	16,793	2,475	188,131	31,638	16.8
Skipjack		11.7	107,321	12,533	295,452	44,171	15.0
Bonito		4.7	19,141	896	314,593	45,067	14.3
Neritic tablefish[6]							
Pompano		65.4	1,301	851	1,301	851	65.4
Spotted sea trout		28.2	5,198	1,467	6,499	2,318	35.7
Scup (sea bream)		17.8	17,855	3,183	24,354	5,501	22.6
Bluefish		13.7	3,851	529	28,205	6,030	21.4
Butterfish		11.4	4,801	548	33,006	6,578	19.9
Spot		9.3	9,897	917	42,903	7,495	17.5
Flatfishes[6]							
Atlantic halibut		47.0	264	124	264	124	47.0
Pacific halibut		17.9	35,800	6,412	36,064	6,536	18.1
New England flounders		12.4	80,371	9,948	116,435	16,484	14.2

[1]Meats only.
[2]Meats only, live weight/4.17.
[3]Heads off.
[4]Used 5.0 conversion factor.
[5]Meats only, live weight/7.14.
[6]Conversion factor 0.90 to gutted weight as usually landed and sold.

Table 6-4. Values at dockside of principal 1967 U. S. fishery landings—cont'd

	Cents/pound		Totals (thousands)		Cumulative totals (thousands)		
Item	Live	Other	Pounds	Dollars	Pounds	Dollars	Cents/ pound
Mid-Atlantic and Chesapeake flounders		16.4	15,486	2,547	131,921	19,031	14.4
Gulf and South Atlantic flounders		21.5	5,397	1,163	137,318	20,194	14.7
Other flounders		8.2	44,243	3,620	181,561	23,814	13.1
Round bank fishes							
Haddock[7]		18.8	59,078	11,094	59,078	11,094	18.8
Sablefish[7]		15.1	4,242	641	63,320	11,735	18.5
Cod[7]		12.6	32,133	4,060	95,453	15,795	16.5
Cusk[7]		10.3	1,030	106	96,483	15,901	16.5
Rockfishes[7]		10.0	13,283	1,328	109,766	17,229	15.7
Lingcod[7]		9.4	5,129	484	114,895	17,713	15.4
Pacific ocean perch[7]		9.3	9,256	861	124,151	18,574	15.0
Wolffish[7]		9.2	302	28	124,453	18,602	14.9
White hake[7]		9.1	1,680	153	126,133	18,755	14.9
Red hake[7, 8]		6.6	974	64	127,107	18,819	14.8
Ocean perch (redfish)	3.9		71,409	2,799	198,516	21,618	10.9
Whiting (silver hake)	3.1		69,543	2,156	268,059	23,774	8.9
Smaller pelagic fish[9]							
Shad[6]		12.6	6,337	800	6,337	800	12.6
Mackerel	9.1		23,671	2,144	30,008	2,944	9.8
Mullet[6]		7.9	30,853	2,431	60,861	5,375	8.8
Jack mackerel	4.0		38,405	1,533	99,266	6,908	7.0
Fish for reduction and industrial use							
Pacific herring	2.4		18,299	431	18,299	431	2.4
Atlantic herring[10]	2.3		69,859	1,641	88,158	2,072	2.4
Gulf industrial fish[11]	2.0		101,367	1,988	189,525	4,060	2.1
Pacific industrial fish	2.0		2,617	52	192,142	4,112	2.1
Menhaden	1.2		1,163,708	14,391	1,355,850	18,503	1.4
Alewives	1.1		101,127	1,551	1,456,977	20,054	1.4
Anchovies	1.0		69,625	704	1,526,602	20,758	1.4
Atlantic industrial fish[12]	1.0		107,816	1,096	1,634,418	21,854	1.3

Summary

Group	Dollars (millions)	Pounds (millions)	Cents/pound
Mollusks	63	167	37.7
Crustaceans	161	292	55.0
Salmons	49	217	22.4
Snappers and basses	8	32	24.6
Tunas	45	315	14.3
Neritic table fish	8	43	17.5
Flatfishes	24	182	13.1
Round bank fishes	24	268	8.9
Smaller pelagic fish	7	99	7.0
Fish for reduction and industrial use	22	1,634	1.3

[7]Conversion factor 0.6 round to gutted as landed.
[8]Part of catch not used as industrial fish.
[9]Used directly or for canning.
[10]Some canned as sardines.
[11]Chiefly for canned pet food, about half young croakers.
[12]Includes large quantities of red hake.

Table 6-5. Value and landings of marine fisheries of the 20 leading nations in 1967

Country	Value (millions of dollars)	Landings (thousands of metric tons)			Cents/pound			Cumulative totals	
		Total[1]	Valuable species[2]	Clupeoids	Valuable species	Clupeoids	Overall	Dollars	Tons
Japan	1,933	7,803	1,891	505	16.0	5.4	11.3	1,933	7,803
U.S.S.R.	1,051[3]	5,332	183	1,676	(19.1)	(5.4)		2,984	13,135
China (mainland)	460[4]	3,434[5]						3,444	16,569
United States	427	2,382	1,231	627	11.8	1.3	8.2	3,871	18,951
Spain	323	1,428	287	197	13.1	7.1	10.3	4,194	20,379
France	263	820	200	74	26.3	10.5	14.6	4,457	21,199
Philippines	262	751	61	89	22.1	12.8	15.9	4,719	21,950
India (1968 prices)	186	904	102	405			9.4	4,905	22,854
United Kingdom	175	1,026	44	147	16.8	2.6	7.8	5,080	23,880
Italy	171	353	89	71	23.3	10.1	22.0	5,251	24,233
Norway	166	3,268	17	1,632	34.2	1.4	2.3	5,417	27,501
Canada	143	1,277	149	402	21.8	1.1	5.1	5,560	28,778
Thailand	132	766	184					5,692	29,544
Peru	124	10,054	88	9,845	3.6	0.5	0.6	5,816	39,598
Indonesia	116[6]	677[7]						5,932	40,275
South Korea	112	749	228	79	6.6	3.9	6.8	6,044	41,024
Denmark[8]	100	1,241	25	405	6.5	1.9	4.5	6,144	42,265
Taiwan	100	442	114	25	13.7	6.9	10.3	6,244	42,707
West Germany	87	651	39	139	4.3	4.5	6.1	6,331	43,358
Malaysia	85	341	75	34	10.6	14.0	11.5	6,416	43,699
SUBTOTAL[9]	5,840	39,588	5,007	16,352					
WORLD TOTAL									50,830

[1] Live weight basis.
[2] Crustaceans, mollusks, salmons, and tunas.
[3] Assuming Japanese prices.
[4] Assuming Hong Kong price of $134/metric ton.
[5] Unofficial 1960 estimate of 5,800 reduced 40.8% for freshwater fish as in 1958.

[6] Assuming Thailand prices.
[7] Total of 1,180 reduced by 503 for freshwater fishes and aquaculture.
[8] Including Faroe Islands.
[9] Excluding China and Indonesia.

Table 6-6. Annual per capita consumption of over 10 pounds of fish and shellfish from 1960 to 1970[*][1]

Country	Edible weight (pounds)	Country	Edible weight (pounds)
Iceland	86.1	United Kingdom	20.9
Japan	71.6	France	20.1
Guyana	54.7	Belgium-Luxembourg	19.3
Trinidad-Tobago	52.3	South Africa	19.3
Portugal	49.1	East Germany	18.5
Denmark	46.7	Indonesia	18.5
Hong Kong	46.7	Surinam	18.5
Singapore	46.7	Thailand	18.5
Sweden	45.1	Peru	17.7
Norway	43.5	Burma	16.9
Philippines	43.4	Ghana	16.9
Taiwan	33.0	Ivory Coast	16.9
Senegal	30.6	Ceylon	16.1
Spain	30.6	Sierra Leone	16.0
Barbados	29.8	New Zealand	15.3
Cambodia	28.2	Australia	14.5
Finland	28.2	Israel	14.5
South Korea	27.4	Italy	14.5
Gambia	26.6	Mauritania	14.5
Malaysia	26.6	Cameroon	13.7
South Vietnam	25.8	Canada	13.7
Venezuela	25.8	Chile	13.7
Greece	22.5	Liberia	12.1
U.S.S.R.	22.5	Netherlands	12.1
Gabon	21.7	United States	11.4
Jamaica	20.9	Ireland	10.5
Panama	20.9	West Germany	10.5
Poland	20.9		

*Modified from Food and Agriculture Organization. 1971. Yearbook of fishery statistics for 1970, vol. 31.
[1]Time period varies; inland countries and certain other countries in which bulk of consumption is of freshwater species are omitted.

point of human nutrition, it is a whole order of magnitude less valuable than fish consumed directly. It may be noted in Table 6-5 that in countries in which a large share of the clupeoid catch is consumed directly (chiefly fresh or canned), the price of clupeoids is much higher.

One of the chief factors determining the total gross value of each nation's landings of raw fishery products is the volume of the higher priced species. Table 6-5 lists the total landings of crustaceans, mollusks, tunas, and salmons. Excluding China and Indonesia, for which data on species composition are not available, it will be noted that out of 5007×10^3 metric tons of valu-

able species, Japan alone accounted for 38%, and the United States for an additional 25%. Spain landed only 6%, and South Korea was fourth with less than 5%.

Table 6-6 shows the per capita consumption of edible fishery products for certain countries. Inland countries and those consuming chiefly freshwater species have been omitted. Among the 55 nations consuming over 10 pounds per capita, the United States ranks fifty-third, with only 11.4 pounds.

It will be noted that fishery consumption is lower in countries with large herds of meat-producing animals such as the United States, Chile, Canada, Australia, New Zealand, and South Africa. Iceland and Japan, with little arable land and extensive fisheries, far outstrip the rest in fishery consumption.

No discussion of consumption of fishery products is complete without the consideration of imports and of industrial use. For example, from 1966 to 1970 between 51% and 60% of our edible supply was imported. Similarly, between 55% and 85% of our industrial fish products were imported.

The edible fishery products imported in 1969 cost $705 million (Table 6-7). Against this we exported only $86 million worth of edible products. In 1969 we also imported $139 million worth of nonedible fishery products, whereas such exports amounted to only $18 million.

If the 9936 million pounds of fishery products imported in 1967 (4516 × 10³ metric tons) is added to the 2382 × 10³ metric tons of domestic catch, the United States supply of fishery products in 1967 totals 6898 × 10³ metric tons. Thus the United States, while ranking sixth in total

Table 6-7. Value of U. S. imports of edible fishery products in 1969

Country	Value (millions of dollars)
Canada	179
Japan	116
Mexico	63
Australia	32
Norway	31
Iceland	24
India	23
South Africa	23
Brazil	17
New Zealand	16
Ecuador	12
Panama	11
Other North American countries	36
Other South American countries	36
Other European countries	36
Other Asian countries	36
Other African countries	9
Other Oceanic countries	7
TOTAL	705

domestic catch and fourth in value of the domestic catch, is probably close to Japan in total volume of fishery products utilized.

POTENTIAL WORLD PRODUCTION OF MARINE FISHERIES

As we rapidly approach the limits of a land-based protein food supply, we need to realistically appraise the total potential protein supply of the oceans. There is too much unfounded optimism on this score. The Commission on Marine Science, Engineering, and Resources states:

> If man's fishing activities continue to be confined to the species now utilized, to the locations now regarded as exploitable, and to the equipment now available, it is unlikely that production could be expanded much beyond 150 to 200 million metric tons—three to four times present levels. But if man's activities were not so confined, far greater quantities of useful, marketable products could be harvested to meet the increasingly urgent world demand for protein foods.
>
> It is, therefore, more realistic to expect total annual production of marine food products (exclusive of aquaculture) to grow to 400 to 500 million metric tons before expansion costs become excessive. Even this estimate may be too conservative if significant technological breakthroughs are achieved in the ability to detect, concentrate, and harvest fish on the high seas and in the deep oceans.*

This optimistic statement is not in accord with what is occurring. There have indeed been great advances in fishing technology, but all these advances, coupled with much greater fishing effort and exploitation of deeper areas, have resulted only in a decreasing catch per unit of fishing effort. Optimism is therefore giving place to genuine concern among fishery scientists as one species after another falls drastically in abundance under the onslaught of ever-increasing numbers of modern fishing vessels with the ever-increasing sophistication of gear and techniques.

The average world catches for a 22-year

---

*Commission on Marine Science, Engineering, and Resources. 1969a. Our nation and the sea, report of the Commission. Washington, D. C. 305 pp.

Table 6-8. Average annual world catch by continent and leading countries from 1950 to 1971 (thousands of metric tons, live weight, excluding whales, but including freshwater fishes, aquaculture, algae, etc.)

	1950-1953	1954-1957	1958-1961	1962-1965	1966	1967	1968	1969	1970	1971
Continents										
Asia	9,390	12,260	16,528	19,210	21,420	22,590	24,250	24,740	26,380	28,160
South America	580	895	3,828	9,175	11,070	12,130	12,880	11,130	14,850	12,880
Europe	6,843	7,918	8,093	9,542	11,530	11,910	11,820	11,220	11,960	12,100
U.S.S.R.	1,869	2,475	2,920	4,262	5,350	5,780	6,080	6,500	7,250	7,340
North America	3,635	4,063	4,165	4,400	4,440	4,360	4,570	4,550	4,870	5,010
Africa	1,503	1,903	2,288	2,865	3,210	3,730	2,220	4,522	4,080	3,750
Oceania	95	103	123	145	190	200	210	200	200	210
Leading countries										
Peru	150	300	3,030	7,630	8,790	10,134	10,520	9,210	12,613	10,611
Japan	4,140	4,900	6,080	6,730	7,102	7,850	8,670	8,620	9,315	9,895
U.S.S.R.	1,869	2,475	2,920	4,262	5,350	5,780	6,080	6,500	7,250	7,340
China[1]	1,450	2,648	5,170	5,800	—	—	—	—	6,255	6,880
Norway	1,680	1,950	1,500	1,650	2,865	3,269	2,804	2,480	2,980	3,075
United States	2,530	2,850	2,830	2,780	2,542	2,431	2,442	2,490	2,755	2,767
WORLD	23,915	29,617	37,945	49,599	56,800	60,498	64,000	63,100	69,600	69,400

[1]Statistics unavailable from 1966 through 1969.

Table 6-9. Estimates of potential sustainable world fishery landings (millions of metric tons)[1]

Author	Year	Biomass from which to harvest	Estimate	Adjusted estimate	Remarks
Thompson	1951		22		
Food and Agriculture Organization, Fisheries Division	1953		34		
Laevastu	1961		21.5		For the Atlantic Ocean only, an increase from an earlier estimate of 12.8
Meseck	1962		100		By 1980 estimates 70 of all species, only 60 of marine species
Graham and Edwards	1962	230	115		Includes only bony fishes taken on continental shelves, no invertebrates
				171	Increased for species they did not include (Schaefer, 1965)
			60		Finally rejected own estimate for an apparent guess of 60
Pike and Spilhaus	1962	180-1,400	175		Stated estimate was 5 times the current landings without whales
				254[2]	
Schaefer	1965	1,045-2,420	200		
				290[2]	
Ryther	1969	240	100		
				145[2]	
Cushing	1969	120-130	40-60		Includes only upwelling areas, 3 to 5 should be added for tunalike fishes

[1]Some estimates may include a few whales or freshwater fishes.
[2]Estimates corrected by a factor of 1.45 to allow for earlier errors in carbon-14 productivity determinations (Nielsen, 1964; Goldman, 1968).

period from 1950 through 1971 appear in Table 6-8. They include both freshwater and marine species. In 1968 the total was 64 million metric tons, of which 56 million metric tons was derived from marine waters.

Fifty million metric tons has been suggested as being about 15% of the world's annual consumption of animal protein. In order for the seas to play a truly significant role in allaying the world's hunger until population control becomes effective, they must furnish much greater landings.

In recent years many estimates have appeared of the world's potential sustainable yield of fishery products. These estimates fall under three headings:

1. Theoretical estimates from data on primary productivity combined with crude estimates of energy losses between trophic levels, of biomass composition at each succeeding trophic level, and of trophic levels of harvest
2. Empirical estimates from the summation of estimates of potential yield of exploited and latent fishery resources based on known fishery yields
3. Empirical estimates from extrapolation of the past trend of fishery landings into the future

Several of these estimates are given in Table 6-9. The annual increase (Table 6-8) was rather steady; the largest, 6.9%, occurred during the meteoric rise in the Peruvian fishery for anchovetas between about 1958 and 1965. The rise was aided by the tremendous growth of the Russian and Japanese high seas fishing fleets. Despite these two great fleets, aided by the new high seas fleets of Poland, East Germany, West Germany, Spain, Great Britain, and other countries, the rate of increase in landings is declining.

The accuracy of these estimates of potential sustainable yield is a question that deserves further exploration. The last five reports in Table 6-9 were serious estimates made from available data but with different methods and interpretation. We will begin by examining the theoretical approach.

Theoretical approach

The estimate of Pike and Spilhaus (1962) is based on an annual (theoretical) photosynthetic production in marine waters of 19×10^9 tons of organic carbon. Their final estimate of 175 million metric tons is apparently a crude guess.

The theoretical estimate in the same year by Graham and Edwards (1962) was based on Nielsen's estimate of 12 to 15×10^9 tons of carbon/year (Nielsen, 1960). They converted this organic carbon to the wet weight of plankton by a factor of 37 (Sverdrup et al., 1942). Assuming a 20% ecologic efficiency for herbivores and 10% thereafter, they arrived at 1 billion metric tons of secondary carnivores, which they reject as being unreasonably large. They then guess at using 70% of the theoretical energy transfer at each trophic level, ending with only 343 million tons, from which they assume a 50% harvest of 230 million tons of bony fishes. They then rejected their own theoretical estimate in favor of an earlier empirical estimate by summation of only 60 million tons.

The estimate of Schaefer (1965) is based on the same amount of photosynthetic carbon as that of Pike and Spilhaus. He attempts refinement by assuming that the ecologic efficiency between trophic levels may be 10%, 15%, or 20%. He then assumes that all clupeoid-like fishes have an average of only 1½ trophic levels (consumer levels). Since about 37% of the world harvest is of these herringlike fishes, he assumes half of the total world harvest of marine organisms is taken at the second trophic level. These assumptions are unwarranted.

I disagree with the apparently prevalent idea that because a fish is capable of straining quantities of water through fine gill rakers that it always swims about openmouthed, eating whatever small plankton happen to be available. Herring stomachs, for instance, will be found crammed with large copepods and pteropods, usually with little or no phytoplankton. I have often watched them feeding, darting about in pursuit of "individual" zooplankters. In autumn, when zooplankton are less abundant, I have found samples of herring with stomachs crammed with sand lances *(Ammodytes)*. Lances themselves would be at about 2½ trophic levels. It is also evident from Table 6-21 that 36% of the clupeoid fishes come from nonupwelling areas, where the type of plankton is often different, and there is more nonplanktonic food.

Ryther also speaks of the short food chain of clupeoid fishes, especially in upwelling areas, stating:

> There seems little doubt that many of the fishes indigenous to upwelling areas are direct herbivores for at least most of their lives.*

He then lists "sardines, pilchards, anchovies, menhaden, and so on" as being most abundant in upwelling areas. The first statement is directly contrary to the findings of Hand and Burner (1959). In the upwelling area of southern California and Baja California, the Pacific sardine *(Sardinops sagax caerulea)* consumed, by weight of organic matter, 89% crustaceans, 4% chaetognaths and fish eggs, and only 7% phytoplankton. Smaller sizes of sardines ate even less phytoplankton. Although Ryther lists menhaden as one of the fishes most abundant in upwelling areas, the shallows and estuaries of the Gulf and Atlantic coasts are not "upwelling areas."

Ryther's estimate of potential fish production (Table 6-10) is based on almost the same estimate of photosynthetic carbon production as that of Schaefer, 20×10^9 metric tons rather than 19×10^9 metric tons. He attempts further refinement by dividing the marine waters into three provinces: oceanic, coastal, and upwelling. Ryther correctly points out that fish of the open ocean, outside of upwelling areas, have a very high average trophic level because of the very small size of the nannoplankton, which are consumed by microzoo-

plankton, and in turn by larger zooplankton, so that the smaller fishes are already in at least the third trophic level. Thus his estimate of the biomass of available fishes is very much less than Schaefer's, only 240 million metric tons. However, his estimate that 40% can be harvested annually seems unrealistically high.

Cushing (1969) estimates production for only the upwelling areas of the oceans. One cannot equate his estimates with those of Ryther by merely adding Ryther's non-upwelling areas, since Cushing shows over 14,958,000 km² of upwelling, compared to Ryther's 360,000 km². Cushing also shows vast areas of oceanic upwelling along divergences that (using his figures for grams of carbon per square meter per day and his time period) can be calculated as an additional 26,897,000 km² in the eastern tropical Pacific. The fundamental differences between their estimates are (1) the large areas that Cushing defines as upwelling areas, (2) the absence from Cushing's final estimate of large and productive coastal areas outside of upwelling areas, and (3) Cushing's postulation of very low trophic levels.

An example of the difference in areas is Cushing's estimate of 1,004,000 km² of upwelling off Peru and Chile as compared to Ryther's estimate of 36,000 km². Cushing placed the outer boundaries of his upwelling areas at the points where the quantity of zooplankton or of phosphate phosphorus is half the maximum from the coast. He vastly improved estimates of the carbon production of upwelling zones by careful estimates of the areas involved at each season, the number of days of upwelling, and the number of zooplankton generations. Because of the difference in approach, the reports of Cushing and Ryther are hard to reconcile. However, Cushing's upwelling areas take in but a very minor portion of the continental shelf, since the great majority of the upwelling takes place off relatively steep coasts and over deep water, often at some distance from land. His areas of

---

*From Ryther, J. H. 1969. Photosynthesis and fish production in the sea. Science **166:**72-76.

Table 6-10. Estimate of potential fish production*

Province	%	Area (km²)	Productivity (g carbon/ m² · yr)	Carbon (metric tons × 10⁹)	Trophic levels	Ecologic efficiency (%)	Fish production (metric tons net weight)
Oceanic	90.0	326 × 10⁶	50	16.3	5	10	16 × 10⁵
Coastal	9.9	36 × 10⁶	100	3.6	3	15	12 × 10⁷
Upwelling	0.1	3.6 × 10⁵	300	0.1	1½	20	12 × 10⁷
TOTAL				20.0			24 × 10⁷

*From Ryther, J. H. 1969. Science **166**:72-76.

coastal upwelling thus extend offshore as far as 290 km (California), 400 km (Peru), 300 km (Canary Islands), 300 km (Benguela), 300 km (Somali), and 175 km (off southwestern Arabia).

Eliminating areas with little or no continental shelf (Table 6-11), only about 4,936,000 km² contains any appreciable

Table 6-11. Relationship of Cushing's upwelling zones to area of the continental shelf (km² × 10³)

Zone	Area
Upwelling areas with little or no shelf	
Guinea Dome	148
Marquesas Islands	8,760
Costa Rica Dome	148
Madagascar Wedge	1,014
Eastern tropical Pacific	26,897
TOTAL	36,967
Upwelling areas with small shelf areas	
Peru-Chile	1,014
Somali-Arabia	226
Flores and Banda	200
California	505
Benguela	629
Canary Current	691
TOTAL	3,265
Upwelling areas adjacent to large shelf areas	
New Guinea	460
Orissa	96
Java	300
Northwestern Australia	300
East Arafura Sea	250
Gulf of Thailand	75
Vietnam	200
TOTAL	1,681

amount of shelf area. Assuming a full 10% of shelf area in this 4,936,000 km² leaves only 494,000 km² of continental shelf in Cushing's estimates, leaving out about 30,506,000 km² of shelf not in the upwelling areas.

We now can make a rough balance sheet between the areal estimates of Ryther and Cushing (Table 6-12).

The chief difference between earlier estimates and Cushing's estimate of primary productivity for the upwelling areas is that he did not use a blanket formula. Instead for each individual area he used rate of vertical upwelling, speed of surface currents, number of days of upwelling, and actual estimates of seasonal primary productivity in grams of carbon per square meter per day. He was thus able to summarize the tons of carbon per year for each of the many areas in great detail. Using Cushing's estimates for the upwelling areas, a summary of primary productivity appears in Table 6-13.

Our final estimate for primary productivity of 28 × 10⁹ metric tons of carbon appears to be exactly the same as Ryther's estimate of 29 × 10⁹ metric tons (20 × 10⁹ multiplied by a factor of 1.45). His estimate includes a larger proportion of what he terms "oceanic," in which the ecologic efficiency is doubtless low.

In a theoretical approach to this problem, we need better information on (1) the efficiency of the energy transfer at each level, (2) the composition of the biomass pro-

Table 6-12. Comparison of areas of marine zones (km² × 10³)

Zone	Ryther (1969)	Cushing (1969)	My estimate
Upwelling areas			
Eastern tropical Pacific[1]	?	26,897[2]	26,897
Around Antarctica	160	0	160
Coastal areas	200	494[3]	494
Nonshelf areas	0	14,464	14,464
Shelf areas[4]	31,000	30,506	30,506
Remaining oceanic areas	330,640	289,639	289,479
TOTAL AREA	362,000	362,000	362,000

[1]Ryther includes oceanic divergences in his coastal zone, which in this table would be in "remaining oceanic areas."

[2]Based on Cushing's tons of carbon per year and grams of carbon per square meter per day with 6 months of upwelling.

[3]See text. Ryther includes some shelf area; Cushing's 494 × 10³ km² is estimated as shelf area.

[4]Includes nonshelf in seas with sills under 100 fm, excludes upwelling portions of shelves. Graham and Edwards (1962) estimate the continental shelves at 24.3 × 10⁶ km², but specify "potentially productive" shelf.

Table 6-13. Summary of primary productivity

Zone	Area (km² × 10³)	Tons (carbon/year × 10⁶)
Upwelling areas		
Eastern tropical Pacific	26,897	1,245.55 (from Cushing)
Coastal (on shelf) areas	494	43.29 (from Cushing)
Noncoastal areas	14,464	1,222.40 (from Cushing)
Antarctic[1]	160	23.52
Shelf areas[2]	30,506	4,423.37
Other oceanic areas[3]	289,479	20,987.24
TOTAL	362,000	27,945.37

[1]Used same rate as for coastal mean, 8.8%.

[2]Used 100 g carbon/m² · year (Ryther, 1969) multiplied by a factor of 1.45 to allow for earlier errors in carbon-14 productivity determinations (Nielsen, 1964; Goldman, 1968).

[3]Used 50 g carbon/m² · year (Ryther, 1969) multiplied by a factor of 1.45.

duced at each trophic level, and (3) the possible harvest from each trophic level. The biomass at the first trophic level of consumers can be estimated from the annual production of metric tons of carbon. Instead of the classic approach of guessing at the ecologic efficiency of this transfer, Cushing carefully analyzed zooplankton volumes from net hauls made through the euphotic zone. Those in the Pacific are summarized by Reid (1962), those in the eastern tropical Pacific by Blackburn (1966), and those in the Peru Current by Flores (1967), Flores and Elias (1967),

and Guillen and Flores (1967). Observations in the Indian Ocean were from Wooster et al. (1967). Where available, we used Cushing's estimate for this first trophic (consumer) level in Table 6-14.

The herbivores at the first trophic level (Table 6-14) are thus assumed to weigh 33.5 × 10⁹ metric tons wet weight. This biomass will vary in composition by area. In the "other oceanic" areas it will probably consist chiefly of microzooplankton and thus not be directly available to fishes; this will apply to a slightly lesser extent to the eastern tropical Pacific and the Marquesas Islands.

Table 6-14. Estimate of first trophic (consumer) level biomass

Area	Primary productivity (tons carbon/ year × 10^6)	Trophic efficiency[1] (%)	Herbivores	
			Carbon production (tons carbon/ year × 10^6)	Wet weight[2] (tons/year × 10^6)
Upwelling areas				
Coastal				
California	30.5	15.82	4.7	83.9
Peru	112.9	11.25	10.5	187.4
Chile	43.6	21.81	7.9	141.0
New Guinea	41.0	3.3	2.4	42.8
Canary	15.7	16.48	2.6	46.4
Benguela	274.6	4.46	12.9	230.3
Somali-Arabia	51.3	7.06	3.7	66.0
Orissa	8.7	16.78	1.5	26.8
Indonesia	64.2	9.90	6.4	114.2
Northwestern Australia	18.5	10.07	4.5	80.3
Gulf of Thailand	20.8	10.00[3]	2.1	37.5
Vietnam	44.2	10.00[3]	4.4	78.5
Antarctica	23.5	10.00[3]	2.4	42.8
Noncoastal				
Costa Rica Dome	16.7	15.76	5.3	94.6
Marquesas Islands	514.5	4.17	21.4	382.0
Guinea Dome			1.6	28.6
Madagascar Wedge	8.7	6.00[3]	0.5	8.9
Eastern tropical Pacific	1,245.6	6.46	80.5	1,436.9
Shelf (nonupwelling)	4,423.4	10.00[3]	442.3	7,895.1
Other oceanic areas	20,987.2	6.00[3]	1,259.8	22,476.7
TOTAL	27,946		1,876.8	33,500.7

[1]Unweighted means when more than one section of coast is involved.
[2]Carbon production multiplied by a factor of 17.85 (Cushing, 1958).
[3]Assumed.

On the nonupwelling portion of the shelf a fraction will be shelled mollusks and a small portion will be consumed by fishes, but the great bulk will undoubtedly consist of copepods and other small invertebrates. In the coastal and noncoastal upwelling zones a somewhat larger share of the algae will be consumed directly by fishes, but the bulk will still be grazed by zooplankton.

Let us use an optimistic 15% ecologic efficiency rate, which may take care of the recycling of organic substances. For the coastal upwelling zone the catch may be derived largely from the second trophic level. The third trophic level is more appropriate for the noncoastal upwelling zone. Perhaps the bulk of the shelf yield may likewise be

as low as the third level. In the eastern tropical Pacific the fourth level may be sufficiently low. For the "other oceanic" areas the trophic level must be higher, averaging at least level five.

This theoretical exercise gives us a total yearly production of fish biomass (including squids, larger crustaceans, and shelled mollusks) of 277 million metric tons (Table 6-15).

Having calculated the annual production of "fish" biomass, the question remains as to the proportion of this biomass that can be harvested if the yield is to be maintained. Differences in opinion between previous authors in the percent of the total biomass harvestable stem largely from differences

Table 6-15. Estimate of fish biomass available (wet weight) by trophic levels

Zone	Biomass of first consumer level[1]	Trophic level of harvest	Assumed ecologic efficiency	Fish biomass available by trophic levels[1]			
				Level 2	Level 3	Level 4	Level 5
Upwelling							
California	83.9	2	15	12.6			
Peru-Chile	328.4	2	15	49.3			
Canary	46.4	2	15	7.0			
Benguela	230.3	2	15	34.5			
Somali-Arabia	66.0	2	10	6.6			
Indonesia	114.2	2	10	11.4			
Thailand-Vietnam	116.0	2	10	11.6			
Northwestern Australia	80.3	2	10	8.0			
New Guinea	42.8	2	10	4.3			
Antarctica	42.8	2	10	4.3			
Costa Rica Dome	94.6	3	15 and 15	(14.2)[2]	2.1		
Guinea Dome	28.6	3	15 and 15	(4.3)	0.6		
Orissa	26.8	3	15 and 15	(4.0)	0.6		
Madagascar Wedge	8.9	3	15 and 15	(1.3)	0.2		
Eastern tropical Pacific–Marquesas	1,819.9	4	15 then 10	(273.0)	(27.3)	2.7	
Shelf (nonupwelling)	7,895.1	3	15 then 10	(1,184.3)	118.4		
Other oceanic areas	22,476.7	5	15 then 10	(3,371.5)	(337.2)	(33.7)	3.4
GRAND TOTAL							
Available at each trophic level				149.6	121.9	2.7	3.4
Remainder at each trophic level				(4,606.9)	(364.5)	(33.7)	
Biomass available to harvest = 277.6							

[1] Metric tons/year $\times$ 10[6].
[2] Figures in parentheses are harvested at a succeeding trophic level.

concerning the trophic levels at which they believe the harvest can be taken. Schaefer (1965) assumed half can be taken at the second and half at the third trophic level, whereas Graham and Edwards assumed the whole harvest to be taken at the third trophic level. Obviously the trophic level of harvest will vary considerably among the different ecologic habitats. Schaefer's use of the second trophic level is very probably the best assumption for the pelagic coastal zones of upwelling. If the anchovetas, for instance, are a little below the second trophic level, this will be balanced by the larger predators taken in the same zone. I agree with Graham and Edwards that the shelf harvest will average closer to the third trophic level. This difference between trophic levels for harvesting in different

zones was recognized by Ryther. Cushing went a step further in his excellent detailed analysis of the world's upwelling areas. However, he seemed to fail to recognize that thermal convection, turbulent mixing, intermittent upwelling, and cabelling are widespread over extensive and highly productive areas. He was apparently preoccupied with tropical and subtropical waters (Table 6-16).

The proportion of the potential biomass that can be harvested on a sustained yield basis will vary widely between the different zones and between the different types and species of organisms. As a general rule the higher the trophic level, the greater the danger of overexploitation. Similarly, species such as shrimp with a very short life-span and high fecundity show

Table 6-16. Previous estimates of "fish" biomass available and potential harvest (millions of metric tons)

Annual biomass[1]	Amount harvestable (%)	Projected harvest	Author
344[2]	50.0	177	Graham and Edwards (1962)
497[3]	50.0	248	Graham and Edwards (1962)
1,515-3,509	8.3-19.1	290	Schaefer (1965)
348	41.7	145	Ryther (1969)
120-130[4]	30.8-50.0	40-60	Cushing (1969)

[1]Adjusted by a factor of 1.45 (see Table 6-9) except for Cushing's data.
[2]Bony fishes only.
[3]All fishes, including squids, etc.
[4]Upwelling areas only.

little or no relationship (within most practical limits) between size of spawning stock and numbers of young shrimp in the next generation. Bearing these limitations in mind I roughly estimate the potential harvest from the theoretical biomass in Table 6-17. My estimate of 94×10^6 metric tons is actually considerably below the total estimate of Ryther, only 65% as large as his adjusted estimate. If my estimate of 47×10^6 metric tons for the shelf areas is added to Cushing's estimate of 40 to 60×10^6 metric tons for the upwelling areas, making 87 to 107×10^6 metric tons, we are in very close agreement for the total.

One important source of nutrients neglected in most theoretical estimates is the dissolved and particulate matter contained in the runoff from the land. Ketchum states:

The effect of river water carrying nutrients into the sea is important in coastal waters and in semiconfined bodies of water such as the Gulf of Mexico. However, in terms of the total oceanic production, river drainage adds only about 1% of the total nutrient requirement each year. Thus, while river drainage is very important locally, its value to the productivity of the sea has been greatly overemphasized by some.*

The importance of land drainage is undoubtedly much greater than the preceding statement would suggest. For example, it

*From Ketchum, B. H. 1969. Productivity of marine communities. In Firth, F. E., editor. Encyclopedia of marine resources. Van Nostrand Reinhold Co., New York. pp. 553-559.

is estimated (Clarke, 1916) that the Mississippi River annually discharges into the Gulf of Mexico 370×10^6 metric tons of sediment. From 1964 through 1966 the fish yield in the Gulf of Mexico was 68.5% as great as that of the Atlantic coast from Key West to Eastport, yet the bulk was taken from Mobile Bay to Port Arthur, a distance of about 300 miles, around the mouths of the Mississippi.

The effect of the Mississippi River sediments that are carried westward along the Louisiana and Texas coasts on the aggregations of brown shrimp is very striking. Where these sediment-laden waters meet a current flowing northward along the Texas coast, they are diverted away from shore onto the continental shelf. Here is where

Table 6-17. Theoretical estimate of potential fish yield (millions of metric tons per year)

Zone	Available biomass[1]	Amount harvestable (%)	Yield
Upwelling areas			
Eastern tropical Pacific–Marquesas Islands	2.7	20	0.54
Other upwelling areas	153.1	30	45.93
Shelf areas	118.4	40	47.36
Other oceanic areas	3.4	15	0.51
TOTAL	277.6		94.34

[1]From Table 6-15.

over 50% of the Texas catch is made (Lindner and Bailey, 1968).

For the entire world Clarke (1916) estimates that the runoff from the land carries 2492×10^6 metric tons/year of dissolved substances, which averages 24 metric tons/km² of land surface. Fifty years later, Alekin (1966) estimates 23 metric tons/km², remarkably close estimates. Clarke's estimate gives an average terrigenous contribution of dissolved substances of 6.9 metric tons/year for each km² of ocean surface. This is nearly equal to the primary productivity of 7.7 metric tons of carbon/km².

Since almost all of this dissolved material flows onto the continental shelves, it should be noted that this amounts to 44 metric tons/year for each square kilometer of shelf area. It appears that the 144 metric tons of photosynthetic carbon/year produced for each square kilometer of shelf compared to only 7.7 metric tons as a world average is not mere coincidence.

Concerning the usually highly productive Sea of Azov, Izhevskii states:

The productivity of the northeastern part of the Black Sea responded to the decreased productivity of the Azov Sea during the reservoir-filling years on the Don (1952-53). According to A. P. Kusmorskaya this part of the sea proved less productive even as compared to the southeastern portion.*

Izhevskii also stated in a later publication that:

The diversion of the Don River in 1952-53 resulted in a sharp decrease in the catches, from 800,000 metric centners in 1951 and 600,000 in 1952 to 35,000 in 1955.†

*From Izhevskii, G. K. 1961. Oceanological principles as related to the fishery productivity of the seas. (Translated from Russian in 1964.) IPST Cat. No. 917, OTS 63-11120. Office of Technical Services, U. S. Department of Commerce, Springfield, Va. 186 pp.
†From Izhevskii, G. K. 1964. Forecasting of oceanological conditions and the reproduction of commercial fish. (Translated from Russian in 1966.) IPST Cat. No. 1854. TT 67-51264. Office of Technical Services, U. S. Department of Commerce, Springfield, Va. 95 pp.

The fisheries adjacent to the Nile delta, especially the sardine fishery, have declined steadily since 1964 because construction of the Aswan Dam has lowered the quantities of incoming nutrients (Commercial Fisheries Review editorials, 1970a).

One point to make concerns the great gap between total primary productivity and even potential yield. It may be noted that the upwelling and shelf areas (exclusive of the tropical Pacific) with a combined total of only about 20% of the primary productivity account for 98.9% of the potential harvest of fishery organisms. A very low order of productivity prevails over most of the deep oceans, excluding only areas of upwelling. This barren area covers 78.5% of the oceans, plus 7.5% of the areas of slightly higher productivity in the eastern tropical Pacific—86% in all. Partly because of the low productivity and partly because of the higher trophic levels, this enormous area, comprising 61% of the entire surface of this planet, has a theoretical potential of only 1% of our fishery harvest.

How well do the theoretical estimates of potential fish yield seem to fit known facts? Ryther gives two examples to authenticate his theoretical approach. First he uses the 110,000 square miles of the New England banks from Hudson Canyon to the Fundian Channel between Georges Bank and the Nova Scotia banks, which Graham and Edwards (1962) estimate contains only 71,875 square miles of continental shelf. Ryther states:

From the information in Tables 2 and 3, it may be calculated that approximately 1 million tons of fish are produced annually in this region. Commercial landings from the same area were slightly in excess of 1 million tons per year for the 3-year period 1963 to 1965 before going into a decline.*

Using the information Ryther gives in Tables 2 and 3 of his article (100 g carbon/m² · year, a 15% ecologic efficiency, his 110,000 square miles, and harvest at the third consumer trophic level), the total

*From Ryther, J. H. 1969. Photosynthesis and fish production in the sea. Science **166**:72-76.

wet weight biomass of all organisms at the third level is only 960,000 metric tons. His harvesting rate of 41.7% yields only 400,000 metric tons, far below the 1 million metric tons actually landed.

Ryther's second example is the Peru-Chile upwelling area, which he estimates as totaling 2400 square miles (6475 km²). Using his figure of 300 g carbon/m² · year and his 20% ecologic efficiency, the wet weight of the biomass would be 3.9 million metric tons at the first (herbivore) level and only 0.8 million metric tons at the second consumer level. Harvested at half at each level as he postulates, at a rate of 40% harvest we derive only 1.9 million metric tons, whereas he states the catch to be about 10 million metric tons and estimates that the guano birds consume an additional 10 million metric tons. This is an order of magnitude between theory and fact.

For the same Peru-Chile region, Cushing (1969) gives an upwelling area of 1,004,000 km² and by his analysis reaches a biomass at the second consumer level of 49.3 million metric tons, which he says would be harvested at that level. The 20 million metric tons that Ryther said could be had by fishermen and guano birds he would produce in an area only 6% as large as that used by Cushing.

The greatest discrepancy between theory and fact is caused by an underestimation of the fertility of inshore areas, especially of those receiving substantial freshwater drainage from fertile lands. Thus the area around the mouths of the Mississippi River between Mobile Bay and Port Arthur has produced for several years about 1 billion pounds of menhaden and other industrial fishes. Disregarding all other fish production, this is 453,000 metric tons in a shelf area of not over 30,000 square miles (77,700 km²). To produce this amount of fish at the second consumer level would require 6.6×10^6 metric tons of carbon per year if the *total* biomass were harvested. Use of Ryther's suggested figure of 100 g carbon/ m² · year for this area gives 7.8×10^6 metric tons of carbon. Primary production in this area then has to be at least two to three times that of the general coastal level suggested by Ryther.

Parsons et al. (1970) assessed the primary productivity in the Gulf of Georgia at 120 g carbon/m² · year, but also stated that allochthonous organic carbon from land drainage was at least as great as the total primary productivity. Stephens et al. (1967, cited by Seki et al., 1968) reported these annual sediments as containing organic carbon and nitrogen in the amounts of 200 and of 27 g/m² · year. Seki et al. (1968) showed that this organic carbon was utilized by bacteria with an efficiency of about 30%, so that the land drainage in this area is contributing about one third of the primary food source. The importance of these sediments as a food source is also well illustrated in southeastern Alaska where shrimp are caught among the fine detritus along the face of melting glaciers.

The weakness of the relationship between primary and even secondary productivity and fishery yield is shown in a report of the Scientific Committee on Oceanic Research group on monitoring in biological oceanography, which states:

Monitoring on an ocean-wide scale of such parameters as chlorophyll-*a*, C^{14} uptake, and zooplankton biomass have been much overemphasized in their direct application to fisheries. A number of examples were discussed to emphasize that application of primary and secondary production data differed very considerably from fishery to fishery.

During the recent METEOR work in the region of Cabo Blanco, a recently upwelled parcel of water, rich in nutrients, was observed to develop a very strong bloom of a *Phaeocystis*-like alga. Subsequently, no grazing herbivores developed, probably because few herbivore species are able to utilize these chain-form phytoplankton. In an ocean-wide chlorophyll-*a* monitoring system such patches would be difficult to assess without additional observations. Similar experiences have been noted off Peru where the *Engraulis* fishery does not correspond with regions of strongest upwelling, and off South West Africa where the

Spanish distant-water trawler fleet has been observed far from upwelling centers, while in the northern Pacific Ocean it has been found that there was no direct relationship between the north Pacific spring bloom and the high seas salmon distribution.*

Empirical approach by summation

Because the theoretical approach obviously could not give a defensible answer to our question of potential yield, a new approach was necessary. The world marine catch in 1958 and 1968 was determined from the statistics of the FAO. The detailed statistics for 1968 appear in Table 6-2. The total marine catch for 1958 (Rounsefell, 1971) was 28 million metric tons. The 10-year increase from 28 to 56 million metric tons (excluding from the 1968 catch of 58 million metric tons a portion of the China catch of freshwater fish) gives an overall rate of increase of 7.15%.

Table 6-18, showing the 1968 catch by types of species for both upwelling and non-upwelling areas, is very illuminating. One of the first facts clearly evident is that the yield of upwelling areas depends on a huge catch of clupeoid fishes. This catch of a few schooling species is highly reminiscent of the golden days of the California sardine *(Sardinops sagax caerulea)* fishery when the industry rebelled against the few conservation measures imposed by the state of California. The idea that one should place confidence in the annual production of enormous quantities of animal protein from a single species of fish is gambling with the future. I was in California when the industry used all its influence to allow the unlimited exploitation of sardines. Despite the limitations imposed by the state, the sardine fishery collapsed.

In thinking of trophic levels one must realize that the bulk of the great catch of clupeoids, about 78% of the 1968 catch in the upwelling areas, is not eaten directly

by humans, but first goes through a whole trophic level (into chickens, etc.) and so is much less important than the gross statistics would indicate. One should note that 58% as many clupeoid fishes are taken from shelf areas as from upwelling areas. Surprisingly, when the yield per area of the rich upwelling areas is compared with the yield of the shelf areas of the world (Table 6-19), the production per square kilometer is almost identical. What the shelf areas may lack in pelagic species is com-

Table 6-18. The 1968 world marine catch by types of species for upwelling and nonupwelling areas (thousands of metric tons)

Species groups	Type of area		
	Upwelling	Nonupwelling	Unclassified
Pelagic			
Neritic			
Clupeoids	13,748	7,911	17
Sea breams	62	304	67
Mackerels	558	3,370	386
Cephalopods	12	1,085	4
SUBTOTAL	14,380	12,670	474
Oceanic			
Salmons		423	
Tunas	250	847	85
SUBTOTAL	250	1,270	85
Demersal			
Flatfishes		1,145	19
Hakes *(Merluccius)*	776		
Other gadoids		8,693	10
Redfishes		952	18
Sciaenids		299	22
Sharks and rays		253	75
Various fishes		261	219
Shrimp and lobsters	219	639	174
Crabs		316	13
Oysters	1	818	
Other bivalves	43	893	
Other mollusks	161	258	36
SUBTOTAL	1,200	14,527	586
Unsorted fishes	1,776	7,841	1,302
TOTAL	17,606	36,308	2,447
Percent of clupeoids	78	22	

*From Scientific Committee on Oceanic Research. 1970. Proceedings of the Scientific Committee on Research. **6:**54-93.

Table 6-19. Comparison of 1968 yields per unit of area from upwelling and shelf regions (thousands of metric tons)

Item	Upwelling area	Nonupwelling shelf area
Demersal species	1,200	14,527
Neritic pelagic species[1]	14,380	12,670
Unsorted fishes	1,776	7,841
TOTAL	17,356[2]	35,038[3]
Yield/unit[2], 14,958 × 10[3] km[2] in metric tons	1.16	
Yield/unit[2], 30,506 × 10[3] km[2] in metric tons		1.15

[1]Excludes the oceanic pelagic tunas and the ocean-feeding salmons.

[2]See Table 6-12; excludes Antarctica and oceanic area of the eastern tropical Pacific.

[3]Includes total area of seas with entrance sills less than 100 fm.

pensated for by the richness of the demersal fauna.

The catch of the shelf area is coming from only a fraction of the area available. Thus for various productive continental shelves, Graham and Edwards (1962) show an average of 20 pounds/acre for bony fishes, or 2.24 metric tons/km[2]. Increasing this 11% (1968 basis) for their omission of invertebrates and elasmobranchs gives 2.52 metric tons/km[2].

The theoretical estimate of total sustainable yield (Table 6-17) gives exactly 50% of the yield coming from nonupwelling shelf areas, but actual statistics (Table 6-19) show that shelf areas yielded over twice as much as upwelling areas and had the same average yield per unit of surface area. This means that the estimates of productivity for shelf areas are too low. This stems (1) from underestimation of the primary productivity caused by failure to adequately sample the shallower portions of the shelf and (2) from failure to fully recognize the role of land-derived nutrients.

I estimated the areas of the continental shelf and the upper slope for each major climatic and geographic area in an article published in 1971. From this summary a list has been derived of the areas of the various shelf and slope regions; it is given by decreasing order of productivity in Table 6-20.

In determining the relative productivity of various areas as shown in Table 6-20, I was partially guided by figures from several sources on the catches of demersal and sometimes other fishes on various banks by unit area. A list of these other sources is given in Table 6-21.

In utilizing the continental marginal areas from Table 6-20 for estimating the demersal yield, I should note that my summation of areas is a little less than that of Heselton (1969), but it is impossible to reconcile the differences, partially because the depth contours used by various authors differ, partially because it is impossible to tell how much shelf different authors assigned to the Antarctic sectors of the oceans, and partially because there is no way to estimate the shelf for the numerous small islands in the Pacific. However, the discrepancies are chiefly in areas of low productivity and therefore have little bearing on the final estimate. The estimate of demersal fish production is given in Table 6-22.

In assigning the yields per square kilometer shown in Table 6-22, I have, if anything, been slightly optimistic. However, the yields given for demersal species for a couple of well-fished areas are closely comparable to estimates by other fishery workers. For the New England banks my estimate of demersal species for the 267 × 10[3] km[2] of shelf and 77 × 10[3] km[2] of slope is 917 × 10[3] metric tons, compared to an estimate by Edwards (1968) of 910 × 10[3] metric tons. For the northeastern Pacific my estimate is 2960 × 10[3] metric tons compared to 1113 to 2269 × 10[3] metric tons estimated by Alverson (1968).

For a total estimate all the pelagic species as well as the bivalve mollusks, gastropods, and crabs must be added to the demersal species of fish.

The neritic pelagic species from the up-

Table 6-20. Continental shelf and upper slope areas listed by relative productivity for demersal fishes (km^2 × 10^3)

Area	Shelf	Slope	Total
Highly productive			
Northeastern Atlantic (except Baltic Sea)	2,017	761	2,778
Northwestern Atlantic south to New England	1,287	347	1,634
Northeastern Pacific	915	143	1,058
Northwestern Pacific (except west Bering Sea)	605	705	1,310
Northwestern subtropical Atlantic (except Bahamas)	557	190	747
Sea of Azov	38	0	38
Northwestern subtropical Pacific south to Sunda Shelf	2,785	364	3,149
Bay of Bengal and Ceylon	172	22	194
Southern Chile	100	24	124
Moderately productive			
U. S. mid- and South Atlantic	271	491	762
Bay of Biscay and west Iberian area	130	13	143
Black Sea	141	65	206
East tropical Atlantic	580	71	651
Western tropical Atlantic	832	187	1,019
Southeast and southwest subtropical Atlantic	583	319	902
Argentina–Falkland Island	1,030	345	1,375
Southwest Pacific (except Chesterfield Islands)	281	1,159	1,440
West Bering Sea–Kamchatka Peninsula	553	86	639
Northeastern subtropical Pacific	164	65	229
East tropical Pacific	95	15	110
Mozambique and Agulhas Bank	247	56	303
North and northwestern Australia and Strait of Malacca	1,463	189	1,652
East Arabian Sea and Persian Gulf	580	10	590
Java and Sulu Seas	400	75	475
Low productivity			
Baltic Sea	478		478
Mediterranean Sea	515	567	1,082
Bahamas and Puerto Rico	132	25	157
Burwood Bank	35	40	75
Northeastern Australia and New Guinea	545	109	654
French and British Pacific Islands	158	195	353
Andaman Sea	205	120	325
South coast of Australia	440	10	450
Red Sea	189	196	385
Tanzania	10	34	44
French and British Indian Ocean Islands	227	217	444
Very low productivity			
Hudson and Baffin Bays and Canadian Straits	1,010	150	1,160
South Georgia and South Orkney Islands	17	103	120
Chesterfield Islands	27	86	113
Kerguelen Islands	52	275	327
Extremely low productivity			
Arctic Sea (except Hudson Bay, etc. listed separately)	3,980	2,350	6,330
Antarctica	0	3,434	3,434

Table 6-21. Annual fish yield for various areas by catch per square kilometer (metric tons per square kilometer)

Area	Period	Demersal	Pelagic	Total
Iceland Banks[1]	1956-1958	3.250	0.594	3.844
Eastern Bering Sea[2]	To 1960	2.018		
Barents Sea[1]	1956-1958	1.760	0.089	1.849
Gulf of Maine[1]	1956-1958	1.423	0.527	1.950
Grand Banks[1]	1956-1958	1.323	0.022	1.345
Nova Scotia Banks[1]	1956-1958	1.211	0.314	1.525
North Sea[1]	1956-1958	1.121	1.861	2.982
Middle Atlantic shelf[1]	1956-1958	0.863	6.075	6.938
Oregon-Washington[2]	1956-1960	0.504		
Baltic Sea[1]	1956-1958	0.460	0.392	0.852
British Columbia, southeastern Alaska[2]	1956-1960	0.336		
Adriatic Sea[1]	1947-1953	0.280	0.235	0.515
Northeastern Pacific[3]	1968	2.399		
North Sea[4]	1965			4.887
Samoa[5]	1967		0.002	
Gulf of Mexico, Mobile to Port Arthur[6]			5.830	
Peru-Chile-Ecuador upwelling area[7]	1968			11.895

[1]Graham and Edwards (1962), bony fishes only.
[2]Alverson et al. (1964).
[3]Oregon to Bering Sea, 1,058,000 km², includes nonbony fishes and invertebrates.
[4]Holden (1967).
[5]Chapman (1969), tuna fishery.
[6]Rounsefell (1971).
[7]Cushing (1969), 1,004,000 km².

welling areas in 1968 were 96% clupeoids; in fact, about 78% consisted of the Peruvian anchoveta, *Engraulis ringens*. The fact that the Peruvian anchoveta catch cannot be increased was stated recently by a panel of scientists (Commercial Fisheries Review editorial, 1971). They estimated the maximum sustainable yield at 9.5 million metric tons, slightly less than the maximum landed in any 1 year. Inasmuch as the 1968 neritic pelagic catch was only $14,380 \times 10^3$ metric tons, I would calculate the ultimate sustainable yield from this source to be at maximum 15 million metric tons.

The neritic pelagic catch from nonupwelling areas in 1968 was only 14,380,000 metric tons, of which 62% were clupeoid fishes. The Norwegian catch in this category of 2,804,000 metric tons in 1968 fell in 1969 to 2,200,000 metric tons owing to a drop in the catches of Atlantic herring that was not compensated for by fishing efforts off New England and Nova Scotia.

There are a few as yet untapped sources

of clupeoid fishes such as the schools of Atlantic thread herring, *Opisthonema oglinum,* off the west coast of Florida. How well they could stand fishing pressure is pure speculation. Despite early accounts of their tremendous abundance, recent work by Kinnear and Fuss (1971) indicates that the entire population is confined to an area south of St. Petersburg and does not extend over 9 miles from shore; they estimate the entire population as containing a maximum of 750,000 tons. Possibly the catch of the pelagic cephalopods (squids and cuttlefishes) can be increased, as they are consumed sparingly in many countries, although highly esteemed in others. Since the 1968 cephalopod catch was only 1,085,000 tons, it will take a large increase indeed to make much difference. Weighing all these factors, it seems that a potential maximum of 15 million metric tons of neritic pelagic species from the nonupwelling areas is a reasonable estimate.

The oceanic pelagic fishes are primarily

Table 6-22. Estimate by summation of the potential demersal fish production

Productivity	Area $(km^2 \times 10^3)$	Yield/area (metric tons $\times 10^3$)	Total yield
Shelf area			
High	8,476	3.0	25,428
Moderate	7,748	2.0	15,496
Low	5,849	1.0	5,849
Very low	1,106	0.1	111
Extremely low	3,980	0.01	40
SUBTOTAL			46,924
Upper slope area			
High	2,556	1.5	3,834
Moderate	4,188	1.0	4,188
Low	6,660	0.5	3,330
Very low	614	0.05	31
Extremely low	5,784	0.005	29
SUBTOTAL			11,412
GRAND TOTAL			58,336

Table 6-23. Estimate by summation of the total potential world fishery yield by categories of organisms (thousands of metric tons)

Demersal fishes	58,336
Neritic pelagic fishes, upwelling areas	15,000
Neritic pelagic fishes (including squids), other areas	15,000
Oceanic feeding fishes (salmons, tunas, billfishes)	2,000
Bivalves (natural beds)	2,000
Crabs, etc.	1,000
TOTAL	93,336

tunas and billfishes plus the anadromous salmons, which make most of their growth on the oceanic feeding grounds. The 1968 tuna and billfish catch was only 847,000 metric tons despite worldwide fishing by well-equipped fleets. The catching rate per unit of fishing effort is falling in all oceans; only the skipjack, *Euthynnus pelamis,* holds any promise of more yield. The 1968 salmon catch of 423,000 metric tons may eventually be increased because of very intensive management of the remaining stocks, but this may be negated by the uncontrolled high seas fishing such as that conducted by Denmark on the small remaining stocks of Atlantic salmon. I consider 2 million metric tons an optimistic estimate for this category.

The 1968 yield of oysters and other bivalves was 1,711,000 metric tons. Considering only the type of bivalve culture employed in the recent past, it is difficult to see much increase. The output of bivalves has increased only 42% in 10 years despite great efforts in management of the fishery. The natural beds are depleted and attempts at cultivation are nullified by increasing estuarine pollution. The extensive use of mussels could help the picture, but in many

areas the danger of paralytic shellfish poisoning from ingestion of toxic plankton organisms, especially the dinoflagellates such as *Gonyaulax catanella* and others, has discouraged their use. I offer 2 million metric tons as a reasonable estimate for this category.

Although the 1968 yield of crabs was only 316,000 tons, I believe this will continue to rise. The handling and processing of fresh crab meat has been greatly improved so that crab fishing will be expanded to more coastal waters. The deep water crabs such as the snow (or tanner) crab will augment production. I believe 1 million metric tons to be a reasonable estimate in this category.

The total estimate is shown in Table 6-23.

It is highly improbable that this suggested potential world yield will be attained for a long time, if ever. Species after species has been depleted to scarcely profitable levels, while new species and new areas are being exploited. But the world is shrinking fast—new areas and new species are becoming scarce.

A good example of overfishing involves the ocean perch, *Sebastes marinus.* It was scarcely fished until filleting commenced in the late 1930's. The New England banks' yield fell from over 100 million pounds in 1941 and 1942 to 5 million pounds by 1965. The Nova Scotia banks were next; the ocean perch landings of over 100 million pounds in 1948, 1949, and 1951 fell to 12

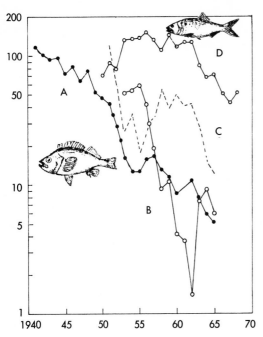

Fig. 6-3. U. S. landings in millions of pounds, 1941 to 1968, of certain species. Ocean perch: *A*, from New England Banks; *B*, from Grand Banks and Gulf of St. Lawrence; *C*, from Nova Scotia Banks. *D* shows the catches of Atlantic menhaden.

million pounds by 1965. Yields in the Gulf of St. Lawrence fell from over 50 million pounds in 1953, 1954, and 1955 to 6 million pounds in 1965. These figures show how we have mismanaged many of our marine species (Fig. 6-3).

Similar stories can be told for haddock, *Melanogrammus aeglefinus;* pollock, *Pollachius virens* (Fig. 6-4); and silver hake, *Merluccius bilinearis* (Fig. 6-5). In the fertile upwelling area of the California Current region the story has been more drastic. The Pacific sardine, *Sardinops sagax caerulea,* once producing a billion pounds a year (Fig. 6-4), is commercially extinct. The Pacific mackerel, *Scomber japonicus,* has also fallen tremendously in abundance (Fig. 6-5).

The Atlantic menhaden, *Brevoortia tyrannus,* considered by many early biologists to be inexhaustible, has fallen in abundance since the very intense fishing of the late 1950's (Fig. 6-3).

In Alaska (Fig. 6-6) the landings of salmon, *Oncorhynchus* spp., fell from over 500 million to 200 million pounds, but

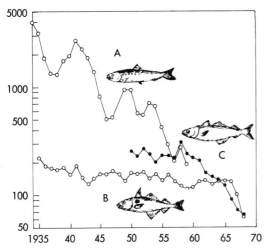

Fig. 6-4. U. S. landings of certain species, 1934 to 1968, and estimate of biomass of the California sardine. *A,* California sardine (biomass in short tons × 10³); *B,* haddock (pounds × 10⁶); and *C,* pollock (pounds × 10⁵).

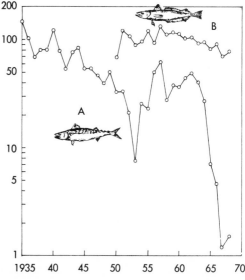

Fig. 6-5. U. S. landings, 1935 to 1968, of, *A,* Pacific mackerel and, *B,* whiting or silver hake in millions of pounds.

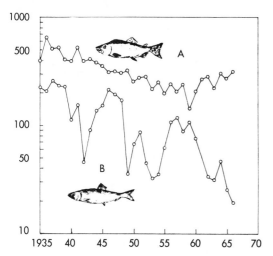

Fig. 6-6. Alaska landings, 1935 to 1966, of, *A*, salmons and, *B*, herring in millions of pounds.

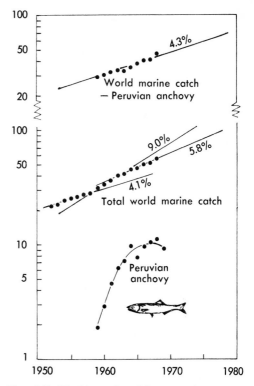

Fig. 6-7. World marine fishery landings (metric tons × 10⁶) showing rates of annual increase with and without Peruvian anchovies.

there have been signs of some recovery. The fisheries for herring, *Clupea harengus pallasi,* have fallen from over 200 million to about 20 million pounds.

Why has the world catch continued to rise slowly while the United States catch remains static? There are several factors. Some of the underdeveloped countries have only recently commenced using enough modern fishing gear to fully exploit their fisheries. A good example is the meteoric rise of the Peruvian fishery for anchovetas, *Engraulis ringens* (Fig. 6-7), which is presently the world's largest fishery from the standpoint of sheer volume. Even this fishery has reached peak production.

Several nations have built large fleets of high seas fishing vessels, some accompanied by floating factory ships. These scour the seas of the world, gradually bringing into use all formerly latent fishery resources. Inevitably in this process, some of the less resilient species must suffer a severe decline.

The failure of United States fisheries to keep pace with the remainder of the world over the past 30 years has resulted in the inability to supply the demands of an expanding population. We now import about two thirds of all our fishery products.

In the face of the falling abundance of practically all of the historically fished species, we have tried to bolster our output by fishing new species and by fishing species inhabiting the deeper waters at the edge of the continental shelf and on the upper continental slope. Thus we developed fisheries for king crab, *Paralithodes camtschatica,* in Alaska and for surf clams, *Spisula solidissima,* off the Atlantic coast (Fig. 6-8). These both appear to have reached or passed their peak. Other developing United States fisheries include calico scallops, *Argopecten gibbus,* off eastern Florida; several species of pandalid shrimps in Alaska; Pacific hake, *Merluccius productus;* and Pacific saury *Cololabis saira.* The Atlantic thread herring, *Opisthonema oglinum,* off western Florida awaits exploitation, but this is hampered by legislation against purse seining; as men-

Table 6-24. The 147 principal species of United States fish and invertebrates tabulated by 3-year periods in which their maximum landings occurred and by their habitat group[1]

Habitat group	*Three-year periods*[2] 1929-1931	1938-1940	1952-1954	1955-1957	1958-1960	1961-1963	1964-1966	Total species
Catadromous	1							1
Anadromous	9	4	1		2	1		17
Estuarine benthic	4	1		2		1		8
Shore and estuarine	5					1		6
Quasi-catadromous[3]	3	2½[4]	5	3		2	2½	18
Coastal pelagic	5	4	1	1	2	1	6	20
Oceanic pelagic	2	2	2	1	1	5	3	16
Benthic	11	7	8	7	6	4	18	61
TOTAL	40	20½	17	14	11	15	29½	147

[1]In a few cases two or more species have not been separated in the statistics and have been grouped as one, e. g., the alewife, *Alosa pseudoharengus,* and the blueback, *A. aestivalis.*
[2]The two earlier periods had to be chosen to include years in which complete canvasses of the fisheries were made.
[3]Species spawning in high salinity offshore waters whose young are nurtured in the estuaries.
[4]For an occasional species the maximum may be identical for two different periods; these species are listed as ½.

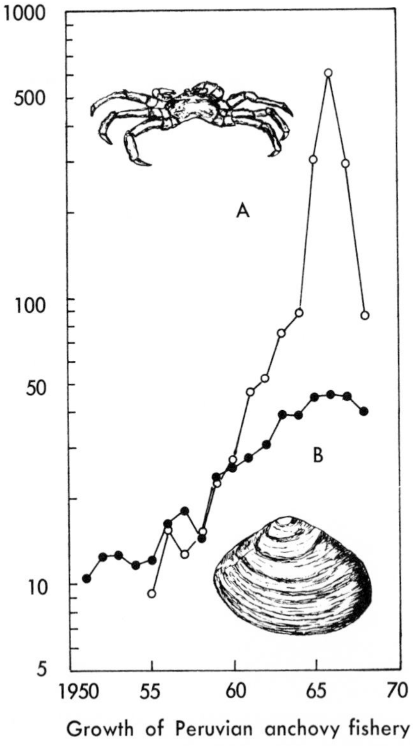
1000
500
100
50
10
5
A
B
1950
55
60
65
70
Growth of Peruvian anchovy fishery

Fig. 6-8. U. S. landings, 1951 to 1968, of, *A,* Alaska king crab and, *B,* Atlantic coast surf clams in millions of pounds.

tioned previously the thread herring, according to Kinnear and Fuss (1971), remain within 9 miles of the shore.

This shift from the more accessible to the less accessible species as species after species fall in abundance is portrayed in Table 6-24. Of the 147 principal species taken in the United States, 41% had their maximum 3-year landings over 30 years ago. In the first four habitat categories 75% of the species fell in abundance after the two initial periods. With such poor management we can never hope to reach the potential sustainable yield.

Empirical approach by extrapolation

A third approach to the estimation of potential fish yield is through the extrapolation of existing catch statistics. In Fig. 6-7 the world catch of marine organisms is plotted from 1952 through 1968. There are three distinct rates of increase: from 1952 through 1958 at slightly over 4%/year, from 1959 through 1962 at about 9%/year, and from 1963 through 1968 at about 5.8%/year.

These changes in rate were engendered

chiefly by the rise of the great fishery for the Peruvian anchoveta. At the top of Fig. 6-7 is shown the world marine landings over the 10-year period from 1959 through 1968, excluding the Peruvian anchoveta. This 10-year rate is 4.3%. Since the Peruvian anchoveta fishery is at its zenith, it would appear that the 4.3% rate of increase for the remainder of the marine catch is reasonable.

If we assume that the catch (excluding the Peruvian anchoveta) will increase by 4.3%/year, we should reach the theoretical total limit of 94×10^6 metric tons by 1982. Is this a valid assumption? Any such extrapolation of the world catch must include one or more of three assumptions:

1. The seas have a certain productivity level that can be attained and will be attained regardless of man's effect on the abundance of particular species. Logically this means that the decimation of one species merely results in its replacement by another.
2. Any decline in particular species can always be more than offset by searching out and exploiting hitherto underfished species.
3. New fishing grounds exist that are practically untouched by fishing so that expansion can continue for a very long time.

Apparently there are those who must believe in the validity of these assumptions. Pariser (1969) cites two authors who place the world's sustainable fishery harvest at 500×10^3 (sic) metric tons and two who place it at 2000×10^3 (sic) metric tons. He obviously means 10^6 rather than 10^3, as he makes the same error for several authors with lesser totals. It may be worthy of note that at the 4.3% rate of increase, the 500×10^6 metric tons could be achieved in 56 years and 2000×10^6 in 912 years.

Pariser (1969) assumes that the United States continental shelves can produe 4,490,000 metric tons/year of fish from stocks now unused or underutilized. If this were true, it would triple the present U. S.

catch, which has declined over a 30-year period. However, I find that if one takes the total fishery landings (including freshwater fishes) without attempting the laborious work of sorting out the categories for the years 1969 through 1971, the 4.3% annual increase has fallen during the past 3 years (from 64.3 million metric tons in 1968 to 69.4 million metric tons in 1971) to a mere 2.58% rate of increase.

Another problem in reaching higher levels of production is the waste of fish resulting from pampered eating habits in some countries. To illustrate, Table 6-25 shows the landings in the northwestern Atlantic (New England to Greenland) and in the northeastern Atlantic (Spain to the U.S.S.R., except the Baltic and Mediterranean Seas.) Note that 3.7% of the European landings consist of fishes we largely waste. During World War II when food was at a premium we smoked anglerfish, *Lophius americanus,* from the Boston trawlers and found it excellent, yet the public will not accept it. Delicious sea mussels abound on the New England coast but go unused. The few sharks used are apt to be sold as swordfish.

The intensive advertising campaigns to induce the public to eat more fish usually tout the excellence of products already in short supply, e.g., haddock, halibut, salmon, whitefish, and shrimp. This is a waste of public funds.

Let us examine closely the three assumptions mentioned previously.

ASSUMPTION 1. In certain instances other species do tend to fill the vacuum created by the decimation of a formerly abundant species. Thus Murphy (1966) shows that the northern anchovy, *Engraulis mordax,* is increasing in abundance in the California Current upwelling region once dominated by the Pacific sardine, *Sardinops sagax caerulea.* Similarly, on southwestern Georges Bank the haddock, *Melanogrammus aeglefinus,* abundant in the late 1920's, declined drastically but was replaced by the yellowtail flounder, *Limanda ferruginea.* When the flounder was fished out, it was replaced

Table 6-25. Landings of less desirable species from both sides of the Atlantic in 1968 (thousands of metric tons)[1]

Less desirable species	Northwestern Atlantic	Northeastern Atlantic
Anglerfishes	0.0	40.0
Gurnards (sea robins)	0.0	12.4
Picked (spiny) dogfish	0.0	27.0
Sharks	0.9	30.7
Rays and skates	0.9	52.6
Winkles	0.1	4.2
Conchs	1.0	2.4
Mussels	2.7	243.3
Squids	1.7	20.8
Octopi	0.0	5.2
TOTAL		
Less desirable species	7.3	438.6
Total weight	3,231	11,866
Percent of less desirable species	0.2	3.7

[1]Species common to both sides of the Atlantic (Mediterranean excluded), except the capelin and sand lances, which are taken wholly for reduction.

by red hake, *Urophycis chuss.* In both cases the resulting product was inferior. Whether or not these changes are reversible has not yet been demonstrated.

In many other instances there is no ready replacement. The anadromous species and those dependent on the estuaries are not readily replaced. Each is the product of long periods of evolution. When a species is gone how can it be replaced? Perhaps the virtual demise of the great Antarctic whale herds is convincing enough.

ASSUMPTION 2. This assumption, the continuous availability of new species to exploit, is quickly becoming invalid. During the years of expansion of the Pacific halibut, *Hippoglossus stenolepis,* fishery, the vessels first overfished the Oregon and Washington banks, then moved in succession to Hecate Strait, Dixon Entrance, Cape Spencer, Yakutat, Cook Inlet, Portlock Bank, Trinity Bank, the Shumagin Islands, and finally the Bering Sea. When they were finished the stocks were depleted over the whole range of the fishery. The ability to shift ever farther westward sprang from the building of larger vessels, the change from dory to longline fishing, the change from gasoline to diesel engines, and the development of efficient hauling gurdies. Now with more efficient navigational instruments, the development of better winches, fish searching equipment and so forth, we are fishing deeper waters on the upper slope below the edge of the continental shelf, but these areas are smaller, less productive, and more expensive to fish.

ASSUMPTION 3. The assumption that expansion can continue indefinitely through exploitation of new fishing grounds has several facets. First, why do these hypothetically rich fishing grounds remain unexploited? Are they too distant from ports of landing? Are they too difficult to fish because of ice, stormy weather, or rough bottom? If such grounds exist, can their exploitation cause the world catch to rise while the already exploited banks are yielding smaller and smaller returns in the face of heavier fishing pressure? Will not the exploitation of new grounds, if many exist, merely end in the final decimation of the fish stocks on all banks—a repetition of the history of the halibut fishery?

For example, in the case of one of the world's great fisheries, the cod fishery, Idler and Jangaard state:

In Table 6 the world catch of Atlantic cod is listed by countries; it is evident that the quantity caught increased dramatically from 1948-1956, which was the peak year. Since then the quantity has fluctuated from 2,560 to 3,010 thousand metric tons per year in spite of greatly increased fishing effort. Several fishing areas are now producing only a fraction of the quantity caught only 10-15 years ago; it is estimated, for instance, that the cod population of the Barents Sea is only about 10% of what it used to be. The other chief fishing areas have as yet not reached this point, but increased fishing pressure on the stocks are showing in smaller average size of the fish and the increased effort needed to catch the same amount of fish.*

There is no obvious reason why fishery landings should continue to increase at any particular rate. The landings have not kept pace with the great increase in fishing effort.

The desperate need for more animal protein from the sea in countries with extremely limited arable land is well exemplified by Japan. Despite their huge world-flung fishing fleets, they are unable to increase their catches except by increasing their fishing effort to unprofitable levels. They have experimented with trying to catch in quantity the small shrimplike euphausiids that form the staple food, the "krill," of the once mighty Antarctic baleen whale herds (Commercial Fisheries Review editorial, 1970). The problems include the loss of a month each way for vessels making the voyage, and the attempts to strain quantities from the water have not been notably successful.

However, the Soviet Federal Research Institute of Fisheries and Oceanography (VNIRO) has built machines to produce a protein-rich paste from krill (Marine Fisheries Review editorial, 1973). In 1972 they operated seven factory ships, probably with 70 to 100 vessels, in the vicinity of the Kerguelen Islands in Antarctic waters to take quantities of *Notothenia,* an Antarctic codlike species not living in waters above 4° C. Now they may turn their attention to krill.

---

*From Idler, D. R., and P. M. Jangaard. 1969. Cod fishery. In Firth, F. E., editor. Encyclopedia of marine resources. Van Nostrand Reinhold Co., New York. pp. 129-135.

The risks assumed by any country in relying too heavily on fish meal from a few sources is highlighted by Kolhonen (1974) who shows that world fish meal production in 1972 declined from the 1970 high of 5.32 million metric tons to 3.88 million metric tons, a drop of 27%. Although this drop was partially a result of the effect of the oceanic condition known as El Nino on Peruvian-Chilean anchovetas, the production of fish meal also declined in South Africa, Norway, Canada, and the United States despite enormous increases in prices. During the last quarter of 1969 fish meal prices in New York rose to about $200/short ton. Prices fell slightly but again reached $200 by mid-1972 when the shortage of meal became apparent. By May 1973 the New York price for Peruvian meal reached $480/short ton. By June, when Peruvian meal was too scarce to be quoted, menhaden meal reached an average quotation of $508/short ton—a rise in 1 year of 190%.

Whether the anchoveta of Peru and northern Chile will continue indefinitely to be the major factor in the world's fish meal production may be open to serious question. This warning is contained in the following excerpts from Boerema and Gulland:

Developments in 1972 gave an unexpectedly early confirmation of the relevance of the stock assessment panel's conclusions concerning the instability of the stock. The first indication of an unusual occurrence in the anchoveta stocks was the scarcity of young fish being recruited to the fishery. . . . At the same time, there was increasing evidence of unusual oceanographic conditions. Direct observations in 1971 did not indicate any abnormality, but an unusual occurrence of a tropical crab *(Euphilax)* in the second half of this year was noted along the coast, and the percentage of adult female anchovies that were in spawning condition in August-October was lower than usual.

Early in 1972 the Institute noted an intrusion of warm, tropical water in the offshore area in the extreme north of the Peruvian coast, which thereafter penetrated further southward and developed into a full-scale El Nino. During the rest of the year the temperatures of the surface waters off Peru have been several degrees above normal, though the abnormality has been less pronounced and less persistent in the south.

So far as adult fish are concerned, the unusual environment conditions seem to have no direct harmful effect. However, the warm water concentrated the fish in local areas of cooler water, and the fish also tended to move south. . . .

More serious was the drop in recruitment. As already mentioned, a failure of recruitment was detected as early as January 1972, and the actual level of recruitment on the basis of catch and effort data was estimated in July 1972 to be only one-seventh of normal. Later evidence suggests that even this figure was optimistic.

. . . When the Expert Panel met in early July it confirmed the Institute's conclusions on the poor recruitment. It also concluded from the decline in the catches between March and June, from the magnitude of the total catch obtained in this period of over 4 million tons, and from the observation that no concentrations of anchoveta had been reported outside the fishing areas (neither further offshore, nor in deeper water, nor further south along the Chilean coast), that most of the adult fish, concentrated by El Nino, had been fished away. Because of a combination of these two factors, the stock was estimated to be at a dangerously low level. The Panel therefore recommended, subject to review in the light of later information, that no fishing should take place until a reasonably good recruitment had brought the stock on the way to recovery.

It is hoped that the fish stocks will soon return to normal following the strict measures taken in 1972, but this will not end the problems of the anchoveta fishery. . . .

The first questions concern the biology of the resource. The events of 1971-72 have shown that, in common with other stocks of similar shoaling pelagic fish, the Peruvian anchovy can undergo sudden and unforeseen changes. Though so far the decline has not been so severe or prolonged as that observed in the Hokkaido herring, the California sardine, or the Atlanto-Scandian herring, these examples of stocks that have reached virtual commercial extinction show how important it is to have a better knowledge of the general factors governing the abundance of pelagic fish stocks. In particular, more understanding is needed on the relative effects of changes in the physical environment, and in the abundance or density of adults, on the numbers of young fish entering the fishery.*

---

*From Boerema, L. K., and J. A. Gulland. 1973. Stock assessment of the Peruvian anchovy (Engraulis ringens) and management of the fishery. J. Fish. Res. Bd. Canada 30:2226-2235.

Suggested readings

Boerema, L. K., and J. A. Gulland. 1973. Stock assessment of the Peruvian anchovy (Engraulis ringens) and management of the fishery. J. Fish. Res. Bd. Canada **30:**2226-2235.

Borgstrom, G., and A. J. Heighway, editors. 1961. Atlantic Ocean fisheries. Fishing News (Books), Ltd., London. 335 pp.

Bullis, H. R., Jr., and J. R. Thompson. 1968. Harvesting the ocean in the decade ahead. Ocean Ind. **3:**52-60.

Cushing, D. H. 1958. Some experiments using the ^{14}C technique. Rapp. Proc. Verb., Cons. Perm. Intern. Exp. Mer **144:**73-75.

Cushing, D. H. 1969. Upwelling and fish production. FAO Fish. Tech. Pap. **84:**1-40.

Edwards, R. L. 1968. Fishery resources of the North Atlantic area. In Proceeding of the conference on the future of U. S. fishing industry, University of Washington, March 24-27.

Food and Agriculture Organization. 1969. Yearbook of fishery statistics for 1968, vol. 26. 320 pp.

Graham, H. W., and R. L. Edwards. 1962. The world biomass of marine fishes. (FAO report of the international conference on fish in nutrition. Washington, D. C., Sept. 19-27, 1961. pp. 3-8.) In Fish in nutrition. Fishing News (Books), Ltd., London. 447 pp.

Hand, C. H., and L. Berner, Jr. 1959. Food of the Pacific sardine (Sardinops caerulea). U. S. Fish Wildl. Serv., Fish. Bull. **60:**175-184.

Hela, I., and T. Laevastu. 1961. Fisheries hydrography. Fishing News (Books), Ltd., London. 137 pp.

Heselton, L. R., Jr. 1969. The continental shelf. Center for Naval Analyses, Doc. AD686 703. Office of Technical Services, U. S. Department of Commerce, Springfield, Va. 44 pp.

Isaacs, J. D., and W. R. Schmitt. 1969. Stimulation of marine productivity with waste heat and mechanical power. J. Conseil **33:**20-29.

Kossinna, E. 1921. Die Tiefen des Weltmeeres. Berlin Universität Institut fur Meereskunde, Veroff, N. F., A. Geogr.-Naturwiss. **9:**1-70.

Meseck, G. 1962. Importance of fisheries production and utilization in the food economy. (FAO report of the international conference on fish in nutrition. Washington, D. C., Sept. 19-27, 1961. pp. 23-27.) In Fish in nutrition. Fishing News (Books), Ltd., London. 447 pp.

Pike, S. T., and A. Spilhaus. 1962. Marine resources, report to the Committee on Natural Resources. NAS/NRC. Publ. 100-E. National Academy of Sciences–National Research Council, Washington, D. C. pp 1-8.

Rounsefell, G. A. 1971. Potential food from the sea. J. Mar. Sci. Alabama **1:**1-82.

Ryther, J. H. 1969. Photosynthesis and fish production in the sea. Science **166:**72-76.

Schaefer, M. B. 1965. The potential harvest of the sea. Trans. Amer. Fish. Soc. **94:**123-128.

chapter 7

🌿 United States fisheries

UNITED STATES FISHERY PRODUCTION BY GEAR AND AREA
General considerations

Statistics for the U. S. fisheries have been reasonably accurate for the past 30 years. They are more accurate for the more important fisheries, especially those using large vessels or those concentrated in a few ports. For minor scattered fisheries on which data were collected only through an annual canvass, the statistics tend to vary in accuracy from one canvass to another and from one locality to another.

Although reasonably accurate insofar as poundage and dockside value are concerned, the statistics have certain built-in defects. The number of fishing craft given is much too high, since many of these craft engage in two or more seasonal fisheries. The number of fishermen is also too high. A "regular" fisherman is defined as one fishing for at least 50% of the year. Many seasonal fisheries last only a few months; yet the statistics count the participants as "regular" fishermen; these men frequently are engaged in other fisheries for a goodly portion of the year. Their numbers are thus duplicated in the totals.

The definition of a "casual" fisherman is one fishing less than 50% of the year, but

how much less is pure guesswork. In 1967 the Pacific coast and Alaska statistics omitted "casual" fishermen.

Another major defect is the failure to show the catches by size of fishing craft.* In New England the otter trawl catches of 539 vessels, many exceeding 150 gross tons, are lumped with the catches of 97 motor boats that are less than 5 net tons apiece.

Most of the data necessary to correct these defects are already on the punched cards fed the computers; their analysis would be invaluable for an intelligent appraisal of the economics of the fisheries.

Despite these handicaps, Table 7-1 shows the marine fishery yield by type of gear and fishery for the continental United States during the year 1967.

---

*"Net" tonnage is derived from Coast Guard measurement of enclosed space. A *boat* is smaller than 5 net tons and is *not a vessel,* as it is undocumented. All *vessels* are documented. Gross tons are a slightly different measurement. An open boat with little enclosed space may be less than 5 net tons and thus be undocumented, but at the same time it may be 6 or 7 or more gross tons. The gross tons are a more accurate measure of true vessel capacity.

Text continued on p. 137.

Table 7-1. Fisheries of the United States in 1967[1, 2]

Type of gear	Motor boats	Vessels	Total gross tons[3]	Nets or other gear	Landings (thousands of pounds)	Value (thousands of dollars)	No. of fishermen	Remarks
Purse seines								
Tuna	0	143	41,943		247,449	29,961	1,602	
Menhaden	0	139	41,380		892,704	10,637	2,409	
Salmon	351	871	24,795		87,495	13,157	6,596	
Herring (Pacific)	0	(25)	(1,250)		17,014	243	(114)	Duplicated in anchovy data (Calif.) (?)
Anchovy-mackerel (Calif.)	0	134	4,690		108,850	2,236	938	
Misc. fish and squid (Calif.)	10	7	160		19,578	600	36	
Mackerel-reduction (North Atlantic)	0	(10)	(1,240)		10,513	449	(99)	Duplicated in menhaden vessel data (?)
Thread herring (Gulf)	0	(3)	(651)		7,750	65	(29)	
Herring (New England)	27	12	927		40,529	932	162	
Striped bass (N. C.)	2	0	10		52	10	5	
Spanish mackerel (Fla.)	5	2	83		720	75	18	
SUBTOTAL	395	1,308	113,998		1,432,654	58,365	11,770	
Towed nets								
Otter trawls, shrimp (Gulf and South Atlantic)	5,738	3,859	203,002		241,352	98,374	16,212	
Otter trawls, shrimp (other)	45	165	7,410		58,556	3,721	574	
Otter trawls, fish (New England)	97	539	40,267		460,232	31,196	3,010	
Otter trawls, fish (other)	89	793	31,833		284,897	16,487	1,802	
Otter trawls, crabs (South Atlantic)	235	179	5,060		12,038	614	512	
Otter trawls, lobster (North Atlantic)	0	(135)	(10,260)		3,976	2,815	(636)	Duplicated in fish otter trawl data (New England) (?)
Otter trawls, scallop (South Atlantic)	0	23	253		1,425	315	68	
Midwater trawls, hake (Northwest)	0	(14)	(1,036)		27,500	220	(42)	Duplicated in fish otter trawl data (other) (?)
Beam trawls, shrimp	1	21	537		2,739	50	65	
Butterfly nets, shrimp (La.)	363	22	2,189		4,571	1,090	711	
SUBTOTAL	6,568	5,601	290,551		1,097,286	154,982	22,954	
Small pot gear								
Small pots, king and tanner crab (Alaska)	29	329	25,092		127,833	14,982	2,923	Includes Dungeness crab fishermen

							Remarks
Small pots, Dungeness crab (Alaska-Calif.)	66	403	8,670	42,562	6,371	—	Includes catch of shrimp pots
Small pots, blue crab (N. J.-Texas)	3,084	377	18,436	100,204	7,193	4,277	Includes catch of stone crabs
Small pots, lobster (Mass.-N. J.)	5,547	58	28,431	24,170	19,169	5,605	Includes green and rock crabs and conchs
Small pots, spiny lobster (Fla.)	388	140	4,040	4,391	2,819	934	Includes octopus
Small pots, spiny lobster (Calif.)	125	57	1,099	776	427	416	
Small pots, sea bass (N. Y.-S. C.)	247	70	2,358	2,651	507	388	
Crab pound nets (Va.)	367	8	1,891	2,379	335	375	
SUBTOTAL	9,853	1,442	90,014	304,966	51,803	14,918	
Line gear							
Troll (Mass. to Fla.)	(773)	(60)	(4,525)	1,872	280	(884)	Duplicated in set and drift gill net data (Atlantic) (?)
Troll, salmon and albacore	4,031	3,447	86,032	77,154	23,518	14,191	
Live bait, tuna (Pacific)	0	191	11,546	20,223	4,120	1,231	
Crab trotlines (Md.-S. C.)	2,753	101	14,634	16,614	1,125	3,100	
Crab trotlines (La.)	518	0	2,590	2,422	178	519	
Longline, halibut (Pacific)	56	253	8,629	42,655	8,853	1,063	Includes other longlines in Alaska and Northwest
Longline (Texas estuaries)	118	0	590	1,457	293	113	
Longline (North Atlantic)	0	29	1,798	7,631	1,057	132	
Handlines, vessels (Ga.-Texas)	0	448	14,429	22,123	5,687	2,038	
Handlines, boats (Ga.-Texas)	1,354	0	6,870	2,040	284	1,360	
Handlines (North Atlantic)	(1,240)	(10)	(6,320)	4,333	431	(1,805)	Duplicated in lobster pot data (Me.-N. J.) (?)
Handlines (Md.)	(61)	0	(305)	152	31	(90)	Duplicated in oyster tong data (Mass.-Fla.) (?)
Handlines (Pacific coast)	(14)	(188)	(4,018)	34	2	(919)	Duplicated in salmon purse seine data (?)
SUBTOTAL	8,891	4,469	147,423	198,710	45,859	23,837	
Entangling nets							
Gill nets, salmon (Alaska-Pacific)	8,441	654	49,470	90,976	19,660	9,886	
Gill nets, sink (New England)	20	9	343	4,305	308	69	
Gill nets, set and drift (Atlantic)	3,789	335	22,103	14,391	1,860	4,474	
Gill nets, set and drift (Gulf)	(65)	(6)	(373)	646	123	(91)	Duplicated in trammel net data (Gulf) (?)

[1] The data for boats, vessels, and number of fishermen that are in parentheses are probably the duplications referred to in the remarks. [3] Estimating 5 gross tons per motor boat. [4] Estimated 1.25 each.
[2] Marine only; excludes Hawaii.

Continued.

Table 7-1. Fisheries of the United States in 1967—cont'd

Type of gear	Motor boats	Vessels	Total gross tons	Nets or other gear	Landings (thousands of pounds)	Value (thousands of dollars)	No. of fisher-men	Remarks
Entangling nets—cont'd								
Gill nets, runaround, (N. Y.-N. C.)	(106)	(11)	(651)		1,279	170	(200)	Duplicated in set and drift gill net data (Atlantic) (?)
Gill nets, runaround (Fla.)	1,261	98	7,677		39,398	4,117	1,930	
Gill nets, eulachon (Columbia River)	(80)	0	(400)		353	51	(80)	Duplicated in salmon gill net data
Gill nets, shad (Ore.)	(63)	0	(315)		507	57	(68)	Duplicated in salmon gill net data
Trammel nets (east Fla.-Texas)	808	29	4,446		12,434	4,020	1,008	
Trammel and gill nets (Calif.)	71	65	1,401		2,749	553	356	
SUBTOTAL	14,496	1,201	86,091		167,038	30,919	17,918	
Dredges								
Dredges, sea scallops (Me.-N. C.)	4	117	13,223		10,167	7,626	1,228	Catches 3 Me. vessels under bay scallops
Dredges, bay scallops (Me.-Fla.)	872	0	4,360		1,277	1,192	872	
Dredges, hard clams (Mass.-Va.)	47	89	2,342		6,609	3,113	317	Includes 1 vessel (west Fla.)
Dredges, soft clams (Md.)	130	90	1,820		6,632	1,846	407	
Dredges, surf clams (N. J.)	121	103	5,652		42,122	4,217	362	
Dredges, rangia (N. C.)	(0)	(9)	(54)		87	27	(11)	Duplicated in oyster dredge data (Md.-N. C.)
Dredges, mussels (Mass.)	(8)	(1)	(54)		350	54	(10)	Duplicated in hard clam dredge data (?)
Dredges, conch (N. J.-Va.)	0	(8)	(128)		74	10	(18)	Duplicated in hard clam dredge data (?)
Dredges, oysters (New England-mid-Atlantic)	21	42	924		1,355	1,664	267	
Dredges, oysters (Md.-N. C.)	397	224	4,286		13,772	9,287	1,275	
Dredges, oysters (Gulf)	323	426	9,789		17,580	6,864	1,886	
Dredges, oysters (Pacific)	5	30	655		7,420	3,082	77	Includes 2 suction dredges
Dredges, crab (N. J.-Va.)	(7)	(160)	(2,973)		15,062	988	(441)	Includes oysters (New England-N. C.)
Crab scrapes (Chesapeake area)	138	23	874		1,900	674	161	
SUBTOTAL	2,066	1,154	44,025		124,307	40,644	6,852	

							Remarks
Stop seines, herring (Me.)	86	16	690	19,712	465	290	
Haul seines, common, edible fish (N. Y.-east Fla.)	450	53	2,780	17,789	1,295	1,390	
Haul seines, common, edible fish (Gulf)	160	18	1,070	13,192	1,020	543	
Haul seines, common, edible fish (Calif.)	5	0	25	666	69	12	
Haul seines, common, salmon (Northwest)	0	12	133	254	60	36	
Haul seines, common, silver smelt (Northwest)	(70)	0	(210)	902	144	(240)	Duplicated in salmon gill net data (?)
Haul seines, common, alewives (Mass.-Conn.)	(10)	0	(50)	457	15	(17)	Duplicated in set and drift gill net data (Atlantic) (?)
Haul seines, common, sand lance (N. H.)	(1)	0	(5)	23	3	(5)	Duplicated in set and drift gill net data (Atlantic) (?)
Haul seines, long, edible fish (N. C.)	58	0	290	3,190	245	223	
SUBTOTAL	759	99	4,988	56,185	3,316	2,494	
Shoal water hand gear							
Rakes, Irish moss (Me. and Mass.)	(299)	0	(1,495)	5,075	94	(418)	Duplicated in lobster pot data (?)
Rakes, oysters (Mass. and N. C.)	(47)	0	(235)	21	15	(47)	Duplicated in oyster tongs data (Mass.-Fla.) (?)
Rakes, hard clams, (Mass. and east Fla.)	(2,386)	0	(11,930)	4,351	3,573	(2,386)	Duplicated in hard clam tongs data (Atlantic) (?)
Tongs, hard clams (Mass.-N. C.)	2,972	88	15,514	6,010	4,741	3,060	
Tongs, oysters (Mass.-Fla.)	6,216	548	35,464	18,050	11,866	7,439	
Tongs, oysters (Gulf)	1,715	1	8,585	8,608	2,988	1,993	
Tongs, oysters (Calif.)	(17)	0	(85)	288	102	(40)	Duplicated in spiny lobster pot data (Calif.) (?)
Diving outfits, lobsters (New England)	(23)	0	(115)	30	28	(54)	Duplicated in lobster pot data (Me.-N. J.) (?)
Diving outfits, spiny lobsters (east Fla.)	(3)	0	(15)	3	2	(3)	Duplicated in blue crab pot data (N. J.-Texas) (?)
Diving outfits, sponges (west Fla.)	0	9	144	26	304	58	
Diving outfits, abalone (Calif.)	248	41	1,978	885	860	609	
Diving outfits, oysters (New England)	(2)	0	(10)	1	1	(5)	Duplicated in lobster pot data (Me.-N. J.) (?)
Hooks, conchs (Fla.)	(8)	0	(40)	15	4	(8)	Duplicated in sponge hook data (Fla.)
Hooks, sponges (Fla.)	71	3	378	30	137	74	
SUBTOTAL	11,222	690	62,071	43,293	24,715	13,233	

Continued.

Table 7-1. Fisheries of the United States in 1967—cont'd

Type of gear	Motor boats	Vessels	Total gross tons	Nets or other gear	Landings (thousands of pounds)	Value (thousands of dollars)	No. of fisher-men	Remarks
Minor craft-dependent gear								
Dip nets, eulachon (Columbia River)	(26)	0	(130)		648	62	(53)	Duplicated in salmon gill net data (?)
Dip nets, silver smelt (Wash.)	(16)	0	(80)		13	2	(40)	Duplicated in salmon gill net data (?)
Dip nets, herring (Puget Sound)	0	(4)	32		142	32	(11)	Duplicated in salmon gill net data (?)
Dip nets, spiny lobster (west Fla.)	(4)	0	(20)		6	4	(4)	Duplicated in spiny lobster pot data (Fla.) (?)
Dip nets, crabs (Md.-N. C.)	(111)	0	(555)		213	27	(111)	Duplicated in crab scrape data (?)
Dip nets, smelt (Calif.)	(1)	(2)	(13)		81	8	(6)	Duplicated in spiny lobster pot data (Calif.) (?)
Dip nets, squid and mackerel (Calif.)	(4)	(33)	(763)		1,069	28	(101)	Duplicated in salmon and albacore troll data (?)
Bag nets, shrimp (N. C.)	103	3	535		333	113	109	
Fyke nets, flounder (N. Y.-Md.)	(57)	(5)	(341)		219	24	(65)	Duplicated in set and drift gill net data (Atlantic) (?)
Fyke nets, alewives (Va.)	(92)	0	(460)		2,200	76	(92)	Duplicated in set and drift gill net data (Atlantic) (?)
Cast nets, shrimp (S. C.)	(2)	0	(10)		34	8	(2)	Duplicated in set and drift gill net data (Atlantic) (?)
Cast nets, mullet (Fla.)	(6)	0	(18)		10	1	(6)	Duplicated in runaround gill net data (Fla.) (?)
Harpoons, bluefin tuna (New England)	(31)	0	(155)		93	8	(44)	Duplicated in lobster pot data (Me.-N. J.) (?)
Harpoons, swordfish (New England)	0	(14)	(781)		318	125	(63)	Duplicated in fish otter trawl data (New England) (?)
Harpoons, swordfish (Calif.)	(16)	(68)	(604)		305	164	(129)	Duplicated in salmon and albacore troll data (?)

							Remarks
Spears, flounders (south Atlantic)	(59)	0	(295)	64	14	(59)	Duplicated in haul seine data (N. Y.-east Fla.) (?)
Spears, flounders (Gulf)	(143)	0	(715)	65	17	(143)	Duplicated in haul seine data (Gulf) (?)
Brush traps, crabs (La.)	(48)	0	(240)	58	44	(48)	Duplicated in blue crab pot data (Gulf) (?)
Drop net, blue crabs (La.)	(101)	0	(505)	605	62	(101)	Duplicated in blue crab pot data (Gulf) (?)
Drop net, spiny lobster (west Fla.)	(7)	0	(35)	8	5	(7)	Duplicated in spiny lobster pot data (Fla.) (?)
Drop dip nets, alewives (S. C.)	35	0	175	2,802	56	85	Duplicated in set and drift gill net data (Atlantic) (?)
SUBTOTAL	138	3	710	9,286	880	194	
Craft-independent gear							
Large fixed gear							
Brush weirs	75	375	97	8,393	228	141	
Traps and pound nets	630	4,546	2,094	94,307	4,053	2,159	
Reef nets	0	0	63	1,281	293	252	
Fish wheels	0	0	8	22	4	8	
SUBTOTAL	705	3,511	2,262	104,003	4,578	2,560	
Intertidal hand gear							
Hoes and forks				6,182	3,677	2,093	
Shovels				546	308	2,016	
By hand				3,374	1,736	3,510	
SUBTOTAL				10,102	5,721	7,619	
Minor nonvessel gear							
Dip nets, shore-operated, alewives (New England)	0	0	(83)	1,853	71	(83)	Seasonal fishermen duplicated (?)
Dip nets, shore-operated, salmon (Columbia River)	0	0	69	154	39	69	
Bag nets, smelt (Me.-N. H.)	0	0	(11)	85	18	(11)	Seasonal fishermen duplicated (?)
SUBTOTAL	69	69	69	2,092	128	69	

Continued.

Table 7-1. Fisheries of the United States in 1967—cont'd

Summary (excluding suspected duplication in gear)

Type of gear	Motor boats	Vessels	Total gross tons	Landings (thousands of pounds)	Value (thousands of dollars)	No. of fishermen	Gear units
Purse seines	395	1,308	113,918	1,432,654	58,365	11,770	1,701
Towed nets	6,568	5,601	290,551	1,097,286	154,982	22,954	12,169
Small pot gear	9,853	1,442	90,014	304,966	51,803	14,918	11,295
Line gear	8,891	4,469	147,423	198,710	45,859	23,837	13,360
Entangling nets	14,496	1,201	86,091	167,038	30,919	17,918	15,697
Dredges	2,066	1,154	44,025	124,307	40,644	6,852	3,220
Haul and stop seines	759	99	4,988	56,185	3,316	2,494	858
Shoal water hand gear	11,222	690	62,071	43,293	24,715	13,233	11,912
Minor craft-dependent gears	138	3	710	9,286	880	194	141
SUBTOTAL, vessel fisheries	54,388	15,967	839,861	3,433,725	411,483	114,170	70,353
Large fixed gear	705	117	3,511	104,003	4,578	2,560	2,262
Intertidal hand gear	0	0	0	10,102	5,721	7,619	7,619
Minor noncraft gears	0	0	0	2,092	128	69	69
SUBTOTAL, nonvessel fisheries	705	117	3,511	116,197	10,427	10,248	9,950
GRAND TOTAL	55,093	16,084	843,372	3,549,922	421,910	124,418	80,303

Gross tons, boats	275,465	Fishermen on vessels	46,185
Gross tons, vessels	567,907	Fishermen on fixed gears	2,560
Average gross tons, vessels	35.3	Noncraft fishermen	7,688
Fishermen per vessel	2.9	All fishermen	124,418
Fishermen on boats[4]	67,985		

Purse seines

Purse seines yielded the largest total catch, over 1.5 billion pounds valued at over $60 million at dockside.

Purse seines differ from haul seines in being retrieved on a boat or vessel instead of on the shore. As the name implies, the bottom of the net (the lead line) is usually pursed or closed, preventing the escape of any fish, before the bulk of the net is hauled aboard the seine boat in order to concentrate the fish. The generic term "purse seine" includes several variations.

Lampara nets. Once the principal net used for California sardines and still used for taking fast-moving small pelagic fishes, the lampara net is a very light net with large meshes in the wings that can be hauled in quickly so that the fish are soon concentrated in the central fine-meshed portion of the net. It can be operated on small vessels and does not require the cumbersome turntables used for larger and heavier nets.

Earlier purse seines. The earlier purse seines were set by two small oar-propelled boats. The net was stacked half and half on the sterns of the two boats with the bight of the net between them. The two boats were rowed around opposite sides of a school of fish, laying the net as they went, until they met. This method was introduced into Alaska from Norway in the 1880's for taking herring for the reduction plant at Killisnoo on Chatham Strait. A similar method is still used in Turkey for taking anchovies in the Black Sea.

This two-boat method was used extensively in New England until very recently for taking mackerel and bluefin tuna, but the two seine boats were powered. The present-day menhaden fishery uses the same method, but the two seine boats are well powered and fitted out with power blocks for hauling in the net.

On the West Coast the pursuit of large fast-moving species such as salmon made speed of setting the net more important. Furthermore, the heavy swells of the Pacific were not conducive to the small seine boat operations conducted along the Atlantic coast, where a large proportion of the seining was in sheltered sounds and estuaries. Thus the oar-propelled seine boats that I once saw surrounding salmon at the creek mouths had to be replaced. The modern West Coast purse seine vessel sets the net from the large vessel itself, which no longer acts merely as a tender and fish carrier as in the menhaden fishery.

There is considerable difference between purse seines according to the species they are designed to capture. For herring or sardines the mesh must be small, so that the net of necessity is bulky. The nets for herring, for instance, may vary from 9 or 10 fm deep in early summer to perhaps 30 fm deep in the autumn when the herring are schooling deeper. For salmon the nets have larger meshes and are less bulky.

Because of the lighter weight of salmon purse seines, numbers of newer vessels have installed a large powered drum on which the net is wound, speeding up net retrieval with less labor; this is illegal in Alaska because of its efficiency.

The large tuna vessels use extremely large purse seines of nylon to capture the large, fast yellowfin tuna. These nets need to be deep enough to reach the thermocline in order to prevent the tuna from sounding and escaping beneath the net. The California tuna seining vessels in 1967 averaged 309 gross tons. In 1942 (25 years earlier) the tuna purse seiners were fishing for the slower moving bluefin, and the 72 tuna purse seiners averaged only 53 gross tons.

During the same period (1942 to 1967) mackerel and sardine purse seiners increased in average gross tonnage from 53 to 68 tons; lampara and ring net vessels increased from 31 to 64 gross tons.

Menhaden purse seines. The menhaden purse seine fishery constitutes a highly specialized fishery operating in the bays, estuaries, and nearshore areas of the Atlantic and Gulf coasts, taking enormous quantities of menhaden for reduction. The two powered seine boats set and retrieve the net; the fish are then taken aboard the attending large shallow draft vessel for transportation to the plant.

Pacific coast–type purse seiner. The net is set directly from the large vessel. The original lampara and ring nets are now used only on small vessels; the larger vessels use purse seines. California's landing statistics are not clearly separated by boat type, but there is a well-marked distinction between the large tuna seiners and those fishing for the small schooling fishes. In 1967 there were 137 tuna purse seiners that landed a total of 244,086,000 pounds. Of this large amount of tuna, 130 million pounds were yellowfin, 99 million pounds were skipjack, 13½ million pounds were bluefin, and the remainder were albacore and bonito. Only the albacore, about 8% of the bluefin, and 75% of the bonito were taken off the coast of the United States; the remainder was caught off Latin America.

In southeastern Alaska 10 herring purse seiners landed 6,050,000 pounds of herring in 1967. As the seines averaged 250 fm compared to 150 fm in the heyday of the reduction fishery, this is a very poor catch indeed. In central Alaska the catch was even lower, 10 purse seines taking only 5,175,000 pounds of herring. The statistics show that nearly 7 million pounds were frozen for bait and presumably most of the remainder were used as fresh bait. In southeastern Alaska alone over 7 million pounds were used as halibut bait in 1927 and 1928. To state that the Alaska herring stocks are grossly underutilized (Rietze, 1972) is to ignore the history of exploitation and depletion that closed the herring fishery long before Peruvian anchovetas were thought of.

Towed nets

Although towed nets yielded the second largest poundage (1,097,000,000 pounds), their catch was by far the greatest in value, $154 million.

Beam trawls. One of the oldest forms of towed net is the beam trawl. This consists

Fig. 7-1. Showing the "dragger" class of New England otter trawlers (5 to 50 gross tons). Small draggers unloading at the famous Boston tea wharf (since demolished) noted for the "Boston tea party."

of a strong beam across the top of the net to keep the mouth open and heavy steel or steel-clad runners attached to each end of the beam to keep it off the bottom. Obviously it can capture fish only if they are close enough to the bottom to pass under the beam. This was the form of trawl introduced into New England in 1905 for capturing groundfish. Although the beam trawl was soon replaced by the otter trawl, many still refer to the larger Boston trawlers as "beam trawlers."

Once prevalent, this gear has all but disappeared because of its restricted width, shallow opening, and difficulty and danger of handling in rough water. Statistically, in Puget Sound two beam trawls (24 feet wide) took 11,000 pounds of shrimp, and in southeastern Alaska 21 beam trawls (average 33 feet wide) took 2,730,000 pounds of shrimp.

Otter trawls. In discussing otter trawls one must note the great disparity between the small trawls used in estuaries and the large trawls that sweep the offshore banks. Trawls are also rigged somewhat differently according to the species sought. Therefore a discussion by type of species is justified.

CRAB TRAWLS. In the south Atlantic area from North Carolina to Georgia small vessels take blue crabs by otter trawl. In North Carolina the vessels averaged 18 gross tons, in South Carolina the otter trawlers were all under 5 net tons, and in Georgia about three quarters of the boats were below 5 net tons.

SCALLOP OTTER TRAWLS. In the south Atlantic area 23 small vessels (11 gross tons) fished for the offshore calico scallops. They took 1,425,000 pounds, of which 1,410,000 pounds were calico scallops.

LOBSTER OTTER TRAWLS. In recent years a fairly profitable fishery developed using otter trawls for northern lobsters on the offshore banks from New England to Virginia with vessels in the various states averaging from 58 to 102 gross tons.

In southern New England 73 vessels landed 2,695,000 pounds: 2,610,000 pounds of lobster, 65,000 pounds of flounders, and 15,000 pounds of haddock. In the mid-Atlantic area 51 vessels landed 1,090,000 pounds, including 742,000 pounds of lobster, 160,000 pounds of butterfish, 80,000 pounds of scup, 45,000 pounds of squid, and 27,000 pounds of rock crab. In the Chesapeake Bay area 11 vessels landed 190,000 pounds, all northern lobsters.

SHRIMP OTTER TRAWLS. Our most valuable fishery is for shrimp, and the great majority are caught by shrimp otter trawls. Unlike the modern fish trawl, the otter boards are attached directly to the wing of the net. Throughout the southern fishery for penaeid shrimps the majority of the vessels fish two trawls simultaneously, one on each side, from a single warp and a bridle.

In northern New England 101 vessels fished for pandalid shrimp; 56 vessels averaged 29 gross tons, while the remainder of the fleet (45) were all motor boats of less than 5 net tons. They landed 6,970,000 pounds of shrimp.

In central Alaska 35 shrimp trawlers averaging over 60 gross tons caught 39 million pounds of shrimp. These small Alaska shrimp were valued at only 4 cents/pound, whereas 102 million pounds of the larger penaeid shrimp landed in Texas were valued at 45 cents/pound.

FISH OTTER TRAWLS. Fish trawls vary in mesh size with the size of the fish sought. The doors are attached to the wing of the net by long "pennants." These long cables between the net and the doors scare fish into the net over a wider area than the width of the net itself. On rough bottom the footrope is often rigged with large rollers to carry the net over obstructions. On the bottom of the cod end a bull hide is often used for chafing gear. The headrope usually has floats at intervals to keep the net opening as high as possible above the bottom.

In New England in 1967 there were 539 fish otter trawls; of these approximately 60% were in the 5 to 50 gross ton or small "dragger" class; about 25% were "large

Table 7-2. New England landings by fish otter trawls in 1967 (thousands of pounds)

Species	Landings	Maine	Massachusetts	Rhode Island	Connecticut	Percent of expected[1,2]			
						Maine	Massachusetts	Rhode Island	Connecticut
All	460,232	91,698	300,257	65,363	2,914				
Percent, expected[3]		19.9	65.3	14.2	0.6				
Reduction (unclassified)	84,586	1,494	33,382	48,511	1,199	8.9	60.4	403.9	236.0
Ocean perch	71,409	62,154	9,254	1	0	437.4	19.8	—	0
Haddock	95,835	2,288	93,360	187	0	12.0	149.2	1.4	0
Whiting (silver hake)	59,852	20,726	37,811	1,219	96	174.0	96.7	14.3	26.7
Yellowtail flounder	52,352	78	46,414	5,793	67	0.7	135.8	77.9	21.3
Cod	37,172	1,451	34,257	1,176	288	19.6	141.1	22.3	129.1
Blackback flounder	21,030	103	16,205	3,842	880	2.5	118.0	128.7	698.4
Dab	7,288	753	6,484	51	—	51.9	136.2	11.7	0
Food (unclassified)	6,854	915	5,915	24	—	67.1	132.1	2.5	0
Pollock	5,939	419	5,514	6	0	35.4	142.2	0.7	0
Gray sole	5,612	528	4,772	312	0	47.3	130.2	39.1	0
White hake (*Urophycis tenuis*)	1,892	588	1,265	39	0	156.0	102.4	14.5	0
Scup	1,651	0	181	1,240	230	0	16.8	529.9	2,300.0
Cusk	1,359	132	1,227	—	0	48.9	138.3	0	0
Lemon sole	1,551	—	1,533	18	0	0	151.3	8.2	0
Butterfish	1,264	0	15	1,238	11	0	1.8	691.6	137.5
Red hake (*Urophycis chuss*)	1,354	0	1,265	87	2	0	143.1	45.3	25.0
Fluke	1,138	0	434	657	47	0	58.4	405.6	671.4
Wolffish	523	14	479	—	0	13.5	140.1	—	0
Lobsters	722	0	721	0	1	0	153.1	0	0
Squid	466	0	14	428	24	0	4.7	648.5	800.0
Sea herring	448	0	95	352	1	0	32.4	550.0	300.0
Angler	358	0	354	4	0	0	151.3	7.8	0
Halibut	156	55	101	0	0	177.4	99.0	0	0
Skates	175	0	157	1	17	0	137.7	4.0	1,700.0
Mackerel	57	0	7	47	3	0	18.9	587.5	882.4

[1]"Percent of expected" is the ratio of actual landings of a particular species in a state to the amount of the species expected if it occurred in the same relation to the total of the species as the percent of all species in the state bear to the New England total.

[2]The underlined figures indicate the state in which each particular species is of the highest importance.

[3]"Percent, expected" is the landings of all species in a state divided by the New England total.

draggers" with 51 to 150 gross tons; the remaining 15% were motor boats of less than 5 net tons.

There are at least three rather distinct fisheries involved. The ocean perch, *Sebastes marinus*, fishery that originated in the 1930's in Gloucester has shifted largely to Maine as the deep banks in the South Channel have become depleted. It is pursued to a large extent by older vessels of the large dragger class. This is the same fishery that accounts for Maine's large catches of white hake, which frequent the same deep water mud holes (80 fm and deeper) between the shallower banks. Table 7-2 has been compiled to illustrate the distinct fisheries involved.

The largest fishery is carried on by the large (over 150 gross tons) otter trawlers and medium draggers on the farther offshore banks (Georges Bank and the Nova Scotian banks).

A large fishery for silver hake (whiting) is conducted by the small draggers fishing the inshore banks from Ipswich Bay, Massachusetts, into southern Maine.

The Rhode Island fleet, which does not include any of the large otter trawlers, fishes off southern New England and southern Georges Bank largely for younger fish of several species to be used for reduction. Fishing farther south, they also take fair quantities of scup, butterfish, fluke, and squid.

The Connecticut fleet of motor boats and small draggers also fishes for reduction plants, but additionally takes fair quantities of blackback flounder and scup.

In 1967 in the mid-Atlantic area there existed a total of 283 fish otter trawls, of which only eight were less than 5 net tons. They landed 44,238,000 pounds, including 9,485,000 pounds of silver hake (whiting), 7,800,000 pounds of various species for reduction, 6,535,000 pounds of scup, 5,477,000 pounds of yellowtail flounder, 4,930,000 pounds of fluke, 3,170,000 pounds of blackback flounder, 1,870,000 pounds of butterfish, 1,195,000 pounds of red hake, 1,140,000 pounds of squid, and 450,000 pounds of sea trout.

In the Chesapeake Bay area only 3 of 86 otter trawlers were less than 5 net tons. They landed 17,563,000 pounds, of which 6,215,000 pounds were unclassified fish for reduction. The chief species in the remainder were scup (4,630,000 pounds), fluke (2,165,000 pounds), sea bass (1,265,000 pounds), butterfish (605,000 pounds), squid (585,000 pounds), blackback flounder (575,000 pounds), striped bass (475,000 pounds), and sea robins (325,000 pounds).

In the south Atlantic in 1967 fish otter trawls were used only in North Carolina; the 128 vessels averaged 44 gross tons. They caught 13,487,000 pounds, of which 4,630,000 pounds were for reduction. The remainder included 3,770,000 pounds of flounder, 1,325,000 pounds of sea trout, 915,000 pounds of croaker, 590,000 pounds of king whiting, 635,000 pounds of sea bass, 450,000 pounds of scup, 360,000 pounds of swellfish, 350,000 pounds of butterfish, and 300,000 pounds of spot.

In the Gulf 69 otter trawlers for fish in Mississippi and Louisiana averaged 58 gross tons. An additional 28 nets reported in the statistics were presumably operated by undertonnage boats. They landed a total of 101 million pounds, of which all but a little less than 1 million pounds was used for reduction or animal food. Most if it was canned for pet food. The species consisted chiefly of croakers, spot, and cutlass fish.

In California 88 fish otter trawls operated from Santa Barbara north. Six were undertonnage boats; the remainder averaged about 37 gross tons. They landed 32,285,000 pounds, consisting of 19,370,000 pounds of flounders, 7,485,000 pounds of rockfishes, 2,590,000 pounds of fish for reduction and animal food, 1,395,000 pounds of sablefish, 705,000 pounds of lingcod, and 315,000 pounds of California halibut. This otter trawl fishery replaces the paranzella net (two-boat trawl) fishery that operated for years out of San Francisco, chiefly taking flounders around the Farallon Islands.

In Washington and Oregon 147 fish otter trawlers averaged 50 gross tons. They

Table 7-3. Catch per vessel according to area of landing by Washington and Oregon fish otter trawl in 1967 (thousands of pounds)

Species	Puget Sound	Coastal areas	Total catch
Ocean perch[1]	147	32	15,350
Flounders	129	252	25,585
Cod	93	8	9,135
Lingcod	63	23	7,135
Rockfishes[2]	74	80	11,190
Hake	14	1	1,370
Ratfish	11	0	1,025
Sharks	13	0	1,250
Skates	13	0	470
Tomcod	2	0	210
Sablefish	3	3	420
Pollock	1	0	95
AVERAGE PER BOAT	563	399	

[1]*Sebastes alutus.*
[2]Exclusive of *Sebastes alutus.*

landed a total of 76,315,000 pounds. They fished from northern California northward into Hecate Strait. The principal species were flounders, ocean perch, rockfishes, cod, and lingcod. However, the 93 Puget Sound vessels operated to a larger extent on grounds off British Columbia, extending into Hecate Strait, whereas the vessels from the coastal areas fished chiefly in more southern waters (Table 7-3).

Midwater trawls. In 1967 midwater trawls were used only in Washington. Fourteen vessels (average 74 gross tons) used nets with an average mouth width of 42 yards. They landed 27,500,000 pounds of hake.

Butterfly nets. Butterfly nets are a specialized gear used in Louisiana for catching shrimp in the shallow bayous. Each boat has a net on each side fastened to a rigid frame that is in turn fastened to a rigid beam protruding from the side of the vessel. The vessel literally pushes the twin nets (hence the term "butterfly") through the water. In 1967 22 vessels and 363 boats used 782 nets (two per boat) and landed 4,750,000 pounds of shrimp.

Small pot gear

Small pot gear includes the small variety of maze, barricade, or trap gear. With landings of 305 million pounds valued at $52 million, this gear was third in both catch and value.

All of these forms of gear require that the animal voluntarily enter an enclosed space from which it cannot readily escape, usually because of an inability to find the entrance, the disappearance of the entrance from the falling of the tide, or an inability to return against the strong current by which it entered.

These devices vary in size from small light traps easily held in one hand to the huge salmon traps with leaders over half a mile long formerly used in Alaska and Puget Sound. This discussion will concern the smaller types.

Pot gear (trap gear). Pot gear devices can be made of metal, wooden slats, cane, wire, or plastic. They may be round, cylindric, cubic, rectangular and boxlike, or flat. They may be made wholly or partially of rigid material, or they may be made entirely of webbing except for rings or rodlike supports. Some are made collapsible for ease in carrying or in storing large numbers on a small deck.

The principle is rather simple. The fish or crustacean is lured into the trap by the smell and/or sight of bait (some species will voluntarily enter unbaited pots). The bait is usually placed in a wire or web bag secured in the center of the trap. The fish or crustacean reconnoiters until it finds the entrance into the trap. (There may be more than one entrance.) The entrance is usually the truncated end of a cone that projects into the trap. Gears will be illustrated and described more fully in Chapter 8. Since the physical dimensions, type of construction, and areas fished will vary with the species sought, each pot fishery will be treated separately.

NORTHERN LOBSTER POTS. The number of lobster pots in use in Maine exceeds the number of all other types of pot gear used throughout the United States. Along the rocky coast of Maine and New Hampshire a total of 733,400 pots caught 17,205,000 pounds of northern lobsters and 1,695,000 pounds of rock crabs, *Cancer irroratus.* In southern New England a total of 156,800 pots took 4,190,000 pounds of lobsters, 71,000 pounds of rock crabs, and 6000 pounds of conchs.

In New York and New Jersey a total of only 17,800 pots caught 700,000 pounds of lobsters, 12,000 pounds of conchs, and 9000 pounds of sea bass.

SPINY LOBSTER POTS. Spiny lobster pots are used on both coasts of Florida. On the east coast they caught 1,675,000 pounds of spiny lobsters, *Panulirus argus,* and 3000 pounds of blue crabs; on the Gulf coast of Florida they took 2,655,000 pounds of spiny lobsters, 45,000 pounds of stone crabs, *Menippe mercenaria,* and 13,000 pounds of groupers. In California they took 450,000 pounds of spiny lobsters and 325,000 pounds of rock crabs.

CRAB POTS. Crab pots vary somewhat in size and shape with the region and species sought.

Green crab pots. Operated only from Maine to Rhode Island green crab pots took 65,000 pounds of green crabs, 55,000 pounds of rock crabs, and 7000 pounds of northern lobster.

Blue crab pots. Blue crab pots are used from New Jersey to Texas. They caught 95,824,000 pounds of blue crabs— 49,455,000 pounds from the Chesapeake Bay area, 21,765,000 pounds from the south Atlantic area, 23,930,000 pounds from the Gulf, and only 674,000 pounds from the mid-Atlantic area. In the Chesapeake Bay area they also caught 3,425,000 pounds of swellfish and 30,000 pounds of conchs.

Stone crab pots. Stone crab pots are used only in Florida, taking 124,000 pounds of stone crabs from the east coast and 800,000 pounds from the Gulf coast.

Dungeness crab pots. Dungeness crab pots are used from California to central Alaska for the large Dungeness crab, *Cancer*

magister. They caught 11,620,000 pounds in central and southeastern Alaska, 19,120,000 pounds in Washington and Oregon, 10,725,000 pounds in northern California, 930,000 pounds from the San Francisco area, and only 7000 pounds farther south.

King crab pots. Used only in Alaska, king crab pots took 127,715,000 pounds of king crab, *Paralithodes camtschatica.*

Snow (tanner) crab pots. Snow crab pots were used only in central and southeastern Alaska and took 120,000 pounds of snow crabs.

OCTOPUS POTS. Octopus pots took 12,000 pounds of octopus in Puget Sound and 5500 pounds in northern California.

SHRIMP POTS. Shrimp pots were used in Puget Sound, taking only 19,000 pounds. In southeastern Alaska they took only 39,000 pounds and in central Alaska 100,000 pounds.

FISH POTS. In the mid-Atlantic area fish pots are used chiefly for sea bass, taking 780,000 pounds; incidentally they captured 91,000 pounds of lobsters, 32,000 pounds of red hake, and 20,000 pounds of tautog. In Chesapeake Bay they took 300,000 pounds of sea bass plus a few lobsters and freshwater catfish. In North Carolina they caught 1,355,000 pounds of sea bass and 15,000 pounds of swellfish. The South Carolina and Georgia catch was only 58,000 pounds of sea bass.

Line gear

Line gear was fourth in 1967 both in poundage caught (700,000,000 pounds) and in value ($46 million).

Handlines. Handlines are extensively used along the Atlantic, Gulf, and Pacific coasts. Some are used for a variety of species, whereas others are used in specialized fisheries. From Maine to Massachusetts they took 113,000 pounds of smelt, *Osmerus eperlanus mordax,* principally in winter through the ice. They took 2,325,000 pounds of cod from New Jersey to Maine, 865,000 pounds of striped bass from New Hampshire to Maryland, 208,000 pounds of bluefish from Massachusetts to Maryland, and 122,000 pounds of mackerel from Massachusetts to New Jersey. Altogether from Maine to New Jersey, 10 vessels and 1240 motor boats used handlines.

In the south Atlantic states of Georgia and Florida (east coast) handlines took 918,000 pounds of red snappers and 461,000 pounds of groupers. In the Gulf of Mexico handlines are also an important gear for the offshore subtropical bank fishes, accounting for 12,847,000 pounds of various snappers, 6,928,000 pounds of groupers, and 538,000 pounds of jewfish, warsaw, and grunts. Additionally, a smaller boat fishery operating near the shore and in the estuaries took 162,000 pounds of king and Spanish mackerels, 148,000 pounds of sea trout, *Cynoscion,* and 135,000 pounds of red and black drum. Along the west coast of Florida handlines took a variety of subtropical carangids: bluefish, blue runner, crevalle, amberjack, mojarra, and permit, totaling 134,000 pounds. Of the sea breams in the same area, they took 74,000 pounds of sheepshead and 53,000 pounds of scup.

On the Pacific coast, a few handlines were used in Puget Sound, taking 16,000 pounds of rockfishes, 15,000 pounds of lingcod, and a few dogfish. However, handlines are very important in California. California has an extensive small boat handline fishery, chiefly for deep water benthic fishes, abundant on the reefs and uneven rocky bottoms of the area. They took 1,828,000 pounds of rockfishes, 167,000 pounds of lingcod, 2,401,000 pounds of sablefish, 243,000 pounds of flatfishes, 83,000 pounds of sculpin, 296,000 pounds of sea basses, and 191,000 pounds of groupers. Of the epipelagic species they took 56,000 pounds of yellowtail, 66,000 pounds of king croaker, 21,000 pounds of Pacific mackerel, 8000 pounds of pompano, and 41,000 of dogfish. The California epipelagic species cannot be accurately separated from and so are included in albacore troll gear.

Troll gear. Troll gear differs from handline gear chiefly in that the bait or lure is towed through the water. This form of gear is of little importance in New England. In Massachusetts the sole catch was 2400 pounds of bluefin tuna. In Rhode Island the total catch of 12,000 pounds was chiefly striped bass and bluefin tuna with a few bluefish.

In New Jersey troll gear took 3000 pounds of bluefish and a few striped bass. In North Carolina the sole catch was 23,000 pounds of king mackerel. On the east coast of Florida the catch totaled 1,240,000 pounds, consisting chiefly of 1,056,000 pounds of king mackerel, 74,000 pounds of Spanish mackerel, and 14,000 pounds of sea trout.

In the Gulf troll gear was used only on the west coast of Florida, with a total catch of 591,000 pounds, consisting chiefly of 247,000 pounds of king mackerel, 129,000 pounds of Spanish mackerel, 154,000 pounds of dolphin (dorado), and 43,000 pounds of sea trout.

Troll gear is of great importance, however, on the Pacific coast. Here a distinction may be made between troll gear used for tuna and for salmon.

GEAR FOR ALBACORE TUNA. Albacore are taken in large quantities by troll gear operating along the coast, often far offshore. In Washington the albacore catch was taken by 83 vessels and 4 motorboats and amounted to 1,240,000 pounds; in Oregon 715 vessels and 113 motorboats took 20,642,000 pounds. The California records do not separate the catches by albacore troll gear and the catches by vessels using live bait. The catch of both gears in California was 17,663,000 pounds of albacore; presumably the largest share was taken by troll gear. The recorded 11,555,000 pounds of skipjack and 11,305,000 pounds of yellowfin tuna taken by lines in California was presumably taken largely by the live bait vessels.

GEAR FOR SALMON. From Monterey Bay north, California salmon trollers landed 3,950,000 pounds of king salmon and

3,450,000 pounds of coho salmon. In Oregon and Washington salmon trollers landed 15,280,000 pounds of coho salmon, 3,215,000 pounds of pink salmon, 3,015,000 pounds of king salmon, 410,000 pounds of rockfishes, 315,000 pounds of lingcod, and 84,000 pounds of halibut. It will be noted that salmon trollers are usually fishing deeper and closer to the coast than albacore trollers and hence tend to catch other benthic species.

In southeastern Alaska salmon trollers took 8,470,000 pounds of salmon, of which 4,150,000 pounds were king salmon and 3,995,000 pounds were coho salmon. In central Alaska a few trollers took 230,000 pounds of salmon.

Longlines. Longline gear consists of a long main line with gangions or dropper lines at intervals, each terminating in a hook. The longline is coiled in long lengths; each such coil is kept in a wooden tub or in a triangular-shaped piece of canvas; hence each length unit is termed a "tub" or a "skate" of gear.

Longlines may be set with the baited hooks on or near the bottom, but can also be used at middepths in the water column for deep-swiming tunas and swordfish.

In 1967 in New England longlines took 6,720,000 pounds. This really comprised at least three rather distinct (and somewhat seasonal) fisheries. The smaller lobster vessels take advantage of a late spring coastal appearance of mature haddock and cod, and they took 2,550,000 pounds of cod and 2,560,000 pounds of haddock with longlines. During the fall months these small boats fish in deeper water, up to 80 to 100 fm, for white hake (720,000 pounds), cusk (339,000 pounds), halibut (127,000 pounds), and pollock (108,000 pounds). Some of the vessels fish at middepths in summer and took 346,000 pounds of swordfish and 13,000 pounds of bluefin tuna. A few of the motor boats fish in the bays for winter flounders (70,000 pounds) and a few striped bass.

The few longlines in New York and New Jersey took principally cod (105,000 pounds), swordfish (260,000 pounds), bluefin tuna (32,000 pounds), and sharks (6000 pounds).

In Virginia longlines took 145,000 pounds of swordfish, 23,000 pounds of tuna, and 4500 pounds of striped bass.

In the south Atlantic area longlines were used principally in fresh waters for catfish and bullheads, but on the east coast of Florida heavy longlines took 1,310,000 pounds of sharks.

Most of the longlines in the Gulf are used for freshwater catfish and bullheads, but they took 35,000 pounds of sea catfish. In Texas they caught 970,000 pounds of black and red drum, 407,000 pounds of spotted sea trout, 45,000 pounds of sheepshead, and 15,000 pounds of flounders.

Crab trotlines. Crab trotlines are specialized longlines without hooks but baited at intervals for taking blue crabs. In the Chesapeake Bay area they took 13,650,000 pounds, and in the Carolinas they took another 2,965,000 pounds. In the Gulf they are used chiefly in Louisiana and caught 2,420,000 pounds of blue crabs.

Entangling nets

During 1967 entangling nets were fifth in volume of catch, with 167 million pounds, but only sixth in value of catch, with $31 million. Entangling nets rely on the fish swimming into a net of fine mesh that the fish does not perceive either because of darkness or because of turbidity of the water. There are two types; the gill net is of such a size that after the fish thrusts its head into a mesh it cannot withdraw because the mesh catches on the opercle. Gill nets are highly selective for the size of fish caught because a small fish can swim through and too large a fish cannot get its head into the mesh.

Trammel nets are composed of two, or usually three, layers of netting. The outside nets have very large mesh through which the fish swims readily. The inside net, sandwiched between the coarse mesh layers, is of very fine light mesh. The fish in swimming pushes a pocket of the inner fine net through a mesh of the coarse net and is then confined in a fine mesh bag.

Gill nets. Gill nets differ chiefly in the size of mesh used for different species and sizes of fish and in the mode of operation.

ANCHOR, SET, OR STAKE GILL NETS. In the anchor, set, or stake mode of operation, the gill nets are placed in a certain position and the fish must swim into them. In New England the anchor or "sink" gill net is used out of Gloucester, Massachusetts, and Portland, Maine, for taking bank fishes. The nets are anchored on the bottom. In 1967 there were 29 anchor gill net operators who took 960,000 pounds of pollock, 1,810,000 pounds of cod, 145,000 pounds of haddock, 145,000 pounds of white hake, 75,000 pounds of winter flounder, 100,000 pounds of dogfish, and some miscellaneous species, the total being 4,160,000 pounds.

DRIFT GILL NETS. Drift gill nets are employed extensively throughout the world. In fisheries for anadromous species they are used in wide stretches of streams, drifting seaward with the current. This movement of the net makes it more difficult to avoid by fish migrating upstream. They are also used in the open sea where large vessels may put out miles of gill net.

Where the records permit, gill nets used for particular species have been kept separate.

Common drift gill nets. In New England from New Hampshire to Connecticut 88 gill nets landed only 165,000 pounds: 140,000 pounds of mackerel, 16,000 pounds of alewives, and a few of other species. In New Jersey and Delaware 49 drift gill nets accounted for 565,000 pounds, including 180,000 pounds of bluefish, 170,000 pounds of mackerel, 140,000 pounds of menhaden, and 22,000 pounds of white perch. In Chesapeake Bay 857 drift gill nets landed 2,570,000 pounds. Of this total, 625,000 pounds were mackerel, 950,000 pounds were striped bass, 355,000 pounds were spot, 262,000 pounds were white perch, 125,000 pounds were black drum, and 95,000 pounds were sharks.

In North Carolina 19 drift gill nets landed 54,000 pounds: 34,000 pounds of bluefish and assorted species. In the Gulf 22 drift gill nets off west Florida caught a total of 155,000 pounds, including 115,000 pounds of Spanish and king mackerel, 33,000 pounds of pompano, and 5000 pounds of common sturgeon.

In California 104 drift gill nets plus 16 trammel nets (catch recorded together) landed 2,765,000 pounds. The difference between the two environments is illustrated by the catches in central and southern California, and these data are presented in Table 7-4.

Obviously the various gill nets used differed considerably, from the huge mesh, heavy twine used for sharks to the fine mesh, light nets used for herring and smelt.

Smelt drift gill nets. In Washington and Oregon 80 smelt drift nets in the Columbia River caught 353,000 pounds of smelt (eulachon).

Shad drift gill nets. In coastal Oregon 36 shad drift gill nets took 375,000 pounds of shad and 17,000 pounds of striped bass.

Salmon drift gill nets. Salmon drift gill nets are treated separately both because of their great importance and because they are seldom operated far from the influence of large rivers. In Washington and Oregon 1883 nets landed 4,952,000 pounds of king salmon, of which 80% was from the Columbia River. Of 5,177,000 pounds of coho salmon, 72% was also from the Columbia River. Of 3,607,000 pounds of sockeye salmon, 98% was taken in Puget Sound as well as 100% of the 1,809,000 pounds of pink salmon. The Columbia River contributed 836,000 pounds of shad and 312,000 pounds of steelhead as well as 196,000 of the 347,000 pounds of sturgeon.

In southeastern Alaska 321 salmon drift nets landed 6,528,000 pounds of salmon, which included 20,000 pounds of steelhead trout. In southeastern Alaska they are operated chiefly on the Stikine River flats where

Table 7-4. Catches to illustrate environmental difference by species in central and southern California using gill or trammel nets

	San Francisco to Santa Barbara (pounds)	San Pedro to San Diego (pounds)
Flounders, general	61,000	0
Sea herring	38,000	0
California halibut	280,000	57,000
Sharks	248,000	212,000
King croaker	83,000	189,000
Perch	29,000	43,000
White sea bass	167,000	946,000
Barracuda	0	257,000
Smelt (Atherinidae)	0	48,000
Black sea bass	0	30,000
Flying fish	0	23,000
TOTAL CATCH	930,000	1,835,000

the muddy waters of the Stikine hide the nets from the wary salmon. Night gillnetting of salmon is not always successful even in clear waters because bioluminescent organisms make the net appear as a shimmering curtain.

In central Alaska 1197 drift salmon nets were used to take 16,000,000 pounds of salmon. Of this 9,583,000 pounds were the prized sockeye. The Copper River flats form the largest gill net area in central Alaska, but the nets are also used near a number of smaller streams.

In western Alaska 2126 drift nets took 33,993,000 pounds of fish, of which 33,723,000 pounds were salmon and 269,000 pounds were sea herring (obviously taken with a few smaller mesh nets). Sockeye constituted 76% of the salmon. Salmon gill nets take nearly all of the western Alaska salmon catch, largely in Bristol Bay in and near the mouths of Nushagak, Kvichak, Naknek, Egegik, and Ugashik Rivers.

RUNAROUND GILL NETS. Runaround gill nets are a specialized type of gill nets that fishermen use chiefly in shoal water. A long gill net is laid entirely around a school of fish, and they then attempt to frighten the fish. Since the net sinks to the bottom in the shoal water, the frantic fish dash into the gill net.

In the mid-Atlantic region 45 runaround gill nets captured 617,000 pounds, of which 334,000 pounds were bluefish and 237,000 pounds were striped bass. In North Carolina 72 runaround nets caught 662,000 pounds, of which 212,000 pounds were black mullet, 188,000 pounds were bluefish, 114,000 pounds were spot, and 48,000 pounds were weakfish.

On the east coast of Florida runaround gill nets are an important gear; 303 runaround nets took 11,264,000 pounds, of which 2,995,000 pounds were mullets, 3,567,000 pounds were king and Spanish mackerels, 1,083,000 pounds were bluefish, 795,000 pounds were spot, 132,000 pounds were king whiting, 124,000 pounds were black and red drum, 470,000 pounds were weakfish, and 122,000 pounds were sheepshead.

In the Gulf 1044 runaround nets on the west coast of Florida, plus 10 in Alabama and Mississippi, landed 28,134,000 pounds, of which 16,517,000 pounds were mullet, 7,074,000 pounds were king and Spanish mackerels, 1,660,000 pounds were sea trout, 236,000 pounds were bluefish, 239,000 pounds were blue runner, 294,000 pounds were black and red drum, 215,000 pounds were crevalle, 101,000 pounds were alewives, 155,000 pounds were spot, 88,000 pounds were sheepshead, 91,000 pounds were tenpounder, 79,000 pounds were pompano, and 69,000 pounds were mojarra.

Trammel nets. On the east coast of Florida 84 trammel nets landed 372,000 pounds, of which 171,000 pounds were pompano, 91,000 pounds were sea trout, 51,000 pounds were spot, and 25,000 pounds were mullet.

In the Gulf 638 trammel nets operated in 1967. They took 12,061,000 pounds: 119,000 pounds of freshwater species and 11,942,000 pounds of marine fish. Over half, 6,761,000 pounds, were mullet, 2 million pounds were sea trout, 1,570,000 pounds were black and red drums, 587,000 pounds were pompano, 250,000 pounds were sheepshead, 106,000 pounds were croaker, 134,000 pounds were king and Spanish mackerels, 65,000 pounds were king whiting, 50,000 pounds were spot, and 43,000 pounds were flounders.

The catches of 16 California trammel nets were not separated from drift net catches.

Dredges

Dredges ranked sixth in 1967 in volume of catch (125 million pounds), but fifth in dockside value ($41 million). Dredges are a rigid rectangular metal frame to which is attached a holding bag, usually made chiefly of metal rings. One or both of the long bars of the frame may have teeth for digging mollusks out of the bottom.

Oyster dredges. Oyster dredges vary somewhat in the width of the frame to fit the power of the towing vessel; most commonly they measure from 3 feet to a maximum of about 6 feet across the mouth.

Clam dredges. Clam dredges differ from oyster dredges by having longer teeth to dig out buried clams, by having a longer and larger bag, by using heavy weights to increase the digging ability, and often by having a hose connection to pump jets of water toward the bottom just ahead of the dredge.

Sea scallop dredges. Sea scallop dredges are very large dredges, about 9 to 12 feet across the mouth; the scraping bar has no teeth but the angle is adjustable. The bag is chiefly made of heavy metal rings, except for the top, which, to save weight, is of sash cord. They are usually used on the offshore banks by motor vessels. The larger vessels will tow two dredges. In the cold waters of Maine sea scallops are found in the brackish estuaries (where the bay scallops live in areas farther south). As a consequence, in Maine sea scallop fishing is largely a small boat fishery. The most important sea scallop fishery on the offshore banks uses large draggers and is centered in New Bedford.

Crab scrapes. Crab scrapes are small nets about 1 yard in width on a rigid frame used in very shallow water, especially in areas with vegetation, to capture blue crabs while they are molting. In Maryland and Virginia during 1967 there were 161 small boats using 322 scrapes. They landed 1,905,000 pounds: 1,800,000 pounds of soft-shell blue crabs, 130,000 pounds of hard-shell blue crabs, and 3000 pounds of terrapin.

Large fixed gears

Large fixed gears have suffered a great decline over the years as fisherman using mobile gear have accused the owners of fixed gear of monopolizing fixed sites and have often succeeded politically in having fixed gear eliminated. As late as 1945 they still produced 500 million pounds annually, which by 1967 had shrunk to 105 million pounds, ranking the gear seventh in volume but only ninth in value, with a mere $4.5 million.

Large fixed traps include weirs, floating traps, and pound nets. All operate on the principle of fish striking a barrier and following along it through a narrow entrance into a large enclosure. Some of these traps are very ingenious, leading the fish into successively smaller enclosures (with narrower entrances) until the fish are confined in a space from which they can be readily removed.

Brush weir. The simplest large fixed gear is the brush weir. The lead from shore is usually made of branches stuck into the soft bottom. The heart may also be made of brush. The last pot or enclosure from which the fish are removed by seining may be made of webbing.

There are 91 weirs in Maine that took 8,145,000 pounds of herring and 55,000 pounds of mackerel. Five weirs in New Hampshire took 60,000 pounds of alewives, 12,000 pounds of smelt, and a few eels. One brush weir in Puget Sound took 117,000 pounds of sea herring. In Puget Sound these "brush" weirs are really made of wire and are used to supply fresh herring bait to halibut vessels. The "brush" is evergreen branches suspended in the pound, which serves as a conservation measure because the herring spawn adheres to these branches.

Floating traps. Floating traps are fairly small traps usually fished in protected bays, especially river mouths. At one time there were a number in the lower Penobscot River taking Atlantic salmon. In Maine they took 295,000 pounds of mackerel, 11,000 pounds of sea herring, and a few Atlantic salmon, smelt, and sturgeon. In Massachusetts they caught 970,000 pounds of mackerel, 45,000 pounds of pollock, and small quantities of other species. In Rhode Island they landed over 7 million pounds, incuding 5,175,000 pounds of scup, 590,000 pounds of mackerel, 112,000 pounds of cod, 90,000 pounds of butterfish, 60,000 pounds of bluefish, 480,000 pounds of squid, 69,000 pounds of striped bass, 125,000 pounds of sea robins, and 50,000 pounds of silver hake.

Pound nets. Pound nets are larger than the floating traps previously mentioned and, being supported by pilings, can be fished in exposed locations that are difficult for most floating traps.

In New England 30 pound nets were used

for marine species; these were employed only in Massachusetts, chiefly on Cape Cod. They took 3,560,000 pounds: 960,000 pounds of sea herring, 870,000 pounds of squid, 750,000 pounds of mackerel, 490,000 pounds of scup, 300,000 pounds of bluefin tuna, 70,000 pounds of pollock, 35,000 pounds of striped bass, 22,000 pounds of bonito, and smaller amounts of bluefish, butterfish, sea bass, and shad.

In the mid-Atlantic area 102 pound nets caught 4,620,000 pounds, of which 2,190,000 pounds were menhaden. Some of the more valuable items were 135,000 pounds of striped bass, 65,000 pounds of swellfish (all in New York), 100,000 pounds of bluefish (all in New Jersey), 225,000 pounds of butterfish, 15,000 pounds of tuna, 21,000 pounds of flounders, 39,000 pounds of tautog, 16,000 pounds of scup, and 5000 pounds of sturgeon.

In the Chesapeake Bay area 1062 pound nets caught 51,645,000 pounds of fish. This included 25,800,000 pounds of alewives, 20,340,000 pounds of menhaden, 3,240,000 pounds of swellfish, 870,000 pounds of striped bass, 1,275,000 pounds of shad, 380,000 pounds of butterfish, 1,870,000 pounds of spot, 1,015,000 pounds of sea herring, 400,000 pounds of flounders, 405,000 pounds of weakfish (sea trout), 25,000 pounds of mackerels, 300,000 pounds of white perch, 25,000 pounds of scup, and other species.

In North Carolina 849 pound nets landed 13,490,000 pounds. This included 3,770,000 pounds of flounders, 1,325,000 pounds of sea trout, 915,000 pounds of croaker, 590,000 pounds of king whiting, 635,000 pounds of sea bass, 450,000 pounds of scup, 350,000 pounds of butterfish, 360,000 pounds of swellfish, 300,000 pounds of spot, and various other species.

Salmon traps. Salmon traps once took the major share of the salmon catch from the Shumagin Islands to Puget Sound but they have been legislated almost out of existence.

In Puget Sound two pile-driven salmon

traps operated on Indian reservations took only 90,000 pounds of salmon. In southeastern Alaska, four floating salmon traps caught only 57,000 pounds.

Fish wheels. Fish wheels are a very specialized and efficient form of gear in which large paddle wheels covered with webbing, revolved by the force of the current of a large river, capture salmon swimming upstream during the spawning migration. They originated on the Columbia River where they were built by the pioneers. They were subsequently built on the Taku River in southeastern Alaska to take king salmon and on the Yukon River to take salmon to dry for winter feed for sledge dogs. They were legislated out of the Columbia River by the more numerous votes of the gill-netters. They survive now on the Yukon River where eight fish wheels took 22,000 pounds of salmon.

Reef nets. A very specialized gear, reef nets were developed by the Indians of Puget Sound to take the salmon bound for major rivers, especially the Fraser River. They took advantage of long reefs perpendicular to the shore with dense growths of giant kelp, *Macrocystis*. They cut a channel across the reef through the kelp. A blanket-shaped net was suspended between two small boats (originally yellow cedar dugout canoes). Ropes at intervals led the salmon over the net. Lookouts on the masts of the boats signaled when to raise the net. In 1967 a total of 63 reef nets took 1,280,000 pounds of salmon.

Haul and stop seines

Haul and stop seines operated along the shores doubtless antedate the operation of nets from boats. Although small haul (or beach) seines can be operated without the use of a boat to lay the net, this is unusual except for recreation. In many places haul seines are semipermanent installations that operate, whenever fish are in the vicinity, from a fixed point, and the hauling ropes are brought in with mechanical or steam winches. At Sand Island in the Columbia River haul seines for salmon were operated for a number of years with the hauling done by teams of horses. The seines are a wall of webbing with corks on the top line, or corkline, and lead weights on the lead line. The net is hung with plenty of slack so that it billows out while being hauled, which helps to keep the fish from finding holes under the net or leaping the corkline. Ordinarily they are operated in shoal water, but for some benthic species, especially flatfishes, they are sometimes used in water sufficiently deep so that the corkline is submerged until the net is partially retrieved.

Stop nets and seines. Stop nets and seines are a form of gear peculiar to the New England herring fisheries. When schools of the small herring suitable for canning enter a bay or bight of the coast, a long wall of webbing is stretched across the mouth, thus impounding the herring in a natural enclosure from which they can be seined at leisure and sold to the canneries. In this fishery one cannot easily define a single unit of fishing effort. It may take several seines joined together to imprison herring in a bight with a wide mouth.

The stop net and seine operation is a small boat fishery. Sixteen small motor vessels, which averaged 16 gross tons, and 86 motor boats under 5 net tons were used in 1967; a total of 19,710,000 pounds of herring were sold.

Shoal water hand gear

Shoal water hand gear includes the hand-operated gears, rakes, and tongs that are used from small craft in relatively shoal water. A distinct separation has been made between this shoal water vessel fishery and the intertidal zone fishery that depends on boats only for transportation.

Rakes. In determining the number of rakes operated, the statistics for "casual" fisherman have been divided by 3. In New England 597 rakes in 1967 took 6,013,400 pounds: 5,060,000 pounds of Irish moss, 865,000 pounds of hard clams, 40,000 pounds of soft clams, 31,000 pounds of mussels, and 15,000 pounds of sea urchins.

In the mid-Atlantic area 1278 rakes collected 3,050,000 pounds, including 2,760,000 pounds of hard clams, 265,000 pounds of soft clams, and 25,000 pounds of mussels. They also took 3000 pounds of terrapin and 12,000 pounds of other turtles.

In Virginia 100 rakes collected 182,000 pounds of hard clams. In the south Atlantic area 176 rakes took 185,000 pounds: 163,000 pounds of hard clams and 21,000 pounds of oysters.

Tongs

OYSTER TONGS. Oyster tongs are operated from small boats, seldom in water over 20 feet deep, except for a small number of patent tongs that do not have handles.

CLAM TONGS. Clam tongs are essentially the same as oyster tongs, but they usually have an extra bar around the inner concave side of each half of the rake to keep the smaller and smoother clams from sliding out.

Diving outfits. Diving outfits are in reality a subtidal extension of hand collection, operating with small craft.

Intertidal hand gear

Hoes. In evaluating the actual number of participants in the hoe fishery, the number of "casual" fishermen has been divided by 3. In New England 1748 persons took 4,165,000 pounds of soft clams, 800,000 pounds of sandworms, and 750,000 pounds of bloodworms. The last two items are for a highly specialized bait trade, principally in New York City, for sportfishermen. They also took 370,000 pounds of mussels and a total of 8000 pounds of various clams. In New Jersey 22 hoes took 60,000 pounds of soft clams.

Forks. A very minor gear, statistics for forks were only recorded in Massachusetts where 17 forks took 31,600 pounds: 22,700 pounds of sea mussels and 8900 pounds of oysters.

Shovels. Shovels are used principally for taking fast-burrowing clams. In California three shovels took only 600 pounds of hard clams. In Washington and Oregon 1958 shovels took 486,000 pounds: 224,000 pounds of razor clams and 262,000 pounds

of hard clams. In central Alaska 58 shovels took 60,000 pounds of razor clams.

Hand collection. Hand collection is done chiefly in the intertidal zones for mollusks and crustaceans. There is also a noncommercial sport fishery in Maine in which the anadromous smelt are caught by hand as they migrate into the brooks to spawn. In enumerating the fishing units for this curious type of fishing gear, the number of "casual" fishermen has been divided by 3. In 1967 in New England 82 persons took 54,000 pounds of periwinkles and cockles and 5000 pounds of conchs. In New Jersey and Delaware in 1967 468 persons picked up 855,000 pounds of hard clams and 50,000 pounds of soft clams. In the Chesapeake Bay area 96 persons took 135,000 pounds of hard clams, 16,000 pounds of soft blue crabs, and 1000 pounds of conchs.

In the south Atlantic area 341 persons picked up 785,000 pounds of oysters and 17,000 pounds of hard clams. In the Gulf 90 persons picked up 90,000 pounds, including 88,000 pounds of oysters and a few hard clams and bay scallops. On the Pacific coast oysters picked up by hand in California (17 persons) are included under the statistics for tongs, and oysters picked up in Washington and Oregon (280 persons) are included under the data for dredges.

In southeastern Alaska 2050 fishermen picked up 380,000 pounds of kelp with adherent herring eggs (worth over $1/pound at dockside in 1967), 45,000 pounds of oysters, and 4500 pounds of abalones. In central Alaska 100 persons collected 22,000 pounds of kelp with herring eggs.

Fyke or hoop nets. Although akin to pot gear, fyke or hoop nets are separated because they are usually set without bait. Sometimes they are set in a stream so that fish will enter while following the current, and sometimes they are set in still water with a pair of wings to lead fish into the entrance. They may be of rigid material, but they are usually a cylinder of wire or webbing supported by metal rings. Chiefly a freshwater gear, they are used to a limited extent in salt water, especially for taking flounders in shoal bays. In such use they are set on the bottom completely submerged and held in place by anchors; the wings are kept vertical by leads and floats.

Bag nets. Bag nets are used in Maine and New Hampshire to catch smelt, *Osmerus eperlanus mordax,* in the estuaries of the larger rivers. An excellent illustration of a bag net set under the ice on the Penobscot River is shown in Atkins' (1887) article. This fishery is carried on during the fall and winter months, at which time these anadromous fishes are congregated in the fresh and brackish waters of the estuaries. In 1967 in Maine and New Hampshire 22 bag nets captured 75,000 pounds of smelt.

Although the bag nets in New England are fished only for smelt and according to Atkins they are only 25 to 30 feet wide, the bag nets used in North Carolina are 25 yards wide and are fished from small motor boats. The 118 bag nets used in North Carolina in 1967 caught 335,000 pounds, of which 315,000 pounds were shrimp and 18,000 pounds were blue crab.

Spears. A very ancient gear, spears were used by all primitive peoples and still survive in certain minor situations. In New Hampshire and Massachusetts 71 spears took 29,000 pounds of eels. In New York 10 spears took 49,000 pounds of eels and 1000 pounds of fluke. In the south Atlantic area 102 spears captured 62,000 pounds of flounders and 1500 pounds of mullet. In the Gulf 183 spears took 65,000 pounds of flounders.

Harpoons. Harpoons are similar to spears in that they are thrust or thrown into the animal. However, harpoon heads become detached from the shaft after throwing. The head is so made that when the attached line is pulled the head tends to turn so that it remains firmly anchored in the flesh.

In New England harpoons captured 295,000 pounds of swordfish and 116,000 pounds of bluefin tuna. In California harpoons landed 305,000 pounds of swordfish.

Brush traps. Brush traps are merely brush suspended along the banks of canals or bayous to entice blue crabs to seek their shelter while shedding. In Louisiana 48 motor boats produced 52,000 pounds of soft-shell crabs and 7000 pounds of freshwater shrimp.

Drop dip nets. Drop dip nets are a cross between a dip net and a pot. The net on one or two hoops is left on the bottom with some bait; after a time it is lifted out quickly on a line.

The same term is applied in South Carolina to 100 nets that took 2,802,000 pounds of alewives, but this is not the same net as used in the Gulf.

Along the west coast of Florida 128 nets took 6000 pounds of spiny lobsters. In Louisiana 9952 drop dip nets (101 motor boats) took 575,000 pounds of crabs plus a few freshwater crawfish.

ECONOMICS OF FISHERIES BY TYPES OF GEAR AND VESSELS

The summary given in the official statistics and my summary prepared from the component parts of the official data differ considerably. In Table 7-1 all of the effort data shown in parentheses are considered to be duplications (as indicated in the remarks column) and consequently do not enter into my totals.

A comparison between my summary and the official summary is shown in Table 7-5. Even after removing all indicated and suspected duplication I have accounted for about 37% more fishermen, about 5% fewer vessels, and about 2% fewer motor boats (but the official total also includes "accessory" motor boats).

These discrepancies in the data indicate that caution must be exercised in reaching conclusions concerning the economics of the fishery based thereon. For instance, it is well known that under the present quota system of regulation the halibut fishery is highly seasonal, so the great majority of the halibut vessels also engage in other fisheries. But which fisheries? When? For how long? Obviously fishermen do not make their total living from 1 or 2 months of

Table 7-5. Comparison of my summary (Table 7-1) with the official summary

Item	My summary[1]	Official summary	Difference +	Difference −
Number of vessels (fishing)	15,967	12,482	3,485	
Total gross tons (vessels)	567,907	478,184	89,723	
Average gross tons	35.3	38.3		3.0
Motorboats (fishing)	54,388			839
Motorboats (including accessory)		55,227		
Total number of fishermen	124,418	118,979	5,439	
Fishermen on vessels	46,185	48,133		1,948
Fishermen on boats				
Regular (including shore)		43,676		
Casual (including shore)		27,170		
Total on boats	67,985[2]	70,846		2,861
Fishermen in noncraft fisheries	10,248[3]	?	10,248	
All boat and shore fishermen	78,233	70,846	7,387	
All boat and shore fishermen[4]	78,233	57,261[5]	20,972	

[1]After removal of all indicated and suspected duplication.
[2]Excluding one half of casual fisherman.
[3]Excluding two thirds of casual fishermen in intertidal and minor noncraft gears.
[4]"Casual" fishermen of the official statistics are divided by 2, since they are by definition fishing less than 50% of the time.
[5]Excluding one half of casual fishermen to approach my basis.

fishing. Some engage in other fisheries; some are otherwise employed and use seasonal fishing as a means of supplementing their income.

Since there is duplication and uncertainty about some of the data, I have attempted in Table 7-6 to choose examples of fisheries least subject to these imperfections in data. In Table 7-6 the catch and value columns for each fishery include the catches and values of minor fisheries utilizing the effort data (numbers of craft and of fishermen) that are presumably duplicated, as shown in Table 7-1. Unfortunately there are many fisheries in which the range of sizes of fishing craft is considerable. I attempted to discount this to the extent possible by showing the average gross tonnage of the fishing craft in each fishery.

Table 7-7 summarizes data for the boat and vessel fisheries; they do tend to give a picture of the fisheries despite the inconsistencies in the source data. Obviously the values given in the table for the catch per vessel and per fishermen are low for several reasons: (1) the duplication of numbers of vessels and fishermen engaged in two or more seasonal fisheries cannot be removed from the source data as presented, (2) the averaging of the dockside landings of fishermen on motor boats and vessels does not take cognizance of the differences in efficiency or investment, and (3) the dockside value gives little or no clue to actual earnings, which depend on the method of payment. Each fishery tends to differ in percentage of earnings used for expenses and for vessel amortization. In some cases fishermen are entrepreneurs sharing in the earnings; in others they are wage earners.

From Table 7-7 it is clear that the inshore fisheries of boats and small vessels are fully as important as those conducted by the larger vessels. These boat and small vessel fisheries have never enjoyed the prestige or political advantage of the larger vessel fisheries, probably stemming from their lack of organization. They operate from many small and widely scattered points, whereas the larger vessels operate from larger and fewer ports. Also, because of the large investment in individual vessels, many of the larger

Text continued on p. 159.

Table 7-6. Analysis of craft-dependent U. S. fisheries in 1967 by size of craft

Fishery	Fishing craft		Average gross tons		Motor boats (%)	Catch (thousands of pounds)	Value (thousands of dollars)	Total gross tons	No. of fishermen
	Boats	Vessels	All craft	Vessels					
Haul seines, long (N. C.)	58	—	5.00	—	100	3,190	245	290	223
Purse seines, striped bass (N. C.)	2	—	5.00	—	100	52	10	10	5
Handlines, boats (Ga.-Texas)	1,354	—	5.00	—	100	2,040	284	6,870	1,360
Dredges, bay scallops (Me.-Fla.)	872	—	5.00	—	100	1,277	1,192	4,360	872
Crab trotlines (La.)	518	—	5.00	—	100	2,422	178	2,590	519
Longlines, fish (Texas estuaries)	118	—	5.00	—	100	1,457	293	590	113
Tongs, oysters (Gulf)	1,715	1	5.00	10.0	100	8,608	2,988	8,585	1,993
Haul seines, fish (Calif.)	5	—	5.00	—	100	666	69	25	12
Crab pound nets (Va.)	367	8	5.04	7.0	98	2,379	335	1,891	375
Pots, lobster (Me.-N. J.)	5,547	58	5.07	12.0	99	33,702	19,731	28,431	5,605
Tongs, hard clams (Mass.-N. C.)	2,972	88	5.07	7.4	97	10,361	8,314	15,514	3,060
Hooks, sponges (Fla.)	71	3	5.11	7.7	96	45	141	378	74
Crab trotlines (Md.-S. C.)	2,753	101	5.13	8.6	96	16,614	1,125	14,634	3,100
Tongs, oysters (Mass.-Fla.)	6,216	548	5.24	8.0	92	18,050	11,866	35,464	7,439
Trammel nets (east Fla.-Texas)	808	29	5.31	14.0	97	13,080	4,143	4,446	1,008
Pots, blue crab (N. J.-Texas)	3,084	377	5.33	8.0	89	100,873	7,308	18,436	4,277
Gill nets, set and drift (Atlantic)	3,789	335	5.36	9.4	92	21,405	2,212	22,103	4,474
Crab scrapes (Chesapeake Bay)	138	23	5.43	8.0	86	2,113	701	874	161
Gill nets, salmon (Pacific)	8,441	654	5.44	11.1	93	93,541	20,008	49,470	9,886
Haul seines (N. Y.-east Fla.)	450	53	5.53	10.0	89	17,853	1,309	2,780	1,390
Gill nets, runaround (Fla.)	1,261	98	5.65	14.0	93	39,408	4,118	7,677	1,930
Butterfly nets, shrimp (La.)	363	22	5.69	17.0	94	4,571	1,090	2,189	711
Haul seines (Gulf)	160	18	6.01	15.0	90	13,257	1,037	1,070	543
TOTAL BOAT FISHERIES	41,062	2,416	5.26	9.7	94	406,964	88,697	228,677	49,130
Pots, spiny lobster (Calif.)	125	57	6.04	8.3	69	1,145	537	1,099	416
Diving outfits, abalone (Calif.)	248	41	6.84	18.0	86	885	860	1,978	609
Pots, sea bass (N. Y.-S. C.)	247	70	7.44	16.0	78	2,651	507	2,358	388
Pots, spiny lobster (Fla.)	125	57	7.65	15.0	73	4,405	2,823	4,040	934
Dredges, soft clams (Md.)	130	90	8.27	13.0	59	6,632	1,846	1,820	407
Trammel and gill nets (Calif.)	71	65	10.30	16.1	52	2,749	553	1,401	356

Dredges, oysters (Gulf and Atlantic)	741	692	10.46	16.3	52	32,794	19,260	14,999	3,428
Otter trawls, scallops (south Atlantic)	0	23	11.00	11.0	0	1,425	315	253	68
Haul seines, salmon (Northwest)	0	12	11.08	11.1	0	254	60	133	36
Troll, salmon and albacore (Pacific)	4,031	3,447	11.50	19.1	54	78,528	23,710	86,032	14,191
Gill nets, sink (New England)	20	9	11.83	27.0	69	4,305	308	343	69
Purse seines, Spanish mackerel (Fla.)	5	2	11.85	29.0	71	720	75	83	18
Otter trawls, crabs (south Atlantic)	235	179	12.22	21.7	57	12,038	614	5,060	512
Diving outfits, sponges (west Fla.)	0	9	16.00	16.0	0	26	304	144	58
Dredges, hard clams (Mass.-Va.)	47	89	17.22	26.3	35	7,033	3,176	2,342	317
Dredges, oysters (Pacific)	5	30	18.71	21.0	14	7,420	3,082	655	77
TOTAL BOAT AND SMALL VESSEL FISHERIES	6,030	4,872	11.26	19.0	55	163,010	58,030	122,740	21,884
Purse seines, salmon (Pacific)	351	871	20.29	26.5	29	87,529	13,159	24,795	6,596
Otter trawl, shrimp (Gulf and south Atlantic)	5,738	3,859	21.15	45.2	60	241,352	98,374	203,002	16,212
Purse seines, herring (New England)	27	12	23.77	66.0	69	40,529	932	927	162
Beam trawls, shrimp (Puget Sound-Alaska)	1	21	24.41	25.3	5	2,739	50	537	65
Dredges, surf clams (N. J.)	121	103	25.23	49.0	54	58,558	5,205	5,652	362
Longlines, halibut (Pacific)	56	253	27.93	33.0	16	42,655	8,853	8,629	1,063
TOTAL BOAT AND MEDIUM VESSEL FISHERIES	6,294	5,119	21.34	41.4	55	473,362	126,573	243,542	24,460
Handlines, vessels (Ga.-Texas)	0	448	32.21	32.2	0	22,123	5,687	14,429	2,038
Purse seines, anchovy-mackerel (Calif.)	0	134	35.00	35.0	0	125,864	2,479	4,690	938
Otter trawls, shrimp (New England and Pacific)	45	165	35.29	43.5	21	58,556	3,721	7,410	574
Otter trawls, fish (except New England)	89	793	36.09	39.6	10	312,397	16,707	31,833	1,802
Pots, crab (Alaska and Calif.)	95	732	40.82	45.5	11	170,395	21,353	33,762	2,923
TOTAL MEDIUM VESSEL FISHERIES	229	2,272	36.83	40.1	9	689,335	49,947	92,124	8,275
Live bait, tuna (Pacific)	0	191	60.45	60.5	0	20,223	4,120	11,546	1,231
Longlines, fish (north Atlantic)	0	29	62.00	62.0	0	7,631	1,057	1,798	132
Otter trawls, fish (New England)	97	539	63.31	85.3	15	464,526	34,275	40,267	3,010
Dredges, sea scallops (Me.-N. C.)	4	117	109.36	112.8	3	10,169	7,626	13,223	1,228
TOTAL LARGE MEDIUM VESSEL FISHERIES	101	876	68.41	75.7	10	502,547	47,078	66,834	5,601
Purse seines, menhaden (Atlantic)	0	55	242.36	242.4	0	448,536	5,780	13,330	969
Purse seines, tuna (Atlantic and Pacific)	0	143	293.31	293.3	0	247,449	29,961	41,943	1,602
Purse seines, menhaden (Gulf)	0	84	333.90	333.9	0	707,716	8,606	28,050	1,440
TOTAL LARGE VESSEL FISHERIES	0	282	295.47	295.5	0	1,403,701	44,347	83,323	4,011
TOTAL ALL CRAFT	53,716	15,837	12.03	35.9	77	3,638,919	414,672	837,240	113,361

Continued.

Table 7-7. Compilation of craft-dependent fisheries (from Tables 7-1 and 7-6)

	Average gross tons		Catch (thousands of pounds)			Value (dollars)			Vessel fisheries (%)	
	All craft	Vessels	Per 10 gross tons	Per craft	Per man	Per 10 gross tons	Per craft	Per man	Catch	Value
Fisheries by vessel size										
Boats	5.3	9.7	17.80	9.36	8.28	3,879	2,040	1,805	11.18	21.39
Boats and small vessels	11.3	19.0	13.28	14.95	17.45	4,728	5,323	2,652	4.48	13.99
Boats and medium vessels	21.3	41.4	19.44	41.48	19.35	5,197	11,090	5,175	13.01	30.52
Medium vessels	36.8	40.1	74.83	275.62	83.30	5,421	19,971	6,036	18.94	12.04
Large medium vessels	68.4	75.7	75.19	514.38	89.72	7,044	48,186	8,405	13.81	11.35
Large vessels	295.5	295.5	168.47	4,977.66	349.96	5,322	295,471	11,056	38.57	10.69
TOTAL	12.0	35.9	43.46	52.32	32.10	4,953	5,962	3,658	99.99	99.98
Fisheries by gear										
Purse seines	71.1	85.6	125.76	893.73	121.72	5,123	36,410	4,959	41.72	14.18
Towed nets	23.9	46.0	37.77	90.17	47.80	5,334	12,736	6,752	31.96	37.66
Small pot gear	8.0	28.3	33.88	27.00	20.44	5,755	4,586	3,473	8.88	12.59
Line gear	11.0	23.0	13.48	14.87	8.34	3,111	3,433	1,924	5.79	11.14
Entangling nets	5.5	11.3	19.40	10.64	9.32	3,591	1,970	1,726	4.86	7.51
Dredges	13.7	29.2	28.24	38.60	18.14	9,232	12,622	5,932	3.62	9.88
Haul and stop seines	5.8	12.1	112.64	65.48	22.53	6,648	3,865	1,330	1.64	0.81
Shoal water hand gear	5.2	8.6	6.97	3.63	3.27	3,982	2,075	1,868	1.26	6.01
Minor craft-dependent gears	5.0	6.7	13.08	65.86	47.87	12,394	6,241	4,536	0.27	0.21
TOTAL									100.00	99.99
Important fisheries by gear and species										
Purse seines, tuna	—	293.3	59.00	1,730.41	154.46	7,143	209,517	18,702	6.80	8.23
Purse seines, menhaden	—	297.7	215.73	6,422.33	370.57	2,571	76,525	4,416	31.77	3.47

Purse seines, anchovy-mackerel	—	35.0	268.37	939.28	134.18	5,286	18,500	2,643	3.46	0.60
Purse seines, salmon	20.3	26.5	35.30	69.91	13.27	5,307	10,510	1,995	2.41	3.17
Otter trawls, shrimp (Gulf and south Atlantic)	21.2	45.2	11.89	25.16	14.89	4,846	10,257	6,068	6.63	23.72
Otter trawls, shrimp (New England–Pacific)	35.3	43.5	89.02	278.84	102.01	5,022	17,719	6,483	1.61	0.90
Otter trawls, fish (New England)	63.3	85.3	115.36	730.39	154.33	8,512	53,892	11,387	12.77	8.27
Otter trawls, fish (except New England)	36.1	39.6	98.14	354.19	173.36	5,248	18,942	9,271	8.58	4.03
Pots, lobster (Me.-N. J.)	5.1	12.0	11.85	6.01	6.01	6,940	3,520	3,520	1.93	4.76
Pots, crabs (Alaska-Pacific)	40.8	45.5	50.47	206.04	58.29	6,325	25,820	7,305	4.68	5.15
Pots, blue crabs (Atlantic)	5.3	8.0	54.72	29.15	23.58	3,964	2,112	1,709	2.77	1.76
Pots, spiny lobsters (Fla.)	7.7	15.0	10.90	24.20	4.72	6,988	15,511	3,022	0.12	0.68
Troll, salmon-albacore (Pacific)	11.5	19.1	9.13	10.50	5.53	2,756	3,171	1,671	2.16	5.72
Live bait, tuna (Pacific)	—	60.5	17.52	105.88	16.43	3,568	21,571	3,347	0.56	0.99
Longlines, halibut (Pacific)	27.9	33.0	49.43	138.04	40.13	10,260	28,650	8,328	1.17	2.13
Handlines, vessels (Ga.-Texas)	—	32.2	15.33	49.38	10.86	3,941	12,694	2,790	0.61	1.37
Gill nets, salmon (Alaska-Pacific)	5.4	11.1	18.91	10.28	9.46	4,044	2,200	2,024	2.57	4.83
Gill nets, runaround (Fla.)	5.7	14.0	51.33	29.00	20.42	5,364	3,030	2,134	1.08	0.99
Trammel nets (east Fla.-Texas)	5.3	14.0	29.42	15.63	12.98	9,318	4,950	4,110	0.36	1.00
Dredges, sea scallops (Me.-N. C.)	109.4	112.8	7.69	84.02	8.28	5,767	63,025	6,210	0.28	1.84
Dredges, hard clams (Mass.-Va.)	17.2	26.3	30.03	51.71	22.19	13,561	23,353	10,019	0.19	0.77
Dredges, surf clams (N. J.)	25.2	49.0	103.61	261.42	161.76	9,209	23,237	14,378	1.61	1.26
Dredges, oysters (Gulf and Atlantic)	10.5	16.3	21.86	22.88	9.57	12,840	13,440	5,618	0.90	4.64
Tongs, oysters (Mass.-Fla.)	5.2	8.0	5.09	2.67	2.43	3,347	1,754	1,595	0.50	2.86
Tongs, oysters (Gulf)	5.0	(10.0)	10.03	5.02	4.32	3,480	1,741	1,499	0.24	0.72
Tongs, hard clams (Atlantic)	5.1	7.4	6.68	3.39	3.39	5,395	2,717	2,717	0.28	2.00
Diving outfits, sponges (west Fla.)	—	16.0	1.81	2.89	0.45	21,111	33,778	5,241	0.00	0.07
TOTAL									96.04	95.93

Continued.

Table 7-7. Compilation of craft-dependent fisheries (from Tables 7-1 and 7-6)—cont'd

Summary

Ranking of important fisheries	Catch	%	Value	%
1	Menhaden purse seines	31.8	Shrimp trawls (Gulf and south Atlantic)	23.7
2	Otter trawls, fish (New England)	12.8	Otter trawls, fish (New England)	8.3
3	Otter trawls (except New England)	8.6	Tuna purse seines	8.2
4	Tuna purse seines	6.8	Salmon and albacore troll	5.7
5	Shrimp trawls (Gulf and south Atlantic)	6.6	Crab pots (Alaska and Pacific)	5.2
6	Crab pots (Alaska and Pacific)	4.7	Salmon gill nets	4.8
7	Anchovy-mackerel purse seines	3.5	Lobster pots (north Atlantic)	4.8
8	Blue crab pots	2.8	Oyster dredges (Gulf and Atlantic)	4.6
9	Salmon gill nets	2.6	Otter trawls (except New England)	4.0
10	Salmon purse seines	2.4	Menhaden purse seines	3.5
11	Salmon and albacore troll	2.2	Salmon purse seines	3.2
12	Lobster pots (north Atlantic)	1.9	Oyster tongs (Atlantic)	2.9
13	Surf clam dredges (N. J.)	1.6	Halibut longlines (Pacific)	2.1
14	Shrimp trawls (New England–Pacific)	1.6	Hard clam tongs (Atlantic)	2.0
15	Halibut longlines (Pacific)	1.2	Sea scallop dredges (Me.-N. C.)	1.8
16	Mullet runaround gill nets (Fla.)	1.1	Blue crab pots	1.8
17	Oyster dredges (Gulf and Atlantic)	0.9	Snapper handlines (Ga.-Texas)	1.4
18	Snapper handlines (Ga.-Texas)	0.6	Surf clam dredges (N. J.)	1.3
19	Tuna live bait (Pacific)	0.6	Trammel nets (Fla.-Texas)	1.0
20	Oyster tongs (Atlantic)	0.5	Mullet runaround gill nets (Fla.)	1.0
21	Trammel nets (Fla.-Texas)	0.4	Tuna live bait (Pacific)	1.0
22	Hard clam tongs (Atlantic)	0.3	Shrimp trawls (New England–Pacific)	0.9
23	Sea scallop dredges (Me.-N. C.)	0.3	Hard clam dredges (Mass.-Va.)	0.8
24	Oyster tongs (Gulf)	0.2	Oyster tongs (Gulf)	0.7
25	Hard clam dredges (Mass.-Va.)	0.2	Spiny lobster pots (Fla.)	0.7
26	Spiny lobster pots (Fla.)	0.1	Anchovy-mackerel purse seines	0.6

vessels are owned by companies that also engage in seafood processing.

SPORTFISHING

The sport fisheries are not covered in the statistics of the commercial fisheries, except in cases where the sportfishermen sells some portion of his catch to commercial dealers for resale. Some sportfishing is in reality a type of subsistence fishing in which a large share of the catch is sold. This is usually by residents of an area who utilize weekends or vacation periods to augment their income. In some cases the sportsman can fish with gear or in some areas or seasons denied to the regular commercial fisherman. For instance, in the Gulf of Mexico large numbers of small shrimp are taken in estuarine areas by hundreds of small otter trawls operated as sportfishing gear. Many of these small shrimp find their way into commercial channels, either surreptitiously or through the guise of bait shrimp. Many are sold to private individuals or directly to eating establishments and do not enter into the statistics of the landings.

There is a growing tendency to evaluate the sport fisheries on the basis of the money expended. This is not a meaningful measure. The true value of sportfishing lies in the recreation afforded.

Although there is some relationship between the abundance of fish and the amount of sportfishing, it is not easily established. Some sportfishermen seek to make substantial catches of edible fish, but many want only the thrill of landing a large fish; others are seeking the pleasure of the outdoors and are not too concerned over the size or edibility of their quarry. These facts serve to explain the taking of tarpon, gars, and sharks that are not usually eaten by the angler. They also explain the dyed-in-the-wool surf caster who will fish for hours and be happy with only an occasional reward.

The sport fisheries in general are highly selective of the species taken. The 1969 *commercial* fisheries statistics show no landings of tarpon, and only Hawaii shows over 500 pounds of marlin. There is considerable exaggeration of the quantities of fish landed by marine sportfishermen. For instance, the Salt-Water Angling Survey by the Department of the Interior for 1960 shows a total marine sport fish catch of 1,380,000,000 pounds, whereas a report by the Outdoor Recreation Resources Review Board (ORRRB), also published by the Department of the Interior, estimated the 1960 sport catch at only 590,000,000 pounds.

I note that the Salt-Water Angling Survey defines sportfishing as the act of catching, or attempting to catch, fish with a hook and line, rod and reel, spearfishing equipment, or bow and arrow, yet in their list of expenditures by sportfishermen they include nets and seines. Furthermore the ORRRB report lists crustaceans and mollusks as objects of a sport fishery. I wonder what they would call wading the shoreline in search of soft-shell crabs or a midnight sortie to hand catch smelt in a spawning brook.

An intensive survey of the sport fishery of California (Miller and Gotshall, 1965) from the Oregon border south about 800 miles to Point Arguello, Santa Barbara County, showed that the sport catch in this extensive area from 1958 to 1960 averaged 4,370,000 pounds, compared to a commercial catch of 82,400,000 pounds; that is, the sportfishermen landed 5% of the total. By species groups the sportsmen landed 92.5% of the cottids (sculpins), 83.1% of the surfperches, 24.1% of the lingcod, 19.9% of the croakers, 11.6% of the rockfishes, and 6.1% of the salmons. They landed only 0.3% of the flatfish and only 1.4% of all other groups. Thus out of the 61,743,000 pounds caught of flatfish and "all other" groups, the sportsmen landed only 699,000 pounds.

A summary of these data (abridged) appears in Table 7-8.

The small surfperches, averaging only about two thirds of a pound, appear to furnish more fishing satisfaction than most of the other species.

It is very difficult to reconcile the 1960

Table 7-8. Annual sport fish catch from the Oregon border to Point Arguello, Santa Barbara County, California, 1958 to 1961

	No. of fish				Total weight (pounds)
Species	Pier and shore	Party boat	Skiff	Skin diving	
Surfperch (15 spp.)	1,204,252	25	8,553	4,923	924,406
Rockfishes (29 spp.)	47,216	682,484	179,779	9,790	1,685,680
Flatfishes (14 spp.)	2,176	12,734	11	0	55,250
Cottids (5 spp.)	46,632	1,718	5,761	1,282	81,010
Sharks, skates, rays (13 spp.)	680,491	111,466	112,710	5,572	40,820
Lingcod	4,357	25,595	18,378	2,923	410,030
Salmons, steelhead	299	37,935	15,582	0	421,110
Striped bass	43,939	30,767	27	0	388,610
White croaker	233,105	1,024	54,681	0	147,290
Jacksmelt	258,276	1,665	12,059	0	108,800
Greenlings (3 spp.)	66,445	521	3,912	2,250	60,791
Topsmelt	42,664	0	0	0	10,670
Jack mackerel	2,522	9,403	1,854	0	8,270
Pacific mackerel	54	3,942	5,226	0	5,260
All other species	28,830	614	991	399	21,937
GRAND TOTAL	2,058,979	800,381	337,171	21,615	4,369,934

Table 7-9. Party boat and commercial catches in California of the most important sport species in 1961

	Sport catch		Commercial catch		Pounds/fish	
Species	Number	Pounds	Number	Pounds	Young[1]	Miller and Gotshall[2]
Barracuda	391,884	1,567,536	177,345	709,379	4.0	
Kelp and sand bass	613,604	613,604	2,584	2,584	1.0	
Yellowtail	42,367	508,404	31,730	380,760	12.0	
Bonito	849,426	3,397,704	2,128,243	8,512,972	4.0	
California halibut	108,011	864,088	81,819	654,554	8.0	
Rockfishes	898,641	1,797,282	5,415,381	10,830,762	2.0[3]	
Albacore	184,891	2,773,365	1,941,549	29,123,244	15.0	
White sea bass	14,082	352,050	27,769	694,224	25.0	
Bluefin tuna	2,268	47,628	994,674	20,882,650	21.0[4]	
Sculpin	26,672	34,674	20,552	26,718	1.3	
Pacific mackerel	113,998	74,099	68,231,000	44,110,194	0.65[4]	0.57
Giant sea bass	310	31,000	3,404	340,363	100.0	
California sheepshead	15,210	47,151	4,065	12,602	3.1	
Lingcod	23,466	187,728	179,992	1,439,943	8.0	
Jack mackerel	28,891	17,335	162,010,510	97,606,304		0.60
Salmon	42,965	433,947	852,669	8,637,907	10.1[4]	
Cabezon	15,971	31,942	4,952	9,904		2.0
Misc. flatfish	9,316	18,632			2.0[3]	
Sablefish	42,965	10,696	6,466,112	1,616,528		0.25
White croaker	21,782	13,069	1,481,940	889,164	0.6	
TOTAL	3,446,720	12,821,934	250,056,290	226,480,765		

[1]Young (1969).
[2]Miller and Gotshall (1965).
[3]Arbitrary.
[4]Computed for individual years.

Table 7-10. Rough estimate of magnitude of sport fish catch on Pacific coast

	Catch in pounds		% Sport of commer- cial
	Sport	*Commercial*	
California			
Party boat catch (1961)	12,821,934		
Other finfish (Oregon to Santa Barbara)	2,417,765		
Other finfish (south of Santa Barbara)	1,208,883		
TOTAL CALIFORNIA FINFISH	16,448,582	560,073,000	2.94
Washington			
Salmon sport fish[1]	3,130,000		
Other finfish[2]	110,000		
TOTAL WASHINGTON FINFISH	3,240,000	102,441,000	3.16
Oregon			
Salmon sport fish[3]	1,022,000		
Other finfish[4]	55,000		
TOTAL OREGON FINFISH	1,077,000	39,247,000	2.74
TOTAL	20,765,582	701,761,000	2.96

[1]Crutchfield and MacFarlane (1968).
[2]Pacific Marine Fisheries Commission. 1966. Eighteenth annual report for 1965, appendix 2. p. 23.
[3]Pacific Marine Fisheries Commission. 1960. Thirteenth annual report for 1960, appendix L. pp. 47-51.
[4]Estimated at one half of the Washington catch.

figures for the 1960 sport catch of 237,000,000 pounds on the Pacific coast when 800 miles of the California coastline accounted for about 4,370,000 pounds. In 1960 the state of Washington sport salmon catch consisted of 122,700 coho salmon and 189,300 chinook salmon. If respective weights of 7 and 12 pounds apiece are assumed, this amounts to only 3,130,000 pounds. Crutchfield and MacFarlane (1968) state that the salmon fishery dominates saltwater sportfishing activities in Washington so completely that most fishermen tend to ignore the existence and potential recreational use of other saltwater resources of the state. The catch of 3,130,000 pounds by sportfishermen is only 3.1% of the total finfish catch of the state.

The party boat catch of the entire state of California is given by Young (1969) and shown in Table 7-9. If the party boat catch of nearly 13,000,000 pounds is added to the amount of sport fish taken in the northern portion of the state by shore, pier, skiff, and skin-diving fishermen, the total is in-

creased to just over 15 million pounds. Estimating the nonparty boat fishery of the coastline south of Santa Barbara County to be half as large as the northern 800 miles, the grand total is 16,448,000 pounds of fish taken by sportfishermen in California in 1961. This is only 2.9% of the state landings of 560 million pounds of finfish and only 5.8% if the state landings caught off Latin America are ignored.

We can now make a rough estimate of the magnitude of the sportfish catch on the Pacific coast (Table 7-10).

Turning to the figure published by the Department of Commerce *(Current Fishery Statistics 6100)* for the sport fish catch of the Pacific coast for 1960 of 237 million pounds, at once an inexplicable discrepancy appears. Whereas the sport fish catch that is accounted for in several published reports is 2.96% of the total commercial finfish catch, a sport fish catch of 33.82% of the commercial finfish catch is shown, a difference of a whole order of magnitude. I am therefore dismissing the remainder of their

extremely rough and possibly biased estimates.

Suggested readings

Crutchfield, J. A., and D. MacFarlane. 1968. Economic evaluation of the 1965-66 salt-water
fisheries of Washington. Wash. Dept. Fish., Res.
Bull. **8:**1-57.

Miller, D. J., and D. Gotshall. 1965. Ocean sport-
fish catch and effort from Oregon to Point
Arguello, California. Calif. Fish Game, Fish
Bull. **130:**1-130.

Young, P. H. 1969. The California partyboat fishery, 1947-1967. Calif. Fish Game, Fish Bull.
145:1:91.

chapter 8

✹ Fishing gears and their characteristics

FISH BEHAVIOR IN RELATION TO FISHING TECHNIQUES

It has already been noted that marine organisms come in many sizes and shapes, they occupy diverse habitats, and their mobility and social behavior cover a wide gamut.

Primitive man could feast on mussels or sea urchin eggs by merely observing the tides and plucking his meal by hand. It has taken a long time to develop much of the sophisticated gear now in use, and we still fail to harvest efficiently many species that do not choose to form dense aggregations at some season of the year.

Although the term "harvesting" is often loosely applied to fishing, it is in all but a very few cases a misnomer. No sane farmer would ride through his pastures indiscriminately shooting down his stock. Fishing is still, despite our modern gear, a form of hunting, whether it be the rape of the sea otter by the "sea wolves" of Jack London or the prosaic tedium of the voyages to the Grand Banks.

There are so many types of fishing gear in use that adequate description would cover many volumes. For instance I have among my books one 536 pages long with numerous illustrations and maps describing the obsolescent primitive fishing by means of thrusting implements, chiefly fish spears, in Poland and the northeastern Slavic territories written by Maria Znamierowska-Prüffer (1957). I also have a scholarly work by Karekin Devedjian (1926), former director of fisheries in Istanbul (then Constantinople), whom I was privileged to meet. He portrays in exquisite detail numerous "dalians," which he calls "madragues," that are pound nets set in the Bosphorus for taking, among other fishes, the huge bluefin tuna on its annual visit to the Black Sea. Practically every dalian has a different layout. On visiting the area it was immediately clear that one cannot describe a typical dalian for bluefin.

In discussing fishing gears it is almost necessary to first define the general types into which the many variations fall. First the difference between motile species and sessile or highly sedentary species must be recognized. For example, all of the mollusks, with the exception of the cephalopods, are either attached or have an extremely limited range of movement. Therefore gears used for the capture of sedentary species will be considered as one major category.

The remainder can be subdivided in several ways. Perhaps the major breakdown

Text continued on p. 168.

163

Fishing gears classified by species behavior, habitat, and type of gear

A. For sedentary (or temporarily vulnerable) species
  1. Shore-operated gear
    a. Hand capture
      Alaska: Kelp or boughs with herring eggs, oysters
      Northwest: Oysters
      California: Spawning grunion
      New England: Periwinkles, cockles, conchs, spawning smelt
      Atlantic–Chesapeake Bay: Hard clams, soft clams, soft-shell crabs
      South Atlantic–Gulf: Oysters, soft-shell crabs
    b. Shovels
      Alaska: Razor clams
      Northwest: Razor clams
      California: Pismo clams
    c. Hoes (or forks)
      New England: Sandworms, bloodworms, soft clams, mussels
      New Jersey: Soft clams
      Massachusetts: Mussels
  2. Hand-operated boat gear (shoal water)
    a. Large rakes
      New England: Irish moss (seaweeds)
    b. Bull rakes
      New England: Hard clams, soft clams, mussels, sea urchins
      Atlantic–Chesapeake Bay: Hard and soft clams, mussels, turtles
      South Atlantic: Hard clams, oysters
    c. Tongs
      Massachusetts-Florida: Oysters, hard clams
      Gulf: Oysters
    d. Hooks
      Florida: Sponges, conchs
  3. Diving gear (shoal water)
    a. Diving outfits
      California: Abalones
      West Florida: Sponges
  4. Towed gear (shoal to deep water)
    a. Oyster dredges
      All coasts: Oysters, rangia, conchs
    b. Bay-scallop dredges
      Maine-Florida: Bay scallops
    c. Toothed dredge, clam
      Massachusetts-Virginia: Hard clams, mussels
      Maryland: Soft clams
    d. Jet dredge, clam
      New Jersey: Surf clams
    e. Sea scallop dredge
      Maine–North Carolina: Sea scallops
    f. Suction dredge
      Northwest: Oysters
      Atlantic coast: Oysters, clams
    g. Kelp harvester
      California: Giant kelp *(Macrocystis)*
B. For motile species, capture aided by their actions
  1. Attracted by food or lure

a. Captured by hook
   (1) Handline
       Northwest (minor): Rockfish, lingcod
       California: Rockfish, sablefish, sea bass, groupers, lingcod, sculpin, flatfish, yellowtail, king croaker
       New England–Maryland: Cod, striped bass, bluefish, mackerel
       South Atlantic–Gulf (vessels): Red snappers, groupers, jewfish
       Gulf, north and west (boats): King and Spanish mackerel, sea trout, red and black drum
       Gulf, west Florida (boats): Carangids and sea breams
   (2) Troll gear, salmon
       Alaska: King and coho salmon
       Northwest and northern California: King, coho, and pink salmons, rockfishes, lingcod, halibut
   (3) Troll gear, albacore
       Pacific coast: Albacore
   (4) Troll gear, regular
       Massachusetts–New Jersey (minor): Bluefin tuna, striped bass, bluefish
       Florida: King and Spanish mackerel, dolphin, sea trout
   (5) Pole and line (live bait)
       California: Yellowfin and skipjack tuna
   (6) Longlines (vessels)
       Pacific coast: Halibut, sablefish, rockfishes, lingcod
   (7) Longlines (boats)
       New England: Haddock, cod, hake, cusk, halibut, pollock, winter flounders
       East Florida: Sharks
       Texas: Drums, sea trout, sheepshead, flounders
   (8) Flag lines
       Atlantic coast: Swordfish, bluefin
b. Captured by clinging to bait
   (1) Crab trotline
       Chesapeake Bay, Carolinas, Louisiana: Blue crabs
c. Captured by scoop net
   (1) Attracted by chum
       California: Mackerel and squid
d. Captured by hoop net
   (1) Baited net
       Gulf: Crabs
       Florida: Spiny lobster
e. Captured in baited pots
   (1) Very large pots
       Alaska: King crabs
   (2) Large circular pots
       Alaska-California: Dungeness crabs
   (3) Large conical pots
       Alaska: Snow crabs
   (4) Small pots
       Alaska (minor): Shrimp
       Northwest (minor): Shrimp and octopus
       California: Spiny lobster, rock crabs
       New England: Lobsters, rock crabs, conchs, green crabs
       New Jersey–Texas: Blue crabs, swellfish, conchs
       Florida: Spiny lobster, stone crabs, groupers

Continued.

Fishing gears classified by species behavior, habitat, and type of gear—cont'd

  2. Avoiding light or seeking shelter
     a. Bunches of brush
       Louisiana: Shedding blue crabs
     b. Earthenware pots
       Japan: Octopus
     c. Scrapes (in vegetation)
       Chesapeake Bay: Shedding blue crabs
  3. Attracted to light
     a. Blanket net (night light)
       Africa: *Sardinella,* mackerel
     b. Hooks (night light): Squid
     c. Dip net (torching): Herring
  4. Migrating upstream (or downstream)
     a. At falls or rapids
       (1) Hanging basket
          Columbia River (obsolete): Salmon
       (2) Dip nets: Salmon, alewives
       (3) Gaff (detachable handle): Salmon
     b. In stream
       (1) Fish wheels
          Yukon River: Salmon, chiefly chums
       (2) Weirs
          New England: Alewives, eels
          Pacific coast (illegal): Salmon
       (3) Fyke (hoop) nets: Eels, river fishes, catfish, baitfishes
       (4) Sturgeon gear: Yesil Irmak
       (5) Gill or trammel nets: Salmon, shad, eulachon
  5. Migrating at night (or in turbid water)
     a. Gill nets, drifting
       Alaska: Salmon, herring (minor)
       Puget Sound: Sockeye and pink salmon
       Columbia River: King and coho salmon, shad, eulachon, steelhead, sturgeon
       California: Sciaenids, flounders, sharks, barracuda, atherinid smelts, flying fish
       New England: Mackerel
       Atlantic: Striped bass, mackerel, spot, bluefish, white perch, drums, sharks
       West Florida: King and Spanish mackerel, pompano
     b. Gill nets, anchored
       New England: Bank fishes
     c. Trammel nets
       East Florida: Pompano, sea trout, spot, mullet
       Gulf: Mullet, sea trout, drums, pompano, sheepshead, croaker, mackerel, king whiting, spot, flounders
  6. Migrating alongshore
     a. Reef net
       Puget Sound: Salmon
     b. Brush weirs
       Maine: Herring, mackerel (minor)
       New Hampshire: Alewives, smelt
     c. Floating traps
       Maine: Mackerel, salmon (minor)
       Southern New England: Scup, mackerel, sea robins, cod, butterfish, bluefish, squid, striped bass, etc.
     d. Pound nets
       Alaska and Puget Sound (only on Indian reservations): Salmon

Cape Cod: Sea herring, squid, mackerel, scup, bluefin tuna, pollock, striped bass

Mid-Atlantic: Striped bass, swellfish, butterfish, bluefish

Chesapeake Bay area: Alewives, menhaden, swellfish, striped bass, shad, spot, sea herring, flounders, sea trout, white perch

North Carolina: Flounders, sea trout, croaker, king whiting, sea bass, scup, swellfish, butterfish, spot

C. For motile species, without their voluntary action
  1. Taken individually
    a. Spear (gig)
       New England: Eels
       Atlantic: Eels, flounders
       Gulf: Flounders
       Tropics (usually with scuba gear): Reef fishes
    b. Bow and arrow: Carp
    c. Harpoon
       Worldwide: Small whales
       California: Swordfish
       New England: Swordfish, bluefin tuna
       Norway: Basking shark
    d. Rifle
       Arctic: Walrus, seals
       Black Sea: Dolphins
    e. Club
       Eastern Canada: Harp seals
    f. Explosive harpoon: Large whales
  2. Taken against the shore
    a. Stop seines
       New England: Sea herring
    b. Haul seines (drag seines)
       Gulf: Mullet, carangids, sea trout, etc.
       Alaska: Salmon
       Northwest: Salmon, herring, silver smelt
       Northern California: Atherinid smelt
       New England: Alewives
       New York–east Florida: Striped bass, scup, bluefish, swellfish, spot, sea trout, mullet, shad, carangids
  3. Taken in shoal water
    a. Cast nets
       Gulf and Atlantic: Mullet, shrimp
    b. Herring rake
       Alaska and Northwest: Bait herring
    c. Butterfly nets
       Louisiana: Shrimp
    d. Bag nets
       Maine–New Hampshire: Smelt
    e. Circle gill nets
       Mid-Atlantic: Bluefish, striped bass
       South Atlantic: Mullet, king and Spanish mackerel, bluefish, spot, sea trout, drums, and sheepshead
       Gulf: Mullet, mackerels, sciaenids, carangids
    f. Filter net (Chinese shrimp net)
       Philippines: Shrimp
       San Francisco Bay (before too polluted): Shrimp
  4. Taken on or close to the bottom
    a. Fyke net with wings
       North Atlantic: Winter flounder

Continued.

Fishing gears classified by species behavior, habitat, and type of gear—cont'd

    b. Danish seine
      North Sea: Flounders
    c. Beam trawl
      Southeastern Alaska–Puget Sound: Shrimp
    d. Paranzella (two-boat trawl)
      Asia: Bottom fish
    e. Otter trawl
      (1) Shrimp
         Alaska: Pandalid shrimp
         New England: Pandalid shrimp
         Gulf–south Atlantic: Penaeid shrimp, blue crabs
      (2) Fish trawls (flat or balloon)
         Northwest: Flounders, ocean perch, rockfishes, lingcod, cod
         California: Flounders, rockfishes, sablefish, lingcod, California halibut
         New England: Ocean perch, bank fishes, flounders, lobsters
         Atlantic: Scup, butterfish, fluke, lobsters, scallops, crabs, silver hake, yellowtail
           flounder, sea trout
         Gulf: Croaker, spot, cutlass fish
5. Taken from surface schools
    a. Lampara
      California: Bait clupeoids, sardines, squid
    b. Purse seine (two-boat)
      Gulf and Atlantic: Menhaden, mackerel, thread herring
    c. Purse seine (regular [may have drum])
      Alaska and Northwest: Salmon, herring
      California: Anchovy, jack mackerel, squid
      New England: Herring
      South Atlantic: Spanish mackerel, striped bass
    d. Tuna purse seine
      Pacific and Atlantic: Yellowfin, skipjack, bluefin tunas
6. Taken from subsurface schools
    a. Midwater trawls
      Northwest: Hake, herring

depends on whether the capture does or does not require voluntary action on the part of the fish. Devices such as traps and mazes, gill nets, and hooks all demand some action by the fish.

Following this general scheme I prepared the foregoing outline in which all fishing gears are classified, not in the classic manner of appearance or operation of the gear, but rather in relation to the habits of the organism to be captured. Support for such a stance is contained in Alekseev (1968) who cites a number of authors who stress the relationship between the basic responses of different species of fish to environmental and artificial stimuli and the methods employed in their capture. This reliance of many fishing gears on the behavior of the fish was recognized a quarter of a century ago by Coker, who stated:

> Most nets are designed to take advantage of known behavior of fish in response to barriers, food, current, spawning impulses and so on.*

I do not attempt to illustrate or discuss all of the fishing gears mentioned in the listing.

*From Coker, C. M. 1949. Maryland's commercial fishing gears. I. The fin-fish gears. Dept. Res. Educ., Maryland, Educ. Ser. **18**:1-37.

CHIEF TYPES OF GEAR AND THEIR USES

Sedentary species

Following the outline, the first discussion deals with sedentary species, in which group are included a few special cases in which a species is temporarily highly vulnerable to capture.

Shore-operated gear. Hand capture, the most primitive type of fishing, is still employed in several fisheries. The harvesting of seaweeds and kelps or purposefully placed evergreen boughs laden with herring spawn was practiced by the Indians of the Northwest and Alaska, who welcomed this source of food in advance of the salmon runs. Herring spawn is now a high-priced item exported principally to Japan.

In the Northwest with its high tides the hand harvesting of oysters is extensively followed. A vessel at high tide distributes floating wooden tubs over the beds to be harvested. At low tide the oysters are picked up by hand and thrown into the tubs, which the vessel retrieves on the following tide.

The grunion, a California smelt, *Leuresthes tenuis,* is picked up as it spawns on the ocean beaches between the retreating surf and the next uprushing wave. This is wholly a sport fishery. In New England the smelt, *Osmerus eperlanus mordax,* ascends small brooks at night to spawn on the hard or gravelly bottom or on vegetation. They are captured by hand. In the cold of very early spring it takes a determined sportsman to wade over rocks slippery with spawn and grab at smelt that rub against his hand in the darkness.

Along most of the Atlantic coast a few oysters and some clams are gathered by hand. Along the south Atlantic and Gulf coasts fishermen collect soft-shell crabs in the shallows as they take advantage of the dark to shed their old shells.

Shovels are used extensively on the Pacific coast for digging clams. Although the hard clam may be taken with an ordinary shovel, for the fast-burrowing razor clam and the geoduck (pronounced "gooeyduck") the shovels have a narrow, long, straight blade that is deeply concave, similar to the blade of a post-hole digger.

Hoes vary from the narrow-tined short-handled hoe (Fig. 8-1) to hoes with wider tines and even some with a solid blade, depending chiefly on the type of beach. They are most useful in areas with a soft bottom to sift out soft clams.

Hand-operated boat gear. The second category comprises hand-operated boat gear for sedentary species. In New England large rakes are used to gather Irish moss and other seaweeds.

The bull rake (Fig. 8-1) is used all along the Atlantic coast for hard and soft clams, mussels, and oysters. In operation the bull rake, with a handle up to 35 feet long, is pulled from astern toward the anchored boat.

Tongs are used along the Atlantic coast for oysters and hard clams and in the Gulf for osyters. The lower pair of hand tongs shown in Fig. 8-1 is for oysters; the pair above has more closely spaced bars for holding clams. The patent tongs, used in deeper water from a boom, are fished in Chesapeake Bay.

Diving gear. Diving gear is used in California for abalones and in west Florida for sponges.

Towed gear. Mollusks are also captured in both shallow and deep water by towed gear. Fig. 8-2 shows a small vessel dredging in a circle in shoal water for surf clams and a vessel in deeper water towing a hydraulic (or jet) surf clam dredge. A hydraulic dredge for soft clams (and shoal water) is also shown.

Sea scallop dredges (Fig. 8-3) vary from about 8 to 12 feet wide and 16 to 18 inches high. The 3-inch steel rings are held together with iron links. The top of the bag is made of sash cord. They are used principally on Georges Bank and the South Channel.

The typical oyster dredge (Fig. 8-3) is used on all coasts, taking oysters and a few rangia and conchs. The size of the dredge will vary with the vessel size. Fig. 8-3 also shows a vessel using a suction dredge.

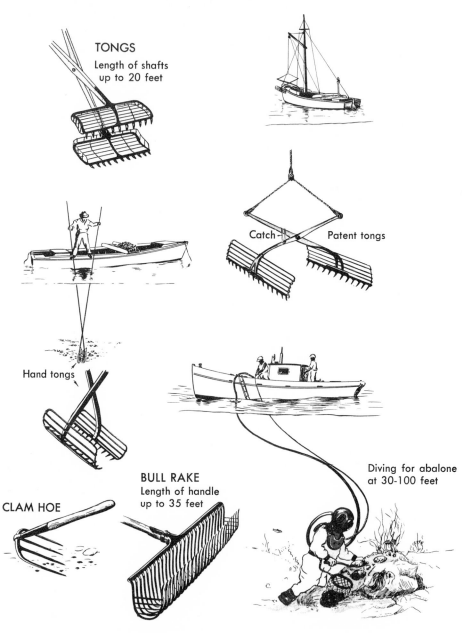

TONGS
Length of shafts
up to 20 feet

Catch — Patent tongs

Hand tongs

Diving for abalone
at 30-100 feet

CLAM HOE

BULL RAKE
Length of handle
up to 35 feet

Fig. 8-1. Mollusk gears operated from shore, boat, or small vessel. (From Sundstrom, G. T. 1957. U. S. Fish Wildl. Serv., Circ. **48:**1-48.)

Operation
fishing in 30-40 feet
of water

Iron stake

Swivel

SHALLOW WATER DREDGE
(N. CAROLINA)

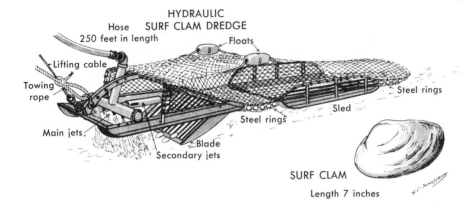

HYDRAULIC
SURF CLAM DREDGE

Hose
250 feet in length

Floats

Lifting cable

Towing
rope

Steel rings

Main jets

Steel rings

Sled

Blade

Secondary jets

SURF CLAM

Length 7 inches

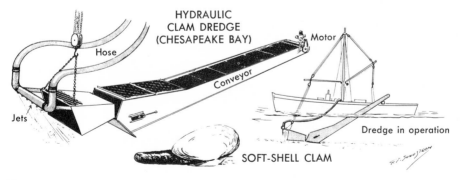

HYDRAULIC
CLAM DREDGE
(CHESAPEAKE BAY)

Motor

Hose

Conveyor

Jets

Dredge in operation

SOFT-SHELL CLAM

Fig. 8-2. Clam dredges for surf, soft-shell, and other shoal water clams. (From Sundstrom, G. T. 1957. U. S. Fish Wildl. Serv., Circ. **48:**1-48.)

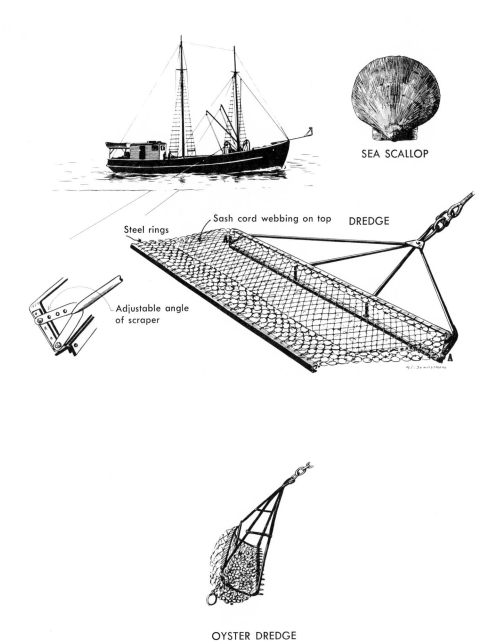

SEA SCALLOP

Steel rings

Sash cord webbing on top   DREDGE

Adjustable angle
of scraper

G.T. SUNDSTROM

A

OYSTER DREDGE

Fig. 8-3. Dredges for sea scallops and oysters. (From Sundstrom, G. T. 1957. U. S. Fish Wildl. Serv., Circ. **48**:1-48.)

Motile species caught by their voluntary action

The second major category of gear is for motile species whose capture is aided by their voluntary action. Perhaps the simplest reaction is the seeking of food, so this discussion will begin with fish attracted by a bait or lure.

Attracted by food or lure. The simplest gear is the handline. In Fig. 8-4 the handline with a light is from the Philippines, but I have seen the Bosphorus at night when it was lit by a string of lights used by sportsmen fishing for bluefish in their beautifully constructed Turkish rowboats. The simple handline has evolved gradually into a line with several hooks.

Although a simple and ancient gear, the handline is still important, especially in the red snapper vessel fishery of the Southeast (Fig. 8-5, *A*), the rockfish fishery of California, and the small boat fishery in the Gulf for Spanish and king mackerels, sea trouts, and carangids.

Pole and line fishing has been chiefly for sport except for the capture of tunas by the live bait boats (Fig. 8-5, *B*).

One of the most tantalizing stimuli to a predator fish is a moving bait or lure. The small vessel shown in Fig. 8-6 is trolling for shallow-swimming pelagic species in the Philippines. Similar gear is used in Turkey for catching bonito. Trolling is a very important method for taking salmon and albacore. Most of the West Coast trollers with offshore vessels fish for both salmon and albacore (Fig. 8-7). Albacore are usually caught farther offshore and closer to the surface than salmon and are sought from California to off southern British Columbia. Salmon are taken from northern California to the Gulf of Alaska.

Longline gear has been in use for a long time and was the main gear employed for bank fishes before the development of the modern otter trawl. On the Atlantic coast the large vessels from which dories were sent out to fish started disappearing in the 1940's. There is still a small vessel–boat fishery for bank fishes along the New England coast, usually by the same boats that fish for lobsters. A few boats long-line for sharks off east Florida, and in Texas they take sciaenids and flounders.

On the Pacific coast the halibut longline vessels fish from the Bering Sea to northern California, taking halibut, sablefish, ocean perch, lingcod, and rockfishes (Fig. 8-8). The miles of gear with baited hooks pass out through a stern chute as the vessel proceeds at full speed. The gear is set on the bottom.

Another form of longline, called a flag line or drift line, is used for taking large deep-swimming tunas, swordfish, and marlins (Fig. 8-9). It is employed extensively by the Japanese.

A novel form of longline called a "trot-line" is used, principally in Chesapeake Bay, for taking blue crabs (Fig. 8-10, *A*). No hooks are used. The bait is tied on the line, usually in a piece of cloth; the crab refuses to let go of the bait as the line is hauled. The crabs strike a roller that knocks them into the rigid mouth of a net towed alongside the boat.

Another way of capturing fish with bait is "chumming" them around a slowly moving boat with chopped bait and then catching them in a scoop net, which is merely a net on a hoop attached to a long handle. This method is used in California for mackerel and squid.

Finally, crabs and spiny lobsters are taken, principally by sportsmen and vacationers, in what is usually called a "hoop" net (not to be confused with the hoop net used in streams). It consists of one, sometimes two, hoops with a bag of netting attached. The net has bait tied in the center. When hauled, the crabs' legs become entangled and they are captured.

A very important gear, especially for crustaceans, is the pot or trap. The largest are those used in Alaska for the king crab. Perhaps the next largest are those used from Alaska to California (Fig. 8-10, *B*) for Dungeness crabs. All pots work on the

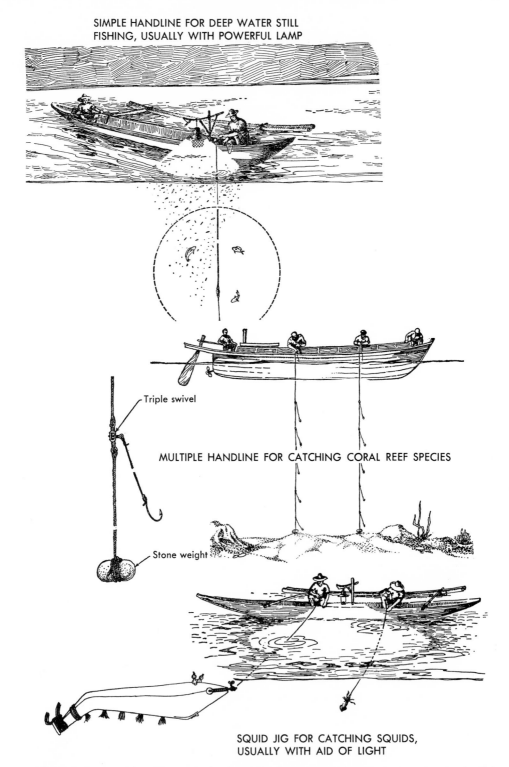

SIMPLE HANDLINE FOR DEEP WATER STILL
FISHING, USUALLY WITH POWERFUL LAMP

Triple swivel

MULTIPLE HANDLINE FOR CATCHING CORAL REEF SPECIES

Stone weight

SQUID JIG FOR CATCHING SQUIDS,
USUALLY WITH AID OF LIGHT

Fig. 8-4. Types of handlines used in the Philippines. (From Umali, A. F. 1950. U. S. Fish Wildl. Serv., Res. Rep. **17:**1-165. [Illustrations by S. G. Duran.])

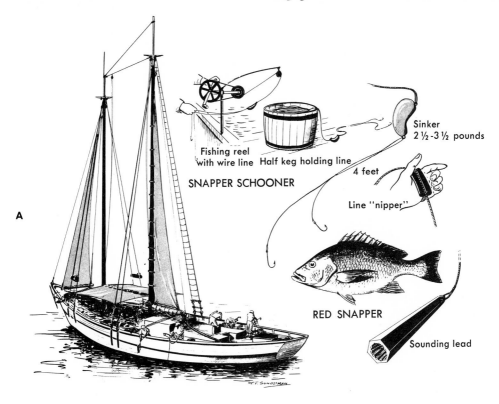

Fig. 8-5. Vessel fishing by lines. **A,** Snapper fishing with handlines. **B,** Tuna fishing with pole and line with live bait for chumming. (From Sundstrom, G. T. 1957, U. S. Fish Wildl. Serv., Circ. **48**:1-48.)

Troll lines used in catching pelagic species

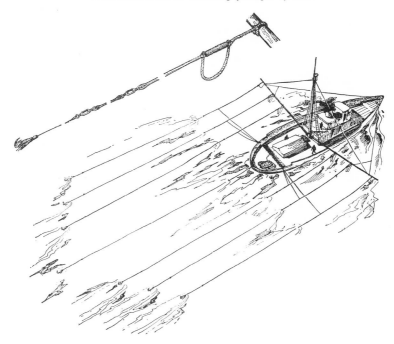

Fig. 8-6. Surface trolling for scombroid fishes. (From Umali, A. F. 1950. U. S. Fish Wildl. Serv., Res. Rep. **17**:1-165. [Illustrations by S. G. Duran.])

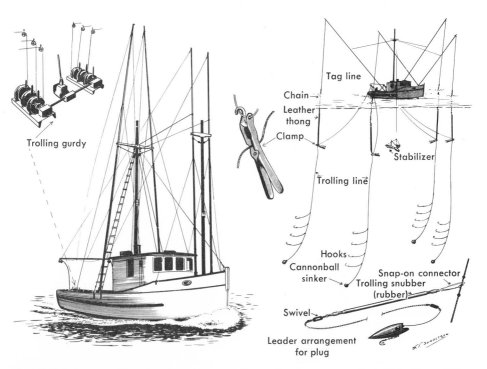

Fig. 8-7. Salmon trolling showing power gurdies and arrangement of multiple lines. (From Sundstrom, G. T. 1957. U. S. Fish Wildl. Serv., Circ. **48**:1-48.)

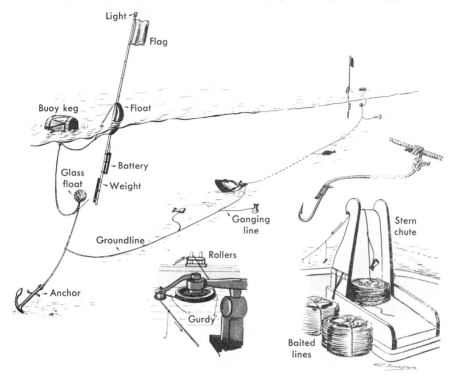

Fig. 8-8. Halibut longline gear showing stern chute for setting gear at full speed and horizontal line pulling gurdy. (From Sundstrom, G. T. 1957. U. S. Fish Wildl. Serv., Circ. **48**:1-48.)

same principle. In order to reach the receptacle containing the bait, the fish or crustacean must pass through a more or less conical-shaped tunnel. In some traps they pass through more than one tunnel, making escape more difficult. Many of the pots have small openings to permit the escape of undersized individuals. Pots come in assorted shapes and are made of different materials (Fig. 8-11). Some are collapsible so that more can be carried on deck.

The cane pots used in Turkey are shown in Fig. 8-12. Devedjian (1926) states that the same pots appear on Byzantine medals struck during the era of Alexander the Great. They are used for lobsters, bearded rocklings, picarels, and shrimps. The size of the pot, the opening, or the spacing between canes varies with the species sought. Fifteen to twenty pots are attached to a mainline. The fishing of pots on a trawl line was adopted some years ago for offshore lobster pots in New England.

In the eastern Bering Sea the Japanese developed a pot fishery for snow (tanner) crabs (Zahn, 1970). They started experimenting about 1965 and finally developed a system of fishing with a typical string of 128 pots on a 3200 m groundline. The line was anchored and buoyed with glass floats and flagged poles; each flag was coded to distinguish the pot gear from the usual tangle nets, which have since been abandoned as too destructive to female crabs. The strings of gear are set about ¼ mile apart. Each pot has a 4 fm gangion fastened to the pot by a bridle in two places to keep the pot upright. The pots themselves resemble a truncated cone with the entrance on the top. The circular base is 45 inches in diameter, and the circular top is 28 inches across. The top, bottom, and middle rings are welded to straight rods to make the pot 22 inches high. The complete pot weighs about 40 pounds. The pots are baited with herring, with herring waste in perforated cups, or

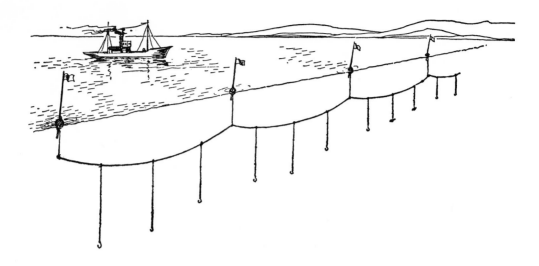

DRIFT LONGLINE FOR CATCHING TUNA,
ESPECIALLY YELLOWFINS

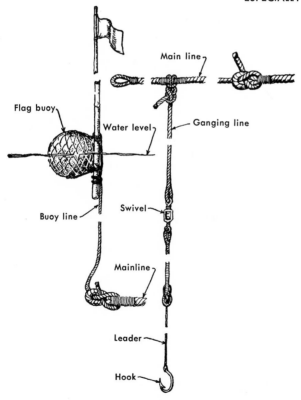

Fig. 8-9. Drift longline or flag line used extensively, especially by the Japanese, for taking deep-swimming tunas and billfishes. (From Umali, A. F. 1950. U. S. Fish Wildl. Serv., Res. Rep. **17:**1-165. [Illustrations by S. G. Duran.])

PATENT CRAB TROTLINE (CHESAPEAKE BAY)

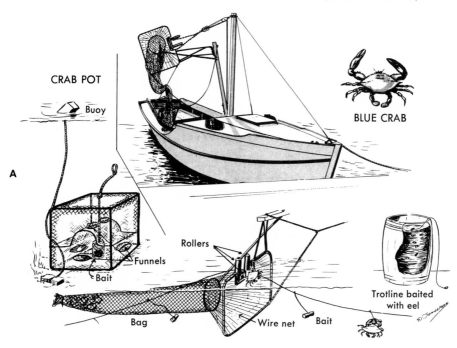

CRAB POT

Buoy

BLUE CRAB

A

Rollers

Funnels

Bait

Bag

Wire net

Bait

Trotline baited
with eel

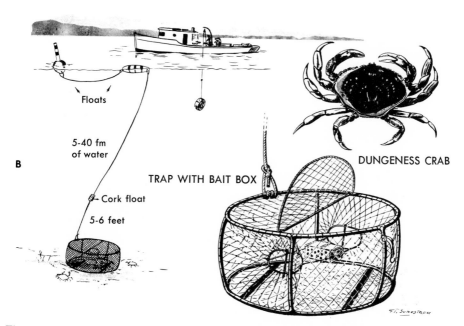

Floats

5-40 fm
of water

B

Cork float

5-6 feet

TRAP WITH BAIT BOX

DUNGENESS CRAB

Fig. 8-10. A, Two most popular gears for the blue crab, *Callinectes sapidus,* of the Atlantic coast, baited wiremesh pot and trotline overhauled by a moving vessel. **B,** Type of pot used for Dungeness crab of the Pacific coast. (From Sundstrom, G. T. 1957. U. S. Fish Wildl. Serv., Circ. **48:**1-48.)

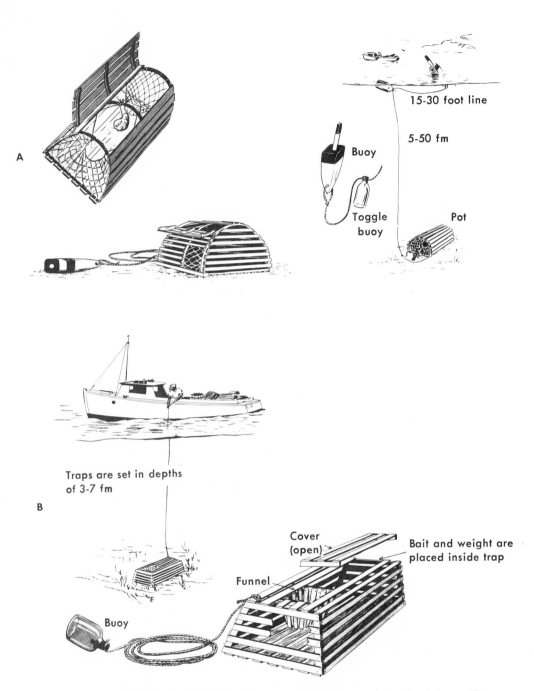

Fig. 8-11. Typical baited pots used to capture, **A,** northern lobster and, **B,** spiny lobster. (From Sundstrom, G. T. 1957. U. S. Fish Wildl. Serv., Circ. **48**:1-48.)

Cane pot for fish and crustaceans

Fig. 8-12. Small cane pots used in Turkish waters for fish and crustaceans. These pots were fished trawl fashion on gangions attached to a mainline. This antedates by several centuries similar trawl fashion fishing of lobster pots in New England. (From Devedjian, K. 1926. Administration de la Dette Publique Ottomane, Constantinople. 649 pp.)

sometimes with Pacific cod. The pots are usually fished 2 to 4 days before hauling.

Large cane pots of different shapes are also used in tropical countries for taking reef fishes. In some localities these pots are made of wire.

Seeking shelter. A second reaction of fish (after feeding) that is sometimes used in their capture is the avoidance of light or seeking of shelter. For example, in Louisiana bunches of brush are put into a bayou to attract blue crabs about to shed their shells. Another example of the shelter-seeking reaction is the use of earthenware pots into which octopi enter (Fig. 8-13). Kask and Hiyama (1947) state that these terra-cotta traps or pots are the main gear for octopi, which are important in Japanese commercial fisheries. Pots are set on a sandy or muddy bottom with little current at a depth of 7 to 20 m and in lines of 20 to 50. The pots are not baited, and they are overhauled daily.

In Turkish waters, Devedjian states that very small earthen pots (35 to 40 cm) are used to catch gobies (without using bait). The pots are placed on the bottom in 4 or 5 m of water by means of a crooked stick. The goby enters to spawn or hide. When the retrieving stick is thrust into the hole by which the goby entered, it is trapped.

Octopus trap

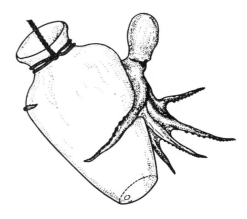

Fig. 8-13. Unbaited terra-cotta pot used in Japan for taking octopi. (From Kask, J. L., and Y. Hiyama. 1947. U. S. Fish Wildl. Serv., Fish. Leaf. **234:**1-107.)

Dip net employed in scooping fish attracted to light

Fig. 8-14. Dipnetting fish at night that are attracted to a torch. This primitive method was once used in New England for taking herring. Called "torching," this method is now being extended to the capture of school fishes by large vessels with elaborate lighting systems. (From Umali, A. F. 1950. U. S. Fish Wildl. Serv., Res. Rep. **17**:1-165. [Illustrations by S. G. Duran.])

Attracted to light. A third reaction of fish that aids in their capture is their attraction to light. Sidel'nikov and Izmest'ev (1971) describe experiments in attempting to take Pacific saury attracted to the ship by lights. Squid were also attracted and could be successfully taken with jig hooks near the edge of the illuminated zone. Experiments in taking African sardines, *Sardinella aurita,* jack mackerel, *Trachurus trachurus,* and Atlantic mackerel, *Scomber colias,* attracted to the ship by a light and captured with a large blanket net are described by Solov'ev (1971). He probably means Pacific mackerel, *Scomber japonicus.*

The light successfully attracted *Sardinella* off west Africa in all but the 7 or 8 days of the lunar cycle with the brightest moonlight. The average catch for each net haul was 3.8 tons. On Campeche Bank in the Gulf of Mexico 67.5 tons of *Sardinella* were caught at 24 light stations. On the shelf off Spanish Sahara 116 tons of Atlantic mack-

erel were taken in five nights; the maximum catch in one cast was 12 tons and in one night 48 tons. Catches were increased 40% to 50% when a larger ring net was substituted for the blanket net.

Fig. 8-14 shows the dipnetting of fish attracted by light from a small dugout with outriggers. Such "torching" was once used in New England to capture herring.

Migration up- or downstream. A fourth way in which the action of fish aids in their capture is through their vulnerability while migrating up- or downstream. This vulnerability is especially acute where fish migrating upstream must pass a rapid or waterfall. A novel form of gear once used at Celilo Falls on the Columbia River but now obsolete was a hanging basket or net suspended in air over the falls into which salmon would leap while attempting to surmount the falls.

Dip nets are used for salmon chiefly in rapids. Usually the operator stands on a

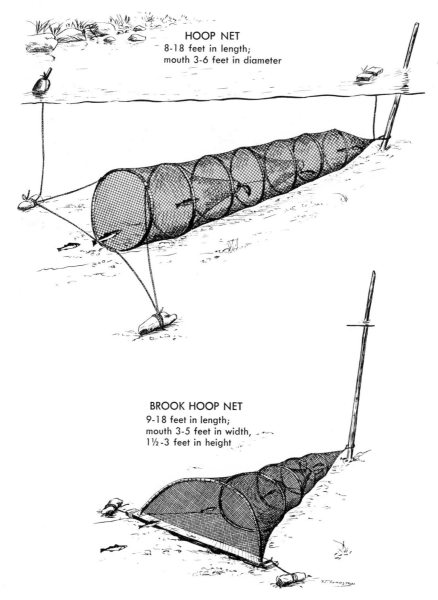

HOOP NET
8-18 feet in length;
mouth 3-6 feet in diameter

BROOK HOOP NET
9-18 feet in length;
mouth 3-5 feet in width,
1½-3 feet in height

Fig. 8-15. Two types of fyke or hoop nets used to capture stream fishes. (From Sundstrom, G. T. 1957. U. S. Fish Wildl. Serv., Circ. **48**:1-48.)

platform. The dip net, with a very large hoop and a long handle, is swept downstream as the fish are ascending. Dip nets are a favorite poaching gear, especially for taking salmon out of uncovered fish ladders.

Dip nets are also used extensively to capture alewives. In New England the alewife streams are owned by the towns. The ascending alewives on the smaller streams must pass through a dipping channel where they are penned up and dipped out, except for a reasonable number that are permitted to ascend into the pond to spawn.

In the pools below waterfalls on small streams a favorite Indian gear is the gaff. This is merely a large hook with line attached that fits on the end of a long pole. As soon as a fish is snagged, the hook becomes detached from the pole and the fish is hauled in.

Other types of gear are used to take migrating fish in less turbulent portions of the streams. One of the most ancient is the weir, but in most places it is now illegal because it is so efficient that it can destroy an entire run of anadromous fish. In New England weirs are used to lead eels into traps as they migrate downstream out of the lakes.

On the Pacific coast the fish wheel to take migrating salmon was developed within the last century, but it has been outlawed everywhere but on the Yukon River, where a few are still used to take salmon for feeding sled dogs. The fish wheel has four wide vanes and is turned by the current of the river. The end of each vane terminates in a piece of webbing with a recurved edge. As the salmon migrate upstream, the huge web scoops on the ends of the vanes lift them out of the water. They slide down the vane and reach a small board chute running obliquely across the vane. As the wheel continues to turn, the salmon slide down the chute into a box at the side of the wheel.

The hoop (or fyke) net is used extensively in streams to take eels, catfish and other river fishes, and baitfishes (Fig. 8-15). In shallow streams the mouth is often made semicircular.

The sturgeon gear used in the Turkish rivers flowing into the Black Sea is novel (Fig. 8-16). Large hooks are fastened by 3-foot gangions to a rope at least 25 fm long. The gangions are spaced a foot apart. By means of a light line and small float, each gangion is kept in a vertical position. According to Devedjian (1926), the sturgeon is snagged by the vent or the gills in passing through the hooks.

Although they are used in estuaries and tidal portions of large rivers, gill nets are also used extensively outside of the rivers. **Migrating at night (or in turbid water).** Gill nets are used extensively for taking

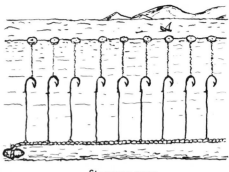

Sturgeon gear

Fig. 8-16. Novel type of unbaited hook gear used to capture sturgeon by snagging in Turkish rivers. (From Devedjian, K. 1926. Administration de la Dette Publique Ottomane, Constantinople. 649 pp.)

salmon (Fig. 8-17, *A*) in the turbid waters of Bristol Bay, on the Copper River flats in Central Alaska, off the mouth of the Stikine River in southeastern Alaska, and in other situations where the water is sufficiently turbid to prevent the salmon from avoiding the net. Farther south they are used off (and in the lower parts) of the Fraser, Columbia, and Sacramento Rivers and in or off the mouths of many smaller rivers. Although they are not separated in the statistics, many of the nets used are trammel nets. Small-meshed nets of fine twine are also used in the Columbia River to take the eulachon, *Thaleichthys pacificus*. In the Northwest many of the gill net boats now use a power-driven drum to haul the net, which is wound around the drum. Drift gill nets are used on all our coasts to take a variety of fishes. In Europe drift gill nets are employed extensively by offshore vessels for catching herring.

A large-mesh gill net is used in shark fishing (Fig. 8-17, *B*); it is usually equipped with large floats and set on or close to the bottom.

In many localities it is easier to fish gill nets by fastening them to stakes or anchoring them to the bottom. A fisherman can usually attend to a larger number of setnets than he can drift nets. Strong tides or winds also discourage drift netting in some locali-

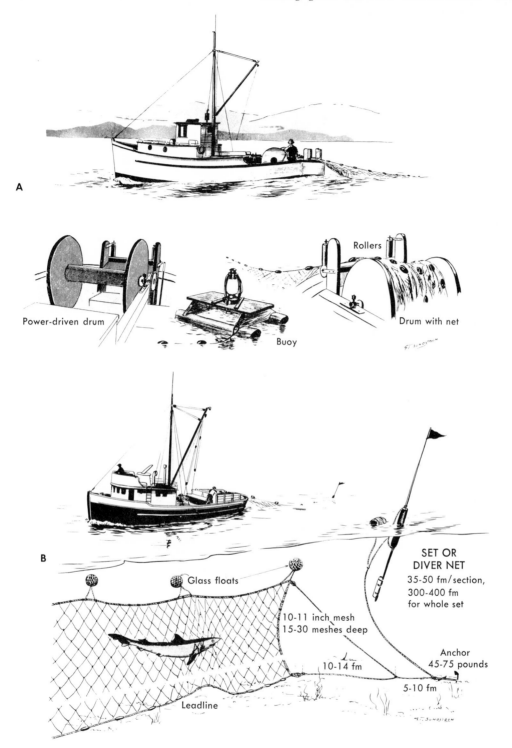

Fig. 8-17. Gill nets used in, **A**, salmon fishing and, **B**, shark fishing. Powered drum for retrieving gill net is being used increasingly in the Northwest. Shark gill net has heavy netting and is set on or close to the bottom. (From Sundstrom, G. T. 1957. U. S. Fish Wildl. Serv., Circ. **48**:1-48.)

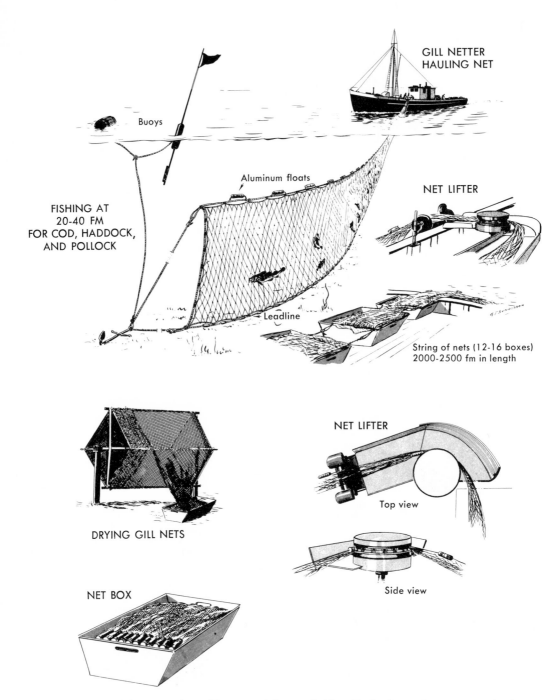

GILL NETTER
HAULING NET

Buoys

Aluminum floats

NET LIFTER

FISHING AT
20-40 FM
FOR COD, HADDOCK,
AND POLLOCK

Leadline

String of nets (12-16 boxes)
2000-2500 fm in length

DRYING GILL NETS

NET LIFTER

Top view

Side view

NET BOX

Fig. 8-18. "Sink" or anchor gill net used by small New England vessels to capture bank fishes, showing method of setting and retrieving nets. (From Sundstrom, G. T. 1957. U. S. Fish Wildl. Serv., Circ. **48:**1-48.)

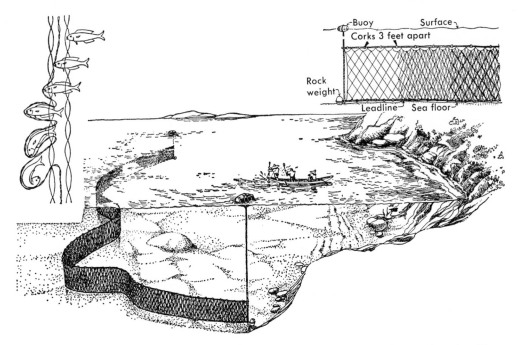

Fig. 8-19. Trammel net illustrating how fish are captured by the three layers of netting. Net illustrated is a Philippine example set on the bottom. (From Umali, A. F. 1950. U. S. Fish Wildl. Serv., Res. Rep. **17**:1-165. [Illustrations by S. G. Duran.])

ties. Where there is a large tidal range, staked gill nets may be set so as to intercept fish leaving an area with the receding tide.

In New England, especially in Gloucester, Massachusetts, and Portland, Maine, a number of small- to medium-sized vessels use what are described locally as "sink" or "anchor" gill nets (Fig. 8-18). Each vessel has three complete sets of nets. One set is left anchored overnight on the fishing ground, the second set is carried on board the vessel to put out when the first set is hauled in, and the third set is on the drying rack. These vessels fish for cod, haddock, and pollock, taking a few other fishes incidentally.

A trammel net (Fig. 8-19) resembles a sandwich. Between two layers of large-mesh heavy webbing is a small-mesh layer of light webbing. Unlike a gill net, the fish pushes a pocket of the fine, loose center layer through one of the large, relatively stiff meshes of one of the outside layers and is thus trapped in a fine mesh bag. Trammel nets have advantages and disadvantages. They are more costly and harder to manage than a simple gill net. Unlike gill nets, trammel nets will catch fish over a wide range of sizes, sometimes an advantage. From the conservation angle their nonselectivity precludes their use in waters in which *any* species must be protected. Large-mesh gill nets are sometimes allowed to fish for king salmon, for instance, while the smaller sockeye are passing unharmed.

Migration alongshore. The sixth type of voluntary action by fish that aids in their capture is a directional migration along the shore. Fish so migrating can usually be led into a trap or enclosure from which they are easily removed. Perhaps the most original method for taking alongshore migrants is the reef net, an ancient gear developed by the Indians of the Northwest to capture salmon. The principle is simple. As the salmon migrate from the ocean toward their

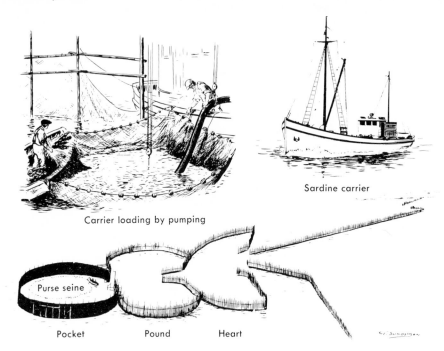

Carrier loading by pumping

Sardine carrier

Purse seine

Pocket   Pound   Heart

Fig. 8-20. A type of impounding net, the brush wier is used for sardines (young herring), *Clupea harengus*, in Maine. (From Sundstrom, G. T. 1957. U. S. Fish Wildl. Serv., Circ. **48:**1-48.)

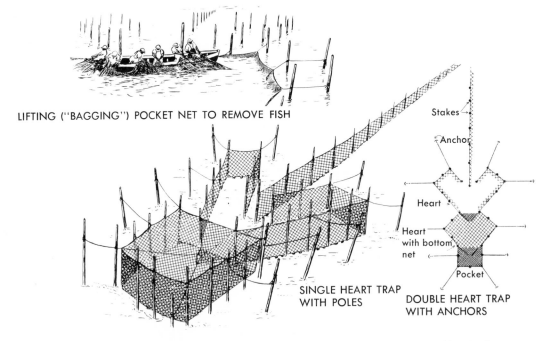

LIFTING ("BAGGING") POCKET NET TO REMOVE FISH

Stakes

Anchor

Heart

Heart with bottom net

Pocket

SINGLE HEART TRAP WITH POLES

DOUBLE HEART TRAP WITH ANCHORS

Fig. 8-21. The Atlantic coast pound net, another type of impounding net, resembles the huge salmon traps once used for Pacific salmon until outlawed by legislation but has lighter piling and less rugged construction. (From Sundstrom, G. T. 1957. U. S. Fish Wildl. Serv., Circ. **48:**1-48.)

natal streams, they must pass through channels among the islands of the San Juan Archipelago. These channels are obstructed in places by rocky reefs running at right angles to the channels. These reefs support a dense growth of the giant kelp *Macrocystis*. The Indians cut narrow channels through these kelp beds to tempt the salmon to take a shortcut across the reef. In this channel the Indians suspend a blanket-shaped net between two anchored boats (originally large dugout canoes). To keep the salmon from swimming under the leading edge of the net, they string a few strands of rope across the channel below the edge of the net. When the lookout signals that a school of salmon is over the net, it is hauled up immediately from both sides.

Somewhat more sophisticated is the so-called brush weir used in Maine and New Brunswick to capture herring for the sardine canneries (Fig. 8-20). It is called a brush weir because the lead and parts of the trap walls consist of saplings of deciduous trees stuck into the soft bottom. On encountering the leafy wall the schools of herring follow it toward deeper water and enter the first chamber, or "heart," of a maze from which they finally reach the spiller, or "pocket," which is made of fine mesh netting and holds the herring until they are taken out with a small seine. These brush weirs do not follow any set pattern; some are merely a wall across the opening of a shallow bay. At high tide the herring can swim over the wall into the bay but when the tide falls they are trapped and seined out. Such tidal weirs are used in other regions where there is sufficient tidal range.

Evolving from the brush weir is the pound net. On the Atlantic coast the more primitive form of the pound net is the so-called floating trap. These were used in Maine for taking mackerel and Atlantic salmon. In southern New England these small pound nets are used to capture a variety of fishes, including scup, mackerel, sea robins, bluefish, and striped bass.

The regular pound net (Fig. 8-21) is much larger, has a much longer lead, and may have two hearts. On Cape Cod near Provincetown they take mackerel, herring, squid, pollock, and even bluefin tuna. They are an important gear from the mid-Atlantic area to North Carolina, catching a great variety of fishes.

The pound net reached its zenith in development in Alaska and Puget Sound where it was the chief gear for sockeye and pink salmon until legislated out of existence, except for a very few on Indian reservations. The impossibility of driving piles in the rocky bottom of many good locations led to the development of the floating salmon trap, now obsolete.

Pound nets of various types are used in many places, but especially where fish perform regular migrations through relatively

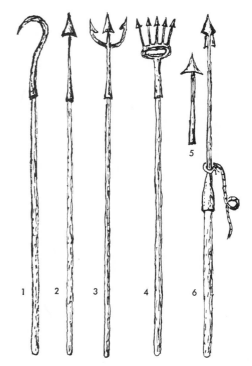

Fig. 8-22. Assorted spears and harpoons. *1,* Gaff. *2,* Lance. *3,* Trident. *4,* Harpoon with five points. *5,* Harpoon (tuna and dolphin) with fixed head. *6,* Harpoon (tuna and dolphin) with loose head. (From Devedjian, K. 1926. Administration de la Dette Publique Ottomane, Constantinople. 649 pp.)

narrow waterways. For example, they are used in the Bosphorus for bluefin tuna and other fishes.

Motile species caught without their voluntary action

Our third major category comprises fishing gear catching motile species in which the actions of the fish itself are not of particular aid in its capture.

Individual capture. The first type of this category of gear is for taking individual organisms. Of these gears the spear is possibly the most primitive. Fig. 8-22 shows the chief types, ranging from the simple gaff to the harpoon. Fig. 8-23 shows a three-headed harpoon from the Philippines.

Spears are used in Atlantic coast estuaries to capture eels, often through the ice. Spearing or "gigging" flounders at night in shoal water either from a skiff or wading is both a commercial enterprise and a popular sport

fishery along the south Atlantic and Gulf coasts. Spearfishing, especially for reef fishes, is a sport of scuba divers.

The hand-thrown harpoon (Fig. 8-24) was practically the only gear used for taking swordfish until it was discovered that they could be taken on midwater longlines. This type of harpoon is also used to a limited extent for bluefin tuna in New England. Nonexplosive harpoons, usually fired from a small cannon, have always been the preferred gear for small whales.

A fleet of small Norwegian vessels has hunted basking sharks, and sometimes small whales at the same time, for centuries. They take these huge sharks along the entire coast of Norway from the Barents Sea to the Kattegat, on the North Sea banks, and west and south of Ireland. The small harpoon, weighing 18 kg, is fired from a small whale gun. The harpoon projectile goes entirely through the shark. Since the steel wire (ap-

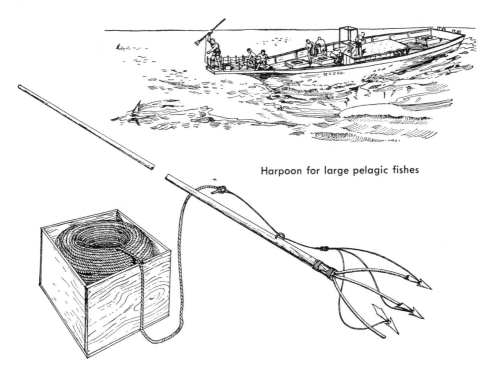

Harpoon for large pelagic fishes

Fig. 8-23. Novel type of three-pronged spear for taking large pelagic fishes in the Philippines. (From Umali, A. F. 1950. U. S. Fish Wildl. Serv., Res. Rep. **17**:1-165. [Illustrations by S. G. Duran.])

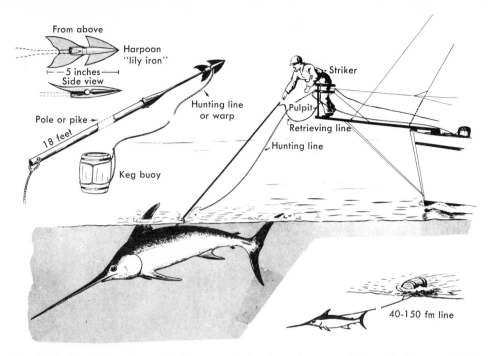

Fig. 8-24. Showing method of taking swordfish with a harpoon. (From Sundstrom, G. T. 1957. U. S. Fish Wildl. Serv., Circ. **48**:1-48.)

Fig. 8-25. Haul seining for pink salmon on the tide flats at the mouth of Ketchikan Creek, Alaska. (Photograph taken in 1904 by John N. Cobb.)

proximately the first 20 m) is attached at the balance point of the harpoon projectile, when retrieved the harpoon turns sideways, forming a toggle from which the shark cannot escape (Myklevoll, 1968). Only the huge liver is retained, and in 1967 53 boats took over 2 million kg of liver.

The rifle must be considered a fishing gear for marine mammals. It is used in the Arctic for walrus and seals and in the Black Sea for killing dolphins. A club, instead of a rifle, is used to kill both adult and newborn harp seals on the pack ice off Newfoundland and Labrador.

In modern whaling the large whales are killed with explosive harpoons fired from powerful whaling guns mounted on fast killer vessels.

Taken against shore. The second type of gear for taking fishes without aid from their own actions is that for catching them against the shore.

The stop seine is used, principally in Maine, to take large quantities of young herring for the sardine canneries. It is a small vessel or boat fishery. When a large school of young herring is observed to enter a cove or bight along the coast, a stop net is quickly placed entirely across the mouth. This may require several nets, quickly lashed end to end, and several small boats. The impounded herring are now seined out of the cove as needed by the canneries.

A second method of fishing against the shore is the use of haul or beach seines (Fig. 8-25), which come in all sizes. For pelagic species the floats keep the top of the net at the surface; for benthic species the

Fig. 8-26. Using a cast net for mullet in the Bosporus. Note extra large leads necessitated by the 4- to 5-knot current.

lead line is made heavier so the net will hug the bottom. The nets are hung full along the corkline and lead line so that in the water the netting forms a vertical arc with the concave side next to the shore. Many beach seines have larger meshes on the wings to facilitate fast hauling. Most have a section of heavier small mesh in the bunt; this often has a bag. Large haul seines are often operated at a fixed location and hauled in with a mechanical winch. They are used on all U. S. coasts for a variety of species.

Taken in shoal water. Some fishing gears are especially adapted to shoal water. Cast nets (Fig. 8-26) are used in the Gulf and south Atlantic for shrimp and mullet, and in many other countries for reef fishes, mullet, pomfrets, etc. The Spanish-style net works best in shoal water. The edges of the net have tucks on the inside, thus forming a continuous pocket along the bottom inside of the net. This net has to touch bottom and be retrieved slowly to keep the lead line on the bottom until all of the fish have been forced into the pocket. The English-style net has lines from the edges that come through the center of the net so that by pulling on the center line the net can be closed to form a bag. It can be used in both shallow and deep water, but must be retrieved quickly to close the bottom of the net.

One form of shoal water gear that is quite effective is the encircling or runaround gill net (Fig. 8-27). It is used from the mid-Atlantic area to the Gulf for mullet, bluefish, striped bass, sciaenids, Spanish and king mackerels, and carangids. The gill net is quietly run around a school of fish in shoal water, and then the fish are frightened and run into the gill net. In Turkey the escape of mullet that leap over the net is prevented by a ring of bamboo poles floating on the surface just outside the net, over which is a layer of fine netting.

Another shoal water gear is the filter net (Fig. 8-28, *A*), which is set in a tidal current to catch shrimp drifting with the tide.

Taken on or close to bottom. To catch fish living on the bottom the chief gears are towed nets. However, in New England and

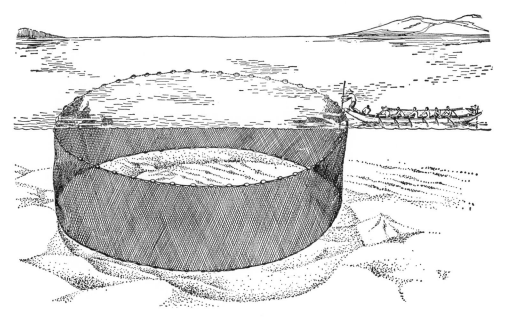

Fig. 8-27. Encircling gill net, used extensively in the middle and south Atlantic and Gulf states and in Asia for mullets and some other estuarine species. (From Umali, A. F. 1950. U. S. Fish Wildl. Serv., Res. Rep. **17:**1-165. [Illustrations by S. G. Duran.])

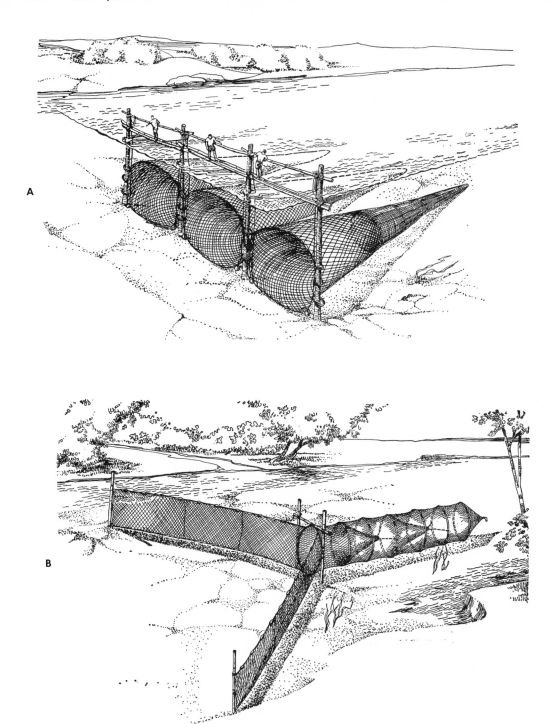

Fig. 8-28. A, Tide-actuated filter net for taking Philippine shrimp is similar to the Chinese shrimp nets once used in San Francisco Bay. **B,** Fyke net with wings for taking fish in shoal water moving with a current. (From Umali, A. F. 1950. U. S. Fish Wildl. Serv., Res. Rep. **17:**1-165. [Illustrations by S. G. Duran.])

New York it was formerly common to catch winter flounders with fyke nets set in a few fathoms of water. These nets had long wings to guide the flounders into the net and were set entirely with anchors. A more common type of fyke net is shown in Fig. 8-28, *B*.

Perhaps the earliest form of towed net for benthic species was the beam trawl (Fig. 8-29). The headrope is fastened to a long wooden beam, and each side of the net is fastened to a steel runner. The disadvantages are the low height off the bottom, the restriction of the length of the beam to what

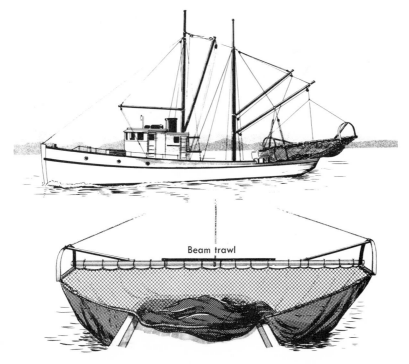

Fig. 8-29. Beam trawl used for shrimp fishing in Alaska. (From Sundstrom, G. T. 1957. U. S. Fish Wildl. Serv., Circ. **48**:1-48.)

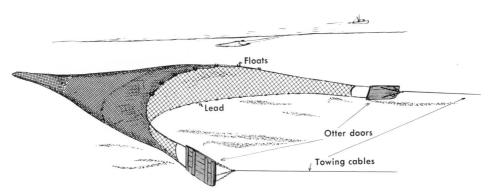

Fig. 8-30. Shrimp otter trawl. (From Sundstrom, G. T. 1957. U. S. Fish Wildl. Serv., Circ. **48**:1-48.)

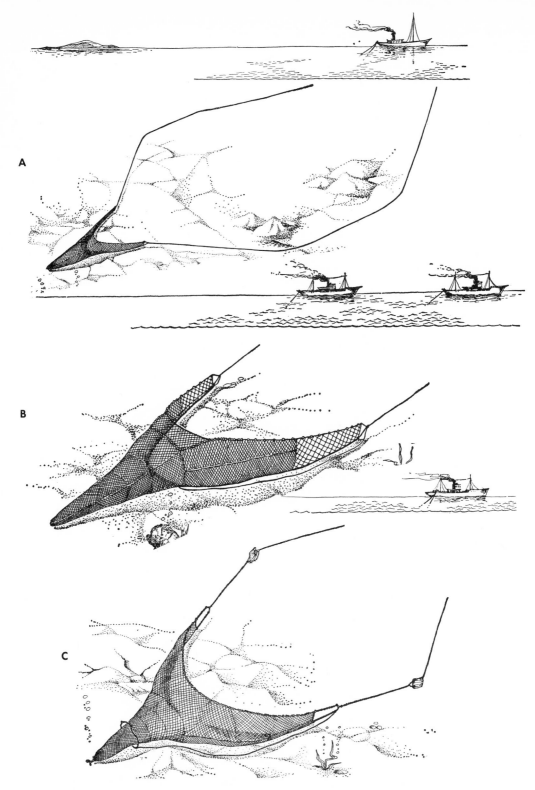

Fig. 8-31. Additional forms of towed nets. **A,** Danish seine (or trawl). **B,** Two-boat trawl. **C,** Vigneron-Dahl otter trawl. (From Umali, A. F. 1950. U. S. Fish Wildl. Serv., Res. Rep. **17:**1-165. [Illustrations by S. G. Duran.])

can be handled, and the difficulty of handling the awkward gear in rough weather. Today only a few survive and are fishing for shrimp in the inside waters of Puget Sound and southeastern Alaska.

The otter trawl and shrimp trawl (Fig. 8-30) are essentially the same, but the otter trawl for fishing bank fishes, rockfishes, and sea breams usually has larger floats on the headrope and fishes much higher off the bottom. They are both used on all U. S. coasts for shrimp, bottom fishes, and sciaenids.

The two-boat trawl (Fig. 8-31, *B*) is still used in some countries. It was formerly used under the name "paranzella net" for taking flatfish around the Farallon Islands off San Francisco.

Whereas the otter boards in the shrimp trawl are fastened directly to the wings, the majority of fish trawls use the Vigneron-Dahl modification (Fig. 8-31, *C*), with the boards far in advance of the wings. The net spreads better and the ropes scare fish into the net so that the same size net takes more fish than in the shrimp trawl.

The Danish seine (or trawl) is used extensively in the North Sea for flatfish (Fig. 8-31, *A*). It combines all the features of a beach seine and a trawl. There are no otter boards. The long ground ropes are set out at wide angles to the net. The vessel then pulls the ropes in while moving slowly ahead, the ropes scaring all the flatfish in the area toward the net.

Most of the larger otter trawl vessels being built today are stern trawlers with a ramp across the stern of the vessel up which the huge net can be drawn. This greatly speeds up retrieval of the net as well as permitting fishing operations under stormier conditions.

Taken from surface schools. A fifth group of gears is designed for capturing surface schooling fishes without voluntary action on their part. Perhaps the oldest of these is the lampara net (Fig. 8-32). It is a small light seine that can be used on a relatively small vessel and can be retrieved quickly. The wings have large meshes and can be hauled in rapidly, confining the fish in the bunt. The lampara net took the bulk of the California sardine catch until the advent of the modern purse seine. It is still used in California for squid and by small vessels for various shore fishes. The tuna vessels still using live bait carry a lampara net to use from a powered skiff when they need a fresh live bait supply.

The menhaden purse seine (Fig. 8-33) is set out and retrieved by two powered seine boats that circle the school of fish in opposite directions. They are now equipped with modern power blocks for seine retrieval. The large so-called menhaden purse seiner is merely a transport vessel that carries the seine boats (on davits) and the fish. This form of seining is now confined to the Gulf and Atlantic menhaden fishery and to mackerel seining in the North Atlantic.

The ring net (Fig. 8-34, *A*) is still used in some countries and is one step in the evolution of one-vessel purse seining (Fig. 8-34, *B*). On the Pacific coast some of the salmon seiners are using huge powered drums for reeling in the net (Fig. 8-35, *A*). Salmon nets are much less bulky than the fine mesh nets used for anchovies, herring, and sardines and so are amenable to this innovation.

The tuna vessels use a very large nylon purse seine for yellowfin tuna, skipjack tuna, and bluefin tuna. These huge seines were made possible by the simultaneous development of synthetic fibers and the power block for hauling such a heavy net. These purse seines are sufficiently deep to reach the shallow thermocline in tropical waters. This cold water prevents the very fast-swimming yellowfin from sounding beneath the lead line and escaping before the net can be pursed. The U. S. tuna seiners each carry four to five small boats, about 6½ feet long with 100 HP outboard motors that can make 40 knots. They are used to herd together a scattered school of yellowfin tuna. When frightened into a tight school, they can be captured with a shorter net.

TUNA BAIT FISHING WITH LAMPARA SEINE

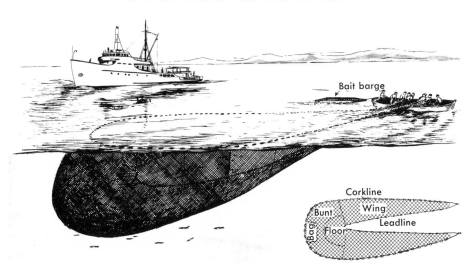

Fig. 8-32. Lampara net is useful for smaller vessels and for seining tuna bait. (From Sundstrom, G. T. 1957. U. S. Fish Wildl. Serv., Circ. **48**:1-48.)

MENHADEN PURSE SEINING

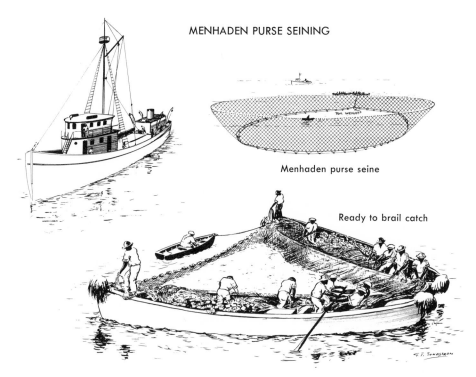

Fig. 8-33. Menhaden purse seine operated from two small seine boats using large vessel merely as a carrier. (From Sundstrom, G. T. 1957. U. S. Fish Wildl. Serv., Circ. **48**:1-48.)

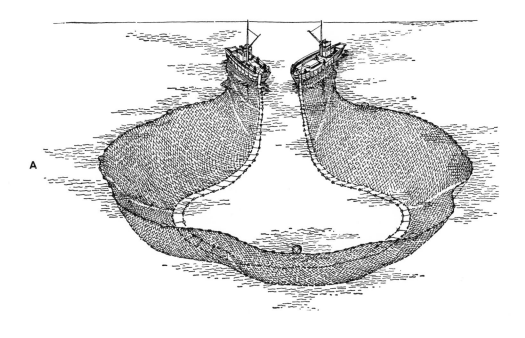

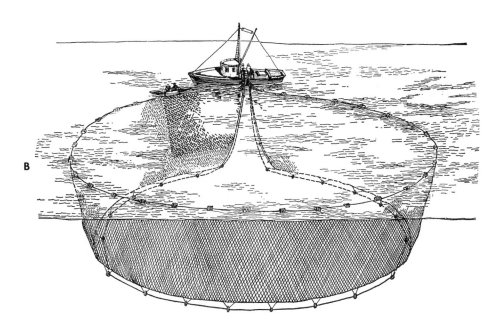

Fig. 8-34. Seining from vessels. **A,** Ring net operated from two vessels is still used in some countries and is the precursor of the purse seine, **B.** (From Umali, A. F. 1950. U. S. Fish Wildl.. Serv., Res. Rep. **17**:1-165. [Illustrations by S. G. Duran.])

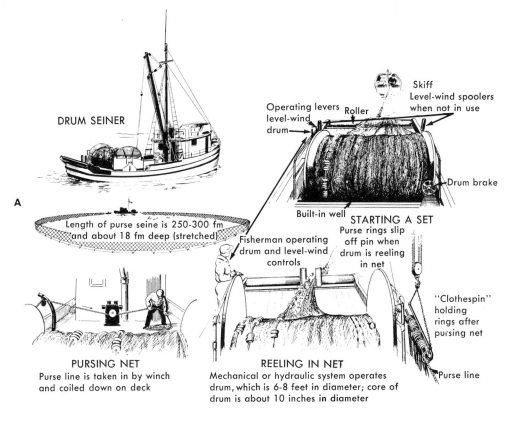

DRUM SEINER

A

Length of purse seine is 250-300 fm and about 18 fm deep (stretched)

Operating levers level-wind drum

Roller

Skiff Level-wind spoolers when not in use

Drum brake

Built-in well

STARTING A SET

Purse rings slip off pin when drum is reeling in net

Fisherman operating drum and level-wind controls

"Clothespin" holding rings after pursing net

PURSING NET

Purse line is taken in by winch and coiled down on deck

REELING IN NET

Mechanical or hydraulic system operates drum, which is 6-8 feet in diameter; core of drum is about 10 inches in diameter

Purse line

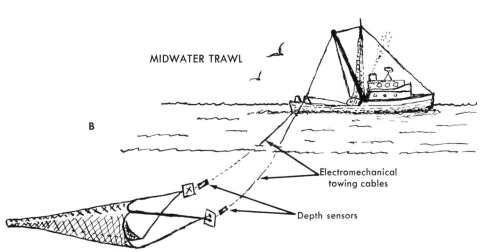

MIDWATER TRAWL

B

Electromechanical towing cables

Depth sensors

Fig. 8-35. A, Drum seining is the use of a purse seine that is retrieved by winding on a powered drum and is used chiefly for salmon in the Northwest. **B,** Midwater trawl is used for capturing schooling fish when the schools are in the water column below the surface. (**A** from Sundstrom, G. T. 1957. U. S. Fish Wildl. Serv., Circ. **48:**1-48; **B** from Johnston, L. J., and W. L. High. 1970. In Pacific hake. U. S. Fish Wildl. Serv., Circ. **332:**1-152.)

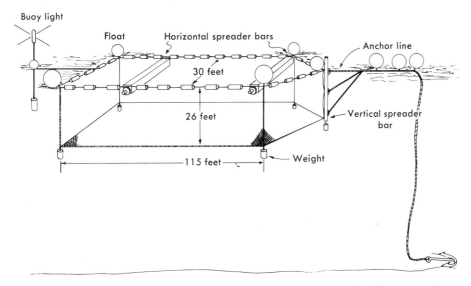

Fig. 8-36. Norwegian-developed pound net adapted for towing to bring live young fish into sheltered waters and retain them until they have digested the "feed" in their intestines so that they will be ready for salting or canning. (From Glanville, A. 1956. FAO Fish. Bull. **9:**113-129.)

Taken from subsurface schools. The last category of gear is that for capturing fish that school off the bottom but beneath the surface layers. This problem is being solved by the development of the midwater trawl (Fig. 8-35, *B*). In experiments in hake fishing off the Washington-Oregon coasts, eight models of nets were tested with mouth openings varying from 50 × 50 feet to 80 × 80 feet and suitable for vessels with 650 HP to as low as (some nets) 330 HP. The earliest version of the midwater trawl (Glanville, 1956), called the Larsen midwater trawl, was first tried in 1948 for taking herring off the coast of Jutland. It is a square-mouthed net varying from 4 to 10 fm in the mouth, without otter boards, and towed by two boats. It was adopted in Scandinavia and other parts of Europe for catching herring, sprat, anchovies, mackerel, and other pelagic fish. It has the advantage that it can be operated by small vessels (about 40 to 200 HP) with the aid of an echo sounder.

In addition to gear used strictly for catching fish, I will mention the holding of live fish. In the sardine fisheries it is important

that the young herring (or sprats or sardines) not have their intestines crammed with copepods or pteropods. In southeastern Alaska during the years when herring were being pickled by the mild Scotch cure method, it was customary to anchor a square-shaped pound net in a sheltered cove close to the fishing grounds. When a school was surrounded by a purse seine, the vessel hauled in only a portion of the net. Then a smaller tow boat fastened a bridle to the bow and stern and towed the seine vessel sideways through the water (the seine with its captured herring trailing close against the protected side of the vessel) to the pound.

Fig. 8-36 shows a pound net developed in Norway (Sherman, 1969) into which sardines can be transferred immediately after capture. The vessel is then free to continue fishing while the net is towed slowly to a sheltered anchorage. The practicality of this method has not yet been demonstrated. When the herring contain chiefly "red feed" (copepods), they are ready for salting in one to several days. When they are filled with "black feed" (pteropods), it is very difficult to get them clean enough to salt without their retention of a horrible taste.

Suggested readings

Alekseev, A. P., editor. 1968. Fish behavior and fishing techniques. All-Union Conference, Murmansk, U.S.S.R. (Translated from Russian in 1971.) IPST Cat. No. 5938, TT 71-50010. Office of Technical Services, U. S. Department of Commerce, Springfield, Va. pp. 1-192.

Glanville, A. 1956. The Larsen mid-water trawl. FAO Fish. Bull. **9:**113-129.

Johnson, L. J., and W. L. High. 1970. Midwater trawling equipment and fishing technique for capturing hake off the coast of Washington and Oregon. In Pacific hake. U. S. Fish Wildl. Serv. Circ. **332:**1-152.

Kask, J. L., and Y. Hiyama. 1947. Japanese fishing gear. U. S. Fish Wildl. Serv., Fish. Leaf. **234:** 1-107.

Myklevoll, S. 1968. Basking shark fishery. Comm. Fish. Rev. **30:**59-63.

Sidel'nikov, I. I., and E. M. Izmest'ev. 1971. Peculiarities in the behavior of Pacific saury and squid with fishing at light. In Fish behavior and fishing techniques. IPST Cat. No. 5938. Office of Technical Services, U. S. Department of Commerce, Springfield, Va. pp. 57-61.

Solov'ev, Y. 1971. Results of experimental fishing of commercial items at light in the Atlantic. In Fish behavior and fishing techniques. IPST Cat. No. 5938. Office of Technical Services, U. S. Department of Commerce, Springfield, Va. pp. 91-95.

Sundstrom, G. T. 1957. Commercial fishing vessels and gear. U. S. Fish Wildl. Serv., Circ. **48:**1-48.

Umali, A. F. 1950. Guide to the classification of fishing gear in the Philippines. U. S. Fish Wildl. Serv., Res. Rep. **17:**1-165. (Illustrations by S. G. Duran.)

Zahn, M. C. 1970. Japanese tanner crab fishery in eastern Bering Sea. Comm. Fish. Rev. **32:**52-56.

part four

🌿 Marine populations

chapter 9

✌ Natural fluctuations in abundance

GENERAL CONSIDERATIONS

The size of a population depends on so many factors that it is virtually impossible to determine the normal or average size of any natural population. For most marine populations annual fluctuations in total abundance are a normal phenomenon. These fluctuations tend to be minimal in those populations dwelling in stable environments and maximal in the reverse situation. Environment in this sense includes both biological and nonbiological factors.

Fecundity may also play an important role in fluctuations. Organisms with a low fecundity tend to have more stable survival rates. Species with a high fecundity may recover quickly from the effects of a low spawning stock and thus exhibit wider fluctuations.

The underlying theory of population size is well and succinctly expressed by Sette, who states:

Fishing theory says that the annual increase in a population is a function of population size and environmental capacity. If a population "fills" its environment, births and deaths are equal and the population is in equilibrium. When fishing takes place, catch mortality is imposed, the population is reduced below the environment's capacity, births exceed "natural" deaths and the population tends to increase toward the environmental limits. With very intense fishing and a very low population level, the reproductive increase is near its maximum, natural mortality near its minimum, but the annual increase is low because there are few spawners. When fishing is very light and the population near the environmental limits, the spawning population is large but the back-pressure from the environmental limit depresses reproduction or increases natural mortality, or both, so that the annual increase is again small. At some level of population size intermediate between these extremes, where the spawning stock is moderately large and back-pressure from the environment moderately gentle, the annual increase is maximal. Of course, at any level, the population size will be in equilibrium when the annual catch equals the annual increase, but the annual harvest that can be sustained without disturbing the equilibrium will be maximal at the level of population abundance that affords the maximum annual increase.*

These relationships between the number of spawners, the number of survivors, and the surplus available to the fishery are shown in Fig. 9-1, illustrating the point emphasized by Sette in the foregoing quotation. With a low number of spawners the rate of increase is very steep, but the low

---

*From Sette, O. E. 1961. Problems in fish population fluctuations. Calif. Mar. Res. Comm., CalCOFI Rep. **8:**21-24.

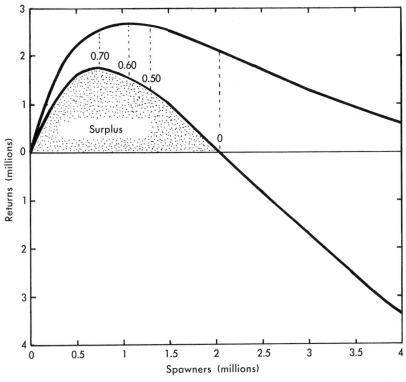

Fig. 9-1. Reproduction curve for Karluk River sockeye salmon for the fish spawning in the years 1890 to 1928 showing for various numbers of spawners the number of adults returning to the river in subsequent years. Lower curve shows for each number of spawners the difference (surplus if plus) between the number of spawners and the number of adults in the next generation. Figures along the curve are the equilibrium points for several fishing rates. (Modified from Rounsefell, G. A. 1958. U. S. Fish Wildl. Serv., Fish. Bull. **58:**83-169.)

population precludes a large numeric increase. With a large number of spawners the "back-pressure" of the limited environment causes such a low survival that the total population actually decreases. Obviously with no fishing the population illustrated will oscillate around a total of 2 million adults. The maximum annual increase and the opportunity for maximum harvest occur with a spawning population of about 750,000.

From the foregoing it becomes apparent that the two chief causes of fluctuations in the abundance of exploited populations are changes in the intensity of fishing and changes in the capacity of the environment. Many of the factors that limit the environmental capacity—spawning space, oxygen,

temperature, salinity, etc.—are covered in Chapters 3 to 5 concerning limiting factors. Limiting factors are themselves subject to fluctuation, and these variations exert a profound effect on populations. Such environmental changes may be sporadic or cyclic, long-term or short-term, reversible or irreversible. This discussion will begin with long-term environmental changes.

EFFECTS OF LONG-TERM CHANGES IN TEMPERATURE

Through evolutionary changes organisms become adapted to specific environments and to specific means of coping with the environment, e.g., the inherited capacities to perform long migrations through specific water masses, to follow specific currents, to store sufficient fuel to enable survival for long periods of scarcity, or to expend energy for long journeys. Such inherited traits may determine the types of substrate required for spawning or the tolerance ranges of salinity, temperature, and oxygen at different life history stages. Obviously the population size of any organism depends on the extent of suitable habitat. This means that shifts in the composition of or in the area occupied by a water mass can greatly expand or restrict the size of a population both in number and in depth or geographic range.

Much has been written about the effect of long-term changes in temperature on the abundance of stocks of fish. Unfortunately in the majority of cases the estimation of fish abundance has been the yield along a particular stretch of coastline; in these cases it is often impossible to be certain whether the population abundance was drastically changed or whether the fish merely remained offshore or moved to another portion of the coast. For instance, in commenting on the albacore fishery of southern California, Clemens and Craig (1965) state that ". . . the fishery was nearly a complete failure for 7 seasons (1928-1934)." This failure of the albacore fishery was blamed on a shift of migration routes caused by a change in ocean temperatures. Such a drastic change in ocean temperatures is not borne out either by their own curve of annual sea temperatures at La Jolla (their Fig. 9) or the sea surface temperature anomalies given by Roden (1961).

In 1925 W. C. Herrington and I made a thorough analysis of the abundance of albacore during the 1915 to 1925 period using a link-relative index in which the logarithms of the individual catches of each boat were compared in other years only to catches of the same boat made on the same or the adjacent date. This index showed a continuous smooth decline in abundance from the beginning to the end of the period; plotted logarithmically it formed a straight line, showing a continuous rate of decline.

Permission to publish this index was withheld on the grounds that such a catastrophic decline could not be caused by falling abundance. However, if one examines the California albacore catches (Fig. 9-2), it would indeed appear that the population reached a very low state of abundance from which it took many years to recover. This decline, although apparently real, was not necessarily caused by the fishery.

There is considerable disagreement among biologists as to the effect of long-term temperature fluctuations on the actual abundance of populations; there is rather general agreement that such changes can modify the areas accessible to various species. This in itself does not necessarily increase or decrease the total numbers of a species, especially if the total number is controlled by factors on some distant spawning ground. In fact the availability of a larger area may even have a deleterious effect by subjecting the population to more fishing pressure. A good case in point is the establishment and rapid increase of a fishery for Atlantic salmon in the waters of west Greenland as a result of the recent warming of the Arctic seas. The salmon spawn principally in the streams of New England, the Maritime Provinces, Quebec, Newfoundland, and Europe. In these areas they are basically a sport fish, but now they are additionally subjected to a heavy commercial fishery.

Since the favorable temperature range for each species has both an upper and a lower limit, the northward extension of range by means of a northward shift of isotherms may also cause a northward movement of the southern boundary of the range with no net gain in area.

Climatic changes sometimes cut off remnants of a population in a portion of their former range that is still suitable, leaving a relict population separated from the main body by an impassable environmental barrier. One example is the lobster, *Homarus vulgaris,* in the Sea of Marmara, extending into the Black Sea. At the central fish market in Istanbul, Devedjian (1926) estimated

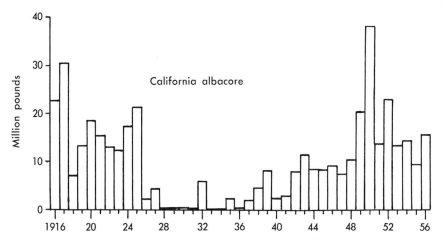

Fig. 9-2. Albacore catches in California from 1916 to 1956 illustrating the natural decline in abundance that practically eliminated the fishery for over a decade.

annual landings of 30,000 lobsters from this isolated population.

That long-term natural fluctuations both in total species biomass and in the relative abundance of different species are normal phenomena is indicated in studies by Soutar and Isaacs (1969). Sediment cores gathered in the Santa Barbara Channel, California, were taken from an area where anaerobic conditions permit the accumulation of undisturbed sediments. These cores show varves caused by winter runoff from the land and a less dense summer layer of diatom frustules. In general the varves are thought to be equivalent to a single year, thus yielding a time-biological record. From the scales deposited in these varves it was possible to estimate the abundance of several species over a period of 1850 years to the present. The Pacific sardine, *Sardinops sagax caerulea,* showed about 12 periods of occurrence over this period of years. The average time between occurrences was 80 years, with a range of 20 to 150 years. Both the northern anchovy, *Engraulis mordax,* and the Pacific hake, *Merluccius productus,* were present in greater numbers. The anchovy was most abundant about 1500 years ago and declined steadily for 12 centuries. The hake exhibited wide changes in abun-

dance, with peaks about every 300 to 350 years. Whether these changes in apparent abundance were real or an artifact caused by shifts in areal distribution during different periods of time in accordance with climatic shifts can only be conjectured.

Long-term changes in abundance within historic time as related to climatic trends have been studied for the New England region (Taylor et al., 1957) and for the northeastern Pacific (Ketchen, 1956; Bell and Pruter, 1958). Air temperatures increased, especially during the winter months, at New Haven, Connecticut, from a low in 1815 of nearly 3° F below the 174-year average (1780 to 1953) to a high in 1930 of about 3.5° F above the average. Such changes in air temperatures appear to reflect changes in sea temperatures. The Arctic Sea has warmed appreciably since 1921; the North Sea and the North Atlantic from the British Isles to the west coast of Greenland have warmed since the 1920's. These changes have been accompanied by changes in the distribution of marine forms. A large cod fishery sprang up along the west coast of Greenland, the cod now being caught about 300 nautical miles (555 km) farther north than formerly according to Taylor et al. (1957); however, Bell and Pruter

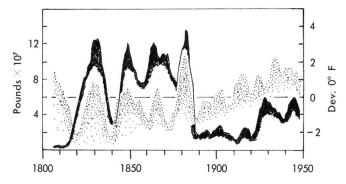

Fig. 9-3. Mackerel landings in New England (black) and air temperature deviations 3 years earlier at New Haven, Connecticut (stippled). Curves are smoothed by a 5-year moving average. Note the apparent correlation from 1820 to 1890 and the subsequent lack of any relationship. (Modified from Taylor, C. C., et al. 1957. U. S. Fish Wildl. Serv., Fish. Bull. **57:** 293-345.)

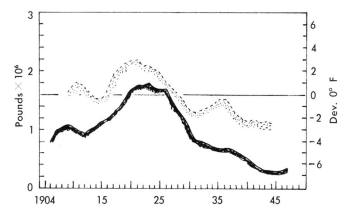

Fig. 9-4. Lobster landings in Rhode Island (solid line) compared to differences in January and July surface water temperatures at Boothbay Harbor, Maine, shown as deviations from the mean difference (dotted line). The decline in the mean difference shows the result of the general warming trend. (Modified from Taylor, C. C., et al. 1957. U. S. Fish Wildl. Serv., Fish. Bull. **57:**293-345.)

(1958) claim that the rise of the Greenland cod fishery was based on economic and other factors unrelated to abundance.

The landings of Atlantic mackerel, *Scomber scombrus,* after the fishery became well established in 1820 were positively correlated with the air temperatures at New Haven 3 years earlier over the 71-year period from 1820 to 1890 (Fig. 9-3). Since 1890 there has been little tendency toward any correlation between temperature and mackerel landings.

A study of the lobster landings showed a great increase in abundance toward the north, but a decline in the southern portion of the lobster's range. Maine landings of lobsters rose between 1940 and 1945 from 7.6 to 19.1 million pounds and continued at a high level. Landings increased during the same period in Massachusetts, the Bay of Fundy, and western Nova Scotia. Landings in Rhode Island decreased steadily from 1927 to 1945, and in the mid-Atlantic states lobsters declined steadily and sharply from 1921 to 1950 (Fig. 9-4).

The long-term warming trend in the

North Atlantic, commencing in the 1920's, was paralleled by a warming trend in the northeast Pacific, but the decline in temperature after about 1930 did not occur in the Pacific (Ketchen, 1956). Ketchen attempts to show a relationship between halibut abundance and the air temperatures lagged by 12 years. The validity of this relationship is vigorously attacked by Bell and Pruter (1958). They also believe that much of the description of the increases in the stocks of cod and other fishes in the Barents Sea and other northern seas that has been attributed to warming of the water is suspect because of the inadequacy of the fishery statistics on which abundance estimates were based.

EFFECTS OF LONG-TERM CHANGES IN SALINITY

Estuarine-dependent species show the greatest effect of changes in salinity. This is especially true of the oyster, *Crassostrea virginica*. In Texas the periods of drought, during which river flow is far below average for several years, cause drastic decreases in oyster abundance.

In a correlation of white shrimp abundance in Texas with rainfall, which reflects salinity in the estuaries, Hildebrand and Gunter (1953) showed that over a 15-year period there was a positive relationship that seemed higher (correlation coefficient of 0.631) for rainfall the previous year than in the current year ($r = 0.419$). By using a multiple correlation of shrimp abundance from their data with the present and the two previous years' rainfall as the independent variables, I obtain an R of 0.89, which is highly significant.

Izhevskii (1961) attributes cyclic changes in salinity on the inner shelf of the Barents, Greenland, and Norwegian Seas to changes in air temperature (and hence in rainfall) caused by pulsations in the strength of the Gulf Stream.

LUNAR PERIODICITY

Although this discussion is concerned with fluctuations in abundance, it seems appropriate to mention other changes that coincide with the lunar cycle. Some of these are changes in the success of fishing that do not necessarily have any connection with actual abundance. Before fishermen possessed electronic fish detectors they had to rely on their senses to know where to set their nets. The ocean is a big place, and setting a net without sufficient information will usually result in a "water haul." In many areas of the world fishermen find the schools of smaller fishes by the glow of the many phosphorescent plankton. However, on clear nights with a bright moon the phosphorescence is difficult to see. Catches are therefore larger and more numerous during the darker portion of the lunar cycle. In fishing for sardines, for instance, the vessels might fish in the evening until moonrise and then head for port.

In southeastern Alaska the herring schools are detected by the fish flipping at the surface as they are feeding. Most catches are made during the dim light of early evening or early morning. An unpublished study I made of the catches showed a fortnightly rhythm in landings corresponding with the fortnightly cycle of higher tides. This of course is a question of availability to the fisherman. The reason for the relationship can only be speculated on, but it is possible that the swifter currents and eddies of the higher tides served to concentrate the herring into fewer and denser schools.

Lunar periodicity in spawning has been shown for both invertebrates and vertebrates. The European oyster, *Ostrea edulis,* in Holland was shown by Korringa (1957) to emit more larvae at both full moon and new moon spring tides than during neap tides.

The grunion, *Leuresthes tenuis,* one of the silver smelts (Atherinidae), spawns strictly in accordance with the tides (Thompson and Thompson, 1919). Spawning occurs during the period from March through August but only for a few hours in total. The eggs are spawned on surf-swept beaches at night, a few minutes after a spring tide has started to ebb. The eggs remain in the warm sand until the next spring tide washes them out of the sand a fortnight later, whereupon the eggs hatch almost immediately and the larvae are swept out to sea.

Suggested readings

Bell, F. H., and A. T. Pruter. 1958. Climatic temperature changes and commercial yields of some marine fisheries. J. Fish. Res. Bd. Canada **15:** 625-683.

Clemens, H. B., and W. L. Craig. 1965. An analysis of California's albacore fishery. Calif. Fish Game, Fish Bull. **128:**1-301.

Hildebrand, H. H., and G. Gunter. 1953. Correlation of rainfall with the Texas catch of white shrimp, Penaeus setiferus (Linnaeus). Trans. Amer. Fish. Soc. **82:**151-155.

Ketchen, K. S. 1956. Climatic trends and fluctuations in yield of marine fisheries of the northeast Pacific. J. Fish. Res. Bd. Canada **13:**357-374.

Korringa, P. 1957. Lunar periodicity. In Hedgepeth, J., editor. Treatise on marine ecology and paleoecology, memoir 67, vol. 1, chap. 27. Geological Society of America, National Research Council, Washington, D. C. pp. 917-934.

Sette, O. E. 1961. Problems in fish population fluctuations. Calif. Mar. Res. Comm., CalCOFI Rep. **8:**21-24.

Soutar, A., and J. D. Isaacs. 1969. History of fish populations inferred from fish scales in anaerobic sediments off California. Calif. Mar. Res. Comm., CalCOFI Rep. **13:**63-70.

Taylor, C. C., H. B. Bigelow, and H. W. Graham. 1957. Climatic trends and the distribution of marine animals in New England. U. S. Fish Wildl. Serv., Fish. Bull. **57:**293-345.

chapter 10

🌿 Determination of population units

WHY KNOWLEDGE OF UNIT STOCKS IS NEEDED

Herring have been taken from Alaskan waters for many years. Plants were built close to the known fishing grounds, but after a few years the fisherman were usually forced to go farther afield for their catches. Many reasons have been advanced to account for this shift in the fishing grounds. Some have held that the herring were being caught in greater quantities than could be compensated for by reproduction; others, that the operations of the fishery have frightened them away from their usual haunts. Still others have thought that there might exist a great offshore body of herring that for some reason did not always approach the coast annually in equal numbers, and that did not always chance to enter the same bays. . . .

If there were assumed to be such a great offshore body of herring coming inshore whenever and wherever currents or enemies impelled it, then it is only reasonable to suppose that, if they were caught in such quantities as to greatly reduce their numbers, the consequent scarcity would be felt throughout the range covered by this great body.

. . . Regulations would have to take into account the dependence of the whole area and fishing in one place might have to be curtailed for the good of another.

On the other hand, if we were to assume that each little region had schools of its own, that did not intermingle to any extent with those of neighboring regions, then it would be easy to understand how excessive fishing might greatly reduce the numbers in one locality without affecting the supply in any other, and it might take a number of years for the few fish remaining in any such limited region to multiply themselves to a point approaching their former abundance. Such a condition would lead to each locality being separately regulated according to the conditions prevailing there.*

The dilemma described illustrates that the importance of knowing whether or not a fishery for a particular species depends on one or several stocks can scarcely be overemphasized. In deciding on the validity of the existence or nonexistence of separate stocks or races one must examine the available evidence. Sometimes a specific character is either present or absent and no statistical analysis is required. This is most apt to be true of some intergeneric or interspecific character.

The evidence of differences within a species must be subjected to statistical tests that will measure the probability that any differences found are significant and not merely a result of random variability. There are two kinds of evidence. One kind is direct evidence such as that resulting from the

---

*From Rounsefell, G. A. 1926. Report of progress in Alaska herring investigations. Pac. Fisherman **24**:20-21.

release and subsequent recapture of marked individuals. The other kind is indirect evidence such as slight morphologic differences that must be examined statistically. If indirect evidence does not show any significant difference in fish from two localities, it does not mean that direct evidence from marking may not still show some degree of intermingling.

This last statement brings to mind some haddock I tagged at Mount Desert Island, Maine, in the month of June during each of the years 1938 through 1942. A good proportion of the marked haddock released in 1938 were recaptured on Browns Bank off southern Nova Scotia; in the subsequent 4 years these Mount Desert haddock obediently returned to Georges Bank. Long studies show that the Browns Bank haddock grow considerably slower than those of Georges Bank, and the two banks are separated by the deep Fundian Channel. Despite all this evidence to the contrary, the tagging indicated that there is some slight degree of intermingling.

DIRECT POPULATION EVIDENCE FROM MARKING

In conducting marking experiments to determine the existence and extent of intermingling of fish from two or more localities, several factors should be kept in mind.

Is there a significant fishery throughout the region being studied? Obviously recaptures can be obtained only where fish are taken. In tagging herring in the mid-1930's in southeastern Alaska we wanted to know if the Sitka-spawned herring responsible for the intense fishery in lower Chatham Strait, especially around Cape Ommaney, were of the same group that was formerly abundant in the central area of Chatham Strait from Security Bay and Point Gardner to Kootznahoo Inlet. Lacking any remaining fishery in central Chatham Strait to provide a chance for tag recoveries, our only recourse was to tag and release herring at Cape Bendel in Frederick Sound where it debouches into central Chatham Strait to find

out whether any of them would be taken in lower Chatham Strait. Our failure to obtain recaptures would seem to indicate little if any intermingling, but without a local fishery one could also postulate very poor survival of the marked herring.

When seaward-migrating young salmon are marked to determine what proportion of the adults subsequently return to their natal stream on their spawning migration, it is not enough to examine the salmon returning to the home stream. It is necessary to examine the adults ascending other streams in the general vicinity with equal thoroughness if any quantitative expression for the degree of straying from the natal stream is desired.

Necessary assumptions concerning marked individuals

In order to justify the interpretation of the statistical significance of any differences in the proportion of recaptures from different areas, one must make the following assumptions concerning the marked individuals:

1. The marked individuals had the time and opportunity to become randomly distributed in the group of which they were a part prior to the recaptures to be analyzed.
2. The marked individuals behaved in the same manner as the unmarked individuals. Marks can affect speed of movement, predilection to predation, feeding ability, and ease of recapture by certain fishing gears.

As an example of a marking-recapture experiment, we may assume that spawned-out salmon carcasses in five streams were observed in a search for a missing two-fin combination of adipose and dorsal fins by which the smolts were marked in a prior year while descending Cedar Creek on their way to the sea. The question to be tested is if the adult salmon returning from the sea ascended the five streams without choice or if the marked individuals tended strongly to return to their natal stream. Analysis of

Table 10-1. Analysis of a marking-recapture experiment

Stream	Salmon examined (thousands)	Marks		x	x^2	$2x^2/m$
		Observed (m + x)	Expected (m)			
Rocky Creek	40	2	20	−18	324	32.4
Falls Creek	10	6	5	1	1	0.4
Cedar Creek	20	40	10	30	900	180.0
Bear Creek	30	8	15	−7	49	6.6
Duck Creek	20	4	10	−6	36	6.6
TOTAL	120	60	60			226.6 df = 4
				Chi-square of 1% =		13.277
Cedar Creek	20	40	10	30	900	180.0
Remaining creeks	100	20	50	−30	900	180.0
TOTAL	120	60	60			360.0 df = 1
				Chi-square of 1% =		6.635

the hypothetical data (Table 10-1) is usually accomplished by the use of a chi-square test (X^2).

The analysis of Table 10-1 indicates that the great majority of the salmon indicated a strong preference to return to their natal stream, since there is less than one chance in 100 that the chi-square would exceed the 1% value in homogeneous samples.

INDIRECT EVIDENCE CONCERNING POPULATION UNITS
Occurrence and abundance of parasites

The use of the occurrence and abundance of parasites is mentioned in Chapter 11 in efforts to distinguish between sockeye salmon of Asiatic and North American origin (Margolis, 1963). Over 20 years earlier it was shown by Nigrelli and Firth (1939) that the ocean perch, *Sebastes marinus,* is parasitized by *Sphyrion lumpi,* an external copepod parasite. From nearly 5000 specimens over an 11-month period they discovered that 10% of the ocean perch along the Maine and Massachusetts coast were infected; this fell to 5% farther offshore in the channel between Cape Cod and Georges Bank. However, numerous samples from the redfish population in the deep hole just north of Browns Bank off the southern tip of Nova Scotia showed no parasites. Fewer

samples farther north along the Nova Scotia coast (from Sable Island, Roseway, Liscombe, and Banquereau Banks) were also not parasitized.

Morphometric and enumeration data

Time and effort can be saved by careful choice of the characters to be measured or observed for a subpopulation study. The number of characters selected depends on the available time; one must usually choose between an adequate number of observations on a few characters or small samples, perhaps inadequate, of a larger number of characters. Preliminary study may aid in selecting a few characters with a useful range of variation. The usefulness of any particular character will vary from one group of fishes to another. Vertebral count has been a very useful character for herring, but years ago the Halibut Commission tried it for halibut and found only an occasional fish that did not have the same number of vertebrae as the rest and so had to abandon it.

One should avoid using more than one of a set of correlated characters that are merely another expression of the same thing, or at least be sure that two such characters are not given double weight in interpreting the significance of any differences. Among the Salmonidae for instance, the

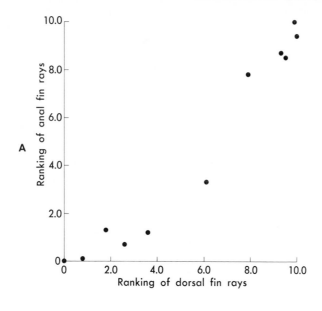

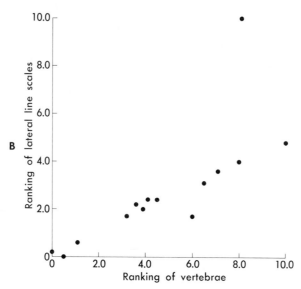

Fig. 10-1. Showing the close correlation in species of Salmonidae between, **A,** the ranking of the number of dorsal and anal fin rays and, **B,** the ranking of number of vertebrae and lateral-line scales. (From Rounsefell, G. A. 1962. U. S. Fish Wildl. Serv., Fish. Bull. **62**:235-270.)

number of vertebrae and the number of lateral line scales are closely correlated, as are the number of dorsal and anal fin rays (Fig. 10-1).

In interpreting the significance of differences between enumeration characters, observe whether or not the variances of the samples are correlated with their means.

Fig. 10-2 shows the correlation between the means and the 20th and 80th percentiles of the number of pyloric caeca in several species of the Salmonidae family. In such cases a small difference between two small means may be fully as significant as a larger difference between two large means. To correct for this in the preceding analysis, the rank-

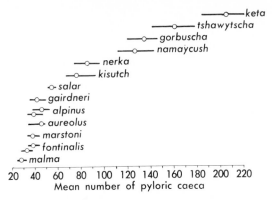

Fig. 10-2. Showing in Salmonidae the mean numbers of pyloric caeca and the 20th and 80th percentile range to illustrate correlation between means and their variances. (Modified from Rounsefell, G. A. 1962. U. S. Fish Wildl. Serv., Fish. Bull. **62**:235-270.)

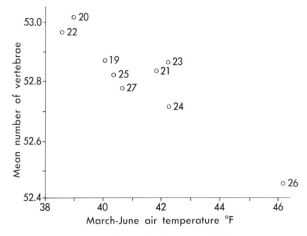

Fig. 10-3. Showing the mean vertebral count of Prince William Sound herring of nine year classes and the March through June air temperature. (Data from Rounsefell, G. A., and E. H. Dahlgren. 1932. Bull. U. S. Bur. Fish. **47**:263-291.)

ings of each character (on a distance scale of 0 to 10 from the lowest to the highest mean) were converted to logarithms.

A statistically significant difference between sample means of a character, e.g., number of vertebrae, should not necessarily be interpreted as denoting a population difference between the samples. One must first be able to discount variations between samples caused by such factors as size, age, or year class. In Prince William Sound, Alaska, the mean vertebral count of nine year classes of herring was significantly correlated (r = –0.85) with the March through June air

temperature of the year each year class was spawned (Fig. 10-3). Obviously it is not safe to make comparisons of vertebral counts between localities except for members of the same year class.

In comparing counts of some characters, e.g., gill rakers, one should be extremely cautious in comparing counts from small specimens with those from large specimens. In most cases counts are higher for larger specimens, suggesting either difficulty in distinguishing rudimentary rakers or the actual formation of additional rakers as the arch grows.

Other genetic differences

Crossbreeding is not usually valuable in defining stocks or geographic races of the same species, but it may prove of value in defining the closeness of the relationship between species within a genus or even between genera. The same probably applies to the chromosomes, but polyploidy is possible.

Coloration is generally considered to be more or less a species character, but there are often slight color differences between geographic stocks of the same species.

Blood characteristics have become an important tool for distinguishing species and are sometimes useful in the determination of subpopulations. Various characteristics and techniques are used:

1. Antigen differences in red blood cells (Some species show differences between isolated gene pools.)
2. Agglutination by hemagglutinins or antibodies of red blood cells (Ridgway, 1957)
3. Antigenetic properties of blood serum proteins (Cushing, 1956)
4. Chemical composition of blood (usually by paper chromatography) (Farris, 1957; Ridgway et al., 1961)

Population differences or similarities

Some population differences are probably genetically controlled; others are more probably wholly or chiefly phenotypic responses to the environment at some stage(s) of the life history. In either case the occurrence and persistence of a difference between fishes of two areas would indicate little intermingling regardless of genetic relationships.

Age composition. The age composition of samples from two areas is most apt to be of value in species such as clupeids that normally exhibit wide variation in spawning success. Close similarity between age groups in such species can be of value in suggesting that the populations in the two areas were exposed to very similar environmental conditions on the spawning grounds.

An interesting case of such similarity is

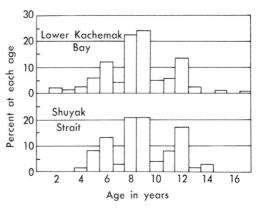

Fig. 10-4. Age histograms of Pacific herring caught in Shuyak Strait, Afognak Island during July 1926 and in lower Kachemak Bay, Cook Inlet in August 1926. The localities are about 90 miles apart. (From Rounsefell, G. A. 1930a. Bull. U. S. Bur. Fish. **45**:227-320.)

shown in Fig. 10-4. The two localities are about 90 miles apart. The Shuyak Strait fishery occurred only during midsummer; the Kachemak Bay fishery commenced in late summer near the mouth of the bay, and the herring continued up the bay toward their wintering location in Halibut Cove.

The two age distributions were compared statistically by computing chi-square (Table 10-2).

The formula for X^2, the measure of divergence, is:

$$X^2 = S(x^2/m)$$

where:

$$m = \text{Number expected}$$
$$m + x = \text{Number observed}$$

Where the expected number is the same for both distributions, x^2 and x'^2 may be added before dividing by m.

It will be noted that the chief item, 1.603, contributing to X^2 was caused by a few more young fish in the Kachemak Bay sample. This would seem to be expected if, as surmised, Kachemak Bay were the home of this race and Shuyak Strait the summer feeding area. It is not unlike the former migrations of the sardine, *Sardinops sagax caerulea,* in which only the larger and older sardines migrated each summer from Cali-

Table 10-2. Comparison of herring age distributions in Shuyak Strait and lower Kachemak Bay, Alaska*

	Observed			Expected		Differences		Measure of divergence	
Age (yr)	Shuyak Strait, July 15, 1926 (m + x)	Lower Kache-mak Bay. August 25-28, 1926 (m' + x')	Sum	Shuyak Strait (m)	Lower Kache-mak Bay (m')	x	x'	x^2/m	x'^2/m'
1									
2		5							
3		3							
4	1	5	14	3.3	10.7	−2.3	2.3	1.603	0.494
5	6	14	20	4.7	15.3	1.3	−1.3	0.360	0.110
6	10	30	40	9.5	30.5	0.5	−0.5	0.026	0.008
7	2	9	11	2.6	8.4	−0.6	0.6	0.138	0.043
8	16	55	71	16.8	54.2	−0.8	0.8	0.038	0.012
9	16	58	74	17.5	56.5	−1.5	1.5	0.129	0.040
10	3	12	15	3.6	11.4	−0.6	0.6	0.100	0.032
11	6	14	20	4.7	15.3	1.3	−1.3	0.360	0.110
12	13	33	46	10.9	35.1	2.1	−2.1	0.405	0.126
13	1	5	10	2.4	7.6	0.6	−0.6	0.150	0.047
14	2								
15		1							
16									
17		1							
TOTAL	76	245	321	76.0	245.0			3.309	1.022

$$X^2 = 3.309 + 1.022 = 4.331, \text{ df} = 9, P = 0.90$$

*Data from Rounsefell, G. A. 1930a. Bull. U. S. Bur. Fish. **45:**227-320.

fornia as far as the British Columbia coast.

A good illustration of the utility of year class abundance in indicating stocks is afforded by Fig. 10-5, which shows the age classes of herring in a few localities in southeastern Alaska. Note that the ages in 1929 commence with 2 years, those in 1930 with 3 years, so that the same year classes are plotted beneath each other. (See Fig. 10-6 for localities.)

The Cape Ommaney herring (from the spawning areas adjacent to Sitka) show the same dominant 1926 year class as Coronation Island and Point Gardner. However, Douglas Island (from the Auke Bay spawning population) has a dominant 1923 year class that is almost entirely lacking south of Kootznahoo Inlet. The Kootznahoo Inlet samples exhibit dominant year classes in both 1923 and 1926. The Noyes Island stock (from the Klawak-Craig spawning ground) has dominant year classes in both 1926 and 1927. The local population from Peril Strait has a dominant year class in 1927 but very few in the 1926 class.

Whether the samples from Favorite Bay at the mouth of Kootznahoo Inlet represent a remnant of the Kootznahoo Inlet spawning population, abundant in the last century but since depleted, or a mixture of the Douglas Island population with herring from the southern end of Chatham Strait is conjectural.

Size composition. Differences in growth rate can result in considerable differences in the size distribution of fish of the same age from various localities. Fig. 10-7 shows the size distribution of southeastern Alaska

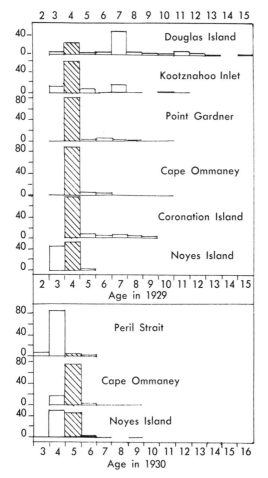

Fig. 10-5. Ages of Pacific herring, *Clupea pallasi,* at several localities in southeastern Alaska in 1929 and 1930, showing marked differences in the dominant year classes. (Modified from Rounsefell, G. A., and E. H. Dahlgren. 1935. Bull. U. S. Bur. Fish. **48**:119-141.)

herring of the 1926 year class (in their fourth summer) caught during the summer of 1929. Those from Point Adolphus in Icy Strait and from Affleck Canal were considerably smaller. Fig. 10-8 shows the same 1926 year class captured during their fifth summer in 1930. The median size of the Larch Bay herring of the 1926 year class showed an increase of 11.6 mm from June 1929 to June 1930.

Much of this growth seems to take place during the summer months. It should be noted in Fig. 10-9 that during an 80-day

period in 1930 the 5-year-olds increased about 6.5 mm in length at Larch Bay. However, there was considerable variation among the 10-day periods. This is not unusual in schooling fishes, but it does imply that size must be evaluated with caution in racial studies.

The comparison of growth curves can be accomplished in several ways. Perhaps the simplest and the one requiring the least calculation is to use the t test (Fisher, 1930). To illustrate, the growth curves for the month of August for herring from Kachemak Bay in Cook Inlet and from Elrington Passage in Prince William Sound will be compared using published data.

One can reach approximately the same result by considering the probability of all of the differences having the same sign. If there were not a significant difference, then the positive and negative signs should appear with about equal frequency. Of the eight differences in Table 10-3, all the signs are the same. From the binomial distribution:

$$(½ + ½)^8$$

all will be of the same sign, by chance, less than twice out of 253 trials. This method of merely considering the signs is less reliable than using the actual values when they are available.

The fact that the growth curves are significantly different between two localities does not rule out the possibility of some intermingling. The extent of such intermingling, if any, is difficult to ascertain by indirect means.

Royce (1957) points out that once a difference between two subpopulations has been demonstrated the important question is the degree of intermingling that occurs. He suggests that whereas the degree of overlap of a character in two populations (Fig. 10-10) does not evaluate the amount of intermingling, it does set an upper limit on the amount of intermingling and can thus be of value when marking experiments show that some unspecified degree of intermingling occurs.

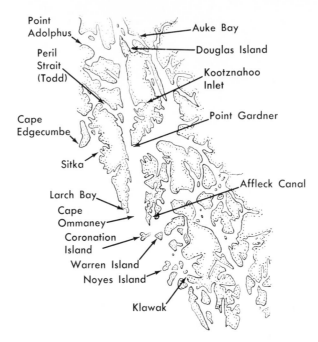

Fig. 10-6. Localities in southeastern Alaska referred to in Figs. 10-5 to 10-9.

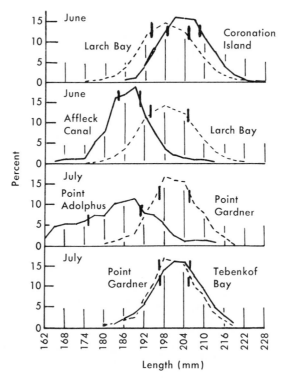

Fig. 10-7. Size distributions of 1926 year class herring caught in the summer of 1929. The first and third quartiles are marked. (Modified from Rounsefell, G. A., and E. H. Dahlgren. 1935. Bull. U. S. Bur. Fish. **48**:119-141.)

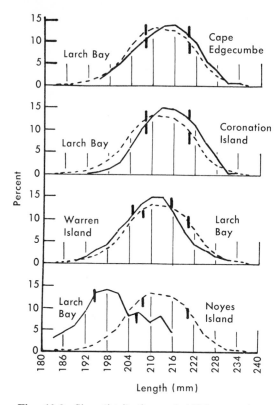

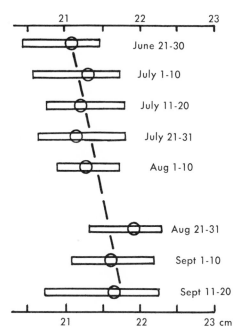

Fig. 10-8. Size distributions of 1926 year class herring caught during July 1930. The first and third quartiles are marked. (Modified from Rounsefell, G. A., and E. H. Dahlgren. 1935. Bull. U. S. Bur. Fish. **48:**119-141.)

Fig. 10-9. Showing the median and the first and third quartiles of the length distributions of 5-year-old Larch Bay herring during the summer of 1930. (Data from Rounsefell, G. A., and E. H. Dahlgren. 1935. Bull. U. S. Bur. Fish. **48:**119-141.)

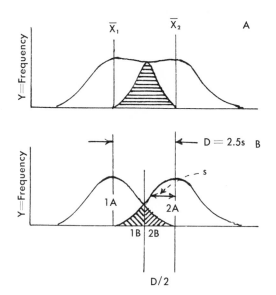

Fig. 10-10. A, Showing the curve resulting if populations intermingle to the full extent of overlap. **B,** Showing the concept of overlap of two distributions of a character, size, or number in which the standard deviations are similar and the curves are assumed to be normal. (**B** modified from Royce, W. F. 1957. U. S. Fish Wildl. Serv., Spec. Sci. Rep. Fish. **208:**7-28.)

Table 10-3. Comparison of growth curves for herring from two localities*

Age (yr)	Length of herring (mm)		Difference (mm)
	Cook Inlet	Prince William Sound	
4	220.2	205.0	15.2
5	224.9	220.8	4.1
6	252.5	231.4	21.1
7	263.0	243.0	20.0
8	268.1	250.0	18.1
9	272.6	261.6	11.0
10	273.7	261.0	12.7
11	279.4	266.9	12.5

$$SX = 114.7$$

$$n' = 8$$
$$n = (n' - 1)$$
$$s^2 = Sx^2/(n' - 1) = 30.585$$
$$s = 5.53$$
$$t = \bar{x}\sqrt{n'}/s = 6.87$$
$$SX^2 = 1,859.21$$
$$(SX)^2/n' = 1,644.51$$
$$Sx^2 = \overline{214.70}$$

$\pm t$ for n of 7 = 3.499 at P of 0.01, t/2 = 1.75, so that the probability of a difference as great as 6.87 occurring by chance is extremely remote.

*Data from Rounsefell, G. A. 1930a. Bull. U. S. Bur. Fish. **45**:227-320.

In Fig. 10-10, *B*, Royce shows two normally distributed curves with equal standard deviations and with a difference between the means of 2.5 standard deviations. The equation involved is:

$$D = (\bar{x}_2 - \bar{x}_1)/\bar{s}$$

in which $\bar{s}$ is computed from the pooled variances:

$$\bar{s} = \sqrt{\frac{S_1(x - \bar{x})^2 + S_2(x - \bar{x})^2}{n_1 + n_2 - 2}}$$

However, as intermingling approaches the maximum possible according to the amount of overlap, representative sampling of the total of both populations should yield a curve approaching that shown in Fig. 10-10, *A*, in which the shaded portion is the joint contribution to the total.

It is suggested that although normal dis-

tributions are useful in arriving at statistical tests and inferences, the platykurtic curve is more usually encountered in biological data.

If, as suggested previously by Royce, the amount of overlap between the distributions of any character in two populations is possibly ascribable to intermingling, then the distance between the two means should decrease with time. One method of evaluating this is to compare the distribution of a character in any year class sampled in successive years. Eight comparisons between the vertebral count of herring of the 1926 and 1927 year classes showed no significant differences between succeeding years of sampling. Furthermore, among the eight comparisons, those of the fifth year showed 4 with higher means and 4 with lower means (Rounsefell and Dahlgren, 1935).

Suggested readings

Cushing, J. E. 1956. Observations on serology of tuna. U. S. Fish Wildl. Serv., Spec. Sci. Rep. Fish. **183**:14.

Farris, D. A. 1957. A review of paper chromatography as used in systematics. U. S. Fish Wildl. Serv., Spec. Sci. Rep. Fish. **208**:35-38.

Nigrelli, R. F., and F. E. Firth. 1939. On Sphyrion lumpi (Krøyer), a copepod parasite on the redfish, Sebastes marinus (Linnaeus), with special reference to the host-parasite relationships. Zoologica **24**:1-10.

Ridgway, G. J. 1957. The use of immunological techniques in racial studies. U. S. Fish Wildl. Serv., Spec. Sci. Rep. Fish. **208**:39-43.

Ridgway, G. J., J. E. Cushing, and G. L. Durall. 1961. Serological differentiation of populations of sockeye salmon, Oncorhynchus nerka. Int. N. Pac. Fish. Comm., Bull. **3**:5-10.

Rounsefell, G. A. 1930a. Contribution to the biology of the Pacific herring, Clupea pallasii, and the condition of the fishery in Alaska. Doc. 1080. Bull. U. S. Bur. Fish. **45**:227-320.

Rounsefell, G. A. 1962. Relationships among North American Salmonidae. U. S. Fish Wildl. Serv., Fish. Bull. **62**:235-270.

Rounsefell, G. A., and E. H. Dahlgren. 1935. Races of herring, Clupea pallasii, in southeastern Alaska. Bull. U. S. Bur. Fish. **48**:119-141.

Royce, W. F. 1957. Statistical comparison of morphological data. In Contributions to the study of subpopulations of fishes. U. S. Fish Wildl. Serv., Spec. Sci. Rep. Fish. **208**:7-28.

chapter 11

✍ Marking as a tool for research and management

WHY ORGANISMS ARE MARKED

The primary reason for marking is the need for distinguishing single individuals or a small group of individuals from the remainder of the population so that when they are recaptured biologists may arrive at certain inferences concerning them.

There are instances in which a group of fish may bear a natural mark by which they can be distinguished from other fish of the same stock. The very abundant 1904 year class of Norwegian herring was distinguished by an extra large initial growth band on its scales. Similarly, salmon sometimes have scales with characteristic growth bands that serve to distinguish fish of the same species even from different tributaries of the same river. The difference in the species of their parasite or in the degree to which they are parasitized has also been used to distinguish fish of the same species but of different origin.

Margolis (1963) found two species of parasites in sockeye salmon that have a limited distribution in fresh water and apparently live as long as their host. *Triaenophorus crassus* (subclass Cestoda) in the muscle is found only in stocks originating in western Alaska (essentially Bristol Bay). *Dacnitis truttae* (class Nematoda) in the intestine is known to occur only in some sockeye from Kamchatka. Fig. 11-1 shows the location of samples in which either of these parasites were found from 1955 to 1959.

Natural marks may occasionally be purposely developed. Hughes (1968) has succeeded in selectively breeding lobsters that he reared to maturity in the hatchery, so as to produce young lobsters of a coloration differing from that normally occurring (except rarely) in nature. Instead of the normal coloration of a dark green shell with small spots of brown, white, yellow, and red, he has succeeded in obtaining young that are all red and also some that are lemon spotted.

Since lobsters are normally 2 years old before attaining a size large enough to carry a tag, this may prove to be an important tool in assessing the contribution of artificial rearing and in determining the movement of lobsters of different age and size.

However, the occurrence of natural marks is too uncertain, and the marks are usually too difficult to interpret to serve in more

• *Triaenophorus*
○ *Dacnitis*

Fig. 11-1. High seas locations in the North Pacific of catches of sockeye salmon infected with *Trinaenophorus crassus* or *Dacnitis truttae* from 1955 to 1959. (From Margolis, L. 1963. Int. N. Pac. Fish. Comm., Bull. **11**:101-156.)

than a few special cases. Therefore biologists must normally mark and release organisms if the several types of information needed for adequate conservation measures are to be obtained from the recaptures.

What are these facts or attributes that can be inferred from the recapture of marked fish? Basically the information gleaned relates to species and race distinctions, geographic distribution, migrations, spawning, age and growth, rearing methods, and mortality rate.

Species distinction. One of the earliest uses of tagging was the marking of immature salmon and sea trout in Britain to discover whether the young, which were difficult to distinguish, always returned in the adult form as the same species identified in the immature stage.

Race distinction. Marking is employed to determine whether groups of fish marked in different localities intermingle to any degree, or whether subpopulations or races exist in different areas.

Geographic distribution. The marking and recapture of fish reveals the geographic distribution of any group of fish (provided fishing offers an adequate opportunity for recapture over the whole area). When young stages can be marked and recaptures continued over a considerable period of time, one may also determine the areas occupied by fish of successively greater size or age. This is often of importance in determining which areas suitable for young fish are contributing to specific offshore fisheries.

Frequency of spawning. The first really

successful tagging was of salmon in the Penobscot River in 1873 by Atkins. He discovered by marking kelts (spawned-out adult Atlantic salmon) that the majority only spawned every second year.

Spawning migrations. Many fishes make long spawning migrations that are difficult to understand without this useful tool. Tagging experiments have shown that many of the king salmon taken as far north as southeastern Alaska enter and ascend the Columbia River to spawn. Similarly, mature halibut from as far away as the Aleutian Islands migrate to the Gulf of Alaska off Yakutat to spawn (Thompson and Herrington, 1930).

Migration routes. Marking is especially valuable in determining migration routes. For example, in southeastern Alaska pink salmon can enter the myriad waterways of the Alexander Archipelago through several straits on their way to their natal streams to spawn. To assure adequate seeding of each stream, intelligent conservation requires knowledge of which routes are used by salmon spawning in different streams. Continuous marking at the entrances of these straits during the migration period has shown the routes used. In some cases the early and late salmon runs to the same stream use different routes.

Speed of migration. The speed of migration is important in certain circumstances. In determining the effect of barriers in delaying the upstream migration of salmon, it becomes vital to know the rate of progress, because the salmon must reach its spawning bed before exhausting its supply of stored fuel.

Age and growth. Recapture of marked fish over a long time may show the increased size at successive ages. For some species such as shrimp, which periodically shed their exoskeletons, or fish in tropical waters, which may not form definite annuli on their scales, this is an extremely valuable method of age assessment. Where sufficiently large numbers of carefully measured fish are liberated, growth rates may be determined.

Even for species with decipherable annuli on their scales, the corroborative evidence from recaptured fish may be very useful in scale interpretation.

Rearing methods. Marking has been widely used to check the success of various methods of rearing fish, especially the salmonids. The fast growth of young fish in the hatchery up to the time of release may appear desirable, but on the other hand, growth alone is not always a sufficient criterion of future survival. By marking and releasing numbers of fish reared under different conditions of feeding, handling, and temporal and spatial methods of release, it is possible through comparison of the recaptures to evaluate methods to improve hatchery efficiency in terms of adult fish.

Mortality rate. The most useful and necessary information concerning any population is knowledge of the mortality rates. For humans the mortality rate is very accurately calculated by insurance actuaries. Without the birth and death certificates and occupational and geographic data available to the actuary, the fishery biologist does the next best thing; he marks individual members of the population. Circumstances may warrant the making of certain assumptions such as the representativeness of the sample of fish marked, their even distribution through the population (or at least that all the population is equally vulnerable to the gear fished), and the tagged individuals acting and being acted on as wholly normal individuals. It is then often possible to calculate from the rate of recapture of the tagged individuals relative to the untagged portion of the population at the time of tagging, the rates of fishing and natural mortality.

TYPES OF MARKS

The choice of one of several general types of marks depends on many factors: size of the organism to be marked, speed of marking, degree of permanency desired, ease of handling the fish, manner of recovery, etc. The chief types are mutilation, vital stains, dyes, tattooing, and tags.

Mutilation

The mutilation method is used chiefly for marking large numbers of very small fish, especially when recovery is not anticipated for a long time, when the fish will be much larger. Consequently, a mark with great permanency is desired. This method has been used on several species but chiefly on salmonids. Because the young salmonids are very small in comparison to the adults, few tags are suitable for marking. Pink salmon fry 1½ inches (3.8 cm) long have been successfully marked by excising fins, and the adults recaptured 1½ years later when they returned from the sea to spawn.

Because of the natural occurrence of fish with one fin missing, it is usual to excise two fins. The fins excised can include the dorsal, adipose, anal, left and right ventral (pelvic), and left and right pectoral fins. It has been shown by Barnaby (1944) that fewer sockeye salmon smolts survive to return as adults with a pectoral fin excised than with other fins removed; therefore excision of the pectoral fin is not recommended. This leaves only 10 two-fin combinations. Some biologists have attempted to increase the number of combinations by using a half-dorsal or a half-anal mark, clipping off half of the fin at the base. As reported by Slater (1949), fins not cut off at the very base tend to regenerate. My personal experience would suggest that these latter two marks are fraught with uncertainty, since only extremely careful and slow marking of fairly large fingerlings can guarantee against portions of the fins regenerating. These partially regenerated fins cause little difficulty in recognition in the normal two-fin combination. However, the distinction between a partially regenerated dorsal fin and one supposedly half excised can be tenuous.

In addition to fin removal there have been attempts to mark some of the more bony fishes by clipping notches in the edges of the opercle or maxilla.

Fish are occasionally marked by punching holes in the fin membrane or cutting the tip off a fin. Lobsters are also sometimes marked temporarily by punching or notching the telson or uropods. Such marks are very temporary and soon become unrecognizable.

Clams and other hard-shelled mollusks are sometimes marked by notching or etching the shell with a file or drill. They have also been marked with waterproof colored cement or plastic.

Another form of mutilation is by branding. R. A. Nesbit, in an unpublished study, tried both hot and cold branding in the late 1920's, but the marks tended to become illegible as the fish grew. Sea herring were branded by Watson (1961) by burning through scales and skin with several resistance wires heated with electricity from a 12-volt battery. The marks of the individual wires were not distinguishable for more than 2 to 3 days. The mark might be useful for very short-term experiments.

Branding has been used for several years on small salmon. The small branding irons (copper with tips of solid silver) are either heated in boiling water (212° F) or chilled with liquid nitrogen (−324° F) for "freeze branding." It is stated that the brand grows in size with the fish and can last its lifetime (Commercial Fisheries Review editorial, 1968).

Vital stains

The use of vital stains to mark fish and shellfish has recently been employed on a large scale. Early experiments involved staining starfish by immersion in a weak solution of stain (Loosanoff, 1937). Others have tried staining salmonids and invertebrates by mixing stains in their feed. Shrimp are marked in the Gulf of Mexico by hypodermic injection of small amounts of dye dissolved in distilled water (Dawson, 1957; Costello, 1959). The dye first colors the entire shrimp, but in about 24 hours the dye is all concentrated in the gills, so that the head (actually the thorax) is brightly colored, and the shrimp can be readily separated from its nondyed companions. This successful technique is extremely useful in studying many aspects of shrimp biology

and can be used for other invertebrates. The chief advantages over earlier methods are that the mark is not affected by molting and that it can be used on very small individuals.

Since there are only two or three colors of dye available, the number of experiments that could be carried out the same year has been strictly limited. E. F. Klima, however, found that the easily observed dye could be supplemented by small local injections of a fluorescent pigment, which could then be detected by examining recovered specimens under ultraviolet light, thus multiplying the possible number of simultaneous experiments.

For experiments involving only a very short period of time, immersion staining has its uses. For example, pink salmon fry are marked by immersion and returned to a stream. Within a few hours or days some of them are recaptured as they migrate downstream to the sea, and the proportions of colored fry to the noncolored fry in the samples captured permits an estimate of the total number leaving the stream. The use of stain by immersion is particularly suitable for temporary marking of larval forms both because they are too delicate to permit handling and because it permits the staining of the vast number that must be marked in order to obtain sufficient recaptures.

Fluorescent and phosphorescent dyes

Biologists have experimented with the use of fluorescent or phosphorescent dyes by themselves for marking. An advantage of this technique is the ability to discriminate between experimentally dyed specimens and organisms merely discolored or naturally possessing colors that may cause confusion. Very minute quantities of different-colored fluorescent dyes can be separated with a fluorometer by their difference in wavelength.

Tattooing

Strictly speaking, tattooing consists of forcing small quantities of inert material beneath the skin by means of needles. A single area may be marked, using different colors for different experiments, a letter or number may be inscribed, or a combination of different colors may be used. Kask (1936) marked a number of halibut on the white side, injecting India ink with a hypodermic syringe, but found the marks became unidentifiable after 3 months. More recently, colored latex injections at the base of the dorsal fin have been successful over a period of a few months.

For temporary marking, tattooing with electric needles is currently employed for large numbers of small salmonids because of its rapidity.

Tags

The most prevalent method of marking is to attach to the exterior or place inside an organism some readily identifiable foreign object termed a tag. Tags are classified according to several criteria, including material used, method of attachment, place where attached, and method of recovery. A general classification system by Rounsefell and Kask (1945) lists 18 types; Rounsefell and Everhart (1953) list 21 types. Some types were never used extensively or have become obsolete as new and improved tags have replaced them; the obsolete types are omitted here.

Materials used in tags. With the development of new materials, especially plastics, many of the materials formerly used have been abandoned. Materials in vogue are various plastics, nickel, Monel Metal, silver, aluminum, stainless steel, titanium and tantalum wire, and magnetic steel.

The material chosen depends on several factors:

1. *Time before recovery.* For short-term experiments one may use material such as aluminum that, although tough and having the great advantage of light weight, is subject to corrosion, especially if not of high purity. Therefore aluminum cannot be recommended for experiments in which recoveries are expected over many months or even years.

Calhoun et al. (1951) found both Vinylite and cellulose acetate disks for Petersen tags inferior to cellulose nitrate, because the first two tended to become brittle and crack. Cellulose nitrate disks, however, also become brittle if held a few years in storage. They also discovered that nickel, Monel Metal, and silver used for pins or wire were inferior to stainless steel or tantalum.

2. *Place of attachment.* For external attachment noncorrosive material is imperative for any long-term experiments. For body cavity tags, loose within the body cavity, nonstainless steel can be used.

3. *Method of recovery.* The material used depends somewhat on the method of recovery. For the recovery of tags by electromagnets from fish meal, obviously only metals with magnetic properties are usable.

Methods of recovery. Divergent types of tags have been developed to suit the manner in which they can best be recovered by the fishery. The major recovery methods are by slight, by transmittal of sound, by electromagnet or electronic detector, and by radioactivity.

BY SIGHT. The use of tags that are visible is the most common method. Detecting tags on live fish is restricted to special experiments such as identifying bass on their nests or observing live salmon on their shallow spawning beds; these external tags must be conspicuously colored and of large size. Oversize Petersen disk tags with a sharply contrasting colored spot in the center have been used successfully.

The recovery of tags from fish in catches requires tags that can be easily spotted by the fisherman while sorting or handling his catch. It is essential to take into account the exact manner in which the fishermen in a particular locality handle their catch in order to ensure placing a tag where it is not easily overlooked. For instance, it may be vital to successful recovery that an opercle tag be placed on the left or right cheek of a fish according to how the fish are held in cleaning. If fish of a certain species are customarily cleaned individually on the fishing vessel soon after catching, an internal (body cavity) tag may be used.

BY TRANSMITTAL OF UNDERWATER SOUND. Tags have been developed that emit low frequency sound from a small battery-powered transducer for several hours. These permit following the individual fish from a boat. Such tags have been most useful in determining the movements of anadromous fishes in finding and passing through fishways and quiet forebays above large dams.

The first crude sonic tags have been greatly reduced in size through advances in the use of miniaturized components, so that instead of being always attached externally they can be inserted into the stomach of a fish as large as a salmon. Sonic tags have been used on salmon, lobsters, shad, sharks, and even tried on whales.

BY ELECTROMAGNET OR ELECTRONIC DETECTOR. Detection by the electromagnet method is most useful for small species taken in enormous numbers and processed without scrutiny or handling of the individual fish. Tags with magnetic properties are usually placed in the body cavity. During processing an electromagnet separates the tags from the fish meal as it travels along a conveyor toward the meal grinder.

Use of an electronic detector, placed in a conveying line prior to processing of the fish, permits examination of the whole fish itself, and is a superior method for determining the locality of capture since catches from two or more localities may become mixed in the fish meal. It is more expensive than magnetic recovery both in number of personnel and expense of equipment and operation, and as with most electronic equipment, it is difficult to keep in operation.

An improved electronically recoverable type of tag has been developed for implanting in very small fish (Bergman et al., 1968). A tiny tag, 1×0.25 mm in diameter, of stainless steel wire was coded with colored epoxy stripes. The tag can be implanted in fish as small as 40 mm in total length, usually in the snout, with a special machine. The tag is magnetized after implantation. The tag is detected in mature fish by an electronic coil that yields an audio response.

BY RADIOACTIVITY. Tags have been developed with a very low level of radioactivity, very similar to the radium dial of a wristwatch. Such tags are detected with an instrument that measures radioactivity near the conveying line on which the fish are moved from the vessel into the plant.

Attachment of tags. No one tag serves all purposes, largely because of differences in the sizes of fish to be marked, in the expected size increases before recovery, and most importantly, in the great differences in the structure of the species to be marked. This is reflected in the methods of tag attachment, which are as follows:

1. To the muscles by a filament that enters and leaves the muscle tissues. The filament may be a rigid shaft or pin or a flexible wire, thread, plastic filament, or tube. Tags that can be so attached include the Atkins, Petersen, hydrostatic, and spaghetti tags.
2. To bone by one or two shafts or pins that pierce the bone. The tags used include the bachelor button, Archer, strap, smelt, and Petersen (also attached to muscles) tags.
3. To fin membranes by one or two shafts. The tag generally used is the Archer tag (also attached to bone).
4. Anchored in muscles by projections on the tag that enter the muscles but do not pass through. These include the barb, harpoon, and hook tags.
5. Encircling tags that depend on their shape for attachment. These include the collar, jaw, and some carapace tags.
6. Internal tags that are placed inside the body cavity, from which the name "body cavity tags" originated.
7. Anchored by material within the body cavity with a filament piercing the body wall for external visibility. This is called the internal anchor tag.
8. Tags that depend for attachment on the continued elasticity of the material. These tags include rubber collar tags and some carapace tags.

Table 11-1. Some successful tags currently in use

Type	Name	Where attached	Material		Retention time	Principal species	Minimum species size	How recovered
			Tag	Attachment				
Petersen	Petersen	Dorsal muscle	Plastic	Metal pin or wire	Long	Flatfish Salmonids	Small Medium	Sight
	Petersen	Opercle	Plastic	Metal pin or wire	Medium	Gadoids	Medium	Sight
	Petersen	Shell	Plastic	Metal pin or wire	Long	Scallops	Medium	Sight
	Small Petersen	Tail	Plastic	Metal pin or wire	Short	Shrimp	Medium	Sight
Barb	Dart	Dorsal muscle	Plastic tube	Nylon barb	Long	Tunas, marlins	Large	Sight
	Serrated spear	Dorsal isthmus	Flat plastic	—	Medium	Lobsters, crabs	Large	Sight
	Smelt	Opercle	Bent plastic	—	Short	Smelt	Small	Sight
Body cavity	Body cavity	Body cavity	Flat plastic	—	Very long	Various	Tiny	Sight
	Magnetic	Body cavity	Steel	—	Very long	Industrial	Tiny	Magnet or electronic
Implanted	Magnetic	Snout	Steel wire	—	Very long	Various	Tiny	Audio-electronic
Atkins	Hydrostatic	Dorsal muscle	Plastic tube	Plastic or steel bridle	Long	Gadoids	Medium	Sight
	Atkins	Dorsal muscle	Metal or plastic	Bridle or filament	Medium	Various	Medium	Sight
	Spaghetti	Dorsal muscle	Plastic tube	Knot or metal clip	Long	Tunas	Medium	Sight
	Herring	Dorsal muscle	Bent plastic	Plastic tube	Long	Herring	Small	Sight
Internal anchor	Internal anchor	Body cavity	External marker	Metal chain to marker	Long	Various	Tiny	Sight
Bachelor button	Bachelor button	Opercle	Metal and plastic disks	Metal shaft	Medium	Gadoids	Medium	Sight
Strap	Strap	Opercle	Metal strip	Metal shaft	Long	Halibut	Medium	Sight

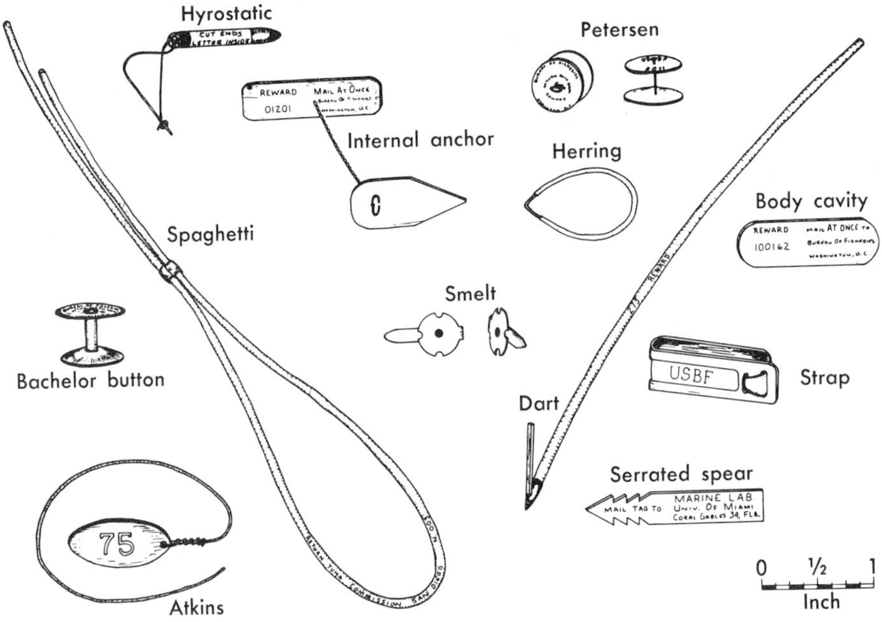

Fig. 11-2. Chief tags in current use listed in Table 11-1.

Obviously some of these methods of attachment are superior to others, and some are best adapted to specific situations. For example, tags depending on the continued elasticity of the material are not useful for long-term experiments. A collar tag is poor, as the fish cannot expand in girth.

Tags in current use. Many types of tags have been tried; only a score can be rated as really successful. Rather than create confusion by including the long list of unproved or unsatisfactory tags, Table 11-1 and Fig. 11-2 show only those tags that are currently most successful under the qualifications as to species, size of organism, etc. that are given.

SELECTION OF MARKS FOR SPECIFIC EXPERIMENTS

A marking experiment should always be designed to answer some specific question. By first posing a question a decision can be made as to what type and quantity of evidence will be sufficient to yield an answer within the definable limits of accuracy. Once the minimum evidence required is determined, the method of marking may be selected. As a first approach, Table 11-2 shows the advantages and disadvantages of several general methods of marking. Mutilation by fin clipping, for instance, can be used on very small fish, and when properly done is quite permanent. However, the individuality of the mark is very low, since only a few marks are available. The recovery of marked individuals is also rather difficult, requiring either intensive canvassing of the fishery or a carefully scheduled representative sampling of the catches.

For some experiments the marking of very large numbers of small individuals is of such overriding importance that tattooing, for instance, may be in order.

In experiments in which the individual fish *must* be identifiable, there is no good substitute for tagging because each tag can be given an individual number. A great variety of tags have been devised, and from experimental evidence they are being continually improved. To aid in the first step of selecting the proper tag, Table 11-3 summarizes the chief attributes of the better

Table 11-2. Attributes of marking methods affecting their selection

Item	Mutilation	Injection	Immersion	Tattooing	Tagging, sight recovery	
					No	*Yes*
Duration of experiment						
Few days			x			
Few weeks			?	x		
Few months		x		?		x
Few years		?			x	x
Several years	x				x	x
Individuality of mark						
Very low			x	x		
Low	x	x			x	
High					x	x
Size when marked						
Very large						x
Large						x
Medium	x	x		x	x	x
Small	x	x	x	x	x	x
Very small			x			
Recovery method						
Own sampling			x	x		
Monitoring machine					x	
Intense canvassing	x	x		x		
Light canvassing						x
Numbers to be marked						
Low						x
Medium						x
High	x	x			x	x
Very high			x	x		
Organism to be marked						
Crustacean		x	?			x
Bivalve mollusk	x					x
Small schooling fish	x	?			x	x
Juvenile fish	x	?		x		x
Large fish						x

types currently in use, with the exception of the magnetic and radioactive tags that in essence are body cavity tags that can be recovered nonvisually but otherwise possess the same attributes.

Even after selection of the specific type of tag, there are certain details that bear watching. The color of an externally visible tag may be very important. Although there is some conflicting evidence, according to most investigators a red-colored external tag appears to be the most attractive to predators. J. E. Watson (personal communication) reports that for the herring-type Atkins tag he devised using yellow plastic tubing,

the returns were five times better than with the green, and no red-colored tags were recovered.

For attaching Petersen tags (Fig. 11-3), stainless steel pins or wire have been shown to be superior to those made of nickel or silver. The same is true of wire bridles for Atkins tags.

Experiments have shown that the hydrostatic Atkins tag fastened through the dorsal muscles yields better returns when attached by a bridle than by a curved loop. Others have found that the single nylon filament used to attach Atkins tags to the muscles is inferior to the heavier braided nylon.

Table 11-3. Attributes of visually recoverable tags affecting their selection

Item	Petersen	Dart	Atkins With tag	Atkins Without tag	Body cavity	Internal anchor	Bachelor button	Strap	Jaw
Skill needed to tag									
High	x					x	x		x
Medium	x		x	x	x				
Low		x		x					
Amount of fish handling									
High	x		x			x	x		x
Medium	x		x	x	x				
Low		x						x	
Structure of fish									
Bony	x	x	x	x	x	x	x	x	x
Soft, light bones	x	x	x	x	x	x			
Place of attachment									
Opercle	x						x	x	
Jaw									x
Body cavity					x	x			
Muscles	x	x	x	x					
Hampering of fish									
High									x
Medium	x		x	x		x	x	x	
Low		x		x	x	x			
Cause of predation									
High	x		x						
Medium	x		x	x		x	x		
Low		x		x		x		x	x
None					x				
Minimum size markable									
Large		x					x		
Medium	x	x	x				x		x
Small				x	x	x			
Very small					x	x			
Tag retention periods									
Short							x	x?	
Medium	x	x	x	x			x		x
Long	x	?	x	x		x	x		x
Very long					x				

For tagging the skipjack (striped tuna), Marr (1961) states that the dart tag yielded several times higher recoveries over those obtained using the best spaghetti tag. (Tubing has a monofilament core of nylon, and the ends are fastened with a clamp in place of a knot.) He attributes this to the ability to hook, tag, and release a skipjack in 4 to 7 seconds using the dart tag, whereas 20 seconds are required with the spaghetti tag.

The manner in which fish are recaptured may influence the proportion and the sizes recaptured. Hartt (1961) found that salmon marked with Petersen tags were more easily held by gill nets. As a result, smaller salmon that would otherwise pass through the nets were retained. Although this fact may tend to yield a larger proportion of recoveries, it may be undesirable from the standpoint of interpretation of the data, since in analyzing the data from a marking experiment it is important that one be able to assume that marked individuals do not differ from the remainder of the population to any significant degree, including their chances of being captured.

Fig. 11-3. Affixing a Petersen disk tag to the opercle of a haddock lying on a measuring board. (Courtesy National Marine Fisheries Service, Woods Hole, Mass.)

CAPTURE AND HANDLING OF LIVE FISH

The success of a marking experiment, *especially* one for the purpose of determining mortality, often depends on how the fish are captured and handled. Iversen and Idyll (1960) obtained 22% recoveries of pink shrimp captured in 15- to 20-minute hauls with a small otter trawl (try net) of 15- to 20-foot spread, whereas recoveries from shrimp captured in 1-hour hauls of a large commercial otter trawl were only 14%. Similarly, tagging of haddock from otter trawls on the offshore banks was unsuccessful, but tagging of hook-caught haddock from small line-trawl boats gave good results (Rounsefell, 1942).

Fish caught by gill net can sometimes be tagged successfully, but Hartt (1961) found that on the high seas tagging recoveries were consistently poor from salmon taken in gill nets. This is largely because of the need to use long nets to take the scattered fish and the impracticability of hauling the nets from a small boat. Baited longlines gave higher returns than gill nets; however, much the highest proportion were returned when salmon were taken by purse seines.

Equally important as the method of capture is the subsequent handling. Large agile fish easily injure themselves against hard surfaces and should usually be held in some type of padded cradle. For exceptionally large fast-swimming fish the total elapsed time between capture and release may be the most important factor. As mentioned previously, Marr (1961) obtained much better recoveries by marking skipjack tuna with a dart tag, which required 7 seconds, than with a spaghetti tag, which required 20 seconds for the whole operation.

Many investigators have used various narcotizing solutions to quiet fish prior to marking. Others prefer not to use such means; opinions remain divided.

For small schooling fish such as herring, continuous release of individual fish encourages predation. A number of marked fish should be released as a school.

For releasing marked shrimp, Costello

(1959) developed plastic containers locked with a lump of salt, which dissolves slowly enough for the container to reach the bottom before opening. The released shrimp quickly bury themselves in the soft bottom.

Suggested readings

Bergman, P. K., K. B. Jefferts, H. F. Fiscus, and R. C. Hager. 1968. A preliminary evaluation of an implanted coded wire fish tag. Wash. Dept. Fish., Fish. Res. Pap. **3:**63-84.

Costello, T. J. 1959. Marking shrimp with biological stains. In Idyll, C. P. Proceedings of the Gulf and Caribbean Fisheries Institute, eleventh annual session. pp. 1-6.

Hartt, A. C. 1961. Problems in tagging salmon at sea. ICNAF North Atlantic Fish Marking Symposium, May, 1961, Contribution No. 24. p. 29.

Margolis, L. 1963. Parasites as indicators of the geographical origin of sockeye salmon, Oncorhynchus nerka (Walbaum), occurring in the North Pacific Ocean and adjacent seas. Int. N. Pac. Fish. Comm., Bull. **11:**101-156.

Marr, J. C. 1961. Note on the recovery rate of tagged skipjack, Katsuwonus pelamis, and the effects of handling. ICNAF North Atlantic Fish Marking Symposium, May, 1961, Contribution No. 1. pp. 1-2.

Rounsefell, G. A. 1963. Marking fish and invertebrates. U. S. Fish Wildl. Serv., Fish. Leaf. **549:**1-12.

Rounsefell, G. A., and J. L. Kask. 1945. How to mark fish. Trans. Amer. Fish. Soc. **73:**320-363.

Thompson, W. F., and W. C. Herrington. 1930. Life history of the Pacific halibut. I. Marking experiments. Rep. Int. Fish. Comm. **2:**1-137.

chapter 12

℣ Population dynamics

In order to intelligently manage a fishery, some of the most important factors to know are the following:

1. The actual size or a good estimate of the relative abundance of the population
2. The age and size composition of the population
3. The age at maturity
4. The mortality rates from fishing and natural causes

Changes from time to time in these items tell a story for which management must seek the causes, whether they result from natural factors beyond human control or from some type of activity by man, beneficial or otherwise, such as changes in fishing rate or enhancement of the environment. The special case where organisms are closely confined is covered in Chapter 16; the harvesting of fish or shellfish from natural waters, without confinement, will be discussed in this chapter.

GENERAL INDICATIONS
OF DECREASING ABUNDANCE

Certain changes in an exploited population are viewed with suspicion as signs that the abundance may be decreasing, although there may be alternative explanations. For example, because of the natural fluctuations in abundance that occur normally in some species, especially the clupeoids with their high fecundity and enormous annual changes in the success of reproduction, all decreases in abundance cannot be blamed on overfishing; the decrease may be only a temporary natural phenomenon unconnected with man's activity.

Similarly, changes in ocean temperatures or the presence or absence of particular water masses can cause long-term trends in the abundance level quite independent of other factors. Sporadic outbreaks of disease also affect marine organisms.

One question that always arises in population estimates is the degree of accuracy required for reasonable management of a fishery. This can depend on several factors. The first question is how important is the fishery? If the fishery is comparatively minor in economic importance, it is highly unlikely that sufficient funds will be provided for a really sophisticated (and expensive) investigation. Moreover, any detailed results will be of only temporary value unless there is some type of continuous monitoring to maintain up-to-date information. Nevertheless, some indications can be obtained at lesser expense and may prove quite adequate for the purpose.

This leads to a second question. What

kind of control is it possible to exercise over the quantities and the portions of the population to be harvested? Unless control can be exercised over a narrow range, there is little need for very accurate estimates of population size.

The third question is how large are the natural short-term fluctuations in abundance? If natural fluctuations are great, as with shrimp, the size of the population one year may have little bearing on the size in the next year. Here the most meaningful statistics are growth and mortality rates for regulation of the harvest of the current year's crop. An estimate of the *annual* population prior to the fishing season may then have some predictive value.

The signs of possible decrease in abundance that could indicate a sufficient depletion to impair future productivity are (1) a decrease in the average age or size, (2) species composition changes, (3) overpopulation by prey species, (4) shrinkage of the area inhabited, (5) shifts in fishing areas, and (6) a fall in the catch per unit of effort.

Decrease in average age or size

A decrease in the average age or size can be caused by a greater than normal recruitment of young into the fishery, causing a disproportionate number of younger fish. In such a case, however, there should not be a decrease in the yield without a large drop in fishing effort.

A virgin fishery when first exploited will usually show a decrease in older and larger fish as the accumulated older fish are removed. This is normal and necessary if the population is to be reduced sufficiently to obtain the maximum sustainable yield. This size reduction is a temporary condition; should it continue instead of stabilizing there may be trouble.

Species composition changes

Changes in the proportions of different species caught by a fishery can imply that one or more species is declining in abundance. This can occur because species differ both in their vulnerability to any specific type of fishing gear and in their capacity to withstand fishing pressure. This last often depends on how long the individual fish are vulnerable to the fishing gear before reaching maturity. Halibut, for instance, have such a high age at maturity that they cannot withstand fishing with otter trawls, which takes them at a much younger age than the hook-and-line fishery.

Overpopulation by prey species

If a prey species becomes very abundant in relation to its normal predator, it may be a sign that the predator species is declining in abundance. The most obvious example of this is the abundant stunted populations of bluegill sunfish that crowd ponds with depleted populations of largemouth bass. Depletion of predators may well be the chief cause of the overpopulations of alewives in the Great Lakes.

Shrinkage of area inhabited

As a species becomes less abundant it tends to occupy less territory. This may be a manifestation of population pressure. There are two good examples. When the Pacific sardine was abundant, the schools of older and larger fish migrated annually as far north as British Columbia, where a fishery was carried on for a number of years. After the very successful spawning of 1934 of striped bass in Chesapeake Bay, the young bass were soon abundant as far north as the Penobscot River, where they were caught along with Atlantic salmon in the famed Bangor Pool.

Shifts in fishing areas

A good example of a shift in fishing grounds concerns a herring reduction plant in southeastern Alaska that operated from 1883 until forced to close in 1928 for lack of fish in adjacent waters (Fig. 12-1). Located near the center of Chatham Strait, the plant depended heavily on the herring of Kootznahoo Inlet. (See Fig. 10-6, p. 220.) The plant fished until as late as 1923

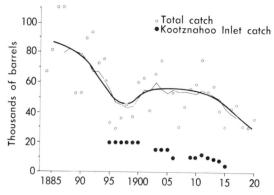

Fig. 12-1. Catches of herring by the reduction plant at Killisnoo in southeastern Alaska from 1884 to 1920. Trend line smoothed once by 7-year moving average.

by a Norwegian method of seining with two oar-propelled seine boats attended by an engine-propelled vessel. Their radius of operation was only about 50 miles, so they could not fish new grounds as the abundance fell near their home base. As late as 1900 they still obtained 20,000 barrels of herring a year from the inlet, but the population continued to decline. By 1915 the inlet furnished only 5000 barrels. From 1927 to 1929 all the herring plants in southeastern Alaska, using modern purse seine vessels, received only 1300 barrels a year from the inlet.

Where more mobile vessels are involved, the shift may continue for some time. When the ocean perch, *Sebastes marinus,* became depleted on the New England banks, the otter trawl vessels moved first to the Nova Scotia banks and, as they were depleted, on to the Gulf of St. Lawrence. They have now run out of new banks to deplete.

Fall in catch per unit of effort

A fall in the catch per unit of fishing gear can be a sign of depletion or of a temporary decline in population size, as often occurs naturally in certain species. To confirm a decline in population size one should compare the number of units of gear. If the units have increased significantly, the decline in catch per unit may be partially or largely caused by increased competition between units of gear. However, in such a case the total yield should be larger. Poor catches can result from changes in availability of the fish caused by fluctuations in oceanic conditions or loss of fishing time because of inclement weather. It is well to critically examine the units of gear from time to time to determine whether there has been a significant increase in the efficiency of the individual unit. Such an increase in efficiency can mask a decline in abundance for a time.

DIRECT ESTIMATION OF POPULATION SIZE
Enumeration of populations

A few populations can be estimated by direct count at one or more stages of their life history. The portion of an annual run of adult salmon that escape through the fishing gear as they migrate to their natal stream can be counted as they pass through openings in a weir or up a fishway. Of course the next problem is to be able to allocate the marine catches of salmon to definite streams in order to estimate the total population of individual streams. This can be done with some assurance for some of the major sockeye salmon streams, but even here the larger rivers have different populations going to different lake systems. In Bristol Bay salmon bound for several river systems mingle in the estuarine waters where they are gillnetted, creating a complex situation.

For the pink salmon, *Oncorhynchus gorbuscha,* of which all the adults invariably mature in their second year, this total run (catch plus escapement) can be related directly to the number of adults in the spawning escapement two seasons previously. For salmon that mature at more than one age it is necessary to take samples of the catch and/or escapement to obtain data on the portions of the run produced by each of several brood years. Since the scales of Pacific salmon become progressively more difficult to read for age as the adults approach maturity, in order to obtain legible scales it is desirable to take scale samples from the catch at frequent intervals before the fish ascend the river. Even this can be fraught with some danger if the fishery is using a selective gear such as gill nets. In such case the sizes (and therefore ages) of the fish in the catch may well differ significantly from those in the spawning escapement. Because of sexual dimorphism, the selectivity of gill nets has at times resulted in an escapement in which the smaller males may outnumber the females by as much as two or three times.

Counts of the total population of salmon smolts descending a stream to the sea have been made in a number of experimental streams. The chief objectives are twofold:

1. To determine freshwater survival from an estimated number of ova. (This requires knowledge of the fecundity and number of female spawners.) The survival rates can then be related to variations in such parameters as stream flow, primary productivity, winter temperature on the spawning beds, etc.

2. To determine marine survival of smolts. This is often accompanied by marking samples of smolts during their downstream migration to determine the relationships between smolt size, sometimes season of migration, and ultimate survival.

Counts of fur seals have been used extensively to determine population size. The observer usually counts the number of harems and then attempts to estimate the average number of females per harem in the different rookeries. The idle bulls are counted separately. Recently this method has been checked by tagging pups and later determining the ratio of tagged to untagged pups.

Summation of area counts

Usually there is no way to count an entire population. However, for many benthic organisms the same result can be obtained within fairly narrow limits by counting the number of individuals on randomly selected

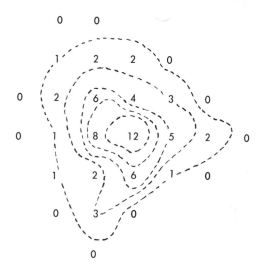

Fig. 12-2. Showing a hypothetical example of a diagram for estimating a population by plotting contours of equal abundance, obtaining areas, and making a summation.

areas of known size. As with all methods there are pitfalls. Seldom does one encounter a wholly uniform area, and practically any species will be more abundant in one spot than in another.

As a first example, there exists a uniformly sloping beach on which the clam population is to be determined. The simplest method is to sample a transect of predetermined width from as high on the beach as clams occur to their greatest depth of water. This will give the population per linear foot of beach. If the substrate varies, several transects may be necessary.

If the organisms are scattered over the surface of a bank it may be necessary to take small area samples on some sort of grid. Then contours should be drawn of equal abundance. As a hypothetical example, Fig. 12-2 shows the average number of organisms at each point, which, for the sake of accuracy, is perhaps the average of 10 samples of 1 m². Then contour lines of equal abundance are drawn at convenient intervals. The lines shown are contours of 1, 3, 5, 7, and 9 organisms/m². Summation of the areas in square meters multiplied by the average abundance between successive contour lines yields an estimate of the population. For conventional sampling gear a substitute could involve pictures taken at a specified distance above the bottom and then a count made of the organisms in a known area.

Marking and recovery

A third direct method of estimating populations is through the marking, release, and subsequent recovery of marked individuals. Rupp (1966) gives a concise exposition of a convenient method for calculating results from both marking experiments and from data in which any particular attribute of certain individuals can be obtained at different time intervals. He terms this a ratio method, defining the following symbols:

N_1 = Total population at time 1
p_1 = Decimal fraction of N_1 consisting of one kind (e.g., males or marked individuals)
M = Number of certain individuals (e.g., males or marked individuals) added or removed between time 1 and time 2
F = Number of other kind of individuals (e.g., females or unmarked) added or removed
N_2 = Total population at time 2
p_2 = New decimal fraction of one kind (e.g., males or marked) among N_2 individuals at time 2

For these symbols Rupp adopts the convention that M and F will be positive or negative depending on whether the certain individuals specified are added to or removed from the population. The two structural equations to show the relationships of these quantities are:

$$p_2N_2 = p_1N_1 + M$$

and

$$N_2 = N_1 + M + F$$

By substituting the second equation into the first he derives a basic estimating equation as follows:

$$N_1 = \frac{M - p_2(M + F)}{p_2 - p_1} \qquad (1)$$

This basic equation is usable for population

estimates when p_1, p_2, M, and F are known or can be estimated, and p_1 differs from p_2. If they do not differ, a population estimate is not possible.

As a hypothetical example of the use of equation 1 it may be assumed that at time 1 the catches were 60% haddock and 40% cod, and that at time 2 after capturing 400,000 haddock and 200,000 cod the ratio has changed to 45% haddock and 55% cod. What are the original numbers?

$$N_1 = \frac{-400,000 - (0.45)(-600,000)}{0.45 - 0.60}$$

$$= 866,667$$

The original number of haddock is 0.60 × 866,667 or 520,000; the original number of cod is 0.40 × 866,667 or 346,667.

From equation 1 when only one kind is added or removed so that F = 0, Rupp derives equation 2:

$$N_1 = \frac{M - p_2M}{p_2 - p_1} \qquad (2)$$

If 1000 marked fish are released into a population in which there are no marked fish, so that $p_1 = 0$, then if in fishing 0.05 are found marked, $p_2 = 0.05$ and:

$$N_1 = \frac{1000 - 0.05(1000)}{0.05 - 0} = \frac{950}{0.05} = 19,000$$

If the 1000 marked fish were taken originally from the same population to which they are returned, then:

$$p_2N_1 = p_1N_1 + M$$
$$p_1N_1 = 0$$
$$N_1 = N_2$$

so that by substituting for p_1N_1 and N_2:

$$p_2N_1 = 0 + M$$
$$N_1 = M/p_2 \qquad (3)$$

Rupp points out that this equation, which is the basic Petersen equation, is biased at small sample sizes; he refers to equation 3.7 of Ricker, in which:

$$\hat{N} = \frac{M(C + 1)}{R + 1}$$

where:

$\hat{N}$ = Estimate for each sample taken
M = Number of fish marked
C = Size of the sample
R = Number of marked fish among sample

If instead of estimating N_1 one requires a direct estimate of N_2, Rupp suggests changing the equation to:

$$N_2 = \frac{M - p_1(M + F)}{p_2 - p_1} \qquad (4)$$

All of these formulas, to give accurate results, make certain assumptions:

1. Natural mortality does not differ between marked and unmarked fish.
2. Marked and unmarked fish are equally vulnerable to the fishing gear.
3. Either the marked fish mix randomly with the unmarked fish or fishing effort is spread out in proportion to the number of fish present.
4. Recruitment is either negligible during the period of mark recovery or the recruits can be identified by size and/or age and left out of the computations.
5. All fish retain their marks, and all marked fish caught are reported.

Egg and larvae sampling

Another method of estimating population size is by sampling to determine the concentration of eggs and larvae. This of course estimates the number (or weight) of mature adults. It requires several items of information:

1. The average fecundity
2. The rate at which the eggs and larvae develop at different temperatures
3. If individuals spawn more than once, and, if after spawning commences, it is continuous or irregular in occurrence

The task of sampling is formidable, since it requires close spacing in distance and time. However, it does permit making estimates of populations that are either not being fished or are not easily estimated from the amount, volume, distribution, or type of fishing effort.

Perhaps the most ambitious program for estimating spawning populations by this method has been carried out by the California Cooperative Oceanic Fisheries Investigations in the California Current system between the Oregon-California border and the southern tip of Baja California.

Over this large area station lines perpendicular to the coast were spaced at 40-mile intervals. Plankton tows were made with a No. 30xxx grit gauge (heavy bolting silk) net of 1 m diameter. The forward 1 m is cylindric; the conical section is about 3 m long. Oblique tows were made from 140 m (depth permitting) to the surface at 1½ to 2 knots, keeping the towing cable at a 45-degree angle and retrieving the net at the rate of 20 m/minute (Ahlstrom, 1966).

An Atlas-type current meter suspended in the mouth of each net measured the water strained (calculated from the revolutions multiplied by the net mouth area multiplied by the length of the water column needed to cause one revolution of the current meter) (Ahlstrom, 1953). Each haul was expressed as a "standard haul"; i.e., the number of eggs and larvae obtained were adjusted to the number in 10 m³ of water strained per unit of depth fished. If the vertical distribution of the eggs and larvae is fully encompassed, this value is equivalent to the number under 10 m² of sea surface.

Usually the entire sample was sorted for eggs and larvae. In the year 1951 out of 1437 samples, 1262 were sorted in their entirety; for the remaining 175 samples, aliquot portions were sorted.

The number of eggs in a sample was expressed as the number of eggs spawned per day. This requires that the eggs be sorted according to their approximate age from the date of spawning. For instance, California sardine (or pilchard), *Sardinops sagax caerulea,* eggs were sorted into four categories according to the hours of age at the time of collection:

A = Within 24 hours
B = Within 24.1 to 48 hours
C = Within 48.1 to 72 hours
D = Within 72.1 to 96 hours
Unclassified = Deteriorating eggs, age uncertain

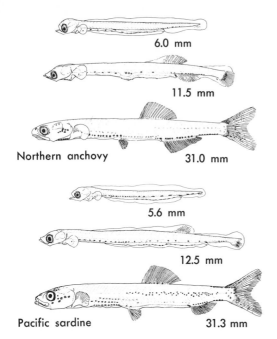

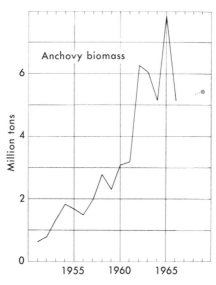

Fig. 12-3. Early life history stages of northern anchovy and Pacific sardine. In each case the two top figures are larvae and the bottom figure is a metamorphosing specimen. (From Ahlstrom, E. H. 1966. U. S. Fish Wildl. Serv., Spec. Sci. Rep. Fish. **534**:1-71.)

Fig. 12-4. Total spawning biomass of anchovies off the West Coast between San Francisco and San Lázaro, Baja California, calculated from the numbers of anchovy larvae collected each year. (From Vrooman, A. M., and P. E. Smith. 1971. Calif. Mar. Res. Comm., CalCOFI Rep. **15:** 49-51.)

The larvae were all classified in millimeter length categories (Fig. 12-3).

In analyzing these data (chief species were the sardine, *Sardinops sagax caerulea,* and the anchovy, *Engraulis mordax*), it was found that the numbers of larvae of both species decreased markedly with an increase in size (Ahlstrom, 1966). Over a 9-year period from 1951 to 1959 despite an enormous increase in the numbers of anchovy larvae, the numbers in each 3 mm size category fell off at about the same rate each year. This being the case, the total number of all larvae collected each year adjusted for catch per 10 m² of sea surface was used in determining relative abundance from year to year.

Since the anchovies were not being exploited sufficiently to obtain any meaningful measure of abundance from catch records, their abundance was estimated by comparing their numbers of larvae with those of the sardine in 1958, the last year with a substantial enough sardine fishery to provide a good population estimate (Messersmith et al., 1969). On the basis of fecundity studies, anchovies spawn twice as many eggs as the sardine per unit of weight, so that in 1958 with the larvae ratio between sardines and anchovies 1:18, the anchovies were assumed to be nine times as abundant, amounting to 1.8 to 2.25 million tons off California and Baja California.

The spawning populations of anchovy for 16 years (1951 to 1966) are obtained (Vrooman and Smith, 1971) using the formula:

$$B_a = 98.2L_a$$

where:

B_a = Biomass in millions of tons
L_a = Number of larvae × 10^{12}

The standard error of prediction is about 9% (Fig. 12-4).

Studies of both meristic characters and serum transferrins show three subpopulations—a northern population north of Point Conception, a central one from Point Conception to Ensenada, Baja California, and a southern group from Ensenada to Cape San Lázaro.

Direct observation

As instrumentation becomes more and more sophisticated, direct observation becomes more appealing. As early as 1946 G. B. Kelez attempted to enumerate spawning salmon in a vast number of streams by means of a strip of aerial photographs taken at about 600 feet. Later aerial flights were used to measure the miles of shoreline used by spawning schools of Pacific herring (Taylor, 1955; Skud, 1959).

It can be readily appreciated that aerial photographs are unsuited for benthic species. However, benthic populations are much more easily estimated from catches than pelagic species, since their density is usually more evenly spread over a plane surface. For pelagic schooling species, aerial photography can be very useful.

Aerial photography of pelagic fishes is still in its infancy. Current experiments include the use of high-flying airplanes and earth satellites. The use of varied emulsions, infrared film, and extremely sensitive film for photographing bioluminescence is being tried. Hopefully the total area covered by schooling fish in each film can be integrated by computer. If so, a combination of photography with sufficient ground truth will make estimation of pelagic populations faster, perhaps cheaper, and far more up-to-date than former conventional methods.

Echo ranging

Some of the first attempts to locate schooling fish by echoes are documented by Smith and Ahlstrom (1948). The equipment consisted of both a horizontally directed sonar and a Fathometer, and observations were limited to finding a few small schools of sardines and squid. Within a few years this technique was extended to attempts to gain quantitative estimates of the abundance (or at least relative abundance) of pelagic fish in different areas. McClendon (1968), in describing the EASTROPAC cruises of the R/V *David Starr Jordan,* states that the starboard transducer was aimed at an angle of 10 degrees off the bow and set at a range of 2500 m, and, with approximately a 23 degree width, scanned an area at a 10-knot speed of about 5 square miles/hour. He states that the number of targets along the track lines are estimates of the total population. I believe that his estimates can only be considered to express relative abundance, since measurement of size differences between schools was not attempted.

An acoustic survey of the schools of pelagic fishes along a transect from Cape Hatteras, North Carolina to Cape Canaveral, Florida, is discussed by Klima (1971), but no attempt was made to estimate species or quantity.

Some of the problems of echo ranging are brought out in a detailed FAO manual edited by Forbes and Nakken:

Fishery scientists need population estimates made independently of fishery statistics of catch and effort and tagging experiments, and methods are also required for the rapid exploration of unexploited stocks. An increasing emphasis has been placed in recent years on the problems of direct and speedier estimation of fish populations, and methods of sizing and counting fish with echo sounders and sonars are now developing rapidly. As no manual or textbook at present exists which specifically deals with this subject, the present publication attempts to present a summary of the state of knowledge in the use of acoustics for fisheries resource survey and appraisal.*

They state that in order to obtain the amount of fish (in either weight or numbers) within an area, one must be able to (1) discriminate between species and (2) make synoptic distribution charts of density for each species throughout the area. They

*From Forbes, S. T., and O. Nakken, editors. 1972. Manual of methods for fisheries resource survey and appraisal. II. The use of acoustic instruments for fish detection and abundance estimation. FAO Man. Fish. Sci. **5:**1-138.

do not have complete solutions to these two problems, but show the present state of methods being developed to solve them. One problem is that the swim bladder is responsible for about half the signal returned from those species of fish that possess one. Also, the target strength varies with the aspect of the fish, the lateral aspect returning 10 times as much signal as the dorsal aspect under some conditions.

INDIRECT ESTIMATION OF POPULATION SIZE

Although there is some overlap I have chosen to call direct methods those depending on simple, straightforward, quantitative estimates entailing a minimum of statistical inference. Indirect methods usually require sampling and compilation of large masses of data by which one may estimate the various parameters required to assess population size and composition through sophisticated actuarial techniques.

The description and critique of these methods is beyond the scope of a general text, but I will discuss some of the objectives and aspects of these indirect analyses.

Fig. 12-5, a simplified diagram, shows the major factors involved. The only control exercised by man is a change in the number of fishing units (or achieving the same objective by shorter fishing seasons or restrictions on gear efficiency).

The "availability" is a variable that can cause a great deal of trouble if it fluctuates widely from season to season. It is most apt to vary with schooling pelagic species and to give least trouble in trawl fisheries for benthic species.

Fig. 12-5 is best understood by first considering what happens to a single brood of fish spawned in 1 year. This is depicted in Fig. 12-6. It will be noted that the total weight of a year class increases to the "critical size," at which time the gain in total weight by increase in the weight of the individuals is less than the loss in weight from mortality. This concept is especially important for very fast-growing species such as shrimp, which also have a high natural mortality. In such cases it is especially important that harvesting start soon enough to take the bulk of the catch before the shrimp pass this "critical size."

One important feature that cannot effectively be shown in Fig. 12-6 because of its variability with the species is the age at maturity. If the age at maturity occurs after the year class has almost reached or passed the "critical size," then the question arises as to the number of spawning individuals needed to maintain a sufficient number of recruits,

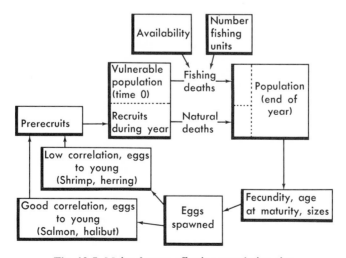

Fig. 12-5. Major factors affecting population size.

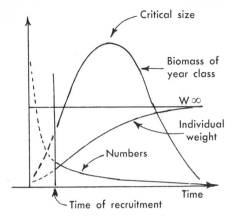

Individual weight

Numbers

Time of recruitment

Fig. 12-6. Changes in numbers and weight of a year class of fish during its life. (Modified from Gulland, J. A. 1969. FAO Man. Fish. Sci. **4:** 1-154.)

because Fig. 12-5 is circular, indicating the cyclic nature of the pattern.

It is thus apparent that to manage a fishery it is necessary to know the age and size composition of the population as well as its size in numbers or weight. In species with very low correlation (except of course at extremely low levels) between the size of the spawning stock and the size of the resulting brood, this restriction is lowered, and the important factors become the harvesting of the year class at such a rate and season so as to capture the majority close to the critical size.

Because of a difference from year to year in the dates at which shrimp, for instance, reach the optimum size for the commencement of harvesting, a shift forward or back of a few days can easily mean a few million dollars' difference in the total value of the catch. This means flexibility in regulations and adequate fast sampling in the field.

The most commonly derived statistic is the catch per unit of fishing effort. Provided there are not wide annual fluctuations in availability to the fishing gear and the number of units of gear remains more or less constant from year to year, it yields a fairly satisfactory measure of relative abundance. It actually measures the average abundance during the year (or during the season when fishing is being carried on).

To convert this catch per unit of effort into actual population size one needs some measure of the total mortality and of fishing mortality. This can be obtained, as mentioned previously, through marking experiments and sometimes through measuring the decrease from year to year in the relative abundance of year classes. This last is difficult to achieve (1) in species with a wide variation in annual recruitment or (2) without means of deciphering ages with reasonable accuracy.

An example of the computation of total population size is taken from Widrig (1954). The notation and relationships of some of the parameters are as follows:

POPULATION

N = Initial population (numbers)
C = Catch
D = Deaths from all causes

MORTALITY RATES, ANNUAL

u = Fraction caught
v = Fraction dying naturally
a = Total fraction dying
s = Total fraction surviving
m = Fishing mortality (if no natural mortality)
n = Natural mortality (if no fishing mortality)

MORTALITY RATES, INSTANTANEOUS

F = Fishing
M = Natural
Z = Total
f = Effective fishing effort

MISCELLANEOUS

Q = Slope (regression) coefficient of Z on f

(1) $\dfrac{dC}{dt} = FN_t$, where $\dfrac{dC}{dt}$ is the catch rate on time and N_t is population size during time dt

(2) $\dfrac{dn}{dt} = MN_t$, where $\dfrac{dn}{dt}$ is rate of natural death on time

(3) $Z = F + M$, or the instantaneous rate of total death

(4) $a = 1 - \epsilon^{-(M + F)}$, or total fraction dying, $1 - \epsilon^{-Z}$

(5) $u = F\,\dfrac{a}{Z}$, or the fraction caught

Widrig states the objective of the method as the question, "what is the ratio between this catch which I observe and the total

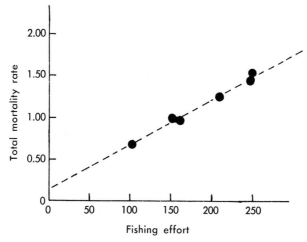

Fig. 12-7. Determining the instantaneous natural mortality rate (M) by determining the slope of the least squares regression line for total instantaneous mortality rate (Z) vs number of units of fishing effort. The intercept of this regression line (Q) at 0 fishing effort yields a Z without fishing mortality, which is M. (From Widrig, T. M. 1954. U. S. Fish Wildl. Serv., Fish. Bull. **56**:141-166.)

stock from which it came?" He then states, "I wish to compute the ratio between the catch and the size of the population from which it came by subtracting the natural mortality rate from the total mortality rate to get the fishing mortality rate. The latter, of course, is the ratio of the catch to the initial stock."

He needed two statistics: (1) the number of fishing units expended to obtain the given catches and (2) the total annual mortality the total stock experienced while yielding the given catches.

Widrig was able to compute total mortality from estimates of stock size in one year to the size of the stock the following year. To do this he had to have information on the age composition of the total catch per unit of effort in order to remove the effect of recruitment during the year.

He next computed the natural mortality (Fig. 12-7) by plotting the instantaneous total mortality, Z, against the number of fishing units (boat days). The slope of the least squares regression line, Q, was then calculated. The intercept of this regression at 0 fishing effort yielded a Z of 0.147. Without any fishing this Z corresponds to

M, the natural mortality. Since $M = Z - F$, at the intercept $M = Z - 0$, or 0.147.

Q was 0.005318, so that for every 100 boat days the total mortality would be increased by 0.5318 units. For 100 boat days the natural mortality was 0.147 plus 0.5318 for fishing mortality, a total mortality of 0.6788. Z therefore corresponds to an a of 49.3%/year. Of this 49.3%, one would infer that the fraction M/Z was that part of the initial population caught during the season, or 0.5318/0.6788, which is 0.7834. So the fraction caught (the rate of exploitation) is $0.7834 \times 49.3\%$, which equals 38.6% with the remainder of total mortality representing the fraction that died naturally, 10.7%.

The initial population for the year, i.e., fish that were fully recruited and therefore sustaining these various rates of mortality, would be estimated by dividing the catch for that year by the rate of exploitation, since:

$$u = C/N$$

and therefore

$$N = C/u$$

That is, N, the initial population, would be

estimated at $1/0.386$, or 2.6 times the catch in that season.

This example from Widrig (1954) of a method of obtaining an estimate of the natural mortality coefficient, M, is an elaboration of a method first devised by Silliman (1943). Similar to practically all statistical estimates, the method depends on certain assumptions that are seldom fully satisfied and that often require considerable manipulation of the data to discount the effect of nonconformity.

For details concerning methods of modification of these basic equations, discussions are given in Murphy (1966), Beverton and Holt (1957), and Ricker (1958).

Suggested readings

Ahlstrom, E. H. 1953. Pilchard eggs and larvae and other fish larvae, Pacific Coast—1951. U. S. Fish Wildl. Serv., Spec. Sci. Rep. Fish. **102**:1-55.

Ahlstrom, E. H. 1966. Distribution and abundance of sardine and anchovy larvae in the California Current Region off California and Baja California, 1951-64: a summary. U. S. Fish Wildl. Serv., Spec. Sci. Rep. Fish **534**:1-71.

Beverton, R. J. H., and S. J. Holt. 1957. On the dynamics of exploited fish populations. Ministry of Agriculture, Fisheries, and Food, Fisheries Investigations, United Kingdom, Ser. II. **19**:1-533.

Cushing, D. H. 1968. Fisheries biology. University of Wisconsin Press, Madison, Wis. 200 pp.

Forbes, S. T., and O. Nakken, editors. 1972. Manual of methods for fisheries resource survey and appraisal. II. The use of acoustic instruments for fish detection and abundance estimation. FAO Man. Fish. Sci. **5**:1-138.

Gulland, J. A. 1969. Manual of methods for fish stock assessment. I. Fish population analysis. FAO Man. Fish. Sci. **4**:1-154.

Messersmith, J. D., J. L. Baxter, and P. M. Roedel. 1969. The anchovy resources of the California Current Region off California and Baja California. Calif. Mar. Res. Comm., CalCOFI Rep. **13**:32-38.

Murphy, G. I. 1966. Population biology of the Pacific sardine (Sardinops caerulea). Proc. Calif. Acad. Sci., Ser. 4. **34**:1-84.

Ricker, W. E. 1958. Handbook of computations for biological statistics of fish populations. Fish. Res. Bd. Canada, Bull. **119**:1-300.

Rounsefell, G. A. 1957. A method of estimating abundance of groundfish on Georges Bank. U. S. Fish Wildl. Serv., Fish. Bull. **57**:265-278.

Rupp, R. S. 1966. Generalized equation for the ratio method of estimating population abundance. J. Wildl. Mgt. **30**:523-526.

Silliman, R. P. 1943. Studies on the Pacific pilchard or sardine (Sardinops caerulea). V. A. method of computing mortalities and replacements. U. S. Fish Wildl. Serv., Spec. Sci. Rep. **24**:1-10.

Skud, B. E. 1959. Herring spawning surveys in southeastern Alaska. U. S. Fish Wildl. Serv., Spec. Sci. Rep. Fish. **321**:1-16.

Vrooman, A. M., and P. E. Smith. 1971. Biomass of the subpopulations of northern anchovy Engraulis mordax Girard. Calif. Mar. Res. Comm., CalCOFI Rep. **15**:49-51.

Widrig, T. M. 1954. Method of estimating fish populations, with application to Pacific sardine. U. S. Fish Wildl. Serv., Fish. Bull. **56**:141-166.

part five

❧ Management of a fishery

chapter 13

✿ Management and regulations

MANAGEMENT TECHNIQUES

The techniques for management of a fish population depend on the amount of environmental control that can be applied, on the particular factors that limit the size of population, and on the part played by man. For valuable species in small bodies of water it is sometimes practical to employ intensive management measures, but for marine species the available management measures are often restricted.

The purpose of management is to exploit a fishery so as to obtain the maximum benefit. The term "maximum benefit" can be interpreted in several ways. For a long time most conservationists considered the maximum benefit to mean the largest poundage of edible fish. Fishery economists, however, disputed this narrow interpretation and pointed out that from the standpoint of the producer (and usually the processors) the maximum benefit accrues when the profits are largest.

Probably the greatest headache in managing marine fisheries stems from the fact that they are a common property resource. Christy and Scott (1965) state that one of the unique characteristics of a common property natural resource is that the amount of effort applied is not subject to the restraints that govern the exploitation of a solely owned resource. This competition between fishermen is clearly shown in the great difference in yield per unit area between private oyster beds and public reefs. One cannot blame the individual fisherman. Whatever he does not catch will be caught by someone else, so that there is no inducement for restraint. Since the resource is public, there is seldom any limit to the number of individuals that can enter the fishery. The only restraint is the degree of profit. As long as there is any reasonable profit, the number of boats will increase until all profit is wiped out.

The lack of restraint on the number of fishermen almost inevitably causes depletion of a fishery. This seldom proceeds far enough to cause a marine species to become extinct, but the species may fall to sufficiently low levels that the fishery is continued only with a waste of capital and labor.

The chief role of man is that of predator, but he may also affect the population in other ways. Fig. 13-1 is a diagram of the various factors that affect a fish population. Management consists in manipulating the action of these factors so as to produce the largest available surplus to be harvested. The continuation of this surplus depends on maintaining a delicate adjustment between

249

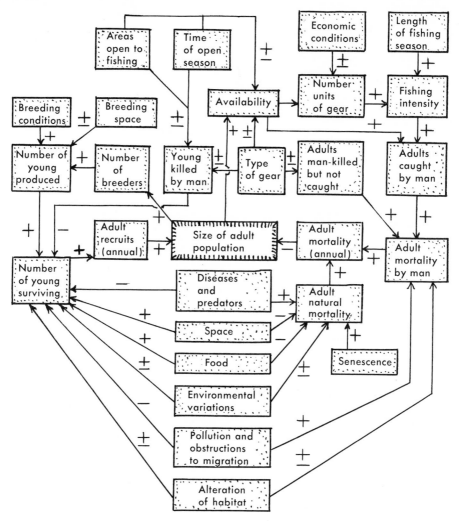

Fig. 13-1. Major and minor factors influencing population size. (Modified from Rounsefell, G. A., and W. H. Everhart. 1953. Fishery science. John Wiley & Sons, Inc., New York. 444 pp.)

the annual mortality (natural and man-induced) and the annual recruitment of adults. Because of the decrease in reproductive potential (or survival value) that invariably accompanies population increase as the curve of population growth approaches an asymptote, the greatest annual harvestable surplus does not usually occur at the highest level of abundance, but rather at some intermediate point. To ascertain with reasonable accuracy the range of abundance within which this optimum level lies may require data covering many years.

As Fig. 13-1 shows, man can affect fish populations in several ways. He can harm populations not only through excessive predation but also by pollution, by obstructing migration to and from spawning areas, by destroying spawning beds, and by altering the habitat in other ways. Habitat alteration is especially harmful in the estuaries that serve as nursery areas for a large proportion of the fishes taken on the continental shelf. It thus becomes apparent that management must be concerned with maintaining or enhancing an environment suitable for all life history stages of an exploited species, which of course includes the same concern for the organisms on which they feed.

Reduction of total fishing mortality

In a great many marine fisheries, especially those in the open sea, the only control the manager has is reduction of fishing mortality. This measure is postulated on the assumption that the present fishing intensity is so great as to have forced the level of the marine population below the point of inflection on the population growth curve, so that the available harvest is below what it would be if the total size of the population were allowed to increase. The point of inflection of the population growth curve is hard to determine. Usually when a species is first exploited its abundance will drop. Some consider that the reattainment of this pristine level of abundance is desirable, but in reality this original level cannot be maintained if there is to be any harvestable surplus.

In some marine fisheries the only management measure possible is control of the amount of the catch, but this measure can be very effective if the population size and the relationship between population size and size of the annual increment of adults are known.

If a fishery is being fully exploited, the restrictions on fishing activity must be approached cautiously. Reducing the amount of the catch by merely decreasing the efficiency of the individual units of gear, for example, may easily destroy all profits and may not even achieve the desired decrease in catch, as the fishermen will be forced to increase the number of units of gear in an attempt to overcome the decreased efficiency of the individual unit. This can sometimes result in higher costs, less profit (if any), and no reduction in fishing mortality.

Selective mortality by the fishery

A second measure, useful in some fisheries employing certain types of gear, is to make modifications in the fishing gear so as to permit the escape of smaller fish. This method is especially applicable to the otter trawl fisheries, but it can be used in most fisheries in which the fish are taken by nets or traps and there is a large size range in the individuals subject to capture. This method requires three items of information concerning a species—the rate of growth, the rate of mortality, and the size selection made by various sizes of net meshes, spaces between laths in pot traps, or other passages for escape.

In applying regulations for selective mortality it should be noted that all of the fish to be harvested each season cannot be caught at one instant. If the minimum size limit is set at the point where an increase in the growth of the individual exactly compensates for increased mortality, there will be some loss in total weight from the death of older fish. (See Fig. 12-6, p. 244.) The amount of such loss depends on the intensity of the fishery. For light intensity the greatest catch may be made without any size limit. Even for heavy fishing intensity a larger take will be made if the minimum size is below the critical point at which growth and mortality balance. However, for fish that mature at a large size it may be necessary to set the limit at or above the critical point to assure a sufficient number of spawners. For species that live to a considerable age the use of a high minimum size may be economically advantageous, as the presence in the population of fish of several ages tends to prevent sudden fluctuations in the catch as a result of the poor survival of fish of one particular year class. Such sudden changes in population size are a great economic detriment to the orderly conduct of any fishing venture.

If the survival of young is high, as in many warmwater species taken in lakes, a minimum size limit may aggravate overcrowding and thus reduce the yield. Any minimum size should be flexible in order to permit adjustments to changes in fishing intensity, growth, and population size.

In actual practice, to save small fish the gear is modified to allow the majority of the small fish to escape. Pound nets and traps are often required to use meshes above a

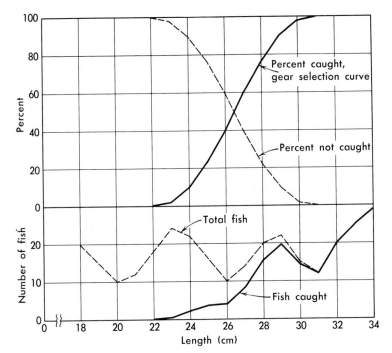

Fig. 13-2. Idealized gear selection curve showing the percentage selection of fish at each length for a particular size of mesh. (From Rounsefell, G. A., and W. H. Everhart. 1953. Fishery science. John Wiley & Sons, Inc., New York. 444 pp.)

specified minimum size in the "pound" or "spiller." Often this measure is designed not so much for the escape of undersized fish of the species sought as for the escape of fish of other species.

In the pot fisheries for crustaceans the pots allow the escape of small individuals. In the lobster fisheries the spacing between the bottom of the pot and the first lath must be of a minimum size. In the king crab pots small circular openings permit the escape of small crabs and many of the female crabs, which are smaller than the males.

Experiments have determined the sizes of fish of different species that escape through the cod ends of otter trawls when meshes of different sizes are used. The percentage of the fish of each available size that escape through the meshes of a cod end forms an ogive curve called a selection curve (Fig. 13-2). The steepness of the slope of the selection curve is related to the speed of towing, as the fish escape through the meshes of the cod end that are kept open by

the outrushing water. If the speed becomes too great, the extra strain on the net tends to keep the meshes closed.

The Danish seine, or "snurrevard," is adapted to saving young fish, since the fish are slowly driven together by the towing warps and brought on board alive, so that small fish can be readily sorted out and released in good condition.

Line trawls take few small fish, but in most bank fisheries the line trawl is supplanted by the more efficient otter trawl. In the Pacific halibut fisheries increasing the size of the hooks results in fewer small fish being caught.

Gill nets are highly selective; each mesh size tends to capture a particular size range of fish. This fact is often used for the protection of small fish.

Size limitations invoke certain biological principles. Most fish exhibit sexual dimorphism with regard to size. On some salmon rivers, for instance, the use of a high minimum mesh size results in catching more females and fewer of the smaller males, so many more males than females reach the spawning beds—an obvious economic waste. Size limitations may have another effect. By catching the larger fish and leaving the smaller ones to breed, we may be decreasing the average size that a species will attain.

When fishing intensity is so heavy that small fish are apt to be netted several times as the fleet tries to catch all the larger fish, savings gear is not always practical. Fortunately it hardly pays a vessel to strain a few large fish from thousands of undersized fish, so when large fish become scarce in an area fishing intensity may slacken.

Savings gear poses many practical problems. Meshes small enough not to permit the escape of many fish of the desired minimum sizes will also take many smaller fish, especially when these smaller fish are abundant and the fish pile against the webbing of the cod end. Since the mesh size of the cod end varies with the species sought, possession of a small-mesh cod end is not evidence of wrong intent. Also, no fishing crew will wish to use savings gear when some vessels are selling undersized fish at a profit. One measure to prevent the capture of small fish and to make the use of savings gear attractive is a strict limitation on the percentage of undersized fish that any vessel may land.

Closure of nursery grounds

Fish of younger age groups usually do not mingle extensively with older fish, but on certain areas of the fishing banks undersized fish tend to congregate. Trawling these areas, even with savings gear, destroys large numbers. Where enforcement is practical, closure of such areas is an effective way to prevent the destruction of young fish. Similarly, Pacific Northwest trout fishermen are prevented from taking young sea-run rainbow (steelhead) trout through the closing of many tributary streams in the spring until the young steelhead migrate to the sea.

In the extensive estuaries of the Southeast it is customary to prohibit trawling for shrimp until the juvenile shrimp reach a specified size. This closure also aids in protecting young croakers and other sciaenids that inhabit the same areas.

Protection of spawning grounds

Only with well-defined spawning grounds is it practical to protect fish in a spawning area. Some biologists contend that whether a fish is caught in the act of spawning or 6 months earlier the net result is the same. The argument for early protection is that fish run a gauntlet of enemies during the year, so chances that any particular fish will spawn are much less 6 months before the spawning season than just before spawning time. One argument favoring closure of spawning grounds is that many fish are especially easy to capture at spawning time. A more cogent argument is that many species are usually in poor market condition during the spawning season.

For species with demersal or adhesive eggs the fishing gear may conceivable damage the already deposited eggs by crushing them, burying them, or tearing up the seaweed or kelps to which the eggs cling.

LAWS AND REGULATIONS
Purpose of fishery regulations

Only a portion of the fishery laws (or regulations) are based on actual conservation needs. Many are for the express purpose of hampering a particular form of gear in order to benefit another gear. Fishermen mustering the most votes win. Certain processors may become involved to promote regulations they hope will increase their supply of raw material, regardless of how it may affect others. For example, shrimp canners can use small shrimp that have a very low value to the fresh or frozen shrimp trade, so they favor the commencement of fishing before the shrimp have reached a size that will result in the optimum harvest.

Types of regulations

The theory that if fewer fish are caught now, more will be available for future fishing is not always true, but it has been so generally accepted for such a long time that it is engraved on the public mind. The popular theories behind most regulations are approximately as follows:

1. A large number of older fish are required for a spawning stock.
2. All smaller fish should be fully protected, since the majority will become big fish.
3. Fish must be protected during the spawning season.

The first theory may be true within certain population limits for a few species, e.g., salmon, in which the small number of eggs is subject to less than normal environmental hazards, so that a connection between the numbers of spawners and of progeny can be established. For many highly fecund species whose eggs are at the mercy of fluctuating environmental conditions, such a connection has not yet been proved, so that maintenance of a large stock of older fish may represent a loss. It cannot be inferred that no connection exists, but rather there may be an upper limit beyond which additional spawning stock is of no advantage. At lower levels the connection may be so obscured by the effect of varying environmental conditions that it cannot be demonstrated without a long series of data both on spawning stock and ecologic factors.

The second theory is often wrong. In the North Sea the shallow waters along the Dutch and Danish coasts support a large population of small plaice stunted from overcrowding; their protection cannot be justified.

The third theory may or may not be true. If the stock of mature fish is low and they are especially vulnerable to capture during the spawning period, protection may be justified. If the fish are not more vulnerable to capture while spawning, the same result can be achieved by reducing the catch during the remainder of the year.

In this chapter I am dealing with regulations that change the amount or type of predation by man. There are two basic ways in which laws can modify man's predation:

1. The total catch can be reduced or limited.
2. Certain portions of the population can be protected.

The first of these two objectives is usually achieved in one of three ways:

1. Lowering the efficiency of the individual fishing unit
2. Placing a ceiling on the number of fishing units permitted to operate (the "limited entry" system)
3. Limiting the total quantity of fish that can be taken during the season (the "quota" system)

The second objective (protecting certain portions of the population) may or may not reduce the total catch but may have other desirable effects achieved by:

1. Changes in the fishing gear to decrease catches of sizes or groups to be protected (the "savings gear" system)
2. Closure of fishing areas dominated by certain sizes or groups of individuals
3. Closed fishing seasons to avoid catching certain sizes or groups
4. Restricting the sale of fish of certain sizes or condition
5. Protection of individuals based on sex or condition

Lowering efficiency of individual fishing unit. Regulations lowering the efficiency of the individual fishing unit are popular because of their ease of enforcement. Typical examples include regulations imposed on the size or type of vessel or gear, closing areas to certain types of gear, placing a bag limit, and restricting fishing time.

REGULATING SIZE OR TYPE OF VESSEL. Size is usually based on net or gross tonnage but sometimes on length measurements. Purse seine vessels fishing salmon in Alaska were for a long time restricted to a 50-foot (15 m) keel length. Many were built with a ridiculously long overhang in the stern in order to gain size without breaking the law. For many years the salmon gillnetters in Bristol Bay were compelled because of vessel regulations to fish dangerous and stormy waters in open boats propelled only by oars and a small sail. Regulating the size or type of vessel is highly artificial and very often increases the cost of operation without a compensatory reduction in total catch.

LIMITING SIZE OF GEAR. Besides fishing vessels, the gear itself is often regulated. Purse seines may be limited in total length and sometimes in depth. Trolling boats once used six to eight lines but now are usually limited to four lines. Fixed gear is sometimes limited to a maximum depth of water; a minimum distance along the shore may be required between successive units, and the length of pound net leaders may be specified. Spiny lobster pots in Florida are limited to a maximum size of 2×3 feet (0.61×0.91 m). Salmon purse seines in Alaska are also restricted to a minimum size because smaller nets are too easily employed for robbing creeks of salmon that have already entered the stream to spawn or are congregated at the mouth before ascending.

REGULATING TYPE OF GEAR USED. Although perhaps the most usual type of restriction, regulations on the type of gear used often spring largely from social and economic factors. They are often based on the desire of the owners of one type of gear to eliminate competition from another. The users of inefficient gear usually stress the great destructiveness of the gear they wish to eliminate. Often they attempt to show that the ownership of the more efficient gear is not so widespread. This is used especially against fixed gear where its operation depends on the ownership or exclusive use of a fishing site.

Restrictions on the gear permitted almost always result in less efficiency, thus increasing the cost of fish. The arguments used are largely social, since they may result in more employment even if at a lower level of productivity. Admittedly a highly efficient gear in a localized area may take too large a proportion of the stock unless some restrictions are imposed.

CLOSING AREAS TO CERTAIN TYPES OF GEAR. Closing a fishing area to some forms of gear while allowing others is usually based either on the high efficiency or on the actual or alleged destructiveness of the banned gear. For example, purse seiners and otter trawlers are often banned from specified inshore areas reserved for local fishermen or sportsmen. When the quantity of fish is low compared to the high number of fishermen, prohibition of an efficient gear may result in more fish per unit of effort expended by the less efficient gear. In a sport fishery in which the individual is seeking recreation rather than a livelihood such restrictions are sometimes desirable. When local fish are part of a widespread population, closing a small area where they are abundant will be a nuisance to the gear banned; the gear will be used to catch fish outside of the restricted area at a greater cost.

BAG LIMIT. One way to lower gear efficiency is through the bag limit, which places a ceiling on the catch of an individual unit during a period of time. Many sportsmen are dissatisfied unless they catch the limit, even fishing long after they wish they were home. Thus in recreational fisheries a limit if of little value unless it is low enough to be often attained.

Commercial fishermen are occasionally subject to bag limits. Both on the Atlantic and Pacific coasts clam diggers are often subject to a bag limit. Also, fish processors occasionally have to restrict the quantity of fish they buy from each boat during the height of a run.

RESTRICTIONS ON FISHING TIME. Limiting fishing time to impair gear efficiency is quite common; other purposes of closed seasons will be discussed later. The actual reduction in fishing power achieved by this method depends largely on the relationship between the time of the closed season and the usual curve of seasonal availability to the fishing gear of the particular species. Closure of fishing for 6 months of the year during which only 10% of the catch is normally caught cannot be expected to diminish the catch by as much as 10%. The fishermen will use the idle time to repair and refurbish their vessels and gear, making them more efficient during the remainder of the year. They also tend to fish longer hours during the open season in an attempt to nullify the effect of the closure on their income.

Even though a closed season covers a sufficient portion of the fishing season to drastically cut the catch of a unit of gear, it nevertheless may not achieve a smaller total catch, which is the only excuse for the restriction. The operators almost invariably respond by increasing the number of units of fishing gear. This is because a fish-processing plant requires a certain minimum volume of raw material in order to stay in business. If the closed season threatens to reduce their catch below this minimum, the operators must employ more units of gear even at the risk of going broke. The net result is very often a higher cost to the producer without a correspondingly meaningful reduction in the total catch.

In order to arrive on the spawning grounds at the proper season, the run to any particular spawning area of an anadromous species is usually of short duration. The date of the occurrence of the peak of this short run may vary by as much as 2 weeks from year to year. Therefore to ensure a spawning escapement regardless of the exact date of the peak of the streamward migration, the usual practice is to have a succession of short closed seasons throughout the fishing season. These short weekly closed periods may vary in length in different years or during runs to different spawning areas from 24 hours to several days, depending on three factors—the size of the run, the number of units of fishing gear, and the size of the escapement needed for the available spawning grounds. In large rivers the speed of migration must be taken into account. The closed seasons may start at staggered times as one proceeds upstream in order to keep pace with the ascending fish.

Limiting number of fishing units (limited entry). The catch may be reduced without lowering the efficiency of the unit of gear, and thus raising the cost, by limiting the number of fishing units. Although efficient,

the limitation of units has been and is consistently fought on the grounds that fish are a public resource and therefore everyone has an equal right to fish for them. The owner of a fixed gear site, one of a limited number of such sites, may have rather exclusive rights when unfavorable conditions or regulations have curtailed the use of other gear. Even mobile gear is sometimes limited in an indirect manner. For instance, in the salmon fisheries of Bristol Bay the number of units of gill net gear was limited unofficially by the fact that the length of the weekly closed season could be and often was changed to allow for the addition of extra gear not contemplated when the regulations for the season were drawn up. By adding more gear the salmon packers merely increased the cost of taking fish without gaining more fish.

In the lobster fisheries it has long been obvious that action is necessary. Maine has required 3 years' residence (formerly 10 years) as a proviso for obtaining a lobster fishing license to prevent a great increase in the number of licenses each time lobsters become abundant. This allows bona fide fishermen to earn a living. The Canadian government limited the number of lobster fishermen in portions of the Maritimes in 1967 and extended the limit to all the Maritimes in 1968. In 1969 they placed the limit on the vessel and not on the operator (Campbell, 1973). Vessels were also classified as A or B; the B boats were those fishing less than a specified number of pots, according to the district, in 1968. It is intended that these B vessels will be phased out of the industry in a period yet to be defined and that the A group will continue. Out of 8349 lobster vessels in 1969, 1990 were classified as B vessels.

In British Columbia the government decided that salmon vessels must be limited. As with the lobsters they were classified into A and B groups. The A vessels could be retired and replaced, but the low-producing B vessels could not be reconstructed or enlarged so they would gradually be eliminated by attrition. Immediately many small A vessels (some less than 25 feet [7.6 m] in length) were used as replacements for larger vessels. Many fishermen with a small A vessel sold it at a top price to someone wanting to use it to exchange for a larger vessel. In June 1970 the law was changed to put vessel exchanges on a ton for ton basis. Under this program the number of salmon vessel licenses has declined steadily from 7639 in 1967 to 5890 in 1972 (Campbell, 1973). This drop in number was accelerated by sharply increasing the cost of a salmon fishing license for group A vessels. This caused many older fishermen to change their vessel from the A to the B category, since they did not expect to fish more than 10 additional years. The higher license fee required of A vessels is being used to buy A vessels and retire them from salmon fishing.

Japan has had limited licensing for many years. The system is rather complicated. The coastal fisheries are in a special category, "Fishing Rights Fisheries," which includes the right to exploit a specified area of water for shellfish or seaweed or the right to operate small types of fixed gear and beach seines from nonmotorized craft. They can obtain a license to use setnets in water shallower than 27 m, and they qualify for a license to use a certain area for fish culture. These rights are monopolistic, and the same laws apply to them as to other property such as land in legal transactions.

The major fisheries are also controlled by licensing. These include fisheries by large vessels, fisheries covering a wide area, and fisheries in which international agreements exist. Licenses are subject to restriction as to the areas to be fished, closed seasons, vessel tonnage, equipment and power, minimum size of fish to be retained, etc. All Japanese fisheries are controlled and the number of licenses is reduced if it is deemed necessary (Asada, 1973).

Quota system of limiting total catch. The third method of reducing total catch that neither decreases the efficiency of the fishing unit nor limits the number of fishermen is the imposition of a limit on the total quan-

tity that can be landed. To be successful this method requires enough biological knowledge of the species to enable a reasonable forecast to be made of the expected size of the population. The reliability of the forecast depends chiefly on two factors: the variability in the success of spawning and therefore in the annual recruitment and the number of age groups in the population.

In the Pacific halibut, *Hippoglossus stenolepis,* fishery in the eastern Pacific each major fishing area is assigned a quota in advance of the season, and when the quota is nearly reached a closing date is set so that the catch will closely approximate the quota. These catch quotas have increased the abundance of halibut but brought other less desirable consequences. As the abundance increased the regular halibut fleet was able to catch the quota in less time, so other vessels turned to halibut fishing, further shortening the season. In some areas it is now only a few weeks long. No one can now make a living from halibut fishing. The bulk of the catch must be frozen, so that there is fresh halibut available for only a short time.

The quota system was employed in the Alaska herring fisheries with indifferent success, since it is extremely difficult to make reliable estimates for a fish with such great variability in spawning success. The many local populations with different age structures as a result of different dominant brood years add to the difficulty.

The Inter-American Tropical Tuna Commission decided in 1960 that yellowfin tuna were being overfished in the eastern tropical Pacific (Joseph, 1973). In 1966 the Commission started regulating the fishery by means of catch quotas. Unfortunately since 1966 the tuna fleet has increased about three times. Consequently, to keep within the quotas the open season for fishing had to be decreased from about 10 months to less than 3 months. The U. S. fleet has been catching the lion's share of the catch, but there has been increasing pressure to make special quota allocations to the developing nations. As this happens many vessels from the larger fleets are shifting to the smaller nations. The whole program is in danger of falling apart.

Other quotas may be mentioned. South Africa sets quotas on the amounts of pilchards and anchovies that can be utilized by individual reduction plants. In 1968 each plant was limited to 12,000 tons of anchovies, with any excess anchovy landings to be deducted from the plant's pilchard quota.

The California fishery for ocean shrimp or prawn, *Pandalus jordani,* has been subject to quotas since 1952. These small shrimp (with a heads-on count of 70 to 160 per pound, averaging about 100 per pound) are protandrous. Since they are males between 1 and 2 years of age and do not develop into females until they are between 2 and 3 years old, the fishery must be light enough to leave a spawning stock of older shrimp. Despite small quotas the three southernmost areas have declined sharply in abundance. The northernmost area off Crescent City is holding its own. The center of abundance of this small shrimp is off the Oregon coast (Dahlstrom and Gotshall, 1969).

Despite accounts of the inexhaustable supply of anchovetas postulated by many a few years ago, Peru has had to set quotas on the catch. During both the 1967 to 1968 and the 1968 to 1969 seasons it was set at 9.5 million metric tons.

Protection of small fish through gear modification. Protection of small fish is sometimes amply justified by biological evidence; occasionally the evidence is not so clear. Such regulations are almost always popular and may serve to reduce the total catch and allow survival of sufficient spawning stock without the necessity of stringent gear restrictions.

The criteria for protection of small fish should include evidence that they are young, fast-growing fish, not just a stunted population, and that they will be available to the fishery at some future date. Sizes that warrant protection should be safely below the "critical" size shown in Fig. 12-6 (p. 244).

The chief modifications of gear to protect small fish are as follows:

1. Minimum size meshes in the cod ends of otter trawls
2. Minimum size meshes in the pots or spillers of traps and pound nets (In a mixed fishery this is often used to protect species smaller than those sought.)
3. Minimum size meshes in gill nets
4. Minimum spacing between the bottom and the first lath in lobster pots and escape ports in crab pots
5. Minimum size hooks in hook-and-line fisheries

Closure of selected fishing areas. Certain areas are often closed to fishing to achieve one or more of the following results:

1. To limit the total catch
2. To protect fish on their spawning grounds
3. To protect fish migrating through areas of restricted extent where they are especially vulnerable to capture
4. To protect young fish on nursery grounds
5. To prevent the harvesting and sale of shellfish contaminated by domestic sewage or an excess of heavy metals or pesticides
6. To prevent paralytic poisoning caused by eating mussels or other mollusks at times when tests show them to be dangerously toxic through the ingestion of certain plankton organisms

The closure of specific areas merely to limit the total catch is seldom practiced. Closure of spawning grounds to fishing is almost universal for anadromous species. Lakeshores are also often closed to protect bass while spawning and guarding their nests.

Closing nursery areas is exemplified in the Pacific halibut fisheries by closure of an area north of Cape Addington that is heavily populated by young halibut. In the Gulf and south Atlantic states the estuaries are usually closed to shrimp trawling each season until the shrimp have reached a reasonable market size.

Closing shellfish areas because of pollution represents a tremendous economic loss.

Restriction of fishing to certain seasons. The widely employed closed season has several purposes; we have already discussed (1) ending fishing on attainment of a fixed quota, (2) permitting anadromous fish to escape through an intense fishing zone, and (3) restricting the efficiency of the individual unit of gear by curtailing fishing time. Other purposes of closed seasons are enhancing the quality and value of the product by permitting fishing only when the fish are in prime condition and permitting the taking of the major share of the catch after or toward the end of the growing season in order to gain considerably more poundage from the same group of fish.

Quality is important to fisheries that produce meal and oil, as the yield of oil is vastly greater during certain seasons. In the absence of official regulations, reduction plant operators have often themselves agreed on an opening date for fishing to avoid fish of low quality. Quality is also often given as the reason for the closing of fishing during spawning seasons. Because of the difficulty in attaining unanimity in such an arrangement and the lack of legal recourse if any operator violates such a privately agreed on opening date, industry sometimes requests government agencies to set an official opening date.

Regulating the fishery with regard to the growing season is especially important in fisheries in which the catch is normally composed chiefly of fish from one year class, e.g., in fishing for shrimp or some of the clupeoids.

Regulations concerning sale. To influence by regulation the sizes of fish that can be legally marketed usually both catching and sale are regulated, but sometimes only the sale is prohibited. Regulations against the sale of small fish are a great incentive for the use of savings gear. The enforcement of the use of savings gear is also easier when the sale of small fish is discouraged.

A related problem is what to do with the small fish that are normally discarded at sea, usually dead before culling. Recent advances in fishery technology now permit processors to recover nearly all of the flesh of these small fish free from bones, skin, scales, and entrails. This flesh can now be made into edible fish products. This may encourage the retention of the small fish usually discarded at sea. At the same time, however, it may encourage the purposeful catching of large quantities of these undersized fish, which in many cases should be permitted to grow to a larger size before harvesting.

Protection based on sex or condition of individual. Unique situations cause restrictions based on sex or condition. The Dungeness crab, *Cancer magister,* of the Pacific coast is usually protected during molting by regulations against taking "soft-shell" crabs. The female Dungeness crab is also protected against possession and when taken must be returned unharmed to the water.

The female northern lobster, *Homarus americanus,* when carrying eggs ("berried") is usually protected and as a general rule can either be returned immediately to the water or brought in unharmed and sold to the state, which then either returns the berried females to the water or retains them to obtain larval lobsters for propagation.

The mature female blue crab, "sponge crab," is protected in some states, but the regulations against their capture and use are often indifferently enforced. The blue crab, *Callinectes sapidus,* has a very high fecundity, and the survival rate of each annual brood fluctuates widely. Consequently, there is some question whether such a regulation is necessary, since abstention from taking them may be an economic waste despite their poor quality at this season.

Regulation of a mixed fishery

The previous discussion is based on regulation of a one-species fishery. As market demand has increased beyond the limits of production attainable from already exploited species, more effort has been expended in taking those species once ignored. Expanded markets stimulated the development of methods for utilizing species formerly not readily salable because of their ugly appearance, e.g., ocean pout, *Macrozoarces americanus;* because of rapid deterioration of their soft flesh when shipped fresh, e.g., hake, *Urophycis tenuis;* or because of the difficulty of handling by the housewife, e.g., ocean perch, *Sebastes marinus.* However, the production by quick-freezing methods of frozen fillets ready for the pan and frozen blocks for cutting into "fish sticks" has placed these species on the desirable list.

This expanded market for once neglected species of fish is the chief reason that fishing vessels once built to engage in only one type of fishing are now designed for speedy conversion from one type of gear to another. Pacific halibut longline vessels once had a small cabin aft of amidships, small hatches forward, and a high stern, but they are now built along the same lines as a purse seiner, with a larger cabin forward, larger hatches for seine brailing or pumping, and a lower stern to permit the easier hauling of seines and the installation of power-operated turntables. The loss in seaworthiness once given by the high stern and smaller cabin aft is partially regained by the high flaring bows. Such vessels purse seine for salmon or herring, long-line for halibut during the brief season, and purse seine for anchovies and jack mackerel in the winter, with perhaps a few longline trips for sablefish, *Anoplopoma fimbria.* The larger offshore trolling vessels troll for both salmon and albacore, and many of them may fish during the winter for rockfishes, *Sebastes* spp.

On the North Atlantic coast the larger otter trawl vessels once fished almost exclusively for haddock, taking cod, gray sole, and other bank fishes that occurred in the same area as the haddock. In the 1950's they commenced fishing purposefully for ocean perch, *Sebastes marinus,* and yellowtail flounder, *Limanda ferruginea.* The smaller otter trawl vessels also fish very extensively for silver hake or whiting, *Merluccius bilinearis,* and pollock, *Pollachius virens.*

Many of the medium-sized otter trawl vessels occasionally join the sea scallop fleet or trawl for offshore lobsters.

Similarly, in the Gulf of Mexico the otter trawl vessels once fished almost exclusively for shrimp. Since the 1950's many have turned to taking so-called trash fish—croakers, spot, cutlass fish, etc.—for the pet food industry. Since about 1969 a number of vessels have been trawling for large croakers, *Micropogon lineatus,* to supply the fresh fish trade of the mid-Atlantic states.

This versatility in fishing vessels and gear is a problem for the fishery administrator. Whenever protection is afforded one species, the bulk of the released fishing effort is thrown on another species. Because of this versatility in the use of fishing vessels, regulations must be made with a broad view of the fisheries as a whole, so that protection of one species does not put undue strain on another.

COMPARISON OF LIMITED LICENSING WITH OTHER METHODS OF FISHERY MANAGEMENT

For over three decades a battle has been going on within the ranks of fishery conservationists, joined in the latter years by the economists. The first full-scale confrontation between opposing sides took place at a panel discussion that I witnessed before the Atlantic States Marine Fisheries Commission at their December 1942 annual meeting in Baltimore. The Commission had passed a motion earlier recognizing ". . . the seriousness of overcompetition in the fishing industry in normal times . . ." and requesting the U. S. Fish and Wildlife Service to report on the feasibility of management plans. At the forum meeting two diametrically opposed views were presented by Herrington (1943) and Nesbit (1943).

Herrington clung to the shibboleth of *optimum yield,* stating that the primary objective was conservation (of fish) and any other objectives such as improved economic and social conditions would be important, but secondary, objectives. Nesbit, on the other hand, decried the waste of capital and manpower implicit in all efforts to increase fishery yields through restrictions on efficiency. With regard to the quota system Nesbit pointed out that when abundance rises the regular fishermen do not benefit, since there are always a large number of new entrants into the fishery. Furthermore, the idea of equating the well-being of the individual fisherman directly with the catch per unit of gear is false, since closed seasons and enforced layovers between trips waste human resources. Using primarily the halibut fishery as an example, Nesbit stated:

The only valid criterion of efficiency is the ratio of what a vessel actually catches to what it is capable of catching in a year under optimum conditions of abundance maintained by scientific management. Proof that the halibut fishery has not gained in efficiency is to be found in the fact that the increases in abundance and yield have not been followed by increased profits per vessel. Originally profits were limited by inefficiency caused by depletion. Now they are limited by legally imposed inefficiency.

It is difficult to escape the conclusion that perhaps half of the vessels and half of the men in the halibut fleet perform no useful service for society and through no fault of their own are prevented from receiving the income and enjoying the standard of living which full application of their ability would make possible.

Now this is an illustration of a perfectly general principle: *whenever and wherever we seek to eliminate inefficiency caused by scarcity by imposing an artificial inefficiency, the two inefficiencies will automatically balance, and the average income of individual fishermen will remain the same.* The total yield will increase and so will the aggregate profit but individual profit will not change. Unless the numbers of fishermen are stabilized, no improvement in abundance will benefit any individual fisherman.

This Commission cannot honestly tell a lobsterman that an increase in size limits will increase his income unless the increase is associated with effective measures to prevent increases in the numbers of lobstermen. It cannot tell a shad fisherman that a weekly closed period will increase *his* income unless new fishermen are prevented from sharing the benefits. The Commission cannot fairly expect cooperation and support from the industry if it refuses to face the indisputable fact that any conservation measure which does not include stabilization or reduction of competition

can do nothing more than increase total yield and spread the work on a low-efficiency and low-income basis. To be sure, from the point of view of the general public, even that is better than continued depletion, but we can scarcely expect fishermen to share our enthusiasm for the public interest unless we can promise them some improvement in their present unenviable position. In the past we conservationists have had a ready answer to the question: What will this proposal do for the fish? But we have never been able to give a satisfactory answer to the fisherman's natural question: What will it do for me?*

EFFECT OF DIFFERENCES IN LIFE HISTORY ON DETERMINING FEASIBILITY OF MANAGEMENT MEASURES

Management measures designed to aid in the most profitable exploitation of a single species must be conditioned by certain facts of its life history. A few of these facts have been mentioned. I have attempted to summarize certain facts for 25 species in Table 13-1. It will be noted at once that the average age at maturity varies from 1 to 12 years and the natural life span from 1 to over 30 years. These two facts alone have a great deal to do with possible management measures. Quite obviously organisms with a long natural life span if not taken one year are available in succeeding years in slightly diminished numbers (except for a few, e.g., Pacific salmons, that die after spawning).

Organisms such as halibut, ocean perch, and green turtles must be permitted a sufficient number of mature individuals. This desirable end can be aided by strict enforcement of size limits *if* there is assurance that captured individuals can and will be released unharmed, or gear can be modified to permit the escape of the undersized individuals. Whereas such a size limit may be feasible for halibut or turtles, it would be worthless for ocean perch, because their swim bladder distends as they reach the surface so that they could not be culled out alive. Whether

---

*From Nesbit, R. A. 1943. Biological and economic problems of fishery management. U. S. Fish Wildl. Serv., Spec. Sci. Rep. **18**:23-53, 61-68.

Table 13-1. Life history facts for 25 species to illustrate their importance to feasibility of management measures

Usual age at maturity (yr)	Species	Life span (yr)	Fecundity	Planktonic life	Parents related to brood strength	Remarks
1	Callinectes sapidus	1-2	High	Long	No	
1	Penaeus aztecus	2	High	Medium	No	
1	Cetengraulis mysticetus	1-3	Medium	Short	No	
1	Sprattus sprattus	1-3	Low	Short	No	
1	Engraulis encrasicholus	2-4	Medium	Short	No	
1-2	Mya arenaria	6+	Very high	Long	No	
1-2	Crassostrea virginica	30+	Very high	Long	No	Protandrous
1-3	Pandalus jordani	3-4	Medium	Long	?	Protandrous, all start as males
2	Oncorhynchus gorbuscha	2	Very low	No	Yes	Die after spawning
2	Sardinella aurita	6-7	Medium	Short	No	
2-3	Osmerus eperlanus mordax	5+	Medium	Short	?	
2-3	Brevoortia tyrannus	6-7	High	Short	No	
2-3	Trachurus symmetricus	15+	Medium	Short	No	
2-4	Melanogrammus aeglefinus	11-22	High	Long	Yes	
2-6	Mugil cephalus	6-7	Very high	Short	No	
3-4	Oncorhynchus kisutch	3-4	Very low	No	Yes	Die after spawning
3-4	Alosa sapidissima	3-6	Medium	Short	Yes	No repeat spawners south of North Carolina
3-4	Merluccius productus	10+	High	–2 yr	?	
3-4	Clupea harengus pallasi	15+	Medium	Short	No	Eggs adhesive
3-5	Merluccius capensis	10?	High	2 yr	?	
4	Morone saxatilis	30+	High	Short	No	
4-13	Chelonia mydas	30+	Low	No	Yes	
6-8	Sebastes alutus	30+	Low		Yes	Ovoviviparous
8-16	Hippoglossus stenolepis	30+	High	Long	Yes	
10	Sebastes marinus	20+	Low		Yes	Ovoviviparous

savings gear is feasible for the smaller rock-fishes taken by otter trawl is somewhat questionable.

For most long-lived fishes the survival of a sufficient spawning stock is attained by maintaining a light fishing pressure combined when possible with any measures that can protect the smaller fish, e.g., closure of nursery areas.

For the very short-lived early-maturing species there is some question concerning the efficacy of endeavoring to provide a large spawning stock. The fecundity of most of these species is so high that conceivably a very few individuals can provide sufficient spawn. This is a debatable question, but we know that for many of these short-lived species it has not been possible to demonstrate any significant correlation between the size of the parent generation and the numbers in the resulting brood. For such a thesis to be true it is necessary to postulate the existence of some spatial relationship with survival so that anything even approaching an average-sized spawning population will oversaturate the environment with young. Since only a small spawning population will suffice, the chief goal of management is to harvest each annual brood at such a size and rate so as to obtain the greatest benefit.

However, the success of reproduction fluctuates considerably from year to year in accordance with natural factors, and this may tend to obscure any causal effect of spawning numbers. Some species with wide fluctuations in annual success of spawning have a long life span. Conceivably this is an evolutionary characteristic permitting the species to survive in sufficient numbers from one favorable spawning year to the next. Should heavy fishing pressure reduce the population during an unfavorable period to such a low level that the remaining adults could not saturate the environment when another favorable year appeared, the resulting brood year might appear abundant in relation to the immediately preceding years, but yet it may not achieve the abundance that the environment would allow. In this case the species, despite wide annual fluctuations in abundance, could continue to decline.

That this theory may have some validity is perhaps indicated by the collapse of the fisheries for Pacific sardines and Atlantic herring and the great decline in such "inexhaustible" species as the Atlantic menhaden and all fisheries with great fluctuations in spawning success. The entries of "No" in column 6 of Table 13-1 must be taken to mean no statistically proved relationship from available data. As the lower limit of parental number is approached, there has to be a relationship and, as I have pointed out, this may occur at a much higher number than that envisioned because of the obscuring effect of variations in environmental suitability.

Cushing appears to share my viewpoint, stating:

Very recently, the recruitment to the Peruvian anchoveta fishery has appeared to fail. Because these animals do not grow very much during their adult lives and because they are not very fecund anyway, the capacity of the stock to stabilize itself cannot be very great. It is unlikely that the stock/recruitment curve can yet be established as

reliably as those shown. . . . However, the fishing mortality is high and the exploitation rate may be about 0.5. At such rates, the stock of California sardines collapsed and the simplest hypothesis is that the collapse was the consequence of the high rate of exploitation. The same form of simple hypothesis is enough to account for the recent collapse of the Norwegian herring and the earlier failure of the Downs stock of herring, both under the pressure of fishing. By far the most important management step is to recognize the possibility that the failure of recruitment might well have been a consequence of heavy fishing.*

USE OF FISH FOR FOOD OR FOR REDUCTION

There is a question concerning the effect of harvesting fish for industrial uses on the supply available for human consumption. Usually industrial fisheries can process all sizes, so that large numbers are taken at a size smaller than that most effective for maintaining the population. Some industrial fishes are not desirable for direct consumption, but in many cases there is direct competition between the two uses. Popiel and Sosinski (1973) list the thousands of metric tons of the principal species used for meal production in 1970:

Anchovies	13,800
Capelin	1,500
Sardines	1,100
Alaska pollock	1,000
Menhaden	850
Herring	600
Sand eel	400
Mackerel	300
Norway pout	300
Horse mackerel	100
Rockfishes	100

They point out that, although edible, very few anchovies are eaten directly in comparison with the abundance of the resource. This may be true in some areas such as Peru, but large quantities are consumed fresh in Turkey, for instance.

Sardines are edible fish, and their continued use for reduction is highly question-

---

*From Cushing, D. H. 1973. Dependence of recruitment on parent stock. J. Fish. Res. Bd. Canada **30**:1965-1976.

able. Herring and mackerel are already intensively exploited, and the catching of large numbers of small herring and mackerel for reduction has reduced their populations to dangerous levels.

The difficulty arises from the ease of catching the dense schools of younger fish with purse seines in large quantities and then processing them at a low labor cost in comparison with their use as food. Furthermore, only certain species are highly desirable as food, whereas the industrial fishery can shift from species to species, always attacking the one most profitable at the moment.

The situation reminds me of the practices of the early Alaska salmon salteries. For many years they cut out and salted only the bellies and discarded the remainder of the fish until laws were finally passed outlawing the waste of edible fish.

Certain fishes such as the Alaska pollock are consumed directly in some countries but used principally for meal in others. In regulating fisheries for species used for both food and reduction a minimum size limit is especially necessary. A quota system is usually based on weight so that by itself the quota is useless for preventing the destruction of great quantities of undersized fish.

Suggested readings

Asada, Y. 1973. License limitation regulations: the Japanese system. J. Fish. Res. Bd. Canada **30**: 2085-2095.

Belyanina, T. N. 1969. Synopsis of biological data on smelt, Osmerus eperlanus (Linnaeus) 1758. FAO Fish. Synopsis 78.

Campbell, B. A. 1973. License limitation regulations: Canada's experience. J. Fish. Res. Bd. Canada 30:2070-2076.

Christy, F. T., Jr., and A. Scott. 1965. The commonwealth in ocean fisheries. The Johns Hopkins University Press, Baltimore. 281 pp.

Cushing, D. H. 1973. Dependence of recruitment on parent stock. J. Fish. Res. Bd. Canada **30**: 1965-1976.

Herrington, W. C. 1943. Some methods of fishery management and their usefulness in a management program. U. S. Fish Wildl. Serv., Spec. Sci. Rep. **18**:3-22, 55-59.

Joseph, J. 1973. Scientific management of the world stocks of tunas, billfishes, and related species. J. Fish. Res. Bd. Canada 30:2471-2482.

Macgregor, J. S. 1966. Synopsis on the biology of the jack mackerel (Trachurus symmetricus). U. S. Fish Wildl. Serv., Spec. Sci. Rep. Fish. **526**:1-16.

Major, R. L., and H. H. Shippen. 1970. Synopsis of biological data on Pacific ocean perch, Sebastes alutus. FAO Species Synopsis 79, NOAA, Nat. Mar. Fish. Serv., Circ. **347**:1-38.

Nesbit, R. A. 1943. Biological and economic problems of fishery management. U. S. Fish Wildl. Serv., Spec. Sci. Rep. **18**:23-53, 61-68.

Rounsefell, G. A., and W. H. Everhart. 1953. Regulations and their effect. In Fishery science, chap. 24. John Wiley & Sons, Inc., New York. pp. 382-396.

part six

Environmental alteration

chapter 14

✻ Effects of engineering projects on estuarine and marine environments

This discussion of the known ecologic effects ensuing from the alteration of marine habitats does not include the effects of dredging unless either structures or deep excavations are involved. Neither does it include the effects of pollutants—industrial, domestic, radioactive, or toxic—but mentions pollutants that may emanate from engineering structures.

POSSIBLE ENVIRONMENTAL EFFECTS

Possible ecologic effects of construction are summarized in the boxed material on p. 268. The material is listed as "environmental" effects in order to include changes in physical parameters that may cause direct or more subtle effects in the ecology of various organisms.

DIRECT EFFECT OF STRUCTURE

Structures may have direct effects on marine organisms. Not all of the effects are adverse; an improved environment may result. Some of the major effects include loss of habitat, thigmotropic effects on certain fishes, provision of shelter for marine orga-

nisms, gain of sheltered habitat, and loss and/or recovery of surf habitat.

Loss of habitat (islands). Loss of habitat occurs most frequently in conjunction with construction of islands. Choice of a construction site for an island between an estuarine or an offshore location depends partially on the economic value of the habitat permanently lost.

ECONOMIC VALUE OF FISHERY HABITAT. It is relatively simple to place a definite economic value on a piece of farmland. It is not difficult to assess the value per acre of the harvest of sedentary or sessile shellfish. The value of an acre to the production, commercial and sport, of motile animals is more difficult to obtain.

Economic value of estuaries. A very large proportion of the sport and commercial fishes, mollusks, and crustaceans are estuarine dependent during some portion of their existence. Together the estuaries and the adjacent coastal waters form an ecosystem. For some species a portion of the catch is taken outside of the estuary, but the estuary is essential to them during their larval and/or juvenile stages. In the Gulf of

Outline of possible environmental effects of construction in marine waters

I. Direct effects of structure itself
   A. Permanent loss of occupied habitat (chiefly by islands)
   B. Thigmotropic effect of submerged structures
   C. Attachment or shelter for marine organisms
   D. Gain of sheltered habitat (lee of islands)
   E. Loss of mainland surf habitat (opposite islands)
   F. Regaining surf habitat (on islands, according to construction methods)

II. Changes in water mass exchange (applies to structures within an estuary or close to its mouth, including hurricane barriers and tidal dams)
   A. Reduction in tidal prism (large islands in regions of small tidal range)
   B. Reduction of deep water exchange (hurricane barriers at entrances to deep estuaries where offshore waters are significantly stratified)
   C. Changes in existing currents
      1. Velocity changes affecting areas of scouring or sedimentation
      2. Changes in direction of currents
         a. Effect on settling areas of larvae
         b. Effect on pollution dispersal or dilution
   D. Shortening of wind fetch (reducing depth of shallow estuaries)

III. Changes in salinity, temperature, turbidity, and oxygen (through change in tidal prism, current direction, velocity, and turbulence)
   A. Shift in areas suitable for different groups of biota (seeking of preferred range of parameters)
   B. Shift in areas of flocculation-induced sedimentation
   C. Changes in amplitude of variation in parameters
   D. Changes in net primary productivity and resultant effect on dissolved oxygen levels
      1. Through increase or decrease in turbidity affecting photosynthesis both in water column and in benthic flora
      2. Through change in length of flushing time affecting retention of excess nutrients and favoring eutrophication
   E. Changes in trophic structure through changes in total plankton consumption by filter feeders caused by changes in total net water movement
   F. Changes in biota of estuary and its use as nursery area through higher range and amplitude of temperature induced by thermal discharges
   G. Shift in area in which certain oyster predators are controlled by intermittent periods of salinity below the predators' tolerance level (favored by longer flushing time and lowered salinity intrusion but also by correct regime of freshwater input)

IV. Changes in substrate
   A. Loss and gain of areas of habitat types by shifts in areas of scouring and sedimentation
   B. Increase in areas of bottom oxygen deficiency induced by reduction in bottom water exchange (hurricane barriers, reduced tidal prisms, and creation of holes deeper than surrounding bottom)
   C. Loss of established benthic communities by excess sedimentation (may eventually be balanced in some instances by gain in and establishment of new communities on areas made more suitable than formerly)

V. Changes in established shoreline
   A. Blocking of alongshore sand transport (by deep excavations into the land) resulting in undernourishment of beaches on the downcurrent side
   B. Filling in and concurrent erosion of shoreline (by construction of peninsulas where there is an alongshore current)
   C. Formation of spits between an offshore island and the mainland

VI. Effects of explosions
   A. Minor explosions, including seismographic
   B. Heavy explosions (e.g., removal of Ripple Rock)
   C. Nuclear blasting

VII. Effects on freshwater supplies
   A. Saltwater intrusion into aquifers

Table 14-1. Economic value of estuaries

| Estuary | Acres of water | | Annual value per acre (dollars) | Capitalized value per acre at 6% (dollars) |
	Low tide	High tide		
Merrimack River[1]	1,350	2,533	451	7,500
Quincy Bay[2]	6,854	7,772	31	500
North River[3]	382	533	244	4,100
Beverley-Salem Harbor[4]	8,031	9,051	75	1,260
Pleasant Bay (Orleans)[5]		7,285	29	483
(quahog bottom)		640	2,142	35,700
Boca Ciega Bay[6]		3,500	400	6,667
Texas estuaries[7]		1,000,000	155[8]	2,600
Delaware River[9]	460,000	460,800	13[10]	210

[1]Jerome et al., 1965.
[2]Jerome et al., 1966.
[3]Fiske et al., 1966.
[4]Jerome et al., 1967.
[5]Fiske et al., 1967.
[6]Taylor and Saloman, 1968.
[7]Odum, 1959.
[8]Includes value for cooling water, navigation, etc.
[9]Shuster, 1959.
[10]Includes only landed fishery values. Shuster (1959) places the capital investment in the Delaware estuary fisheries at $60 million, or $130/acre.

Mexico, for instance, over 95% of the catch of the commercial species are estuarine dependent. Table 14-1 shows the results of some attempts to set a dollar value on estuaries.

The value to marine production of an acre of estuary is underestimated in Table 14-1 because the table omits the principal value—its use as a nursery area for many species of which the largest catches are made elsewhere. For instance, Sykes and Finucane show that 23 species of major importance to commercial fisheries inhabit Tampa Bay during immaturity. They state:

Few constitute important commercial fisheries in Tampa Bay. The significance of the estuary lies more in the growth of species for later harvest in Gulf fisheries than in catches of adults in nursery areas.*

Some notion of the relative productivity of estuaries is given by Odum and Odum

*From Sykes, J. E., and J. H. Finucane. 1966. Occurrence in Tampa Bay, Florida, of immature species dominant in Gulf of Mexico commercial fisheries. U. S. Fish Wildl. Serv., Fish. Bull. **65:** 369-379.

(1959). They state that the deserts and the oceans beyond the continental shelf produce less than 1.0 g carbon/m^2 · day. Continental shelf waters have primary productivity levels comparable to grasslands and mountain forests of 0.5 to 3.0 g carbon/m^2 · day. On a worldwide scale, estuaries, coral reefs, alluvial plains, and intensive year-round agriculture have the highest level of primary productivity, 10 to 25 g carbon/m^2 · day.

The loss of valuable estuarine habitat is decried by Glude:

. . . clam flats, unappealing to some and unrecognized for their true value, are sacrificed to make way for "progress." One fine clam flat in Massachusetts became a huge airport. Others became sites of new factories. Channels were dredged through some, and silt heaped on others.*

Economic value of continental shelf. Much proposed construction will be on nearshore portions of the continental shelf, raising the immediate question of how to place a value on shelf habitat permanently

*From Glude, J. B. 1951. The effect of man on shellfish populations. Trans. N. Amer. Wildl. Conf. **16:**397-403.

lost through construction. Several general approaches result in average values that must be applied with caution to any specific site, especially along coastlines with rapid variations in depth and type of substrate. Values for a number of bank areas are given in Table 6-21 (p. 120). A further interpretation of these values appears in Table 6-22 (p. 121).

For highly productive shelf areas (depths down to 200 m) the annual potential yield of demersal fish and shellfish is about 3 metric tons/km². This includes the New England banks, the northwest Pacific from Oregon to and including the eastern Bering Sea, and the Gulf of Mexico. For moderately productive shelf areas, including the mid- and south Atlantic coasts and California, the average is about 2 metric tons/km². For pelagic fishes the loss of a specific area of bottom will not have as much impact as on a demersal species. That these figures have some validity is indicated by a recent unpublished study on the value of a portion of the Gulf of Mexico shelf between Mobile Bay and the eastern side of the Mississippi delta I made in connection with a study of the ecologic effects of a proposed deep water port (Table 14-2).

Note that Table 14-2 includes only the benthic species; in addition this area produced, chiefly in the shallow estuarine portion inside the shelf itself, tremendous quantities of menhaden as well as oysters and blue crabs. Therefore on an average portion of a highly productive shelf yield can be estimated at about 3 metric tons/km². This value will vary widely; on sandy shifting bottom it will decrease, and on firmer bottom it will increase, especially if there are natural outcroppings. The only safe measure is to make a biological survey of any proposed site.

Thigmotropic effect on certain fishes. Small structures such as buoys and platforms tend to attract both pelagic and benthic fishes. These aggregations are favorite fishing spots for sportsmen, but the areas of the structures themselves are too small to pro-

Table 14-2. Pounds and values per acre of fisheries in the shelf area between Mobile Bay and the Mississippi River delta

Species[1]	Pounds per acre	Value (dollars)	Depth (fm)
Penaeid shrimps	4.7	4.35	0-50
Snappers, groupers, etc.	3.7	1.36	10-50
Large croakers	6.0	0.78	5-50
Pet food fish	15.0	0.30	8-30
TOTAL	29.4	6.79	
Total biomass	38.9		7-34
Totals/km²	7,265.0, or 3.3 metric tons	1,678.0	

[1]This includes only benthic species.

vide food sufficient to have any actual effect on fish populations. The effect of larger structures will be discussed in a subsequent section.

Shelter, or substrate suitable for attachment, for marine organisms

ARTIFICIAL REEFS. Fishing success on artificial reefs in California is possibly two to three times that on nearby natural reefs of similar size (Carlisle et al., 1964; Turner et al., 1969). The biologists conclude that artificial reefs can turn nonproductive nearshore areas into productive fishing areas. The structures initially attract fish from surrounding areas. With time (about 5 years in California) a natural situation is reached whereby both plant and animal populations fluctuate in a manner typical of reef ecosystems.

Succession on the reefs consisted during the first year of a barnacle-hydroid phase, followed by less distinct mollusk-polychaete, ascidian-sponge, and finally encrusting ectoproct stages. Later (during the second and third years) anemones became important, followed by gorgonians (in the third and fourth years). Stony corals first appeared in the fifth year.

Scientists also concluded that their experimental reefs, 25,000 to 50,000 square feet, are minimal for any sustained harvest. They quickly concentrate fish but are soon fished out. An area of at least 200,000 square feet of bottom was recommended to allow the reef to reach equilibrium and permit propagation, so that the harvest can extend over a longer period.

In an attempt to increase lobster populations by the use of artificial reefs, a rock reef of 30,000 square feet (2740 m^2) was constructed in Northumberland Strait, New Brunswick (Scarratt, 1968). It was built on a substrate of hard to gravelly sand of individual sandstone rocks varying in size from 5 to 100 cm in diameter and up to 15 cm thick; the total volume was 1500 m^3.

The prereef epifauna consisted of numerous sand dollars on the sandy bottom, occasional scallops on the gravel, and a few fish, notably sculpins. The reef was colonized gradually by starfish, sea urchins, bryozoans, hydroids, sponges, tunicates, a few fishes, crabs, and a few lobsters. After 2 years the biomass of lobsters on the reef was less than on productive lobster grounds nearby. There was no evidence of larval lobster settlement; colonization was by immigration. This experiment seems to support the conclusions of Turner et al. (1969) that artificial reefs must be quite large to contribute to population abundance.

The epitome of nonsense about artificial reefs is perhaps contained in a report (World Fishing editorial, 1969) stating that a reef of 800 concrete blocks (16 × 8 × 8 inches) produced 14,514 pounds/acre of block surface compared to 1417 pounds/acre on the surrounding natural reefs. The total area of the reef if only one block deep would be only 711 square feet or 0.014 acre! Such reports of fish taken on an area of 70 × 10 feet are entirely misleading.

Artificial reefs are regarded in some areas as a solution to the problem of the disposal of tremendous quantities of solid wastes (Landis, 1970b). Without adequate supervision this can result in a huge garbage dump. During 1968, for example, 10 million metric tons of solid debris, including building rubble, excavation materials, junk cars, and chemical sludge, were dumped into the ocean off U. S. coasts (Brown, 1969). At the National Conference of Solid Waste Disposal Sites, sponsored by the American Public Works Association in Washington, D. C., early in 1971, it was brought out that because of dumping some 20 square miles of the sea bottom in the New York Bight had become a veritable biological desert. According to the National Council on Marine Resources and Engineering Development (1971), environmental and shellfish samples from the sludge dumping areas off the New York Bight and Delaware Bay were found to be grossly contaminated. Similarly, a 12-mile ocean dumping site off Cape May, New Jersey, has been labeled "a dying ocean bottom," and a study is being made to determine what types of material are responsible (Oceanology International editorial, 1971).

RUBBLE ON SLOPES OF ARTIFICIAL ISLANDS. The ecologic effect of an artificial island depends on the type of construction. If the island is the diked-fill type, the slopes will probably be armored with heavy rubble. In 50 feet of water an armored island with a 10-mile circumference and a slope of one on six will have about 16 million square feet of submerged rubble slope. This is 80 times larger than the 200,000 square feet recommended by Turner et al. (1969) as the minimum size for an artificial reef to maintain a self-supporting fish population.

Gain of sheltered habitat. Where offshore islands are sufficiently close to the shore and the prevailing winds and storms blow onshore, it may be necessary to armor only the sides of the island exposed to heavy wave action. In the lee of the island gentler slopes without armor may suffice. If planted with shoreline vegetation, such gentle slopes may provide nursery areas for many species.

Natural beds of sea grasses afford food and shelter, but they are also useful in stabilizing the bottom and reducing turbidity. Artificial sea grass is being considered to replace natural beds destroyed by dredging and to cover bottom areas where natural grass will not grow; the artificial sea grass may be especially useful as a setting material for larval shellfish (Commercial Fisheries Review editorial, 1969).

The ecologic importance of the marine sea grasses is best appreciated by noting the effects of the absence or presence of the common eelgrass *Zostera*. In the far north Landis (1970) reports eelgrass growing under the winter ice of Safety Lagoon near Nome, Alaska, and Cottam and Munro (1954) report it growing as far north as Frobisher Bay, George River, and Foxe Basin on the Atlantic coast. They also mention it growing down the Atlantic coast to North Carolina, the southern limit on the Atlantic coast. On the West Coast it occurs south to San Diego.

In 1931 to 1932 eelgrass was catastrophically reduced by a wasting disease caused by *Labyrinthula* and all but disappeared in many localities. Cottam and Munro (1954) mention that with the loss of their staple food large flocks of eastern brant wandered from place to place and many perished. It also affected the abundance of Canada geese, scaup, black ducks, fish, mollusks, crustaceans, and especially bay scallops.

Invertebrates were also affected; Stauffer (1937) states that practically all the animals once found living on or among the eelgrass disappeared with it, and although the total number of burrowing species fell slightly, they now constitute a much larger proportion of the total population than formerly.

Loss of surf habitat on mainland. A large offshore island adjacent to the coast could decrease the surf on a stretch of mainland shore. This not only could affect the use of the beach by bathers, but it would also decrease the mainland area available for certain species requiring sandy surf-swept beaches, e.g., the grunion or Pismo clam.

Regaining of surf habitat. It may prove more economical not to armor exposed artificial island slopes with rubble but rather to try to stabilize the exposed shoreline by means of stabilized dunes and/or the use of natural and artificial sea grasses.

DUNE STABILIZATION AND SEA GRASSES. The continued existence of some offshore and barrier islands depends on maintaining a ridge of stable sand dunes for protection against the high waves and storm surges of hurricanes and gales. The best method of stabilizing sand dunes is with vegetation, but this is destroyed too often by fire or overgrazing. In some areas the dunes have been dangerously breached by carting away sand for road and building construction or just for use as fill. Even the excessive use of "dune buggies" has contributed to breaking down the dunes.

Long-term experiments in many places suggest the best plants for various localities and the best methods for seeding or planting them and assuring their growth. Adler (1970) suggests fertilizing the dunes with the thousands of tons of sewage sludge now dumped at sea, which he states has caused the deterioration of the benthic environment over about 15 square miles of the New York Bight.

Davis (1957) divides the United States coastline into eight botanical zones for dune stabilization planting, based chiefly on rainfall and temperature regimes. His system is shown in Table 14-3.

Of plants available for use in the different climatic zones, Davis lists less than 50 species in the north Atlantic, south Pacific, and arid parts of the Gulf region, but over 100 in the Florida region. He lists 562 plants that are either numerically important or are involved in coastal changes and stability and gives the region in which each plant may be important. More recent planting experiments have been carried out in North Carolina (Woodhouse and Hanes, 1967; Savage and Woodhouse, 1969) and in Texas (Gage, 1970; Woodard et al., 1970). Gage found snow fences cheaper and more effective than junk cars for accumulating sand.

Experiments with artificial seaweed in a wave tank and in the field show that it increases the net drift of bed water toward the shore, thus maintaining and building beach levels (Price et al., 1969). Similarly, in a study of four sea grasses in Florida, Phillips (1960) found that they aided in silt and detritus deposition as well as in binding the

Table 14-3. Botanical zones suggested for dune stabilization planting*

Region	Shore (miles)	Rainfall (inches)	Temperatures	
			Summer	Winter
North Atlantic	570	50	Mild	Long, cold to arctic
Mid-Atlantic	520	40	Warm	Cold, not severe
South Atlantic	650	50	Hot	Short, mild
Florida	750	40-60	Long, hot	Short, frost rare
Gulf of Mexico	1,600	20-60	Long, hot	Short, occasional frost
South Pacific	400	10-20	Long, hot, arid	Frost rare, irregular rain
North Pacific	900	40-80	Cool to warm	Long, mild
Great Lakes		Moderate	Cool to hot	Long, cold

*Data from Davis, 1957.

substrate and preventing erosion. Erosion prevention in Holland and Britain is also aided along canal banks and bottoms by lining them with very low specific gravity (0.2) filaments of polypropylene foam monofilament (Ocean Industry editorial, 1969; Oceanology International editorial, 1969).

DIRECT EFFECTS OF CONSTRUCTION

Effect of bulkheading. Bulkheading can change the productivity of a shoreline. To assess the effect, a study was made by Mock (1967) in Clear Lake, Texas (an estuary tributary to Galveston Bay). He selected two similar sections of shoreline, one in its natural condition with a gradually sloping shore covered with marsh plants, chiefly *Spartina.* The other section had been altered by a rock bulkhead so that the mean low and mean high tides both occurred along the bulkhead and there was no vegetation left. Ten months of intensive sampling yielded 2.5 times more brown shrimp and 14 times more white shrimp from the natural vegetated shoreline, illustrating the ill effects of bulkheading on productivity.

Effects of changes in substrate. Alteration of the substrate during construction can alter the species composition of the recolonizing animals. Substrate preference was tested on the three important commercial shrimps of the Southeast (Williams, 1958). The pink shrimp, *Penaeus duorarum,* preferred a shell-sand substrate; the brown shrimp, *P. aztecus,* and the white shrimp, *P. setiferus,* preferred softer, muddier sub-strates—loose peat, sandy mud, and muddy sand.

Experiments at the Virginia Institute of Marine Science show that very small hard clams, *Mercenaria mercenaria,* survive in high numbers, escaping predation by blue crabs, benthic fishes, and waterfowl, if after scattering the tiny seed clams the bottom is covered to a depth of 1 to 3 inches with loose aggregates (Commercial Fisheries Review editorial, 1970c). Aggregates tested were crushed oyster shell, pea gravel, and crushed stone. In the covered plots seed clam survival averaged 80%, with a high of 90%, whereas on unprotected plots survival was about 16%, but never over 30%.

Pratt (1953) found that hard clam populations living in sand grew 24% faster than those in an adjacent plot of sandy mud containing much organic matter. Pratt and Campbell (1956) confirmed that the growth of the hard clam is retarded in substrates with a high silt-clay content. Bader (1954) also studied the distribution of pelecypods vs substrate, finding that as the organic matter (food supply) increases, the pelecypods increase until bacterial decomposition of the organic matter becomes the major limiting factor; then the population decreases.

Among the level bottom infauna in south Florida detritus feeders predominate in the very finest sediments, whereas deposit and filter feeders prevail at intermediate grades, with the latter more abundant at a considerably greater particle size than found by Sanders (1960) in the northern waters of

Buzzards Bay (McNulty et al., 1962). A close correlation exists between particle size and body size of the deposit feeders regardless of the type of animal.

Dependence on particle size of the substrate is perhaps greatest among the tube-building polychaete worms. In the Newport River estuary in North Carolina (Kenny, 1969) the polychaete, *Clymenella torquata,* is found in greatest numbers where the median particle size of the substrate is between 0.2 and 0.32 mm and where the salinity remains above 25 $^o/_{oo}$. In the laboratory a drop in salinity to 15 $^o/_{oo}$ resulted in a 50% lethal time of 45 hours. In tests the optimum conditions for tube building are a temperature of 25° C with a salinity of 35 $^o/_{oo}$ and particles between 0.25 and 0.42 mm in size.

Recovery rate of organisms in disturbed substrate. An important question is the length of time needed for the organisms in an area to return to a natural state of equilibrium after a drastic disturbance. Clues can be found in already disturbed areas or in newly created areas. The studies by Turner et al. (1969) (see the discussion of artificial reefs) show in California waters a succession of invertebrates reaching a balance similar to that on natural reefs within 5 years. Recuperation may be faster on nonreef bottoms. In Maryland, Hanks (1968) studied succession in a man-made saltwater pond. Dominant invertebrates became quickly established, following a *Mya-Macoma-Nereis* association similar to that in the nearby estuary. Estimated biomass indicates benthic populations near maximum within the first year. A stable association continued through the second year.

In the Baltic Sea an oxygen deficiency often occurs in the deeper portions of the Bornholm Basin that is occasionally relieved by intrusions of oxygenated oceanic water. Leppakoski (1969) studied the repopulation of benthic organisms following the amelioration of the oxygen deficiency in 1959 and subsequent years. Recolonization continued through 1964. Seven species, especially numbers of *Scoloplos armiger,* were

present by June 1965. In March 1967 the dominant benthic species was *Capitella capitata,* a species unknown in the Baltic. During several years Leppakoski failed to find two lamellibranchs, *Macoma calcarea* and *Astarte borealis,* formerly characteristic of the benthic fauna of the region. This suggests a rather slow recuperation in deeper subarctic waters, but the results could be confounded with the low oxygen levels that have an adverse effect on larval forms of *Macoma* and *Astarte.*

Differences in succession between rock and other hard substrate and softer sediments is shown by Reish (1961, 1962, 1963) in studies of four newly constructed small boat harbors in southern California, one at Alamitos Bay, one at Playa del Rey, and two in Ventura County. At Alamitos Bay there was no indication of succession. Six weeks after the harbor was dredged seven benthic species were found; 39 species were present by 5 months, and 51 species by 9 months, remaining stable for the next 14 months. Of 89 species, 56 were polychaetes, 14 each were mollusks and crustaceans, and 5 were other invertebrates. A year after dredging, the number of species started to fall at some stations, particularly those in the inner reaches of the harbors. This was correlated with a drop in the dissolved oxygen and a sulfide odor. This decrease in the inner basins that did not occur in the main channels was attributed to poor water quality because of the limited circulation.

Colonization of rocks exposed to the sea on new jetties in southern California is fairly rapid, as shown by Hewatt (1935) and Reish (1964, 1969). The green alga *Enteromorpha minima* in the upper zone and *Ulva dactylifera* in the midintertidal zone reach a peak in 3 or 4 months. *Enteromorpha* is gradually replaced by barnacles, limpets, snails, and shore crabs. The upper zone thus reaches a climax in 6 months. In the midintertidal zone *Mytilus* grows rapidly and reaches a climax within a year (Reish, 1962). In central California *Mytilus* took 2.5 years to become reestablished (Hewatt, 1935), probably as a result of much colder water in the areas north of Point Conception.

Succession on hard substrate appears to be more rapid in the warm northern Gulf of Mexico waters than in temperate waters. For 9 months Gaul and Vick (1964) sampled both 2-week and cumulative growth of sessile organisms on buoys suspended in the water column at 15, 35, and 55 feet below the surface at a station 2 miles offshore of the mouth of St. Andrew Bay, near Panama City, Florida, in 60 feet of water. Salinity ranged from 32.5 to 36 °/₀₀, and temperature varied from a midwinter 55° F to a midsummer 85° F. In 12 weeks the buoys were heavily encrusted with invertebrates. Barnacles set heaviest on the bottom floats. The chief species included one gastropod, *Murex recurvirostris;* eight pelecypods; one cirriped, *Balanus amphitrite;* two annelids, *Neanthes* and *Eunice;* and a few juvenile anemones.

Effects of explosions and blasting. Explosions and blasting can be conveniently divided into three categories:

1. Small to medium explosions such as are employed in seismographic work for oceanography or oil exploration or explosions by naval ordnance
2. Heavy explosions such as those used for removal of underwater navigational hazards
3. Extremely large blasts, probably nuclear

The smaller explosions damage organisms over a relatively small area. Aplin (1947) found, using blasts of 10 to 40 pounds each of 60% nitrogel in 10-pound sticks, that fish with swim bladders were severely injured at 50 to 55 feet from the blast, but those lacking swim bladders were largely uninjured. Using 40-pound charges in 4 feet of water a few fish were killed up to 250 feet from the blast. Spiny lobsters, *Panulirus interruptus,* were not injured in two tests at 50 and 55 feet with 20-pound charges.

In Louisiana the effects of one 200-pound and two 800-pound blasts of 60% gelatine dynamite were tested by Gowanloch and McDougall (1945). All three blasts were in relatively shallow water. Shrimp were not injured at 50 feet; croakers, *Micropogon undulatus,* were not injured at 200 feet. However, the use of wooden cages may have minimized the damage.

The Chesapeake Biological Laboratory (1948) in cooperation with the Naval Ordnance Laboratory found that oysters suffered 5% fatalities within 100 feet of a 30-pound charge of TNT and within 200 feet of a 300-pound charge. Lethal damage to crabs was limited to about 150 feet. Weakfish, *Cynoscion regalis,* and striped bass, *Morone saxatilis,* were injured 200 feet from a 30-pound charge.

An extensive study of the effects of seismologic explosions off California by Fitch and Young (1948) is vitiated by failure to give the distances.

Hubbs and Rechnitzer (1952) ran numerous experiments comparing black powder with dynamite. Damage from the slower burning black powder was very slight in comparison with the dynamite.

Crutchfield (1969) summarizes the effects of seismic explorations off Alaska, British Columbia, Washington, and Oregon, concluding that the conventional use of explosives was harmful to fishes with air bladders 150 to 500 feet horizontally and vertically; fish without air bladders and invertebrates were much less vulnerable. He states that the industry in 1 year switched from using 90% explosives to only 10% explosives, substituting pneumatic systems, sparkers, and hydraulic systems.

Thomson (1958) describes the removal of Ripple Rock, a serious navigational hazard in Seymour Narrows, British Columbia. This rock was riddled with passages filled with 2,750,000 pounds of explosive. Evidence from fish placed in cages prior to the detonation shows that fish mortality was confined to less than half a mile from the rock.

Study of the nuclear blast at Amchitka Island may shed some light on the effect of nuclear blasting.

Effects of construction on freshwater supplies. Construction of harbors or terminals by deep excavation into the mainland can endanger freshwater supplies. This can be caused by the cracking of impervious layers, permitting salt water to penetrate freshwater aquifers. A deepened channel may also permit a bottom salt wedge to move farther inland to the detriment of agricultural enterprises dependent on fluvial sources for irrigation water or for flooding of low areas used for such crops as rice.

Habitat loss from deep excavation. The excavation of very deep harbors in mainland areas or the deepening of existing channels can cause the loss of considerable areas of habitat because of the great depth and width required. An ancillary problem is the disposal of enormous quantities of spoil.

INDIRECT EFFECTS OF CONSTRUCTION

Among the indirect effects of construction are changes in water mass exchange, in turbidity, and in salinity and temperature.

Changes in water mass exchange. Manmade barriers affect water mass exchange in various ways. Depending on the type and construction of the barrier, the changes may be detrimental or beneficial.

EFFECTS OF HURRICANE BARRIERS. Hurricane barriers can affect the ecology of an area in several ways but principally through their effect on the amount and type of water exchange. Across the mouths of deeper bays, such as Narragansett Bay, the bottom of the opening through the long levee, which must be left to allow free ingress and egress of ships, will be higher than the surrounding bottom. In effect the barrier is a dam with a spillway. To be effective in preventing floods even on normal tides the current through the opening in the barrier will be swift. The amplitude of the sea level within the barrier will be reduced. I have observed several deep bays in Alaska that have naturally occurring sills with narrow openings; in one deep fjord in particular, near Red Fox Bay on Kodiak Island, the water enters as a turbulent rapid, continuing to enter until about 2 hours after high slack water outside. The outgoing water then flows until about 2

hours after low slack water outside. The water level in the fjord never rises as high nor falls as low as on the outside. This reduction in the tidal prism means a great reduction in total water exchange.

The effect of such a restricted opening with a sill on the composition of the water exchanged will depend on several circumstances. In an exorheic area the net flow will be seaward, and if the outside water is stratified below sill depth, the tendency in deep bays would be for the inside water to maintain a lower surface salinity with a higher salinity at the bottom. Bottom oxygen levels may become quite low below sill depth.

In a shallow bay there is usually little vertical stratification so that in an exorheic area the inside water might normally be expected to maintain a low salinity, whereas such a channel restriction in an endorheic area will raise the inside salinity, e.g., in the Laguna Madre of Texas. In shallow bays the sill depth for the structure would usually be little if any above controlling depth, so that no stagnation should occur.

The Bureau of Sport Fisheries and Wildlife (1962) studied the changes expected if hurricane barriers were placed in the two entrances to Lake Pontchartrain at the Rigolets and at Chef Menteur. The hydrographic portion of these studies, made with a model at the Waterways Experiment Station at Vicksburg, Mississippi, indicates that salinities in Lake Pontchartrain (640 square miles) will not be greatly affected because the two barriers would restrict water exchange by only about 15%. It would, however, lower the nutrient content, since the nutrient-rich waters of the Pearl River flow into Lake Borgne just outside of the proposed barriers.

The effect of the increase in entrance velocity on fish and shellfish is conjectural. The swift entrance current would be a problem for small boats. When the taintor gates are closed for an approaching hurricane, it also would be difficult to lock through all the boats scurrying for shelter.

Restriction of the current to narrow openings will have some effect on the currents, especially near the barrier. There will be changes in the areas of sedimentation because the barrier effectively prevents the continuation of the existing current parallel with the shores.

Preexisting water temperatures inside a hurricane barrier should assume greater seasonal amplitude. This could cause undue stress on some organisms during the summer and winter months. The lessened water exchange will reduce the heat-dissipating capacity of the bay so that any additional sources of heat, e.g., thermal discharges from power or industrial plants, could have a considerable effect on the biota.

EFFECTS OF TIDAL DAMS. The ecologic effects of tidal power have been studied extensively for the Passamaquoddy Project between the United States and Canada. This huge project involves the creation of a high basin (Passamaquoddy Bay) of 70 square nautical miles (239 km²) and a low basin (Cobscook Bay) of 30 square nautical miles (103 km²). Water will flow continuously from the high pool to the low pool. The project will increase tidal range in the entire Bay of Fundy by about 1%. Salinities will be reduced slightly in the northern portion of Passamaquoddy Bay (Trites, 1961). Summer temperatures will increase to 20° C, and winter temperatures will decrease to less than 0° C, with a large ice-covered area.

These changes in tidal range and temperature will have a considerable effect on some of the commercially important organisms. Least affected will be haddock, pollock, and winter flounder, since those presently caught inside the pool areas consist largely of fish that temporarily enter the area; these same fish will be available outside.

Reduction of the areas of the clam flats in the high pool by 95% will result in a drop from 4 to 2 million pounds of soft-shell clams, a loss of $100,000 (Medcof, 1962). Reduced high pool water exchange should increase scallop production from 60,000 to 90,000 pounds of meats, worth about $36,000. The increase in water temperature will cause the teredo, no problem now, to become an expensive pest.

Lobster stocks outside the bay should not be affected. Within the bay, the hatch, survival, and settlement of larvae should increase. Despite a decrease in growth rate, there should be a modest increase in landings (Wilder, 1960).

The passage of Atlantic salmon and other anadromous fish into the lower and upper pools will require fishways and fish collection systems costing $3.5 million for the best and somewhat less for minimum facilities (Bell and Clay, 1960; Hart and McKernan, 1960).

Relocation and increase in the size of herring weirs because of the new water levels was expected to cost $129,000 (Hart and McKernan, 1960). Even if weir fishing inside the project area is discontinued, it is expected that the herring catch can be maintained at least at its present level, since the abundance of herring is not expected to change appreciably.

These Passamaquoddy studies give some insight into what can be expected when the tidal prism of a large, deep estuary in a subarctic area is substantially decreased.

GENERAL EFFECTS OF REDUCED WATER EXCHANGE. Any reduction in water mass exchange affects the physical and, indirectly, the biological characteristics of any semi-enclosed body of water such as an estuary. For instance, it is pointed out by Harleman and Ippen (1969) that any change in channel depth or volume of freshwater discharge relative to the volume of an intruding salt wedge will change the area of shoaling. This is because the region of heavy shoaling coincides with the point at which the velocity near the bottom reverses from a net landward to a net seaward direction.

An excellent example of the effect of a sill in reducing deep water exchange is afforded by Saanich Inlet on Vancouver Island. Behind the submerged 75 m sill the basin is 234 m deep. Waters of the inlet above sill depth are normal; those below are isolated, oxygen-deficient, and usually contain hydrogen sulphide (Herlinveaux, 1962).

One important feature of the tidal flushing of an estuary is pointed out by Ketchum (1951). The classic assumptions are that (1) entering water mixes completely and uniformly with water present in the estuary at low tide and (2) the volume of water moving seaward on the ebb tide escapes and does not return to the area on the next flood tide. Ketchum states that neither assumption is correct, and therefore it is not the total tidal prism but only water that escapes and does not return that is available for the dilution of introduced pollution. This points out the fact that an offshore island, even if placed just outside of an estuary, will reduce the amount of water available for pollution dilution if it decreases the proportion of the estuarine tidal prism that actually escapes during each tidal cycle.

Changes in turbidity. Much of the turbidity in estuaries is from material carried in by rivers. Construction of large upstream reservoirs often drastically curtails this sediment load. Hassler (1958) shows for the Roanoke River that upstream impoundments decreased the turbidity by an average of 90% in July and the maximum turbidity by at least 80% in every month.

Such changes in sediment load can have a twofold effect. The increase in water transparency may increase photosynthesis, but the loss of the sediments may decrease the available nutrients. The negative effect of the high Aswan Dam on the fisheries of the Mediterranean by curtailing the historical influx of sediments from the Blue Nile is an example of the latter effect.

Turbidity within the estuary depends on the sediment load of incoming waters, the depth and wind fetch, and the amount and zone of flocculation, because the colloidal sediments coagulate and sink as the fresh waters mingle with the salt. Sakamoto (1968), using three clay minerals—illite, montmorillonite, and kaolinite—showed that flocculation occurs as the particles flow into seawater because their surface electric charges are neutralized. Obviously construction projects that affect the salinity will also shift the zone of flocculation, thus increasing or decreasing turbidity in some areas of the estuary.

The detrimental effects of high turbidity (Wilson, 1959) include reduction of light penetration and photosynthetic activity; smothering of bottom-dwelling animals and plants; impairment of fish spawning; reduction of waste-assimilation capacities; and effects on shellfish, particularly oysters.

Although oysters can feed in turbid water, Loosanoff and Tommers (1948) conclude that an increase in turbidity usually causes a decrease in feeding, and at high turbidities oysters may cease pumping entirely. Mussels, *Mytilus edulis,* act similarly. Jorgensen (1949, 1955) tested mussels in three suspensions—graphite at 4 to 5 μ, flagellates, and *Nitzchia closterium*—and found that only a small percentage of the graphite particles of the same size as the flagellates were retained by the gills. When mussels dislike their food they interrupt the formation of feeding "mucus" by the gills.

In clear freshwater ponds the volume of net plankton of surface waters is 8 times greater than in those of intermediate turbidity and 12.8 times greater than in most turbid ponds (Buck, 1956). After two growing seasons Buck found the total weight of fish in clear ponds to be 1.7 times greater than in muddy ponds.

Projects that disturb the sediments will, at least temporarily, have a negative effect on the biota. Those that promise to permanently increase turbidity can have far-reaching effects and need to be approached with caution.

It is suggested by Roe et al. (1970) that excessive turbidity might be prevented by forming a plastic film over the sediments through casting from a compatible solvent system, but they fail to mention the effects of such a coating on the infauna.

Changes in salinity and temperature. Contrary to consideration of substrate as the chief deciding factor in the distribution of benthic fauna, Filice (1958) found that in the San Francisco Bay complex salinity is the most important parameter. Correlation was lacking with either pH or oxygen. The number of species in the substrate decreases toward the freshwater source, the largest break in distribution occurring at Carquinez Strait at a salinity of 9.5 $^o/_{oo}$. The riverward fauna contains freshwater, estuarine, and marine species; the seaward fauna is estuarine and marine. Although substrate type influences the distribution of many species, it does not explain the presence of different species in the two faunas, e.g., marine forms are present in the riverward fauna despite the lack of their preferred substrates. The marine species are more abundant at deeper levels, apparently to take advantage of the higher and more stable salinity at these levels.

While studying the zoobenthos of the same area, Painter (1966) found chlorinity changing as much as 6 $^o/_{oo}$ during a tidal cycle; he was thereby forced to use monthly averages. This is not unusual in estuaries; in the Louisiana marshes, over a 2-year period, the salinity at the base station in Hopedale often varied from 3 to 6 $^o/_{oo}$ or more from day to day, depending chiefly on wind direction and velocity (Rounsefell, 1964). Painter agreed with Filice that animals with high population levels seaward of Carquinez Strait were marine and euryhaline, whereas those toward fresh water were euryhaline and freshwater species.

Menhaden, *Brevoortia tyrannus* and *B. patronus,* spawn in high salinity waters off the Atlantic and Gulf coasts. After hatching and early development, the young enter the estuaries, moving up the tributaries in large quantities as far as the upstream limits of saline water where salinity falls to 1 $^o/_{oo}$ or less. The young can tolerate higher salinities, metamorphosing in the laboratory at salinities of 25 and 40 $^o/_{oo}$. Temperatures below 3° C deter movement into the estuaries and may cause mass mortalities (Reintjes and Pacheco, 1966). The critical range of high temperatures for menhaden is discussed by

Lewis and Hettler (1968) in a subsequent section concerning the effects of thermal discharges.

Salinity and temperature ranges are often critical to larval development. The optimum salinity range for hatching eggs of the blue crab, *Callinectes sapidus,* is about 23 to 28 $^o/_{oo}$, and eggs fail to hatch outside of a temperature range of 19° to 29° C. Favorable ranges for the first three stages of larval ecdysis were salinities from 21 to 28 $^o/_{oo}$ and temperatures from 20° to 29° C (Sandoz and Rogers, 1944).

Similarly, Calabrese (1969) showed that embryos of the coot clam, *Mulinia lateralis,* developed satisfactorily within the salinity range of 22.5 to 30 $^o/_{oo}$, with optimum development at 27 $^o/_{oo}$. The favorable temperature range was 15° to 25° C, with the optimum at 20° C. The larvae grew best at salinities from 20 to 27.5 $^o/_{oo}$ and temperatures from 20° to 30° C.

EFFECTS ON FAUNA CAUSED BY PURPOSE AND USE OF PROJECT

Effects of thermal discharges. Thermal discharges have both physical and biological effects on the environment. Effects vary from place to place, depending on such factors as water depth, rate of water mass exchange, ambient air and water temperatures, presence or absence of pollution, level of nutrients, etc. A discharge harmless or even beneficial at one site may be very detrimental at another.

Commenting on heated effluents, deSylva (1969) states that the effects of elevated water temperature from power-generating plants are more extensive and subtle than apparent effect manifested by dead fish and other animals. Temperature increases alter the normal internal physiologic processes of the organism, influence survival of egg and larval stages, alter reproductive rates, and cause changes in the physical environment such as increased evaporation and salinity and decreased oxygen content. The effects of toxins are usually greater at higher temperatures.

During the warmer months even a slight rise in temperature can cause heat deaths in the shallow coastal and estuarine waters of the Gulf and south Atlantic coasts because many species will already be close to their tolerance level. Mussel larvae, for instance, are very sensitive to elevated temperatures at either high (40 $^o/_{oo}$) or low (20 $^o/_{oo}$) salinities. Similarly, Davis and Calabrese (1964) found that reduced salinities reduced the range of temperatures tolerated by the larvae of both hard clams and oysters.

Even in subarctic areas higher temperatures can be critical. The giant sea scallop, *Placopecten magellanicus,* in the Gulf of St. Lawrence is limited to a narrow depth zone because of the effects of water temperature on spawning and adult survival (Dickie, 1959; Dickie, 1959a). High temperatures appear to be directly responsible for some of the sudden mass mortalities of adult scallops in the Gulf of St. Lawrence since 1928. Mortalities as high as 90% have occurred in 2 to 3 weeks. Experiments show that scallops living in water between 5° and 20° C may be killed by temperatures of 21° to 23° C, depending on their previous temperature experience.

Salinity and temperature have synergistic effects. Garside and Jordan (1968) found that stress generated by compensatory osmoregulatory processes and dysfunctions influences rather substantially the temperature that is lethal to both the mummichog, *Fundulus heteroclitus* and the banded killifish, *F. diaphanus.* They conclude that the basis for the primary ecologic separation that exists between various species can be at least partially explained by differential responses to salinity, particularly during the intense insolation and heating of shallow ponds and marshes in summer.

Heated effluents are a serious potential danger to the menhadens, a very valuable and most abundant species. Test temperatures above 33° C caused death in young menhaden. Lewis and Hettler (1968) state that temperatures above 33° C are not uncommon in menhaden nursery areas during the summer and, with more power plants discharging heated waste water, high water temperatures will become an increasing threat to young menhaden. If the water temperature in a nursery area increases gradually, chances of survival are better than if the young are trapped in a discharge of heated water.

This sensitivity to temperature in warm regions is also noted by Mayer (1914), who states that tropical marine animals commonly live within 5° C of their temperature of maximum activity and within 10° to 15° C of their upper lethal temperature. He notes that in tropical forms a change of even a few degrees of heat or cold causes a marked depression in movement.

For the American lobster, *Homarus americanus,* the ultimate lethal level (salinity 30 $^o/_{oo}$, oxygen 6.4 mg/1) was 32.0° C (McLeese, 1956). The lethal temperature level fell as salinity and oxygen decreased. The brown shrimp, *Penaeus aztecus,* withstood a temperature range of 7° to 35° C, but postlarval shrimp showed a decreased tolerance to low salinity below 15° C (Zein-Eldin and Aldrich, 1965).

Very slight rises in temperature have a marked effect on the survival of mature salmon both migrating upstream and on their spawning grounds. This poses a grave problem on river systems such as the Columbia along which large impoundments have increased the river temperature. Any additional temperature rise from thermal discharges may have very serious consequences to salmon populations. This problem must be considered before adding thermal discharges to streams or estuaries that must be traversed by cold-water migratory fishes.

Another effect of heated effluents is a change in species composition within an area. Naylor (1965) states that the biological effects of heated effluents include:

1. Elimination of some species, especially cool water stenothermal forms
2. Increase in abundance of remaining eurythermal species

3. Introduction of immigrant warmwater stenothermal species
4. Increase in abundance of fouling and boring species
5. Acclimatization of warmwater species to temperate regions

In estuaries the mixing of water and the dissipation of heat may be prevented by vertical salinity gradients and the complexities of flushing, thus affecting migratory species such as crustaceans and fish.

Dissipation of waste heat is not simple. Factories using fossil fuel send most of their heat and air pollutants out a stack. When this becomes politically impossible, they can erect huge cooling towers in which the heat will be consumed as heat of evaporation. However, the atmosphere will become supercharged with water vapor, which will have an effect on the climate. In arid regions the water supply for the cooling towers becomes another real problem.

Nuclear plants dissipate all their waste heat into their cooling water. For this reason they have a more immediate problem of thermal waste disposal, even though both fossil fuel and nuclear plants may dissipate equal quantities of heat.

One suggestion for the disposal of waste heat from nuclear plants is to use the heat to cause nutrient-rich water from below the photic zone to be brought to the surface to raise primary productivity and indirectly increase fishery production. This suggestion is feasible only in situations in which deep water comes close enough to the shore to permit an artificial island for the plant without too long a pipeline. Analysis of the costs involved in moving water from a depth of 300 m to the exit of a pipe at 50 m in terms of expected fish production (Martino and Marchello, 1968) does not give any reason for optimism. Martino and Marchello state that with a $10°$ C heat differential and a tube 10 m in diameter, 105,000 kg/second of water could be delivered from a depth of 300 m. This amounts to 9,072,000 m^3/day. This may be compared to the upwelling area off Peru. Cushing (1969) states

that the biologically active areas (479,000 km^2) average about 2½ times the physical areas, which give an upwelling area of 191,000 km^2. At an upwelling rate of 1 m/day, this gives 191.6 billion m^3 of water. The pipeline thus would raise only 0.0047% as much water. The Peru upwelling area yields less than 15 million metric tons of fish per year. Martino and Marchello (1968) estimate production at 1050 metric tons/year, or only 0.007% of the Peruvian production. Even then they estimated their production rate at almost twice that of the natural rate off Peru.

Extensive use of cold, nutrient-rich deep water in tropical regions may lead to irreversible damage to coral reefs. Projects for raising deep nutrient-rich water by the use of the heated cooling water envision using the nutrients in mariculture. Such fertilization would cloud the water and encourage the growth of benthic algae, thus crowding out the coral. This could be disastrous to the reef corals, which need warm transparent water in order to thrive.

Effects of oil spills. Although the scope of this text cannot encompass any lengthy discussion of pollution, I mention oil spills because they are a unique feature of the marine environment and can occur either during the obtaining of petroleum from submarine strata or during the transport of oil by barge, tanker, or pipeline. The effects of an oil spill depend on many factors:

1. One of the most important factors is the type of material spilled, which refers to the degree of refinement of the particular petroleum product. In Buzzards Bay, Massachusetts, a spill of 38,000 metric tons of No. 2 diesel oil from a wrecked barge in September 1969 quickly caused a heavy kill of fish, worms, crustaceans, and mollusks. The much higher toxicity of diesel fuel compared to crude oil was also shown in Baja California when 8000 metric tons of dark diesel spilled at the mouth of a small cove by the *Tampico Maru* caused an immediate and drastic kill of marine organisms.

2. The time elapsing between the spilling

Table 14-4. Chief attributes of petroleum from three sources*

	Santa Barbara	*Gulf coast*	*Middle East*
Asphaltenes	High	High	Medium
Wax	Low	Low-medium	Medium
Aromatics	Medium	Low-medium	Medium-high
Naphthenes	High	High	Medium
Paraffins	Low	Low-medium	Low-medium
Sulfur	Medium-high	Medium	High
Nitrogen	Medium	Low	?
Pour point	Low	Low-medium	Medium-high

*Modified from Straughan, D. 1971. In Kolpack, R. L., editor. Biological and oceanographical survey of the Santa Barbara Channel oil spill 1969-1970. I. Biology and bacteriology, chap. 18. Allan Hancock Foundation, University of Southern California, Los Angeles. pp. 401-426.

and the oil reaching shore is also important. In the Santa Barbara oil spill crude oil was released 7 miles (11 km) offshore, and the slicks remained at sea several days before moving onshore. This delay permitted the evaporation of many of the volatile (and most toxic) components from the crude oil prior to reaching the beach.

3. The type of cleanup methods used affects the severity of the oil spill. When the *Torrey Canyon* ran aground on Seven Stones Reef, 15 miles (24 km) from the coast of Cornwall, England, in March 1967, she lost 119,000 metric tons of Kuwaiti crude oil. This is about 50% larger than the Santa Barbara spill (which occurred over several months), but it was twice as far from shore. However, both the detergents and the dispersants (some kerosene based) used extensively in the cleanup (about 2½ million gallons) were more toxic to marine organisms than the crude oil. They caused heavy kills at subtidal depths and a large part of the mortality along the 140 miles (224 km) of beach. In contrast, at Santa Barbara no dispersants were used inside the 1-mile limit except when oil entered the harbor at Santa Barbara. Beaches were cleaned by spreading chopped straw and then raking it into trucks to be hauled away and burned. Kills of intertidal organisms were not exceptionally heavy (Nicholson and Cimberg, 1971).

Whether the results of the Santa Barbara spill are generally applicable is somewhat doubtful. Santa Barbara crude has a high asphaltene component that is relatively insoluble in water. The aromatic fraction (the most toxic part) is low. Since the relative insolubility keeps the oil at the surface, the volatile components are lost by evaporation, reducing its toxicity.

4. A fourth factor that may sometimes be of considerable importance is freshwater outflow. The outflow of fresh water from estuaries may be a major factor in protecting sheltered nursery areas lying shoreward of the barrier islands. There are two ways for this outflow to be important: (a) the low salinity residual currents flowing out of interisland passes will tend to hold oil slicks offshore except in the face of onshore winds strong enough to create an overriding surface current and (b) the suspended sediments in the freshwater outflow may cause absorption (or sorption) of oil on the suspended detrital particles, resulting in the sinking of large quantities of oil from the surface of the water, as was shown by Kolpack (1971) in the case of the Santa Barbara oil spill.

5. Another important factor when the spill is raw crude petroleum is the source. Straughan (1971) compares the chief attributes of petroleum from three sources in Table 14-4. It is apparent that Middle East crude oil with high aromatics and high sulfur is potentially more dangerous to marine life than California or Gulf coast oil.

The time that elapses before recovery of an area will vary with the extent of the initial damage, the types of substrate, and the prevailing water temperatures. The mortality in the rocky cove of Baja California was very high, but recovery was almost complete 6 years later.

The effects of any oil spill that might occur in the Arctic Sea is a source of worry to both Canadians and Alaskans. Because of the prevailing very low temperatures (impeding biodegradation of the spilled oil) and the delicate balance of nature in the permafrost tundra, it is feared that an arctic spill could be much more disastrous than any yet encountered. As a result Canada is understandably unwilling to permit oil tanker traffic through the rocky ice-ridden Canadian Straits connecting the Beaufort Sea with Hudson Bay.

EVALUATION OF EFFECTS CAUSED BY DIFFERENT TYPES OF PROJECTS

The construction of islands as airports is receiving much attention. Because of the large area required for a modern jet airport, many heavily populated areas have run out of land adjacent to the cities. Furthermore, there is increasing opposition to the inherent noise and air pollution. Even where land can be acquired the cost of removing hills and filling swamps is sufficiently great to suggest the advantages of an island.

The great majority of our coastal cities are on the shores of an estuary, sheltered bay, or harbor. In selecting a site in such a situation the filling in of a portion of the bay or estuary or planting an island in its midst may seem very practical at first glance. It is thus obvious that for some time there will be more demand for airport construction in our valuable wetlands and tidal waters than in truly offshore locations.

The alarming proportions of the loss of habitat by land fill and channelization are described by Chapman:

Channels and spoil banks are now a part of the estuarine environment. Several methods of construction are used that permit varying degrees of control over resulting spoil. Mechanical excavation with bucket dredges or draglines provides good spoil control on a small area. Hydraulic excavation, however, requires large spoil areas and affords poor control unless the spoil is removed from the construction site (hopper dredge) or retained with-

in ring levees. More than 200,000 acres of shallow coastal bays (not including marshes) in the Gulf and South Atlantic areas have been lost by dredging and filling over the past 20 years. In Texas alone, about 700 miles of Federal navigation channels have altered 13,000 acres of shallow bay bottoms and destroyed 7,000 acres of brackish marsh by deepening. Spoil from these channels has filled 55,000 acres of shallow bays and covered 23,000 acres of brackish marsh. It is not known how much estuarine habitat has been obliterated by private channels. Other disadvantages of channelization and spoil dumping include segmentation of bays which promotes shoaling; increased saltwater intrusion; increased flushing time; altered tidal exchange, mixing, and circulation; increased turbidity; and loss of submerged aquatic vegetation. None of these changes, however, are as significant as the direct physical loss of habitat. Advantages of channels and spoil deposition include connection of isolated waters and marshes to make them available as fish nursery areas, provision of routes of escape or refuge for fish during cold periods, improvement of water exchange and circulation, and release of nutrients trapped in bottom sediments.*

The loss of marsh habitat described above in the south Atlantic and Gulf regions has been duplicated in the north Atlantic. Wenk states that:

Of the tidal wetlands along the Atlantic coast from Maine to Delaware, 45,000 acres were lost between 1955 and 1964. An inventory shows that 34 percent of the area was dried up by being used as a dumping ground for dredging operations; 27 percent was filled for housing developments; 15 percent went to recreational developments (parks, beaches, and marinas); and 10 percent to bridges, roads, parking lots and airports; 7 percent was turned into industrial sites and 6 percent into garbage and trash dumps. (In Maryland 176 acres of submerged land in Chesapeake Bay were sold recently for $100 an acre and, after being filled with dredged bay-bottom muck, were subdivided into lots selling for between $4,000 and $8,000 each.)†

Use of the sea as a disposal area for almost anything man wishes to rid himself of

---

*From Chapman, C. 1968. Channelization and spoiling Gulf Coast and South Atlantic estuaries. In Proceedings of the Marsh and Estuary Management Symposium held July 1967 in Baton Rouge, La. pp. 93-106.

†From Wenk, E., Jr. 1969. The physical resources of the sea. Sci. Amer. **221**:167-176.

has been accelerated in recent years. In several countries the solid portions of these wastes are used as fill in so-called land reclamation, especially for extending land seaward to make airports, new harbor areas, or merely valuable waterfront residential property. There is more and more pressure to find a reasonably cheap method for disposing of the enormous quantities of wastes engendered by our cities and industries. For a long time almost any waste that could be dissolved in water or carried in pipes when mixed with water has been piped into the sea. Even this questionable expedient has left behind enormous quantities of solid wastes for which sufficient land disposal areas are not available near our cities and that cannot easily be incinerated without excessive air pollution.

Can a significant portion of these wastes be disposed of by dumping them into the sea without causing significant environmental damage? Many of these waste materials are toxic, some may cover productive bottom with inert material, and others may clutter the bottom with heavy objects, making trawling difficult.

Solid wastes with negligible, if any, toxicity could be used in the filling of artificial islands, but they should preferably be dumped inside a previously constructed perimeter dike. It was proposed by Bostrom and Sherif of the University of Washington (Landis, 1970c) that unwanted solid wastes are best disposed of by dumping off the mouths of rivers, such as the Fraser, where sedimentation proceeds naturally at a rate of 1 to 20 feet/year, so that any dumped material would be buried in a few months. They claim that any chemical effects, such as the solution of metals, would be less than the natural production of such solutions from undersea volcanoes.

Shifting from waste materials to actual construction, the environment could not be significantly affected by such small projects as buoys and small underwater habitations. A few of the larger projects, such as floating bridges over deep water, should also

have no effect. It is technically feasible to construct and lay pipes of large size anywhere on the continental shelf and wherever necessary to bury them in trenches and cover them. There is even a plan to suspend a 36-inch pipeline across the Mediterranean at a depth of 300 feet from buoyant towers 9000 feet apart.

The environmental hazard from a pipeline is not in the pipeline itself, but in the amount of risk of spillage of the contents through breaks or leaks in the pipe. In earthquake areas such breaks can be expected. One questionable practice is the use of pipelines to carry industrial wastes far offshore where the contents are dumped into deep water.

To date most tunnels for rail or vehicular traffic have been over narrow bodies of water. Where tunnels are buried the effect on the environment should be only temporary. Bridges in themselves are not usually harmful to the environment, but the long causeway approaches to bridges can be very harmful. Table 14-5 offers a general summary of the environmental effects of various projects.

Evaluation of the effect of a project on the environment is complex. Effects may be direct or indirect. Table 14-5 shows that normally most minor construction projects have only a negligible or slight effect on the environment. These minor projects do not include minor filling or channel dredging, which, although individually minor, may have a very serious cumulative effect.

The largest offshore construction projects are islands. Not many have been built, but eventually there may be a number. The ecologic effect of such islands will depend both on the site selected and the use to which the island is put. The least desirable site from the standpoint of potential ecologic damage is within an estuary. If it is assumed that geologically an estuary is only a temporary phenomenon, it is clear that any construction that significantly disturbs its circulation and its volume (and perhaps type) of water exchange will hasten its demise. A limited

Table 14-5. Summary of ecologic effects of specific projects

Project	Negligible	Slight	Requires investigation		
			Site	Wastes	Construction
Buoys	x				
Floating bridges	x				
Undersea habitations	x				
Floating airports		x		x	
Floating cities			x	x	
Underwater pipelines	x[1,2]				
Tunnels	x[1]				
Bridges					x[3]
Artificial reefs	x[4]				
Mariculture structures		x[4]			
Hurricane barriers			x[5]		
Tidal dams			x[5,6]		
Submarine storage		x[7]			
Deep excavations by blasting		x[8]			
Offshore platforms	x				
Offshore islands			x	x	x

[1]If buried.
[2]Danger of leaks in earthquake zones.
[3]Depends on amount of channel blocked.
[4]Possible navigation hazard.
[5]Sill depth in relation to basin depth and stratification; effect of restriction of tidal prism.
[6]Effect on thermal range and amplitude.
[7]May be preferable risk in lieu of long pipelines.
[8]Radiation effects not covered.

Table 14-6. Ecologic effects of artificial islands by site and purpose

Item	Air field	Deep water port	Other small islands	Fossil fuel plant	Nuclear fuel plant
Site-independent effects					
Project area habitat loss	xxxx	xxx	xx	x	x
Noise (distance function)	xxx				
Air pollution	xxx			xxx	
Atomic radiation					xxxx
Site in or close to estuaries					
Water exchange reduction	xxxx	x	xx	x	x
Changes in currents	xxx	x	xxx	x	x
Suitable substrate removal	xxx	x	xx	x	x
Thermal discharge effects				xxx	xxxx
Sedimentation, turbidity	xx	x	x	x	x
Salinity, temperature changes	xxx	x	x	xxx	xxx
Waste, toxin accumulation	xxx	x	x	x	x
Dissolved oxygen reduction	xxx	x	x	xx	xx
Site well offshore					
Thermal discharge effects				x	x
Armored-slope reefs *(gain)*	xxxx	xx	xx	x	x

body of water has a limited capacity to assimilate waste products and excessively enriching nutrients. When this ability is impaired, the estuary may slowly or quickly pass the point where it can support a normal fauna. Some artificial islands may be placed in estuaries; some may be located well offshore. The relative effect of these islands according to their use (which also determines size) and their site is approximated in Table 14-6.

Considering only site-independent factors, nuclear-fueled power plants perhaps offer the greatest ultimate threat to human survival. Many of the proposed plans for both fossil-fuel and nuclear-fuel power plants include also a desalination plant. The extra effluent from the desalination plant (Zeitoun et al., 1969) is at a salinity about 15% higher and a temperature 12° to 15° F above the ambient, so that the water will be denser than the receiving water and will tend to sink to the bottom. Since this effluent will usually contain almost no dissolved oxygen and higher concentrations (from 0.12 to 0.15 ppm) of copper, the placement of such a desalination plant within an estuary will be deleterious to benthic organisms; should the estuary have a sill, the basin within may become devoid of all benthic life.

Studies of environmental changes must be planned so that one can judge from the analysis of the data whether or not any significant changes have occurred or will occur. The study must not only be quantitative, but sampling must be designed to permit the identification and thus the discounting of any secular trends operative during the sampling period. A significant difference in population abundance between pre- and postproject sampling could be only a reflection of a long-term trend that can be detected solely by adequate sampling in control areas unaffected by the project.

The biological community concept of botanists and other ecologists has spilled over into marine zoology, especially in efforts to describe benthic assemblages. If one examines the various communities described, one can scarcely escape the conclusion that these "communities" are largely artifacts. As optimum conditions vary from species to species, almost any situation is closest to the optimum for certain species. They will be dominant in that particular area, but to call this grouping of species a community named after one or more dominant species is merely confounding the confusion. The assumption that a "community" is always more or less an organismic unit is unfounded. The best critique of the "community" concept is offered by Mills:

> . . . a variety of complex ecological assemblages exist . . . from loosely integrated aggregations (or even simple co-occurrences of species independently distributed along continua) to highly stable coadapted groups in equilibrium with climate and other ecological factors for long periods of time. Groups . . . in which instability may be biologically produced rather than imposed directly by changes in the physical environment also exist.[*]

The same type of criticism of the classic community concept is given by Jones (1950), who states that the significant environmental factors that may cause the fauna of the sea bottom in the littoral region to become segregated into groups are temperature, salinity, and the nature of the bottom deposit. These three factors interact, and when two are fairly uniform over a large area, the third may be relatively more important.

Much the same philosophy is echoed by MacGinitie, who states:

> . . . Using the locality, rather than the generic names of animals, for naming a community is recommended, for dominants show so much variation that generically named communities lack uniformity. Dominants may be dominant in entirely different communities, and their use to name a community may cause the worker to make very small community areas.[†]

Changes imposed by a project may be very local or widespread. Projects involving

---

*From Mills, E. L. 1969. The community concept in marine zoology, with comments on continua and instability in some marine communities: a review. J. Fish. Res. Bd. Canada **26:**1415-1428.
†From MacGinitie, G. E. 1939. Littoral marine communities. Amer. Midl. Nat. **21:**28-55.

changes in tidal prism, shifts in current direction and/or velocity, and possibly widespread disruptions of the substrate may call for intensive investigation, whereas projects covering only a small area of the offshore continental shelf may require very little study insofar as the biota are concerned.

The actual evaluation of the degree and type of environmental change caused by a project can be more readily accomplished for some of the biota than for others. In areas of strong coastal upwelling, for instance, the benthic fauna is often of minor importance to the overall productivity, which takes place in the overlying water column, resulting in heavy populations of nektonic species. In no case is it easy to measure project effects on highly motile species. Probably any changes in overall primary productivity may give the best index of the overall effect on motile organisms.

Suggested readings

Bader, R. G. 1954. The role of organic matter in determining the distribution of bivalves in sediments. J. Mar. Res. **13**:32-47.

Carlisle, J. G., Jr., C. H. Turner, and E. E. Ebert. 1964. Artificial habitat in the marine environment. Calif. Fish Game, Fish Bull. **124**:1-93.

Chapman, C. 1968. Channelization and spoiling Gulf Coast and South Atlantic estuaries. In Proceedings of the Marsh and Estuary Management Symposium held July, 1967, in Baton Rouge, La. pp. 93-106.

Cottam, C., and D. A. Munro. 1954. Eelgrass status and environmental relations. J. Wildl. Mgt. **18**:449-460.

Crutchfield, J. A. 1969. Effects of mineral and petroleum extraction on living resources of continental shelf waters. In Proceedings of the Gulf and Caribbean Fisheries Institute, twenty-first annual session. pp. 20-36.

Davis, J. H. 1957. Dune formation and stabilization by vegetation and plantings. U. S. Army Corps of Engineers, Beach Erosion Board, Tech. Mem. **101**:1-47.

deSylva, D. P. 1969. The unseen problems of thermal pollution. Oceans **1**:37-41.

Filice, F. P. 1958. Invertebrates from the estuarine portion of San Francisco Bay and some factors influencing their distributions. Wasmann J. Biol. **16**:159-211.

Glude, J. B. 1951. The effect of man on shellfish populations. Trans. N. Amer. Wildl. Conf. **16**:397-403.

Hewatt, W. G. 1935. Ecological succession in the Mytilus californianus habitat as observed in Monterey Bay, California. Ecology **16**:244-251.

Hubbs, C. L., and A. B. Rechnitzer. 1952. Report on experiments designed to determine effects of underwater explosions on fish life. Calif. Fish Game **38**:333-366.

Kolpack, R. L., editor. 1971. Biological and oceanographical survey of the Santa Barbara oil spill 1969-1970. II. Physical, chemical and geological studies. Allan Hancock Foundation, University of Southern California, Los Angeles. 477 pp.

Lewis, R. M., and W. F. Hettler, Jr. 1968. Effect of temperature and salinity on the survival of young Atlantic menhaden, Brevoortia tyrannus. Trans. Amer. Fish. Soc. **97**:344-349.

Martin, W. R. 1960. Predicted effects of proposed tidal power structures on groundfish catches in Charlotte County, N. B. J. Fish. Res. Bd. Canada **17**:169-173.

Medcof, J. C. 1962. Possible effects of Passamaquoddy power project on clams, scallops and shipworms in Canadian waters. J. Fish. Res. Bd. Canada **19**:877-889.

Mills, E. L. 1969. The community concept in marine zoology, with comments on continua and instability in some marine communities: a review. J. Fish. Res. Bd. Canada **26**:1415-1428.

Mock, C. R. 1967. Natural and altered estuarine habitats of penaeid shrimp. In Proceedings of the Gulf and Caribbean Fisheries Institute, nineteenth annual session. pp. 86-98.

Naylor, E. 1965. Effects of heated effluents upon marine and estuarine organisms. Adv. Mar. Biol. **3**:63-103.

Nicholson, N. L., and R. L. Cimberg. 1971. The Santa Barbara oil spills of 1969: a post-spill survey of the rocky intertidal. In Kolpack, R. L., editor. Biological and oceanographical survey of the Santa Barbara Channel oil spill 1969-1970. I. Biology and bacteriology, chap. 17. Allan Hancock Foundation, University of Southern California. pp. 325-400.

Painter, R. E. 1966. Zoobenthos of San Pablo and Suisin Bays. Calif. Fish Game, Fish Bull. **133**:40-56.

Pratt, D. M. 1953. Abundance and growth of Venus mercenaria and Callocardia morrhuana in relation to the character of bottom sediments. J. Mar. Res. **12**:60-74.

Pratt, D. M., and D. A. Campbell. 1956. Environmental factors affecting growth in Venus mercenaria in Narragansett Bay. Limnol. Oceanog. **1**:2-17.

Ralph M. Parsons Co. 1969. Evaluation of construction methods for offshore airports. Federal Aviation Administration, Systems Research and Development Service, final report RD-69-42,

No. AD 693 185. Office of Technical Services, U. S. Department of Commerce, Springfield, Va. 197 pp.

Reintjes, J. W., and A. L. Pacheco. 1966. The relation of menhaden to estuaries. In A symposium on estuarine fisheries. Amer. Fish. Soc., Spec. Publ. No. 3. pp. 50-58.

Reish, D. J. 1969. Discussion of the Mytilus californianus community on newly constructed rock jetties in southern California (Mollusca: Bivalvia). In Reish, D. J., editor. Biology of the oceans. Dickenson Pub. Co., Inc., Encino, Calif. pp. 18-28.

Rounsefell, G. A. 1972. Ecological effects of offshore construction. J. Mar. Sci. Alabama **2:** 1-208.

Stauffer, R. C. 1937. Changes in the invertebrate community of a lagoon after disappearance of the eelgrass. Ecology 18:427-431.

Straughan, D. 1971. What has been the effect of the spill on the ecology in the Santa Barbara Channel? In Kolpack, R. L., editor. Biological and oceanographical survey of the Santa Barbara Channel oil spill 1969-1970. I. Biology and bacteriology, chap. 18. Allan Hancock Foundation, University of Southern California, Los Angeles. pp. 401-426.

Sykes, J. E., and J. H. Finucane. 1966. Occurrence in Tampa Bay, Florida, of immature species dominant in Gulf of Mexico commercial fisheries. U. S. Fish Wildl. Serv., Fish. Bull. **65:** 369-379.

Taylor, J. L., and C. H. Saloman. 1968. Some effects of hydraulic dredging and coastal development in Boca Ciega Bay, Florida. U. S. Fish Wildl. Serv., Fish. Bull. **67:**213-241.

Turner, C. H., E. E. Ebert, and R. R. Given. 1969. Man-made reef ecology. Calif. Fish Game, Fish Bull. **146:**1-210.

Wilder, D. G. 1960. Possible effects of Passamaquoddy tidal power structures on the Canadian lobster industry. J. Fish. Res. Bd. Canada **17:** 553-563.

Woodhouse, W. W., Jr., and R. E. Hanes. 1967. Dune stabilization with vegetation on the Outer Banks of North Carolina. U. S. Army Corps of Engineers, Coastal Engineering Research Center, Tech. Mem. **22:**1-43.

Zeitoun, M. A., E. F. Mandelli, W. F. McIlhenny, and R. O. Reid. 1969. Disposal of the effluents from desalination plants: the effects of copper content, heat and salinity. U. S. Office of Saline Water, Res. Dev. Prog. Rep. **437:**1-203.

chapter 15

❧ Effects of engineering projects on anadromous fishes

ENVIRONMENTAL REQUIREMENTS OF ANADROMOUS FISHES

Anadromous fishes—smelt, shad, alewives, sturgeon, striped bass, lampreys, salmon, and sea-run trout—must ascend streams to reach spawning grounds that are suitable and sufficiently extensive to accommodate them. The exact requirements differ between species depending on their life histories.

The smelt of the Atlantic coast, *Osmerus eperlanus mordax,* although a shore fish of shoal waters, is pelagic in habit. This smelt enters fresh water almost as soon as the ice leaves the streams, seldom swimming more than a few hundred yards upstream whether in a small brook or a river; they may even spawn in slightly brackish water. The spent adults return immediately to the sea. The adhesive eggs sink and stick fast to any grass, stick, or rock they touch. The eggs hatch in 1 to 3 weeks. The young smelt probably descend to the sea in early summer, according to Bigelow and Schroeder (1953). In New England this is often a necessity, as many of the small brooks they use are dry by midsummer.

Another important anadromous smelt, the eulachon, *Thaleichthys pacificus,* found in the Pacific Northwest and Alaska, differs from *Osmerus* in several ways. The eulachon ascends only larger streams such as the Columbia, Fraser, Nass, and Chickamon Rivers, as well as a number of smaller rivers. The fact that they appear in the very early spring made them extremely important to the Indians, as they came at a time when last year's smoked salmon supply was running low. Eulachon are extremely oily; the name "candlefish" derives from the fact that a dried eulachon fitted with a wick can be used as a candle. The adhesive eggs stick to sand grains and hatch in 2 to 3 weeks. The young fish drift down to the sea. Unlike *Osmerus,* many of the adults die after spawning. At the head of Behm Canal I have observed the bodies of spent eulachon that had drifted out from the Chickamon and Unuk Rivers.

The eulachon is very sensitive to high temperatures. Schools enter the Columbia River in late November or early December when the water temperature averages 45° F (7.2° C). Experiments (Snyder, 1970) show that when smelt are exposed to a temperature of 61° F (16.1° C) for 32 hours, 50% die. Most female smelt fail to spawn in water 7° F (3.9° C) above river temperature. Temperature increases of 10° F (5.6° C) killed all adult smelt in 8 days; a 5° F (2.8° C) rise killed 50% in 8 days.

The shad, *Alosa sapidissima,* like the smelt, does not relish swift water. Unlike the smelt, however, it will ascend slow-moving streams for long distances. The nonadhesive eggs are semibuoyant and require sufficient current to move them slowly along the bottom in order to avoid being smothered. They hatch in about 1 week. Shad will spawn successfully in slightly brackish water, which explains the survival of small runs in streams blocked by dams just above tidewater. They will ascend well-constructed fishways that do not require them to leap out of the water; some ascend the fish ladder at Bonneville Dam on the Columbia River.

The alewife, *Alosa pseudoharengus,* normally enters streams containing ponds or lakes; a scant few may enter sluggish streams without ponds. The size of the stream may vary from a large river to one so small that the fish have difficulty in entering. Although a very few do spawn in sluggish streams, the great majority spawn in ponds or lakes, the adhesive eggs hatching in about 6 days. The young feed pelagically in the ponds for a few months and descend to the sea during the summer. The spent adults return immediately to the sea. Based both on the very small numbers of repeat spawners and the large number of dead alewives observed after spawning, I believe that a sizable proportion of the adult spawners die during or soon after spawning.

The sturgeon, *Acipenser* spp., once abounded in all our major rivers. The sea sturgeons ascended larger rivers in early summer to spawn. According to Clemens and Wilby (1961), they ascended several hundred miles to Stuart and Fraser Lakes at the headwaters of the Fraser River, suggesting that they are very strong swimmers. The young remain in the rivers for some time before going to sea, where they make most of their growth.

The striped bass, *Morone saxatilis,* will spawn just above the range of the tide, but they may run far upstream in streams such as the Roanoke; in some places they spawn successfully in slightly brackish water. The chief requirement is enough current to prevent the semibuoyant eggs from settling to the bottom, where they are in danger of being smothered by the sediment. The eggs hatch in about 2 to 4 days. The striped bass may be less anadromous toward the south, e.g., a nonanadromous stock inhabits the Alabama River.

The sea lamprey, *Petromyzon marinus,* will spawn just above the range of the tide or may run farther upstream. They require gravel or small rubble bottoms in moving water. I watched them spawning in Tunk Stream in Maine several miles above tide-water and above some fairly swift stretches of water. They need some mud or sand bottom nearby for the larvae, or ammocoetes, which remain in the bottom of the stream for a few years before transforming into the adult form. The eggs buried in the gravel hatch in a few weeks. The adults die after spawning.

The requirements of the salmonid fishes differ according to species. Their spawning ground and nursery area requirements are described in detail in Chapter 18.

GENERAL EFFECTS OF DAMS

The type of environmental degradation caused by dams depends on such factors as the dam's height, the volume of water stored in relation to the stream's flow, and the season of water storage. There is also a cumulative effect as the number of dams on the same stream multiplies. Laying aside for the moment the blocking of migrations, dams have sundry other and sometimes more subtle effects on the suitability of the environment, especially for salmonids.

One effect is the drowning of salmon spawning riffles. A high dam can flood several miles of gravel spawning riffles. Where one dam succeeds another, there may remain insufficient spawning area or none at all.

A second danger is heightened temperatures. Most salmonids are adapted to cool water. Water in reservoirs rises in temperature. This effect is also cumulative. The numerous dams on the Columbia River have raised the temperature to dangerous levels. This warmer water has increased the incidence of disease among fishes, probably in two ways: not only does the higher temperature favor the disease organisms, but it weakens the salmon by raising his metabolic rate in the face of lowered oxygen levels.

A third danger is the supersaturation of the water with nitrogen gas as tremendous volumes of water thunder down the spillways (Ebel, 1971). This applies even to the run-of-the-river dams with negligible storage. The supersaturated water causes a gas-bubble disease often fatal to salmons.

A fourth danger arises from the drastic changes in fauna. The warmer quiet-water reservoirs harbor warmwater fishes formerly scarce in the cool swift waters. The seaward-migrating smolts must now run this gauntlet of hungry predators.

A fifth effect of dams is the danger of so long a delay in the speed of migration that the salmon may exhaust his supply of energy, stored while feeding in the sea, before he can reach his natal tributary to spawn. In a large river a salmon usually needs a little time to find the entrance to a fishway. Each additional dam adds to the delay.

A sixth effect of many dams comes from the diurnal and weekend changes in flow in step with changes in power demand. These changes in flow can be detrimental to successful spawning in otherwise suitable areas below the dam.

GENERAL EFFECTS OF STREAM DIVERSIONS

The diversion of a portion of a stream's flow can be detrimental to anadromous fish. The volume of such a diversion in relation to the original volume of the stream is most important. Diversion of the major share of the flow through a tunnel into another watershed may destroy all or a large part of a salmon run.

Diversion of water for irrigation also reduces total stream flow despite a certain amount of return flow from the irrigated land. This return flow is likely to contain a much higher content of dissolved salts than the original water. In much of the far west alkali soils occur in irrigated areas. Leaching of basic salts from this soil raises the pH of the water. In some river systems the water in the lower reaches is so high in alkaline salts acquired from these return flows that it cannot be used for irrigation.

Perhaps the chief danger from irrigation diversions is the channeling of downstream migrating smolts into the irrigation canals and thence onto the fields. This danger has been alleviated over the years by screens to divert the smolts back to the main stream.

NEED FOR FISHWAYS TO PROVIDE FOR UPSTREAM MIGRATION

A fishway provides for the upstream and sometimes downstream passage of fish past a dam or a natural barrier. It consists of a water-filled lock, channel, or series of connected pools by means of which the fish may swim past the obstruction.

Fishways are usually expensive to build and operate. The fishery administrator has to decide, often without adequate evidence, whether or not a fishway should be built. The question of what constitutes damage and the responsibility involved is far from a simple matter. Some conservationists believe all damage to a natural resource must be compensated for. From the practical side, this is clearly impossible and not always desirable.

When a dam blocks only a small area, the expense of a fishway may often be wholly disproportionate to the possible benefits. Regardless of who pays the bill it may be economically unsound to build a fishway. In many states such situations are recognized, and the owners of such an obstruction are permitted to compensate for the damage incurred in other ways such as by contributions toward artificial propagation. Evaluation of a commercial fishery to estimate damage caused by the lack of a fishway is readily accomplished; for a sport fishery evaluations are more difficult. If the run of a species has already been destroyed by a dam that has been in existence for many years, the value of a fishway must be estimated on the potential value of the re-established run.

Cost of a fishway is generally weighed against the capitalized value of the present or potential resource that requires it. If the salmon run that depends on the spawning grounds above a proposed dam produces an annual benefit of $2000, the capitalized value of the run is $50,000, using an interest rate of 4%, which is applicable to natural resources conserved by the taxpayer's money in computing benefits from engineering projects. If an adequate fishway can be built for less than $50,000, the cost is a justifiable expenditure from the national viewpoint.

What happens when the fishway cannot be built for $50,000? On the theory that the owner of the dam must compensate for any damages incurred, there are other lines of procedure. It is a matter of policy whether or not a permanent fishery resource should be extinguished by a dam with an estimated useful life of 40 to 60 years. If both the fishway and the dam are of importance to the area, a more expensive fishway may be justified. This is the same line of reasoning adopted when many of the large public dams are constructed despite an unfavorable cost-benefit ratio.

Evaluation of the need for a fishway at a natural obstruction is made in the same manner as for a dam, but there is one difference. A fishway at a natural obstruction, instead of preventing a loss, usually results in the creation of a new resource.

GENERAL REQUIREMENTS AND TYPES OF FISHWAYS
Basic principles for a successful fishway

To be successful, a fishway must be constructed in accordance with the following principles:

1. It should be readily passable by all the migratory species in that particular stream.

2. It should operate at all water levels in the forebay and tailrace of a dam or above and below a natural obstruction.
3. Fish should ascend without injury or exertion of supreme effort.
4. Fish must find the entrance and enter without too much delay.

Types of fishways

Fishways have been in use since very ancient times. Of the many designs and types tried in various places, a few are successful, some have limited success, but the majority are failures. In the following discussion, I have classified the general types according to the type of obstruction at which they are most likely to be used.

Low dams with a gradually sloping face. Although uncommon in this country, dams of this type occur on the salmon and sea trout streams and small rivers of Britain. Here the fishway may consist merely of a long inclined chute or "balk" formed by a long timber or stone ridge running obliquely across the gently sloping face of the dam, forming a trough of low gradient up which salmon can easily swim for a short distance (Menzies, 1934).

Low dams without a sloping face. On the alewife streams of New England the fishway often consists of an inclined timber chute or sluiceway with L-shaped staggered baffles to check the swift flow and to lower the gradient by effectively increasing the length of the fishway (Figs. 15-1 and 15-2). This fishway works fairly well for alewives. It is too turbulent and too swift in places, it does not provide resting pools, and it does not operate satisfactorily on low flows, but the alewives scramble up somehow. When the water is too shallow, they turn on their sides and wriggle up amid great splashing. Although salmon are known to use these fishways, they are basically unsuitable for salmon because of their many turns. The effective width of the channel is actually much less than the width of the sluice, and the many sharp turns cause crosscurrents that create difficulties for large fish. This type of fishway is operable over a fair range

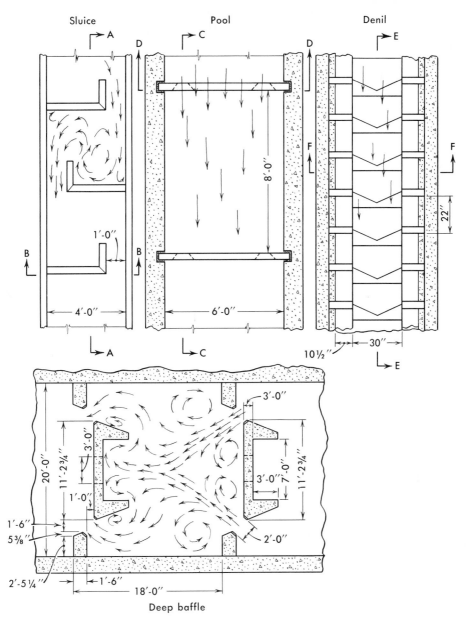

Fig. 15-1. Top view of several types of fishways. (From Rounsefell, G. A., and W. H. Everhart. 1953. Fishery science. John Wiley & Sons, Inc., New York. 444 pp.)

of flows, working as well when almost full as when very low. Although unsuitable for salmon, it works for alewives that prefer (in most streams) to swim up a rapid flow rather than leap over an obstructing weir.

The Denil type of fishway (Figs. 15-1 and 15-2) is very useful for low- to medium-height dams. First developed by Denil in 1938, it has been improved over the years and is used on several salmon streams in the Pacific Northwest. Essentially it is a narrow chute carrying a large volume of water at high velocity, especially on the surface. The force of this stream striking closely spaced baffles aids in maintaining a low velocity near the bottom.

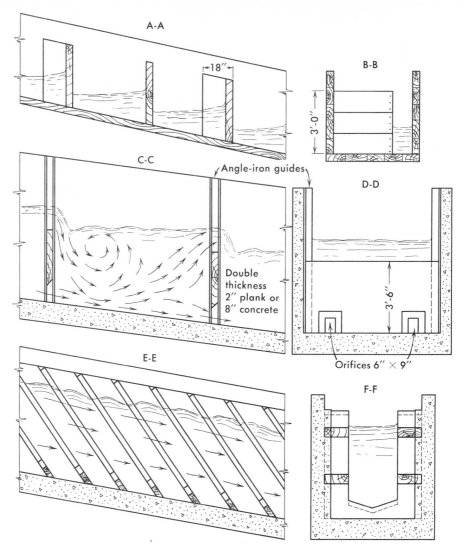

Fig. 15-2. Side and end elevations of several types of fishways. See Fig. 15-1 for locations of sections. (From Rounsefell, G. A., and W. H. Everhart. 1953. Fishery science. John Wiley & Sons, Inc., New York. 444 pp.)

Low to high dams. The most universal type of fishway is the pool type, which is a succession of pools connected by short rapids or low falls and often by a submerged orifice. This fishway is especially advantageous for small streams that cannot spare a large volume of water. The weirs between pools are sometimes solid, especially in narrow fishways. Where water is a major problem, the weir may be notched to permit the fish passage with very low flows. For fish such as alewives that dislike leap-

ing out of the water, this notch in the weir can contain a short chute running into the pool above, up which the fish will readily scramble.

Most large fishways use submerged orifices (Figs. 15-1 and 15-2) so that fish may swim from pool to pool without leaving the water. Such an arrangement is desirable for shad.

Extensive experiments (Gauley, 1960) show that for a group of mixed salmonids—steelhead and king and coho salmon—the difference in elevation between pools has a significant effect on time of passage. In ascending a 6-foot elevation, heights between pools of 1 foot took them 10.6 minutes, 1½-foot differences took them 21.6 minutes, and 2-foot differences took them 32.5 minutes.

The need for efficient fishways became apparent when Bonneville Dam was constructed across the lower Columbia River in the 1930's with little advanced warning to conservationists, threatening the very existence of a prosperous salmon industry. With no previous experience in passing such large numbers of salmonids over such a large structure, with lack of time for adequate experimentation, and with the necessity for avoiding failure, the biologists designed fishways of generous proportions. Each pool was 40 feet wide, 16 feet long, and over 5 feet deep with submerged orifices 2 feet square. The pools had a difference in elevation of only 1 foot. These fishways were a success.

The great cost of construction of such large fishways, often combined with the problem of insufficient space across the face of a dam for both adequate flood spillways and large fishways, was a great stimulus to research on fishway capacity. This has aided greatly both in reducing cost and in ensuring successful passage. For instance, the record hourly count of fish passing up the Bonneville fishway is 4296 salmonids. An experimental ladder only 4 feet wide passed 50 per minute (3000/hour), or about two thirds as many (Elling, 1960).

At Bonneville an ingenious collection system was devised across the face of the powerhouse, whereby salmon approaching the powerhouse could enter a collection tunnel that led them into a large fishway at one side of the powerhouse. In addition to the collection system, this also necessitated an additional large fishway. A new cost-saving idea is the transfer of fish at about the same level from such a collection system into a fishway through pipes that are easily installed. Such a system, if originally installed

at Bonneville, could have saved great expense, since it would have eliminated an extra fishway. The pipe experiments (Slatick, 1970) showed that salmon and trout passed readily through a 0.6 m pipe 82 m in length either with or without illumination.

Natural obstructions. Passage of anadromous fishes past natural obstructions is not a new subject. For a great many years attempts were made to aid salmon trying to pass small falls and rapids in Alaskan streams. During this period the chief method was blasting holes or steps with dynamite. This met with some success in the hands of skillful operators, but it sometimes made matters worse. In some of the smaller streams in Maine runs of alewives were maintained by constructing a series of masonry pools with small falls or rapids connecting them. This method was even used by the pioneers in establishing runs of alewives in hitherto inaccessible lakes, e.g., at Damariscotta.

The blocking of streams to anadromous fish by logging debris, although usually not of natural origin, requires mention. Great efforts have been made in recent years to clear up such log jams throughout the Columbia River basin and in other logging areas.

One of the chief problems in passing fish by a natural rapid is that such rapids usually occur in narrow canyons, so that there is a great difference in water levels between low and high flows. In the famous Hell's Gate Canyon, about 250 miles up the Fraser River, the difference is about 90 feet. Furthermore, such aids must usually function without any means of human control. After considerable study, the International Pacific Salmon Fisheries Commission designed a type of fishway to meet these requirements. It is a baffle-type fishway reminiscent of the alewife sluiceway that, because of the low gradient, can function efficiently with a considerable difference in water level (Fig. 15-1). Even so it was necessary to install several such fishways at different levels to enable salmon to pass through the Canyon at all stages.

NEED FOR SAFE DOWNSTREAM PASSAGE FOR YOUNG

The young of anadromous species migrating downstream may be injured or destroyed in several ways:

1. They may enter an irrigation diversion and be spread on the fields.
2. They may enter a city water diversion and be killed in the reservoir as the water is treated.
3. They may enter a power diversion intake, where two dangers confront them. If it is a small volume diversion with a high fall, they are likely to be chopped up in the turbine impellers. In any case the sudden release of pressure at the outlet may destroy them. This last depends partially on whether they were already somewhat adjusted to pressure just prior to entering the diversion. In such case the effect will be more pronounced.
4. They may leave the forebay of a dam via the spillway. This occurs very often beneath taintor gates at a depth of 50 or more feet, entailing a sudden release of pressure.
5. They may be forced to traverse a very long artificial lake abounding with predator species such as the squawfish that is now a nuisance on the Columbia River (Maxfield et al., 1970).

Various methods of channeling young fish away from dangerous routes have been tried. The huge drum screens in use for many years in major irrigation diversions in the West (Figs. 15-3 and 15-4), although they saved millions of small salmon, have certain disadvantages:

1. High cost
2. Excessive maintenance
3. Need for constant adjustment to compensate for changes in volume of flow
4. Excessive loss of head, requiring widening of canals, despite the "self-cleaning" action of the drums
5. Mechanical limitations in great depths or very wide channels
6. Incomplete efficiency in guiding fish (The rate of flow against the screen is always rather critical.)
7. Limited ability in guiding fry (or eggs) of shad and striped bass
8. Occasional failure when high water brings excessive debris to clog both trash racks and screen meshes

Guiding experiments have been tried with combinations of intensity and frequency

Fig. 15-3. Showing drum screens on a small irrigation diversion. The paddle wheels that turn the drums are on the downstream side.

of sound, rising bubble curtains, hanging chains, electric stimuli, lights, water jets, and louvers. None of these methods were completely successful or reliable, and some were worthless. Brett and Alderdice (1958), for example, experimented with sound, light, bubbles, chains, odors, and dyes without satisfactory results.

The most satisfactory solution to date appears to be the traveling screen moving horizontally and placed diagonally across the stream. A preliminary model is shown in Fig. 15-5 (Bates and Vanderwalker, 1970). In this model the screen was placed at a 20-degree angle to the flow, and the fish (carried downstream tail first) are swept into the bypass. In later models the screen is lifted clear of the water on its return trip to minimize head loss.

In later experiments a somewhat similar

Fig. 15-4. Large irrigation diversion with four of the nine screens raised for overhauling.

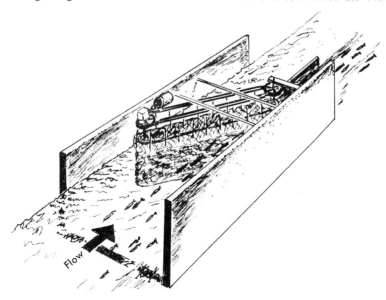

Fig. 15-5. Horizontal traveling screen, model I. (From Bates, D. W., and J. G. Vanderwalker. 1970. U. S. Fish Wildl. Serv., Spec. Sci. Rep. Fish. **608**:1-5.)

type of traveling screen made of heavy large mesh was developed to be placed ahead of the young fish screen in order to remove logs and debris from the stream (Bates et al., 1971).

Suggested readings

Bates, D. W., and J. G. Vanderwalker. 1970. Traveling screens, for collection of juvenile salmon (models I and II). In Preliminary designs of traveling screens to collect juvenile fish. U. S. Fish Wildl. Serv., Spec. Sci. Rep. Fish. **608**:1-5.

Brett, J. R., and D. F. Alderdice. 1958. Research on guiding young salmon at two British Columbia field stations. Fish. Res. Bd. Canada, Bull. **117**:1-75.

Ebel, W. J. 1971. Dissolved nitrogen concentrations in the Columbia and Snake Rivers in 1970 and their effect on chinook salmon and steelhead trout. NOAA Tech. Rep., Nat. Mar. Fish. Serv., Spec. Sci. Rep. Fish. **646**:1-7.

Elling, C. H. 1960. Further experiments in fishway capacity, 1957. U. S. Fish Wildl. Serv., Spec. Sci. Rep. Fish. **340**:1-16.

Gauley, J. R. 1960. Effect of fishway slope on rate of passage of salmonids. U. S. Fish Wildl. Serv., Spec. Sci. Rep. Fish. **350**:1-23.

Maxfield, G. H., R. H. Lander, and C. D. Volz. 1970. Laboratory tests of an electrical barrier for controlling predation by northern squawfish. U. S. Fish Wildl. Serv., Spec. Sci. Rep. Fish. **611**:1-8.

Menzies, W. J. M. 1934. Salmon passes—their design and construction. Fisheries, Scotland, Salmon Fisheries, 1934, No. 1. pp. 1-29.

Slatick, E. 1970. Passage of adult salmon and trout through pipes. U. S. Fish Wildl. Serv., Spec. Sci. Rep. Fish. **592**:1-18.

part seven

❧ Commercial culture of marine organisms

chapter 16

℣ Mariculture

BIOLOGICAL FACTORS

Mariculture consists of the rearing for commercial purposes of marine organisms. This wide definition encompasses everything except the rearing of freshwater and anadromous species in a freshwater environment.

Rearing environment

Some of the biological factors important in mariculture are briefly outlined in the boxed material on p. 303. Among the natural rearing environments, the simplest situation is the use of an area that has no confining boundaries, e.g., an oyster bed that is a portion of the bottom of a bay with the boundaries indicated merely by occasional stakes.

A slightly more sophisticated approach is the use of the same natural environment but confining the organisms within a cage or enclosure. In the first situation one is restricted to rearing nonmotile organisms; the second approach broadens the possibilities to include fishes and other swimming organisms. Perhaps the largest enclosure is the 2500 acres fenced in by a shrimp farm in West Bay near Panama City, Florida. Such fences can be used also as a temporary feature in accordance with the season. At

Yumurtalik (translates "place of the eggs") in the Gulf of Iskenderun on the Mediterranean coast of Turkey, a half-mile woven bamboo fence is placed entirely across the mouth of a shallow bay every spring to confine shoals of young wild mullet (Fig. 16-1). In the fall the grown mullet, heavy with roe, are led into traps as they attempt to leave, presumably on a spawning migration.

Cages can be large wicker baskets, wire or wooden live cars, or large floating enclosures of netting such as the Japanese have long used to rear yellowtail and which are being used in many places for salmons and trouts.

The third category is the use of the natural environment as modified by the release of heated cooling water from a power or manufacturing plant. Such use will usually entail some form of enclosure. It is hoped that the use of this heated water will pay dividends in accelerated growth rates, but it also poses problems in disease control. At Crystal River, Florida, experiments are under way to use the heated effluent of a power plant to extend the length of the growing season for penaeid shrimp being reared in semiraceway environments (Florida Conservation News, 1972). In experiments

Fig. 16-1. Weaving a fence out of bamboo to confine mullet in a bay at Yumurtalik, Turkey.

in rearing sole *(Solea solea)* at Hunterston, Scotland, the use of heated water caused sole to reach market size in 18 months instead of the usual 4 years. It is now planned to cover tanks of seawater with plastic balls to retain heat during the winter because it has been shown that the balls reduce heat losses by up to 70% and evaporation by nearly 90%. Within limits the ball size has no bearing on the results (Commercial Fisheries Review, 1969a).

Catfish, *Ictalurus punctatus,* were reared successfully in Texas in water warmed by the discharge from steam-electric generating stations (Tilton and Kelley, 1971). The catfish were confined in wire cages containing 1 m³ of water that were floated at the surface attached to one line and tended by a small barge pulled along a parallel line. They were fed 3% of their body weight daily. The economics of such a rearing method needs to be worked out.

It is pointed out by Milne (1972) that the heated effluents used may vary somewhat in salinity and may also contain varying amounts of silt, necessitating some type of filtering operation.

The fourth category is the confinement of fish in ponds, permitting the natural water of the adjacent coast to flow through them, usually by means of tidal gates. This does not differ radically in result from the diked Olympia oyster beds in Puget Sound where the high tide overtops the dikes, renewing the water twice a day. Of course for motile species there must be either a netting barrier or a high dike. The high dike has the advantage of allowing the incoming water to be strained for the young of predator species. However, for large active fish such as salmon or yellowtail the netting permits the much larger quantities of water that are desired. In some cases the passage is closed at each end to give the best water circula-

Important biological factors in mariculture

A. Rearing environment
   1. Natural, organisms unconfined
   2. Natural, organisms confined in cage or enclosure
   3. Natural, modified by a thermal effluent
   4 Ponds, natural water flows through, perhaps with tidal gates
   5. Ponds, water stagnant at least for considerable periods
   6. Closed circulating system
B. Sources of young
   1. Natural spawning in area
   2. Captured from wild parents spawning naturally
   3. Reared from spawn of captured wild parents
   4. Reared from parent brood stock
C. Sources of food
   1. Natural food in water or on bottom
   2. Natural food in water flowing through
   3. Natural food aided by fertilizer-induced production, possibly including upwelling
   4. Natural food supplemented with captured or reared live or fresh food
   5. Natural food supplemented with artificial food
   6. Artificial food only
D. Trophic level of organisms reared and their natural food types
   1. Level 1: Algae and vegetation
   2. Level 1½: Mixed plankton, detritus including bacteria and protozoa
   3. Level 2: Zooplankton
   4. Level 3: Benthic invertebrates, forage fishes, scavengers
   5. Level 4: High level feeding, piscivorous predators
E. Niches occupied under natural conditions
   1. Attached or nonmotile: Oyster, clam, mussel
   2. Benthic, only slightly motile: Abalone, scallop, sea urchin
   3. Benthic, nonswimming: Lobster, some crabs
   4. Benthic, swimming: Shrimp, crab, flounder
   5. Bottom to surface: Catfish, etc.
   6. Chiefly near surface: Pompano, mullet, trout
F. Genetic control possibilities
   1. Excellent, known techniques: Trout, catfish
   2. Good, rearing known, can raise to adult: Oyster, clam, lobster
   3. Good to fair, rearing known: Penaeid shrimp, mullet
   4. Speculative
G. Temperature restrictions under natural conditions
   1. Require warm temperatures: Spiny lobster, pompano, milkfish
   2. Require cool temperatures: Northern lobster, trout, European oyster
   3. Reproduction poor in cool temperatures: American oyster
H. Salinity restrictions on reproduction
   1. Reproduce in fresh to saline water: Tilapia
   2. Reproduce in fresh water: Trout, shad
   3. Reproduce in estuaries: Oyster
   4. Reproduce in high salinity: Mullet, drums, eel

tion. Such netting enclosures are used in Norway, Japan, Britain, and Puget Sound, Washington.

The fifth category is the use of ponds in which the water is renewed sporadically as required to maintain optimum salinity levels. This type of brackish water pond is used throughout Southeast Asia but is perhaps best exemplified by the "tambaks" of Java (Schuster, 1949), in which the ponds can receive seawater through canals on high tides as well as freshwater runoff. Maintaining acceptable salinity levels is a difficult problem during exceptionally wet or dry years.

The last category of rearing practices involves the rearing of organisms in a closed circulating system in which the quality of the water can be maintained only by adequate filtration and occasional partial renewal to take care of the buildup of deleterious substances.

Despite the care needed to maintain the suitability of such an artificial environment, it has certain advantages that in the long run may outweigh other considerations. Although the cost in capital and the need of trained personnel will usually rule out this method for volume production of low-cost protein, it may become the most popular method for production of gourmet items. The University of Rhode Island is attempting pilot experiments to determine how much space is required to grow northern lobsters to market size in a closed system (New England Marine Resources, 1973).

Sources of young

One of the most difficult problems in mariculture involves obtaining a sufficient and reliable supply of young organisms. The simplest situation is that in which the new crop of young depends on spawning within the mariculture area or perhaps on the drifting into the area of planktonic larvae from spawning in neighboring waters. This is the situation in some oyster areas, but the setting of the planktonic larvae within the area is usually increased by spreading oyster shells or other substrate material at the proper

time so that the larvae can set before the cultch is covered by fouling organisms.

The second source of young is the capture for rearing within the mariculture area of young produced by the spawning of wild parents outside of the area. This is perhaps the most universal method now in vogue for obtaining young stock.

One example of this source of young is the seining of young pompano, especially along the surf-swept beaches of the east coast of Florida, to stock commercial rearing ponds over a wide area. Another better established example is the capture of wild young milkfish, *Chanos chanos,* to stock rearing ponds and tambaks throughout much of the East Indies and Southeast Asia. The young milkfish are carefully tended and carried long distances in earthenware jars, but the supply is often inadequate.

The Japanese also depend on annually catching many millions of young yellowtail, and this supply is also often inadequate. They also capture very large quantities of elvers, both in the sea and as they ascend streams, to use in rearing eels for a gourmet market. This supply also is apparently inadequate, as in 1972 biologists were sent to Florida to determine whether a reliable supply of elvers could be developed for shipment to Japan.

In most of the oriental brackish water ponds shrimp postlarvae enter ponds that have an inflow of seawater. The shrimp are then raised in the ponds along with milkfish, tilapia, carp, or mullet. Similarly, in the southeastern United States both the entry of wild penaeid shrimp larvae with the tides and the stocking of young reared from captured gravid shrimp are practiced, often in the same ponds (Broom, 1971).

The third method of obtaining young is to rear them from captured wild parents. The present culture of penaeid shrimp depends on capturing gravid females, which are held until they spawn. The young planktonic larvae are then raised through their numerous molts, subsisting on special cultures of algae. However, Mock (1973) states that the Japanese have developed techniques by which shrimp mature sexually, mate, and spawn in captivity. This is not practiced commercially in Japan because large numbers of wild gravid females are available.

The same method has been used for a long time to obtain young of the northern lobster. However, on Martha's Vineyard, Massachusetts, Hughes (1968) now rears lobsters to maturity, which offers the possibility of developing better strains.

The fourth method of obtaining young is to maintain a brood stock of adult fish. This is by far the superior method where possible because it permits genetic manipulation to improve growth rates, disease resistance, and any other desirable characteristics. The outstanding examples of this technique are the rainbow trout and some of the salmons, for which greatly improved strains are available. Donaldson (1971) began the selective breeding of rainbow trout in 1934. After 38 years of selection he matured male trout in only 1 year at a weight of 680 g. Females matured in their second year at 4.5 kg and averaged 9000 eggs. For chinook salmon, *Oncorhynchus tshawytscha,* in the few years from 1960 to 1969 he was able to increase the egg production of 3-year-old females from 3800 to 5400 eggs.

In Puget Sound pan-sized (one-half pound [0.23 kg]) coho salmon are being raised commercially in ponds (Idyll, 1973), and early in 1972, 200,000 pounds (90,000 kg) were sold.

Continued research on other species, including methods for inducing spawning, will doubtless add to the short list of organisms now responsive to this method. For instance, recently the quasi-catadromous gray mullet, *Mugil cephalus,* has been successfully induced to spawn (Kuo et al., 1973).

The shortness of the list of marine fishes (excluding anadromous species) that have been reared from the egg is highlighted by the recent bibliography (May, 1971) on the subject. From 1878 through 1969 attempts were made to rear 75 species of fish. Perusal of the bibliography indicates some success with three species—the mackerel, *Scomber japonicus,* the sole, *Solea solea,* and the plaice, *Pleuronectes platessa*—a very meager result indeed.

A few species breed so heavily in ponds that the ponds are soon overstocked with a stunted population. This applies especially to the tilapias. Tubb states:

> The most important stimulus to fish culture development in South East Asia during the past 20 years was the introduction of the exotic species *Tilapia mossambica.* The readiness with which this fish responded to artificial cultivation and the easiness with which it could be bred and fed, created a furore throughout the region.
>
> Unhappily the extreme fecundity of the species and the fact that it breeds continuously throughout the year have created their own problems and over the past few years the interest in this species has declined. Only in rare cases has any serious attempt been made to apply adequate management techniques to the pond culture of Tilapia.
>
> Considerable success in mono-sex-culture of this species was obtained in Sabah and experimental studies at the Tropical Fish Culture Research Institute, Malacca, have produced hybrids which seem to offer high potential for cultural activities. The crossing of *Tilapia mossambica* and a different species derived from South East Africa results in the production of 100 percent male offspring. These fish have considerable hybrid-vigour and, if segregated, show an excellent growth rate. This hybrid is not as yet widely cultivated.*

It is apparent that one of the biggest problems in mariculture is the obtaining of a sufficient and reliable source of young. Tubb also states:

> There is a small import and export trade in milkfish fry but this has never developed to significant proportions, essentially because most of the countries from where the fry can be obtained do not have supplies adequate for their own requirements.*

Sources of food

The success or failure of a mariculture establishment of any kind is highly dependent on the quantity, quality, and cost of food. The figures often quoted on the weight of fish harvested per unit area are rather meaningless unless accompanied by data on sources and cost of food consumed.

---

*From Tubb, J. A. 1967. Status of fish culture in Asia and the far east. FAO Fish. Rep. **44**:45-53.

The most primitive type of mariculture depends wholly on the natural supply of food in the water column and/or on the bottom. Obviously when this is the sole food supply one cannot normally expect large returns per unit of area, since without a continuous supply of nutrients the primary producers soon exhaust those available, as is illustrated by the normal summer slow-down in algal production.

When sufficient area is available and supplemental feeding is expensive in either material or labor, it is not always economical to feed. In raising sedentary mollusks, for which the area used is continuous with other waters, the food filtered from the water column may be continuously replaced by currents, preventing exhaustion of the supply. For raising mollusks then, it is advantageous to have a continuous flow of water so that the organisms are not just repumping the water they have already pumped. In areas with a high tidal range it is possible to achieve this continuous or almost continuous flow through seaside ponds at little expense. Where tidal ranges are very slight one must consider the cost of pumping water.

In stagnant pond culture probably the cheapest source of food is the elevated algal production resulting from fertilization with organic or inorganic materials. Some experiments are already under way to pump nutrient-rich seawater from below the photic zone into ponds to provide nutrients in lieu of these commercial fertilizers.

The relative importance of each food source in stagnant ponds is explained by Gaudet for warmwater ponds. He states:

Artificial feeding is widely practised. Gains obtained by feeding are hard to determine but in Israel, of 2,000 kg of fish obtained per hectare, probably 400 kg come from natural food, 400 kg more from fertilizers and 1,200 kg from artificial feeding.*

Where large numbers of fish are confined in a limited space it is necessary to provide

*From Gaudet, J. L. 1967. The status of warmwater pond fish culture in Europe. FAO Fish. Rep. **44**:70-87.

all or most of their food. Often this is fresh or live food, e.g., cultured algae to feed larval or juvenile forms. Some larval organisms do well at certain stages on larval brine shrimp, *Artemia salina,* but it is becoming increasingly difficult to obtain brine shrimp eggs from areas not polluted with pesticides. The Japanese, despite the unsuitability of such oily fish, have been forced to feed enormous quantities of anchovies to yellowtail, *Seriola quinqueradiata,* kept in net enclosures, but the supply of anchovies cannot keep pace with the growing need.

There is an increasing demand for manufactured fish food to supplement natural food. The reliance on fresh food can be precarious, and its capture and storage expensive. Furthermore, the artificial feeds can be standardized for content of vitamins and amino acids. Presently these feeds are usually prepared as pellets of any desired size, and the pellets are treated with a coating to withstand leaching when immersed in water.

For organisms cultured in a closed system, the pelleted artificial feeds are highly desirable to prevent fouling of the water.

In discussing artificial feeds, Hastings (1971) stresses certain factors as being independent variables that need to be optimized to obtain the full carrying capacity of a body of water. These factors are as follows:

1. Feed quantity (percent of body weight fed per day)
2. Feed quality (meeting caloric, amino acid, and vitamin requirements)
3. Feeding frequency (number of daily feedings)
4. Stocking rate (number of fish per unit area)
5. Stocking size
6. Time (appears to mean season of the year)
7. Water temperature

Hastings states that it is difficult to optimize these variables for all types of bodies of water from Kotzebue, Alaska, to Homestead, Florida. He does not mention the effect of salinity or the presence of any natural food.

Table 16-1. A suggested high density, restricted ingredient formula for low pesticide fish feed*

	Amount (kg)	Protein (kg)
Fish meal	91	54
Soybean meal (solvent extracted)	272	136
Rice bran (solvent extracted)	272	38
Milo or shorts (wheat)	182	29
Distillers' solubles	45	11
MNC (Milk Nutrients Concentrate)	28	7
Deodorized soybean oil	18	
Vitamin premix[1]	4	
TOTAL	908	275 (30.45%)

With some monitoring of fish meal, milo, and oil source, the total pesticide content in this formula should be below detectable levels or in very low amounts. Price is about the same as any 30% protein concentrate now sold for animal production.

*From Hastings, W. H. 1971. In Proceedings of the first annual workshop, World Mariculture Society. pp. 118-126.
[1]A typical poultry layer-breeder vitamin premix containing pyridoxine in addition is recommended.

There is not complete agreement concerning the use of pelleted feeds containing a "wet mix" that must be kept refrigerated as compared to the use of completely dry feeds. Hublou (1963) gives a formula for "Oregon pellets" used for salmon and trout. The "dry" portion (about 57%) consists chiefly of cottonseed meal and herring meal; the "wet" portion is tuna viscera and a mixture of other fish. It contains a vitamin premix.

Feeding trials at several Oregon hatcheries with chinook and coho salmon revealed a food conversion of 2.0 (obviously the feed mix vs the wet weight of the fish), which at a cost (in the early 1960's) of 12 cents/pound yielded a food cost of 24 cents/pound of fish reared. They hoped to be able to dehydrate the product to eliminate the necessity of refrigeration and also to put it in a practical form for feeding smaller fish (less than 700 fish/pound).

Table 16-2. Vitamin levels recommended for dry trout feeds*

Vitamin	Level per kilogram of feed
Niacin	330-440 mg
Pantothenic acid	110 mg
Inositol	396 mg
Choline chloride	5,286 mg
Biotin	4.4-5.5 mg
Vitamin B_{12}	0.7-1.1 mg
Folic acid	4.4-6.6 mg
Pyridoxine	20-22 mg
Riboflavin	44 mg
Thiamine	11 mg
Ascorbic acid	440 mg
Vitamin K	11 mg
Vitamin E	22-66 mg
Vitamin A	6,608 I.U.
Vitamin D	1,322 U.S.P.

*Data from Phillips, A. M. Unpublished paper.

Hastings (1971) states that 95% of the feeds now in use are dry, because the historical use of fresh or frozen fish and livestock by-products has become too expensive, since they are now largely used in pet and mink feeds. The dry feeds eliminate most of the problems of handling, storage, and water quality. The formula he suggests for a low cost, low pesticide feed is shown in Table 16-1.

Hastings stresses the need for sufficient amino acids in the protein constituents of the diet and gives a list of the required amounts of 10 amino acids based on Mertz' publication (1969) for chinook salmon fingerlings. He also claims that in the future fish meal may become too expensive to compete with vegetable proteins supplemented with synthetic amino acids. Hastings gives a table of the vitamin requirements of trout that are taken from a hatchery manual being prepared by Phillips (Table 16-2).

Trophic levels and food types

The trophic level of a species is of great importance in mariculture because of the high loss of energy between trophic levels. It is not by accident that the fish raised in ponds throughout the Orient for providing low-cost protein are chiefly herbivorous—

milkfish, mullet, carp, and tilapia. These fish will eat some other fare. The milkfish, *Chanos chanos,* will eat both phytoplankton and zooplankton, and large *Chanos* will eat small shrimp in the ponds. Young *Chanos,* after capture, are fed rice flour or egg yolk. In these extensive brackish water ponds (tambaks) little fertilizer is used other than small amounts of green manure, because there is little available organic fertilizer and the low price of the product does not justify inorganic fertilizers, especially since the occasional necessity of draining the ponds would also drain away any dissolved substances. For this same reason pond owners are encouraged to capture their large shrimp from the ponds with fyke nets rather than by the easier method of attracting them by outflowing water.

The importance of the trophic level is emphasized by the necessity of removing as many as possible of all predator species, since their often higher price does not compensate for the fish destroyed. Schuster (1949) found that a 5-inch giant perch (slipmouth), *Lates calcarifer,* one of the principal predators in tambaks, consumed 242 *Chanos* fry in 24 hours in an aquarium.

Niches occupied

The particular habitat normally occupied by a species is of some importance in selecting an organism amenable to any particular type of mariculture. Under artificial conditions some species show adaptability, e.g., catfish, which normally are bottom feeders, quickly learn to feed on the surface.

Attached or nonmotile species have the distinct advantage of not requiring any enclosure, so they may be reared in natural waters. It has been amply demonstrated that the filter-feeding mollusks grow much faster when suspended in the water column than when spread over the bottom. This has at least two other advantages: it protects the mollusks from nonswimming predators and it permits fuller use of the water column so that a great many more individuals can be reared over the same area. Furthermore, it permits the rearing of mollusks in areas with

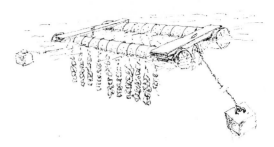

Fig. 16-2. Type of small oyster culture raft used in British Columbia for raising *Crassostrea gigas.* (From Quayle, D. B. 1971. Fish. Res. Bd. Canada, Bull. **178:**1-34.)

water too deep or bottom too soft for conventional bottom culture.

Quayle (1971) states that in British Columbia bottom culture of the Pacific (Japanese) oyster, *Crassostrea gigas,* may produce 2000 pounds of meats per acre per year, but raft culture is capable of producing more than 10 times this amount. He lists the advantages of raft culture (Fig. 16-2) over bottom culture as:

1. More rapid growth
2. Better condition
3. Better flavor
4. No predators
5. Tidal independence
6. Higher production per unit area
7. Better survival

Oysters are also sometimes grown in trays suspended above the bottom. In areas too shoal for suspending long enough strings of oysters from rafts to make it economically feasible, oysters are sometimes grown on sticks thrust into the bottom or on many short strings suspended from wooden racks.

Nonswimming motile organisms such as lobsters usually prefer a firm substrate. Lobsters require more space than bivalves, and the tendency toward cannibalism needs to be overcome. Along the New England coast lobsters are kept in walled-off coves with screened openings to permit the inflow and outflow of the tides. However, this is really a storage operation and is most often used to hold lobsters for a better market.

Swimming crabs, shrimp, and fish must

be confined in tanks, ponds, fenced areas, or floating enclosures. The latter may vary from small cages to large enclosures for such active fishes as yellowtail.

Genetic control possibilities

Genetic control is of great importance in agriculture in developing strains of animals best suited for the production of a desired product, whether it be beef or milk, wool or mutton. Strains of cattle have been bred for resistance to heat or cold, rapid growth, and high food conversion.

The same type of genetic control is not only desirable but perhaps necessary if culture of any particular marine species is to prove economically feasible.

Temperature restrictions

Under natural conditions most marine organisms have a restricted temperature range. Even within their range of tolerance they may be under stress as they approach their tolerance limits. Unless or until it is possible to extend this range, it is impractical to attempt rearing organisms in unsuitable temperatures.

Spiny lobsters, pompano, and tilapia are tropical to semitropical species easily subject to winterkill. The risk of losing an entire pond of fish in one cold snap is too great to make it worthwhile to culture them in an area of occasional winter freezes. The reverse is true of the northern lobster and most of the salmonids. Temperature may also restrict reproduction, e.g., the American oyster does not spawn successfully every year as far north as southern New England.

The temperature requirements for a particular species are not inflexible. In salmonids, for instance, the same species occurs from the Arctic to the subtropics, and there can be little doubt that the southern stocks of these species are far more adapted to elevated temperatures than the northern stocks. In discussing warmwater pond culture in Spain, Gaudet states:

Experiments were also carried out in the culture of rainbow trout (*Salmo gairdneri*) and common trout (*Salmo trutta*) at high temperature (average monthly temperature of 26.9° C. ((80.2° F)) with a maximum of 29° C. ((84.2° F))....

The culture of trout in warm water is made possible by the oversaturation of oxygen of the water, with the use of aquatic plants covering 40 percent of the pond area, with abundant sunshine and shallow water.*

The temperature restrictions on trout and salmon rearing given by Liao and Mayo (1972) are much more stringent. They propose the following limits:

Trout and Pacific salmons
  Adults
    Optimum: 28° to 55° F
    Lethal values: below 30° F, above 75° F
  Fingerlings
    Seriously detrimental: over 6 hours at 65° F, over 48 hours at 60° F
Atlantic salmon
  Adults
    Optimum: 50° to 65° F
    Lethal values: below 31° F, above 80° F
  Fingerlings
    Seriously detrimental: over 6 hours at 80° F, over 48 hours at 75° F

These values are decidedly different from those of Gaudet for rearing rainbow and brown trout in Spain. It is my opinion that Liao and Mayo's values can easily be exceeded on the high side when oxygen levels are also high. In Maine I have caught Atlantic salmon parr on artificial flies in riffle areas when the water temperature exceeded 90° F.

Salinity restrictions on reproduction

Salinity requirements for successful reproduction are important. The salmonids reproduce in fresh water, but the young can soon be acclimated to brackish and even full salinity water, where they grow much more rapidly than when confined to fresh water. The ability to breed for desired traits by holding brood stock is largely responsible for the rapid increase of this commercial salmon and trout culture using brackish and saline rearing ponds. Milne (1972) describes both the floating and alongshore net

*From Gaudet, J. L. 1967. The status of warmwater pond fish culture in Europe. FAO Fish. Rep. **44**:70-87.

enclosures used to hold the salmon in Norway and Britain. A Marine Fisheries Review editorial (1973a) states that in Norway 70 to 80 of these salmon farms are operating and have raised salmon in 3 years using capelin for food. The price in Norway is reported as $1.75/pound ($3.84/ kilo). According to the Sport Fishing Institute (1972), the salmon cost 81 cents/ pound to raise. Two men raise 50 tons in 2 years or 12½ tons/man year, the fish weighing 4 to 8 pounds apiece. Iceland is experimenting with water heated by thermal springs to speed the growth of smolts.

Some species reproduce readily in estuarine situations, whereas others spawn in waters of high salinity. Both of these facts have a bearing on the suitability of sites for the culture of certain species. For stenohaline species requiring high salinity two choices are available: a coastal site where high salinity prevails or an entirely closed system in which the salinity can be controlled. For quasi-catadromous species an estuarine site can be used if either wild young can be captured or if adults can be induced to spawn under artificial conditions, perhaps with pituitary extracts.

ECONOMIC FACTORS

In considering the feasibility of mariculture one must weigh a number of factors in addition to whether or not the rearing of a particular organism is biologically practical. As in any business venture profit depends largely on the amount of margin (if any) between gross sales and costs. Failure to fully recognize all of the costs can result in unexpected losses. There are also certain inherent risks that need to be considered. If not readily evaluated there must be at least provision made for the accumulation of reserve funds to counteract unexpected expenses. These risks may occur sporadically, such as hurricane flooding, disease outbreaks, or failure to obtain sufficient young stock.

Selection of the best site for a mariculture farm entails several factors. The physical and chemical factors are necessarily interwoven with the species it is desired to culture. In many cases they may dictate the species that can be reared.

The first question concerns the use of natural waters vs a closed system. Considering the use of natural waters, in coastal areas of gently sloping shore, low tidal range, and sporadic hurricane tides seaside ponds are subject to occasional inundation and consequent loss of motile species. One solution is to maintain motile species in fenced portions of natural waters or in smaller floating enclosures of netting.

Pollution is a hazard in utilizing natural waters. If present pollution levels are low, one should consider whether the site is in any potential danger of pollution from future development of the area.

After consideration of the costs and hazards of a site it should be compared with the costs of construction and maintenance of a closed system. It is necessary to carefully calculate the cost of pumping water and constructing the ponds. Perhaps ponds could be constructed at a sufficient elevation to avoid losses from high tides and hurricanes. The factor of space can be of overriding importance. However, if the item to be cultured can be sold at a profit using artificial feeds, then the closed system has several advantages over the use of natural waters. The chief advantage of the ponds is the ability to exercise better control over salinity levels. One of the other advantages is the usual tremendous difference in cost between upland and seashore real estate.

In considering the use of natural waters vs a closed system one must include the costs of labor for pond maintenance and the cost of harvesting. Large areas of natural waters or even very large ponds may require floating equipment.

In deciding on the species to be cultured it is necessary to consider the purpose, which is to make a profit. This means that the fish, crustacean, or mollusk must be acceptable to the public. In fact unless one can afford the expense of developing a nonexistent market, it must be a product that the consumer regards highly and is willing to pay for. If the current price is high, one should decide whether the market is large enough to absorb a reasonable quantity without affecting the price.

The degree of processing the product will require before it is ready for marketing can be important. Will quick-freezing and storage facilities be necessary or would these services be provided and at what cost? Merely harvesting the raw product out of the ponds and turning it over to a processor is the same as making dockside deliveries from a vessel and may command only the dockside price. By the freshness and careful

Table 16-3. Examples of economics of aquaculture in ponds*

Item	Examples (numbers from Pillay)					
	I	*III*	*IV*	*V*	*VI*	*VIII*
Organism	Rainbow trout	Carp	Carp	Mullet and carp	Milkfish	Catfish
Country	Ireland	Poland	India	Hong Kong	Philippines	U. S.
Area used						
Acres	35.0	1,371.4	8.6	2.5	12.4	160.0
Hectares	14.2	555.0	3.5	1.0	5.0	64.8
Monetary unit	Pound	Zloty	Rupee	U. S. dollar	Peso	U. S. dollar
Capital investment						
Land	18,000	(30,414)[1]	40,000	(37,500)[2]	150,000	62,370
Ponds	17,000	18,659	49,000	19,000	27,250	50,830
Equipment	(1,854)[3]	6,667	1,022	4,011	470	22,190
TOTAL CAPITAL INVESTMENT	36,854	55,740	90,022	60,511	177,720	135,390
Direct operating costs						
Feed and fertilizer	6,000	1,904	2,644	6,307	5,419	22,900
Labor	2,000	1,172	14,900	1,938	1,234	4,750
Transport to market	1,000		476			(3,849)[4]
Harvesting	(114)[4]			(1,078)[4]	(2,204)[4]	4,380
Maintenance and repair	200	314	140	1,923	750	(1,095)[5]
Depreciation	800	465				5,552
Stock of young	1,500	74	20,000	1,123	4,500	16,300
Pesticides and materials		10				3,628
Unspecified costs		418	7,150	501	84	1,727
TOTAL OPERATING COST	11,614	4,357	45,310	12,870	14,191	64,181
Land rental at 8%[6]	1,440	2,433	3,200	3,000	12,000	4,990
Pond amortization at 10%[6]	1,700	1,866	4,900	1,900	2,725	5,083
Equipment insurance[7]	22	80	12	48	6	258
TOTAL ANNUAL EXPENSE	14,776	8,736	53,422	17,818	28,922	74,512
GROSS SALES	24,000	5,665	58,400	23,692	27,068	102,200
PROFIT BEFORE TAXES[8]						
Plus	9,224		4,978	5,874		27,688
Minus		3,071			1,854	

*Modified from Pillay, T. V. R. 1973. J. Fish. Res. Bd. Canada **30**:2202-2217; see footnotes and text for amendments and additions.

[1]Based on geometric mean ratio of land to pond cost.
[2]Based on $3,000 land rental as constituting 8% of land value.
[3]Based on geometric mean ratio of equipment cost to land cost.
[4]Based on geometric mean ratio of transport plus labor to gross sales.
[5]Based on geometric mean ratio of cost of maintenance plus repair to cost of ponds plus equipment.
[6]Additions to reflect the cost of the capital invested.
[7]Used insurance rate of the Mississippi, U. S. example, which is 1.2% of equipment.
[8]No managerial salaries are shown; if owner also works on farm his salary must come out of profits.

Table 16-4. Economics of brackish water ponds for fish and shrimp in India*

	Their figures (per ha)		My figures (U. S. dollars)	
	Rupees	U. S. dollars	Per ha	Per acre
Capital investment				
Land	6,000	833	833	336
Pond construction	10,000	1,389	1,389	562
Sluices	1,000	139	139	56
Farm buildings	1,100	153	153	62
Farm equipment	1,400	194	194	79
TOTAL	19,500	2,708	2,708	1,095
Annual operating costs				
Fish seed	250	35	35	14
Fertilizers	635	88	88	36
Feeds	120	17	17	7
Wages	1,440	200	200	81
Pond preparation and maintenance	250	35	35	14
Transport	75	10	10	4
Miscellaneous	200	28	28	11
TOTAL	2,970	413	413	167
Depreciation				
Equipment and sluices, 20%			167	68
Buildings and ponds, 10%			154	62
Land rental at 8%			67	27
Communications			10	4
Loan for ½ annual operating cost at 8%			238	96
Managerial salary			300	121
TOTAL ANNUAL EXPENSE			1,349	545
TOTAL PRODUCTION: 1,500 kg/ha 607 kg or 1,335 pounds/acre				
GROSS SALES: 4 rupees/kg (25.3¢/pound)	6,000	833	833	336
NET RETURN	3,030	421		
LOSS BEFORE TAXES			516	209

*Modified from Jhingran, V. G., and V. Gopalakrishnan. 1973. J. Fish. Res. Bd. Canada **30:**2341-2345.

handling of the product a premium price may be obtained.

After deciding what species are sufficiently in demand and command a high enough price to offer hope of a profit, the costs of raising each species must be considered. From the foregoing it is obvious that the cost of raising a pound of each organism will vary considerably, both between species and between culture methods.

In evaluating cost of artificial feed the interactions between percent of protein in the diet, quantity fed, and stocking rate must be known. In feeding catfish (Hastings, 1971) there was a linear response in growth both to percent of protein (25%, 30%, and 35%) and percent of body weight fed (2%, 4%, and 6%). Equal growth resulted from feeding 25% protein at 6% and 35% protein at 4%.

Stocking rate experiments were carried out in which Hastings fed 2%, 4%, and 6% of body weight at 1000, 2000, and 4000 catfish/acre; at all three stocking rates more feed produced more fish, but the 4% level produced the highest profit. The 2% rate did not assure sufficient feed for each fish, whereas at 6% there was excess food that actually caused water quality stress.

Mariculture may be suffering from glowing accounts of its profitability that tempt people into ventures that offer little chance of success. The latest word from the FAO by Pillay (1973) gives 11 examples of aquaculture ventures for which he purports to show "cost-benefit" data. Every one of the 11 is ostensibly making from a reasonable to a handsome profit. In Table 16-3 I show six of the eight examples that use pond culture, and I attempt to make estimates of some costs that his data unaccountably fail to show. The two examples he gives of shrimp farms in Japan and Thailand with no information on size or capital investment I have discarded as useless.

I show (if my estimates are even approximately correct) that two of the six remaining pond culture ventures are failing, one is on the border line, and three appear to be making a reasonable profit (if the lack of information on the tax bite or on managerial salaries is ignored). The tiny size of some of the farms he uses as examples obviously means that they are devoid of much utility in determining what to expect on a scale large enough to be called a viable business venture. The only large farm that he gives any data on (555 hectares) is apparently state owned, and its operation bears no relation to commercial reality.

Unfortunately, Pillay failed to show the quantity and price of the fishes reared. The two examples of pond-reared fish that appear to show a reasonable profit—rainbow trout and catfish—command a higher price than carp or mullet and probably more than milkfish. In the United States mariculture is hampered by the low price that can be obtained for the product in relation to the high cost of labor. For instance Mock (1973) states that in Tokyo live shrimp were selling for $7 to $30/kg, although the average price was $10 to $11/kg. Production costs were about $7/kg. This is a higher price than U. S. fishermen are receiving and so, to be realistic, one must plan to raise shrimp much cheaper than they do in Japan where labor costs are very much lower.

Another instance of peculiar accounting is contained in Jhingran and Gopalakrishnan (1973) in which they estimate (very optimistically) the profit to be expected per

hectare of brackish water pond in India by raising fish and prawns. In Table 16-4 I give their figures plus my own calculations.

The authors state that these are expected levels of production and expenditure and that the return on capital investment of about 15% appears attractive!

Suggested readings

Bardach, J. E., J. H. Ryther, and W. O. McLarney. 1972. Aquaculture: the farming and husbandry of freshwater and marine organisms. Wiley-Interscience, Div. John Wiley & Sons, Inc., New York. 868 pp.

Broom, J. 1971. Shrimp culture. In Proceedings of the first annual workshop, World Mariculture Society. pp. 63-68.

Donaldson, L. R. 1971. Selective breeding of salmonid fishes. In Proceedings of the second annual workshop, World Mariculture Society. pp. 75-83.

Gaudet, J. L. 1967. The status of warm-water pond fish culture in Europe. FAO Fish. Rep. **44**:70-87.

Hastings, W. H. 1971. Fish feeds. In Proceedings of the first annual workshop, World Mariculture Society. pp. 118-126.

Hublou, W. F. 1963. Oregon pellets. Prog. Fish-Cult. **25**:175-180.

Kuo, C., Z. E. Shehadeh, and C. E. Nash. 1973. Induced spawning of captive grey mullet (Mugil cephalus L.) females by injection of human chorionic gonadotropin (HCG). Aquaculture **1**:429-432.

Loosanoff, V. L., and H. C. Davis. 1963. Rearing of bivalve mollusks. (Reprint.) Adv. Mar. Biol. **1**:1-136.

Martino, P. A., and J. M. Marchello. 1968. Using waste heat for fish farming. Ocean Ind. **3**:37-39.

May, R. C. 1971. An annotated bibliography of attempts to rear the larvae of marine fishes in the laboratory. NOAA Tech. Rep., Nat. Mar. Fish. Serv., Spec. Sci. Rep. Fish. **632**:1-24.

Mayer, A. G. 1914. The effects of temperature upon tropical marine animals. Pap. Tortugas Lab. **6**:1-24.

Mertz, E. T. 1969. Amino acid and protein requirements of fish. In Neuhaus, O., editor. Fish in research. Academic Press, Inc., New York. pp. 233-244.

Milne, P. H. 1972. Fish and shellfish farming in coastal waters. Fishing News (Books), London. 208 pp.

Pillay, T. V. R. 1973. The role of aquaculture in fishery development and management. J. Fish. Res. Bd. Canada **30**:2202-2217.

Quayle, D. B. 1971. Pacific oyster raft culture in British Columbia. Fish. Res. Bd. Canada, Bull. **178**:1-34.

Schuster, W. H. 1949. Fish-culture in brackish-water ponds of Java. (First published under the title De Viscultuur in de Kustvijers op Java as publication No. 2 of Inland Fisheries Division of the Agricultural Service of Department of Agriculture and Fisheries, Indonesia; translated from Dutch in 1952.) Published in English as Spec. Publ. No. 1, Indo-Pacific Fisheries Council. pp. 1-143.

Tamura, T. 1970. Marine aquaculture, ed. 2. (Translated from Japanese in 1966.) PB 194051 T in two parts. National Science Foundation, Office of Technical Services, U. S. Department of Commerce, Springfield, Va.

Tilton, J. E., and J. E. Kelley. 1971. Experimental cage culture of channel catfish in heated discharge water. In Proceedings of the first annual workshop, World Mariculture Society. pp. 73-87.

Tubb, J. A. 1967. Status of fish culture in Asia and the far east. FAO Fish. Rep. **44:**45-53.

part eight

❧ Life histories of
commercial species

chapter 17

Chief taxonomic groups and their relative importance

COMMERCIAL MARINE ORGANISMS

In describing the life histories of marine organisms I have tried to select North American examples. Because the life history of many species is imperfectly known, I have made a careful selection, picking out species or groups that exemplify different trophic levels, habitats, and modes of life. For each group one or more typical examples are described with notes on allied species or groups.

The systematic grouping of all commercial marine fauna is shown in Table 17-1. Obviously the table includes several groups of minor economic importance, including five of the eight phyla, i.e., Porifera, Coelenterata, Echinodermata, Annelida, and Urochorda. The three remaining phyla contain 11 classes, of which four are also of minor economic importance.

Only seven of the 18 classes in the eight phyla are of significant importance. Table 17-2 lists the 11 minor groups together with their worldwide production in 1970.

Some of the items of minor importance in Table 17-2 were formerly significant. The sponge industry once flourished on the west coast of Florida; Tarpon Springs was the home port for a large number of sponge vessels manned chiefly by the descendants of Greek sponge fishermen. Tons of sponges were sold at regular public auctions. As recently as 1945 the Tarpon Springs Sponge Exchange auctioned 194,000 pounds of sponges, taken by 76 diving vessels and 115 small hooking boats, for $2,716,000. By 1951 the landings had fallen to 11,683 pounds taken by two diving vessels and 13 hooking boats and worth only $82,128 (Storr, 1964). The industry disappeared from two main causes: the sponge disease epidemics that seriously depleted the sponges and the advent of cheap and acceptable artificial sponges. Perhaps a third factor was the disinclination of the younger generation to adopt the strenuous life of a diver. Today a very few vessels operate as tourist attractions.

Precious corals are used in the manufacture of semiprecious jewelry such as beads for necklaces, bracelets, or rosaries. They are also used for cameos, earrings, and the inlaid decoration of many objects. Coral formerly came chiefly from various parts of the Mediterranean Sea, but recently the chief source has been Taiwan, which in

Table 17-1. Commercial marine organisms grouped by larger taxa

Phylum	Class and subclass	Order and suborder	Chief items
Porifera	Demospongiae	Keratosa	Sponges
Coelenterata	Anthozoa	Gorgonacea	Precious corals
Echinodermata	Asteroidea		Starfishes
	Echinoidea		Sea urchins
	Holothurioidea		Sea cucumbers
Annelida	Chaetopoda		
	Polychaeta		Bait worms
			Palolo worms
Mollusca	Pelecypoda	Filibranchia	Mussels
		Lamellibranchia	Bivalves
	Gastropoda	Aspidobranchia	Abalones, limpets
		Pectinibranchia	Conchs
	Cephalopoda		
	Sepioidea		Cuttlefish
	Coleoidea	Teuthoidea	
		Myopsida	Neritic squids
		Oegopsida	Oceanic squids
		Octopoda	
		Incirrata	Octopi
Arthropoda	Crustacea		
	Malacostraca	Decapoda	
		Natantia	Shrimps
		Reptantia	Crabs, lobsters
	Arachnida	Xiphosura	Horseshoe crab
Urochorda	Tunicata	Ascidiacea	Sea squirts
Vertebrata	Cyclostomata	Petromyzontes	Sea lampreys
	Elasmobranchii		
	Selachii	Squali	Sharks
		Raji	Skates and rays
	Holocephali		Chimaeras
	Pisces		Bony fishes
	Reptilia	Chelonia	Turtles, tortoises
		Crocodilini	Crocodiles
		Squamata	Sea snake leather
	Aves		Guano
	Mammalia	Carnivora	Sea otters
		Pinnipedia	
		Otarioidea	Sea lions, fur seals, walrus
		Phocoidea	Seals, elephant seals
		Sirenia	Manatees, dugongs
		Cetacea	
		Odontoceti	Toothed whales, dolphins
		Mysticeti	Baleen whales

1969 produced 100 metric tons worth $4,410,000, or about $20/pound ($44/kg). In 1970 the quantity was less and the value was $1,838,000. Red coral commands the highest price followed by black coral and white coral, in that order.

Red coral, *Corallium rubrum,* is found only in various parts of the Mediterranean Sea and around the Cape Verde Islands, whereas numerous other species of *Corallium,* including black coral, are available worldwide in tropical and subtropical seas.

Whereas the tropical reef-building corals do not live below about 20 fm (37 m), the precious corals (treelike in appearance) are usually taken in fairly deep water.

Table 17-2. World production of classes of minor importance, 1970

Class	Item	Metric tons (thousands)	Principal sources
Demospongiae	Sponges, *Spongia* and *Hippospongia*	0.2	Greece, Tunisia
Anthozoa	Precious corals, *Corallium*	0.1	Taiwan
Asteroidea	Starfish, *Asterias rubens*	4.7	West Germany, Denmark, Netherlands
Echinoidea	Sea urchins, *Strongylocentrotus*	27.3	Japan, Taiwan
	Sea urchins, *Loxechinus albus*	4.0	Chile
Holothurioidea	Sea cucumbers, *Stichopus japonicus*	12.8	Japan, Korea
	Sea cucumbers, other	4.2	Western Pacific, Indian Oceans
Chaetopoda	Bloodworms, *Glycera dibranchiata*	0.4	Northeastern United States
	Sandworms, *Neanthes*	0.3	Northeastern United States
	Palolo worms, *Eunice viridis*	0.0	Oceania
Arachnida	Horseshoe crab, *Limulus polyphemus*	0.1	United States (Atlantic)
Tunicata	Sea squirt, edible, *Pyura chilensis*	4.0	Chile
	Sea squirt, grooved, *Microcosmus sulcatus*	1.0	Northeastern Atlantic, Mediterranean
Cyclostomata	Sea lamprey,[1] *Petromyzon marinus*	0.0	United States
Reptilia	Terrapins, *Malaclemmys* spp.	0.0	Americas (Atlantic)
	Turtles, green *Chelonia mydas*	0.5	United States to Venezuela
	Chelonia spp.	6.0	Worldwide
	Turtles, hawksbill, *Eretmochelys imbricata*	0.2	Cuba
	Turtles, loggerhead, *Caretta caretta*	0.5	United States to Venezuela
	Marine crocodiles	0.0	Southwestern Pacific
	Sea snakes,[2] *Laticauda calubrina*	0.0	Philippines
Aves	Guano (and eggs)	51.7	Peru
		4.5	South Africa
		0.3	Argentina

[1]Last U. S. catches noted from Pacific coast in 1949 of *Entosphenus tridentatus.*
[2]Skins exported for fancy leather.

According to Tressler and Lemon (1951), the Algerian coral beds lie 6 to 8 miles offshore in 90 to 900 feet (27 to 274 m) of water; the average depth of the Sicilian beds is 650 feet (198 m); in southwestern Japan the coral grows on rocks 30 to 100 fm (55 to 183 m) deep.

The starfish landings must have been used for industrial purposes, most probably for calcium in poultry rations, as they brought only about $11/metric ton.

The dried body wall of the sea cucumber is sold as trepang or more commonly as bêche-de-mer (a French rendition of bichodo-mar, Portuguese for sea slug). According to Beardsley (1971), premium grade bêche-de-mer brings up to $2/pound in Singapore and Hong Kong. He states that there are about 100 known species of sea cucumbers in Truk Lagoon. Three species have commercial value: the black teatfish, *Actinopyga nobilis;* the prickly redfish, *Thalenota aranas;* and the tigerfish, *Holothuria argus.* They are prepared by boiling in water for an hour, then removing the viscera and drying on racks in a drying house at 80° to 85° C for 2 days.

The value of sea urchins is not given but is undoubtedly high, as the roe is a gourmet item.

The Polychaeta include bait worms and the unique palolo worms. The palolo worm,

Eunice viridis, lives in burrows among the coral reefs of the southwest Pacific. Once a year their posterior segments fill with eggs or sperm. Their swarming commences on the first day of the last quarter of the October-November moon and continues for a few days. The anterior end of the worm remains in its burrow, but it casts off the posterior segments, which float to the surface. These wriggling segments, about $\frac{1}{16} \times 12$ inches (1.5×300 mm), are considered a delicacy by the inhabitants of Oceania. The segments reach the surface in enormous quantities a little before sunrise. At sunrise the segments burst and the eggs are fertilized.

Bait worms are worth far more than their volume would indicate. In 1969 they averaged $2.13/pound, about $4700/metric ton. They thus bring between $2 and $3 million/year to New England fishermen.

The horseshoe crab, sole representative of the Arachnida, is an anachronism I have included to illustrate the great variety of life in the sea. In 1969 10,600 pounds taken by otter trawls in Connecticut sold for $1167, or 11 cents/pound. They are of no value as a direct food item but can be used for reduction, and a certain number are used as curios.

The only figure available on the value of sea squirts is $364/metric ton in France. No data are available as to how they are prepared for market.

The last recorded catch of sea lamprey in the United States was a few from the Columbia River in 1949 where they were used for reduction. In colonial days salted lamper eels were a staple commodity along the Atlantic seaboard. One English king is reputed to have died from indigestion as a result of surfeiting himself on his favorite dish, pickled lampreys.

The reptiles are represented by three orders—Chelonia, the turtles; Crocodilini, the crocodiles and alligators; and Squamata, the sea snakes.

The terrapin, which in 1970 produced less than 100 metric tons from the United States to Venezuela, was once important along the Atlantic and Gulf coasts of the United States

from New Jersey to Texas. In the period 1918 to 1921 (figures available for different years in different states) the annual production of terrapin had already fallen to 43,302 pounds valued at $16,444 for this stretch of coast. The Bureau of Fisheries began experiments in 1909 at Beaufort, North Carolina, to rear terrapins for liberation (Hildebrand, 1929). It was discovered that the females on the average lay only about 12 eggs/year. The terrapin grows so slowly that the project was eventually terminated. The small proportion (about 20%) of males in all of the pure stocks raised from several species of terrapin grew even slower than the females, rarely reaching a length of 4 inches.

During this same period of time (1918 to 1921) the annual landings of other marine turtles along the U. S. Atlantic and Gulf coasts were about 150,000 pounds. An additional 12,500 pounds of Mexican turtles were landed in California. Presently most marine turtles are endangered species, chiefly because of the difficulty of protecting them when they come ashore to lay their eggs in sandy beaches.

Marine crocodiles exist in the southwestern Pacific. However, the alligators along the Gulf and South Atlantic coasts that habitually sojourn along the shores of brackish water estuaries and bayous might be classed as semimarine.

The class Aves contributes both guano and eggs. Guano deposits were once one of the chief sources of income in Peru, where it was mined and sold for fertilizer. The guano birds and their rookeries are jealously guarded by the government.

MAMMALIA

Referring back to Table 17-1 there remain only seven classes that contain all of the fauna of major economic importance: Pelecypoda, Gastropoda, Cephalopoda, Crustacea, Elasmobranchii, Pisces, and Mammalia. The worldwide landings of these groups are covered in Chapter 6 on world fisheries except for the Mammalia, which I present in Table 17-3.

Table 17-3. World production of marine mammals, 1970*

Order and subgroup	Item	Number	Principal source
Carnivora			
Sea otter	*Enhydra lutris*	0	North Pacific and Bering Sea (protected)
Pinnipedia			
Otarioidea, walking seals			
Fur seal			
North Pacific	*Callorhinus ursinus*	42,228	Pribilof Islands (U. S.)
		16,306	Commander, Kurile, and Robben Islands (U.S.S.R.)
South American	*Arctocephalus australis*	11,940	Uruguay
Cape	*Arctocephalus pusillus*	81,550	South Africa
Sea lion			
South American	*Otario byronia*	2,950	Uruguay
Steller	*Eumetopias jubata*	?	Entire North Pacific, used by natives for food and hides
Walrus	*Odobenus rosmarus*	?	Arctic, adjacent seas[1]
Phocoidea, crawling seals			
Harp seal	*Pagophilus groenlandicus*	294,555	Canada and Norway
Bearded seal	*Erignathus barbatus*	596	Norway[2]
Ringed seal	*Pusa hispida*	16	Norway[3]
Hooded seal	*Cystophora cristata*	46,713	Norway and Canada
Elephant seal	*Mirounga*	0	(protected)
Sirenia			
Steller sea cow	*Hydrodamalis gigas*	0	Exterminated by 1768
Manatee			
Amazon	*Trichechus inunguis*	0.1[4]	Brazil
Caribbean	*Trichechus manatus*	0	
Cetacea			
Odontoceti, toothed cetaceans			
Dolphin	*Phocoena phocoena*	0.3[4]	Taiwan
	Phocoena phocoena relicta	8.3[4]	Turkey
Beluga (white whale)	*Delphinapterus leucas*	948	Greenland
		178	Hudson Bay[5]
Narwhal	*Monodon monoceros*	?	Greenland Canada[6]
Pilot whale	*Globicephala melaena*	586	Newfoundland to Norway
		152	Japan
Killer whale	*Orcinus orca*	276	Worldwide
Bottle-nosed whale	*Hyperoodon ampullatus*	535	Norway (North Atlantic)

*Data from Food and Agriculture Organization. 1971. Yearbook of fishery statistics for 1970. **30:** 1-476; Kerswill, C. J., and J. G. Hunter. 1970. J. Fish. Res. Bd. Canada **13:**357-374; and Smith, T. G. 1973. Fish. Res. Bd. Canada, Bull. **181:**1-55.

[1]About 280 walrus/year taken by Eskimos in northern Hudson Bay and northern Foxe Basin.

[2]Less than 1,000 bearded seals/year taken by Eskimos in southern Labrador and the Gulf of St. Lawrence.

[3]About 20,000 to 70,000 ringed seals taken annually by Eskimos; see text for Baffin Island take.

[4]Metric tons.

[5]Annual Canadian take of beluga whales about 650 in western Hudson Bay, about 150 in Cumberland and Jones Sounds, and about 200 in the Mackenzie River delta.

[6]About 200 narwhal/year taken by Eskimos along north and east coasts of Baffin Islands.

[7]About 10 bowhead whales are taken annually at Point Hope and Point Barrow, Alaska, by Eskimos for food. This whale was once considered extinct but is now reappearing in small numbers.

Continued.

Table 17-3. World production of marine mammals, 1970—cont'd

Order and subgroup	Item	Number	Principal source
Other beaked whales	*Ziphius, Mesoplodon*	113	Japan
Sperm whale	*Physeter catodon*	22,752	Antarctica
		3,090	Other seas
Mysticeti, baleen whales			
Greenland right whale or bowhead	*Balaena mysticetus*	?	Arctic Alaska[7]
Gray whale	*Eschrichtius gibbosus*	?	North Pacific
Rorquals			
Blue whale	*Balaenoptera musculus*	0	Protected
Bryde whale	*Balaenoptera edeni*	144	Warm seas
Finback whale	*Balaenoptera physalus*	3,002	Antarctica
		2,005	Other seas
Humpback whale	*Megaptera novaeangliae*	3	Antarctica
Minke whale	*Balaenoptera acutorostrata*	3,616	All oceans
Sei whale	*Balaenoptera borealis*	5,194	Antarctica
		5,857	Other seas
Unspecified whales		172	Other than Antarctica

Carnivora

The first order of Mammalia is the Carnivora, which includes the sea otter. This remarkable creature, once abundant from the Kurile Islands to California, was the prime cause for Russian settlement in Alaska and their establishment of Fort Ross just north of San Francisco. The near extinction of the sea otter combined with the enormous decline of the fur seal herds caused their interest to wane and they sold their empire.

Pinnipedia

The Pinnipedia are divided into two superfamilies—the Otarioidea, or walking seals, and the Phocoidea, or crawling seals. The Otarioidea include several species of fur seals. Those on some of the smaller islands were quickly exterminated, but large herds of northern fur seal haul out on the Pribilof Islands (St. Paul, St. George, Otter, and Walrus Islands, and Sea Lion Rock); on the Commander Islands (Bering and Copper [Medny] Islands) on the Soviet end of the Aleutian chain; and on Robben Island (Tyuleniy Island or Kaihyo To) off the eastern shore of Sakhalin Island. Small colonies became reestablished on a few of the Kurile Islands in the 1950's and they reappeared on San Miguel Island off southern California about 1968.

There are several species of the southern fur seals, *Arctocephalus*. Many of the subspecies or races are extinct. They once ranged as far north as the Farallon Islands off San Francisco, but now the most northern group is a small colony on Guadalupe Island off Baja California. Other species occur and are harvested from islands off Uruguay and South Africa. Still other species occur from Australia and New Zealand to the Falkland Islands and other subantarctic islands and on the Galapagos Islands.

Sea lions of three genera occur from Japan to California, south to Cape Horn, and north to Brazil. A fourth genus lives south of Australia and New Zealand.

The walrus, also of the superfamily Otarioidea, lives only in the Arctic and adjacent seas. Although not taken commercially, it is the mainstay of some isolated Eskimo groups such as those on St. Lawrence Island who depend on walrus for meat, hides, and the ivory tusks they employ in native carving.

The Phocoidea, or crawling seals, are also known as the "earless" seals. The best known is the harp seal of the North Atlantic, which Norwegian and Canadian sealers kill on the pack ice. The newborn pups are especially sought for their fur. The sealers also take large numbers of the hooded seal, which is related to the elephant seal. The ringed seal of the Arctic Sea and adjacent seas has closely related species in Lake Baikal and the Caspian Sea. Despite FAO statistics showing only 16 ringed seals taken in 1970, I note that Smith (1973) shows that at only two trading posts—Cumberland Sound and Home Bay on the eastern shore of Baffin Island—the Eskimos traded an average of 12,850 ringed seal pelts from 1961 through 1969, with a 1969 take of 16,127 pelts.

Sirenia

An interesting order of Mammalia is the Sirenia or sea cows, often believed to be the sailors' mythical mermaids. Of the few species, the great northern sea cow, or Steller sea cow, first discovered in 1741, was exterminated by 1768 from the two islands it was known to inhabit, Bering and Copper Islands, in the western Bering Sea. The manatee exists in small numbers in the lower reaches of a few Florida streams. A related species inhabits the Amazon and Orinoco Rivers. The dugong exists in a few localities in the Indian Ocean and the western Pacific. Sea cows have attracted attention as a possible means of controlling aquatic vegetation without the use of chemicals.

Cetacea

The most interesting order of marine mammals is the Cetacea. The slaughter of this group of giant mammals is a dismal story of the failure of international cooperation. The Cetacea are divided into two great groups—the suborder Odontoceti, or toothed cetaceans, and the suborder Mysticeti, or baleen whales.

The toothed cetaceans include a few river dolphins, a large number of ocean dolphins, a few beaked whales, and the sperm whales. I will dismiss the river dolphins. The common dolphin or harbor porpoise is widespread, and some are taken for their oil in Turkey and Taiwan.

The beluga or white whale is widespread in the Arctic and adjacent seas and is the object of fisheries in Hudson Bay and off Greenland. In the Pacific it ranges as far south as Cook Inlet. I have observed schools of beluga chasing schools of herring in shallow-mouthed Halibut Cove Lagoon off Kachemak Bay.

The pilot whale and the killer whale, somewhat larger than most of the numerous species of ocean dolphins, are often harpooned for their oil. The beaked whales comprise a number of species but are nowhere abundant; a few are taken.

The most important of the toothed cetaceans is the sperm whale, which is found in all oceans. Since the slaughter of the major portion of the former herds of baleen whales, the sperm whale is now the major remaining target.

The baleen whales do not possess teeth; instead their upper jaw has great thin plates that strain the macroscopic zooplankton and small fishes from the water. These whalebone plates (baleen) were once split for supports in ladies' corsets.

There are three families—the right whales, the gray whales, and the rorquals. The right whale acquired its name in the early days of whaling as the "right" whale to harpoon. A few still exist in the North Pacific; the Greenland right whale is rare or perhaps extinct.

The gray whale is extinct in the North Atlantic. In the Pacific an effort is being made to save them; the Mexican government is protecting them in Scammon Lagoon and other shallow coastal lagoons in which they breed.

The third group of baleen whales is the rorquals, which are the targets of the Antarctic whaling expeditions. As shown in Table 17-3, the blue whale (the world's largest creature and on the verge of extinction for a long time [Fig. 17-1]) was entirely protected in 1970. Long after the virtual end of the blue whale, the International Whaling Commission still sets whaling quotas called "blue whale units" in which a unit is 1 blue whale, or 2 fin whales, or 2.5 humpback whales, or 6 sei whales. This fiction disguises

Fig. 17-1. An 86-foot blue whale at the shore station at Akutan, Alaska, in 1928.

Table 17-4. Catches of sperm whales and Antarctic baleen whales, 1868 to 1966*

Item	Sperm whales	Baleen whales					Grand total
		Blue	Finback	Humpback	Sei	Total	
Number of whales × 10³	435	365	840	172	186	1,563	1,998
Individual weight (metric tons)	40	100	50	40	20	57.0	53.3
Total weight (metric tons × 10⁶)	17.4	36.5	42.0	6.9	3.7	89.1	106.5
Annual weight (metric tons × 10⁶)	0.174	0.365	0.420	0.690	0.037	0.891	1.065
Annual number	4,350	3,650	8,400	1,720	1,860	15,630	19,980

*Modified from Moiseev, P. A. 1969. The living resources of the world ocean. (First published under the title Biologicheskie resursy Mirovogo okeana; translated from Russian in 1971.) IPST Cat. No. 5954, TT 71-50026. Published jointly by National Science Foundation and National Marine Fisheries Service. Nat. Tech. Inf. Serv., U. S. Department of Commerce, Springfield, Va. 334 pp.

the actual number of whales taken, which means that as one species disappears another is attacked. Perhaps the best way to illustrate how badly the whales are faring is to note that during the nine whaling seasons, 1963 through 1971, the quota of blue whale units has been progressively reduced from 15,000 to 2700. During the entire 9 years only once was the quota actually captured and then by a margin of only 12 units. Very clearly the quotas have always been set high enough to permit the slaughter to go on without hindrance.

The relative importance of whales in the world catch of living marine resources is outlined by Moiseev (1969), who shows the total catch of over a century, from 1866 through 1966. This has been modified somewhat in Table 17-4. This table is somewhat misleading, since it includes catches for many years before the advent of Antarctic whaling. Only a portion of the wide-ranging sperm whales were taken in Antarctica. Moiseev states that in Antarctica during the 60 years of whaling the take was 1,300,000 whales weighing about 65,000,000 metric tons. This would place the average annual take over the 60 years at 21,700 whales weighing about 1,083,000 metric tons.

These average figures by Moiseev fail to

portray the tremendous number taken during the height of the fishery and the subsequent rapid decline. For instance, in the single season of 1930 to 1931 over 25,000 blue whales alone were taken; by the 1950 to 1951 season this had fallen to 7000; by 1958 to 1959 it had dwindled to a mere 1200; and it ultimately fell so low (112 in 1963 to 1964) that protection of the blue whales was finally agreed on. The whalers tried to compensate for the lack of blue whales by turning to finbacks. From over 27,000 finbacks taken in 1960 to 1961, the catch had fallen to less than 2500 by 1965 to 1966, only a 5-year period (McVay, 1966).

Small (1971) states that in the early days of Antarctic whaling (which commenced in 1904 on the South Georgia Islands) a great many whales were killed and lost by the small slow killer boats then in use (he estimates the loss at about 20% of the whales killed until about 1925). In that year the first floating factory ship started to replace the land-based stations. In this early period of whaling the thick layer of body blubber was merely stripped off, the thinner layers on the head and flukes being ignored, and then everything else discarded.

I well recall the shock and outrage of seeing numbers of stripped whale carcasses floating in Port Hobron in the late 1920's. When whales became scarce recovery of the large amount of oil contained in the bones was started. Later whale meat became a staple in some countries. The Japanese especially have long depended on whale meat as a good source of animal protein.

FISHES

There are several opinions on the major groupings of living fishes; we shall not discuss them here. In general, ichthyologists recognize three major groups:

1. The lampreys and hagfishes, called Cyclostomata from the circular, jawless mouth. Some ichthyologists place them on an equal footing with all higher groups, calling them Agnatha from lack of jaws. Other ichthyologists separate the lampreys from the hagfishes.
2. The sharks, rays, and chimaeras, called Selachii, Elasmobranchii, or Chondrichthys from their cartilaginous skeletons. Some experts consider the chimaeras separately from the elasmobranchs and called them Holocephali.
3. The bony fishes, or Pisces. The bony fishes are usually divided into two or three main groups. The lungfishes and the lobefins (Coelocanths) form one or two groups, depending on the author. The bichirs or reedfishes are sometimes included in this group.

The remaining bony fishes form by far the greater portion of the fishes of commercial importance. To those interested in the details of classification I refer to Berg (1940) for the major groupings. The higher bony fishes are very numerous; estimates of the number of valid species vary from under 20,000 to over 40,000. The most modern attempt at a truly phyletic classification is by Greenwood et al. (1966), who list 413 families. Of this great number of families probably less than half are likely to be of commercial importance in the near future.

Suggested readings

Baker, R. C., F. Wilke, and C. H. Baltzo. 1970. The northern fur seal. U. S. Fish Wildl. Serv., Circ. **336**:1-21.

Berg, L. S. 1940. Classification of fishes both recent and fossil. (Reprinted by J. W. Edwards, Ann Arbor, Mich., 1947.) Trans. Inst. Zool. Acad. Sci. U.S.S.R. **5**:87-517.

Greenwood, P. H., D. E. Rosen, S. H. Weitzman, and G. S. Myers. 1966. Phyletic studies of teleostean fishes, with a provisional classification of living forms. Bull. Amer. Mus. Nat. Hist. **131**:341-455.

Hildebrand, S. F. 1929. Review of experiments on artificial culture of diamond-back terrapin. Doc. 1060. Bull. U. S. Bur. Fish. **45**:25-70.

McVay, S. 1966. The last of the great whales. Sci. Amer. **215**:13-21.

Moiseev, P. A. 1969. The living resources of the world ocean. (First published under the title Biologicheskie resursy Mirovogo okeana; translated from Russian in 1971.) IPST Cat. No.

5954, TT 71-50026. Published jointly by National Science Foundation and National Marine Fisheries Service. Nat. Tech. Inf. Serv., U. S. Department of Commerce, Springfield, Va. 334 pp.

Rice, D. W. 1967. Cetaceans. In Anderson, S., and J. K. Jones, editors. Recent mammals of the world: a synopsis of families, chap. 15. The Ronald Press Co. New York. pp. 291-324.

Scheffer, V. B., and D. W. Rice. 1963. A list of the marine mammals of the world. U. S. Fish Wildl. Serv., Spec. Sci. Rep. Fish. **431:** 1-12.

Small, G. L. 1971. The blue whale. Columbia University Press, New York. 248 pp.

Smith, T. G. 1973. Population dynamics of the ringed seal in the Canadian eastern Arctic. Fish. Res. Bd. Canada, Bull. **181:**1-55.

Storr, J. F. 1964. Ecology of the Gulf of Mexico commercial sponges and its relation to the fishery. U. S. Fish Wildl. Serv., Spec. Sci. Rep. Fish. **466:**1-73.

chapter 18

🌿 Life histories of anadromous salmons, trouts, and charrs

The first group of organisms selected for discussion is the Salmonidae, a group of cold-water fishes, most of whom are anadromous in at least a portion of their range. North American Salmonidae include five species of *Oncorhynchus*, four of *Salvelinus*, one of *Cristivomer*, three of *Salmo*, and the introduced *Salmo trutta*, the brown trout or sea trout of Europe. Two related genera, *Hucho* and *Brachymystax*, occurring in Eurasia inhabit chiefly fresh waters. Some taxonomists include the graylings, Thymallidae, and the whitefishes, Coregonidae, in the same family, but their life histories differ and I exclude them from this discussion.

As indicated in Fig. 18-1, *Oncorhynchus* and *Salvelinus* are each closely knit groups. *Cristivomer* is closest to *Salvelinus alpinus* but has some features more characteristic of *O. kisutch* and *Salmo gairdneri*. *Salmo* is a widely divergent group; *S. gairdneri*, the rainbow or steelhead, and *S. clarki*, the cutthroat, are closer to *Oncorhynchus* and *Salvelinus* than to the other two species placed by taxonomists is the genus *Salmo*. The Salmonidae are noted for great plasticity; each species may vary widely both physically and physiologically in different portions of its range, which has led to the naming of many subspecies (Snyder, 1940).

Description

Most anadromous Salmonidae are silvery while in the sea, shading from metallic blue on the back to silvery beneath. Black speckling occurs on the body of all *Oncorhynchus*

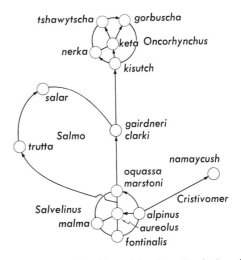

Fig. 18-1. Relationships of the four North American genera of Salmonidae and their component species. (From Rounsefell, G. A. 1962. U. S. Fish Wildl. Serv., Fish. Bull. **62**:235-270.)

327

Table 18-1. Average and maximum weights for Salmonidae

Species	Average weight		Maximum weight		Locality
	lb	kg	lb	kg	
Sockeye salmon	6	2.7			Fraser River
	8.3	3.8			Yes Bay (Cobb, 1930)
	3.9	1.8			Tamgas Stream (Cobb, 1930)
			12	5.4	
Coho salmon	7-8	3.2-3.6	30	13.6	
Chum salmon	9	4.1	45	20.4	
Pink salmon	4	1.8	11	5.0	
Chinook salmon	22	10.0	50	22.7	
			125	56.7	Petersburg, Alaska
Atlantic salmon	10	4.5	30	13.6	Leim and Scott (1966)
Steelhead rainbow	8-15	3.6-6.8	30	13.6	
Sea-run cutthroat	0.5	0.2	3-4	1.4-1.8	
Brown trout or sea trout			13	5.9	Nova Scotia (Leim and Scott, 1966)
			28	12.7	Newfoundland
Eastern charr			3	1.4	Maritimes (Leim and Scott, 1966)
			7	3.2	Record
Dolly Varden charr	4-5	1.8-2.3	25-30	11.3-13.6	Larger streams
			5¼	2.4	Karluk (DeLacy and Morton, 1943)
Arctic charr			3⅕	1.5	Karluk (DeLacy and Morton, 1943)
			10	4.5	Leim and Scott (1966)
			26	11.8	Rare (Leim and Scott, 1966)
Lake trout	3-12	1.4-5.4	25	11.3	Great Lakes (Van Oosten, 1944)
			102	46.2	Record

Table 18-2. Flesh color and texture of selected species of Salmonidae

Species	Flesh color	Flesh texture	Remarks
Sockeye	Bright red	Very firm	Retains color when canned; few early run sockeye often have paler flesh and are canned as cohos (medium reds)
Chinook	Red or white (few may be pink or mixed)	Firm	White fish usually dyed and smoked; red fish canned or sold fresh
Coho	Medium red	Firm	Retains color when canned; better than the drier sockeye for fresh use
Pink	Bright pink	Somewhat soft	Very little fading in canning
Chum	Bright orange	Rather firm	Fades to grayish in canning; excellent fresh or smoked
Atlantic salmon	Almost red as sockeye	Firm	Delicious baked; moister than sockeye
Steelhead	Bright pink to red	Firm	Equal to Atlantic salmon
Lake trout	White to deep reddish orange	Firm	
Golden charr	Deep orange	Firm	Delicious
Dolly Varden charr	White	Somewhat soft	Have taken some with pink flesh

as well as on *Salmo salar, S. gairdneri,* and *S. clarki.* All *Salvelinus* and *Cristivomer* have larger round light-colored spots. Only *Salmo trutta* has both black and light spots on the body. The papers of Evermann and Goldsborough (1907) and Synder (1940) contain excellent color plates.

The weights of anadromous species vary so widely between streams and in response to varied length of sojourn at sea that I merely list the average and maximum weights for anadromous stocks (except for the lake trout) (Table 18-1).

Although introductions of the brown trout were from both resident European freshwater stocks (often called *Salmo fario* or *S. trutta fario*) and anadromous or adfluvial stocks (*S. trutta trutta* or *S. levenensis*), I have noticed that the original stock appears to have no bearing on whether subsequent populations will be anadromous or adfluvial. In Maine brown trout are anadromous in the East Orland, Sheepscot, and Penobscot Rivers. They are so bright and silvery that anglers often think they have caught small Atlantic salmon.

Flesh color and texture. All of the Salmonidae when not in spawning condition have toothsome flesh, regardless of color. Some have a little better flavor, and for commercial purposes the color cannot be disregarded. Sockeye and red-fleshed chinooks were the first to be canned. When the packers started canning pinks there was so much sales resistance to the lighter color that one packer labeled his pinks "guaranteed not to turn red in the can." Table 18-2 lists a few of the characteristics of some species.

Distribution

Salmonidae are boreal to subarctic species distributed widely over the northern hemisphere. The sockeye, the most valuable species, ranges from the Columbia River to the Yukon (which has only a small run) and down the coast of Kamchatka to the northern Kurile Islands and the northern Okhotsk Sea. Commercially abundant runs occur in Kamchatka and on the North American coast from the Columbia River to Bristol Bay (Fig. 18-2). In addition to the

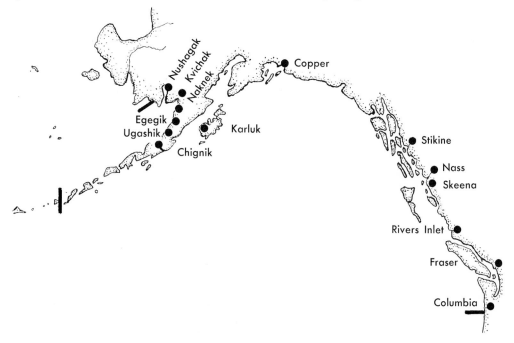

Fig. 18-2. Showing the northern, western, and southern limits of abundance of North American sockeye salmon (black bars). Principal natal rivers are named in the text (black dots).

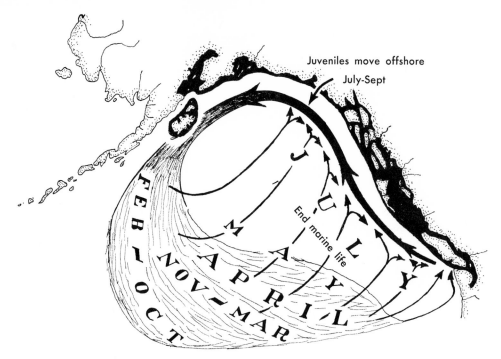

Fig. 18-3. Range of pink salmon during their various life history stages. The blackened shoreline encompasses areas with high spawning populations. The fall-spawned eggs hatch in early spring and the young immediately descend to salt water. The juveniles leave the sheltered inside waters in July to September, moving northwestward in a narrow band about 20 miles offshore. About 12 to 14 months later they return to their natal streams to spawn and die. (Modified from Royce, W. F., et al. 1968. U. S. Fish Wildl. Serv., Fish. Bull. **66:**441-462.)

rivers shown in Fig. 18-2, there are scores of smaller streams supporting sockeye runs.

Pink (humpback) salmon occur from the Klamath River to the mouth of the Mackenzie River (Dymond, 1940) and down the Asiatic coast to Japan. They are commercially abundant from Cape Flattery to the Nushagak River of Bristol Bay, but they are most abundant from southern British Columbia to Kodiak Island. Because young pink salmon go directly to the sea on emerging from the stream gravels, the adults spawn both in large streams and in streams so tiny and shallow that their backs are exposed. Fig. 18-3 shows their areas of abundance.

The following account of the oceanic portion of the life history of the pink salmon is adapted from Royce et al. (1968).

Pink salmon invariably mature at age 2

years. They spawn from about mid-July to mid-October. The eggs (and yolk-sac fry) overwinter in the stream gravels and emerge as fry from February to as late as June in the far north. They proceed directly to the sea, hiding along the stream banks during the day and migrating downstream at night. They feed in small schools along the shores for 2 or 3 months and then leave for the open sea, having grown to between 5 and 6 inches (12.7 to 15.2 cm). The next 12 to 14 months are spent at sea. They first travel north and westward in a narrow dense band about 20 miles offshore (Royce et al., 1968), following the westward-flowing Alaskan Stream (Fig. 18-4). South and west of Kodiak Island the pink salmon that originated from Kodiak Island and eastward leave the Alaskan Stream, cross the Alaska Gyre, and enter the eastward-flowing Sub-

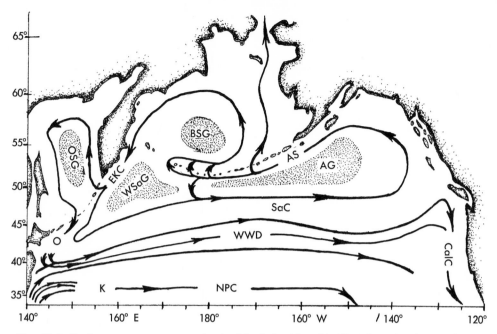

Fig. 18-4. Surface water movements in the North Pacific. (Modified from Dodimead, A. J., et al. 1963. Int. N. Pac. Fish. Comm., Bull. **13**:1-193.)

AG	Alaska Gyre	NPC	North Pacific Current
AS	Alaska Stream	OSG	Okhotsk Sea Gyre
BSG	Bering Sea Gyre	O	Oyashio
CalC	California Current	WSaG	Western Subarctic Gyre
EKC	East Kamchatka Current	SaC	Subarctic Current
K	Kuroshio	WWD	West Wind Drift

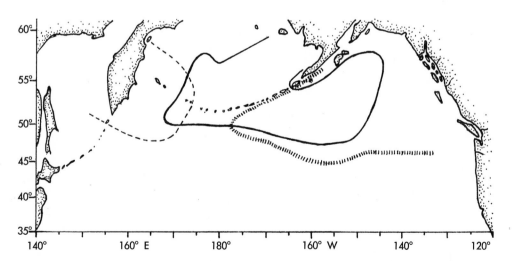

Fig. 18-5. Oceanic range of maturing sockeye salmon. Dotted line indicates Kamchatka salmon; solid line indicates western Alaska salmon; and hachured line indicates other North American salmon. (Modified from Margolis, L., et al. 1966. Int. N. Pac. Fish. Comm., Bull. **20**:1-70.)

arctic Current in which, swimming faster than the current, they approach the coast they left the previous year.

Returning to the sockeye's marine existence, Fig. 18-5 shows that the sockeye from the Columbia River north to Kodiak Island occupy about the same water masses as the pinks from the same areas. Since most sockeye remain 2 or more years at sea, the majority of them complete two or more complete circular (or oval) swings around the North Pacific before they mature and leave the circulating water masses to approach their natal spawning areas. Royce et al. (1968) discuss at length the complicated marine journeys of the Bristol Bay sockeye and the Asian pink salmon.

The Pacific salmons, *Oncorhynchus,* and the steelhead, *Salmo gairdneri,* occupy most of the North Pacific north of about 41° N lat. in winter or 48° N lat. in summer and all of the Bering Sea south of the ice pack. They remain chiefly in the upper 10 m.

The chinook salmon is abundant in the Sacramento–San Joaquin River system and enters all larger streams north to the Yukon, up which they travel the 1504 miles (2402 km) to Dawson at a rate of 52 miles (84 km) a day, and enter some tributaries 3000 miles (4828 km) from the sea. It is no wonder that Gilbert states:

As it enters the mouth of the river, the Yukon king is the richest salmon known to us. It there drips oil profusely when hung on the racks to dry and is, in fact, too rich for most successful canning.*

They occur in low abundance in Kamchatka; they do not spawn as far south as Japan where only an occasional catch is made.

The coho salmon in the past has spawned as far south as the Salinas and Ventura Rivers, and a run exists in Waddell Creek, which empties into the Pacific just north of Monterey Bay. They are abundant from Puget Sound to Cook Inlet, but some occur throughout western Alaska, and a few enter

*From Gilbert, C. H. 1922. The salmon of the Yukon River. Doc. 928. Bull. U. S. Bur. Fish. **38**:317-332.

the Yukon. They occur in low abundance on the Asiatic coast.

The chum salmon together with the pink salmon sustain the Asiatic fisheries. A few chums enter the Columbia. Chum salmon range north to the Arctic Sea where they enter the Mackenzie River as well as the Lena River of Siberia. A large run enters the Yukon, many of them spawning as far as 2000 miles (3219 km) from the sea.

The Atlantic salmon spawns from Norway and Iceland to Portugal and from west Greenland and the eastern shore of Ungava Bay to Maine. Once abundant in the Connecticut, Merrimack, and other southern New England streams, the runs were destroyed years ago by impassable dams, deforestation, pollution, and other causes (Rounsefell and Bond, 1949; Herrington and Rounsefell, 1940).

The steelhead and cutthroat are the Pacific coast relatives of the Atlantic salmon, and like the Atlantic salmon they avoid the colder streams. The steelhead does not range north of the Kuskokwim and avoids the colder rivers in Bristol Bay. The cutthroat ranges south only to the Eel River (DeWitt, 1954) and does not occur north of southeastern Alaska, where all the stocks are anadromous.

The genus *Salvelinus* contains three species that are anadromous over parts of their range. The eastern charr is anadromous to some degree from Cape Cod northward; in some far northern areas the populations are all anadromous. The arctic charr is anadromous in Hudson Bay and arctic Canada but only rarely so at Karluk. The Dolly Varden is anadromous from British Columbia northward to Herschel Island in the Arctic. The Dolly Varden is very abundant in some Alaska streams and has sometimes been canned commercially, e.g., small packs were put up beginning in 1912 and continuing for several years in Kotzebue Sound.

Homing. Anadromous Salmonidae all tend to return, with only slight straying, to their natal stream. When Kelez (Rounsefell and Kelez, 1938) transferred young coho salmon of 10.2 cm from their native river to a second river where he marked and released them, they migrated to the sea and returned as adults to the second river. This ready adoption of the second stream discounts the theory that imprinting at a very early age is the prime factor in homing.

For the species that migrate great distances over the oceans—the Pacific salmons, the Atlantic salmon, and the steelhead—many theories have been advanced as to how they manage to return from faraway places to their home stream. If we conceded that some of the theories could function once the fish make a landfall, their oceanic navigation continued to remain inexplicable. Royce et al. (1968), however, have advanced the theory, based on careful studies of the oceanic occurrence and distribution of different age and size groups of maturing salmon, that they follow the great ocean currents, as discussed previously.

Reproduction

Most North American Salmonidae form a redd or nest in gravel or rubble in which the eggs are buried in egg pits. The lake trout (Royce, 1951) and the golden charr scatter their eggs over gravel or rubble substrate without any attempt at nest building.

Fecundity. Salmonidae produce meroblastic eggs containing a large supply of yolk. The largest eggs occur in the four fluvial anadromous *Oncorhynchus*. There is considerable variation in egg size within species in stocks from different streams, between fish with varying numbers of years at sea, and between different years. The ova vary from about 6.5 to 8 mm in diameter; sockeye eggs are slightly smaller. Eggs of the other genera average somewhat smaller, but 4 mm is about as small as has been found (Rounsefell, 1957a).

Spawning areas and behavior. The basic types of spawning areas and spawning behavior for North American Salmonidae are as follows:

1 Redds built in the streams flowing into the lakes in stream systems containing lakes
2 Redds built in the lake outlet streams just below lakes in stream systems containing lakes
3 Redds built in lake gravels aerated by seepage or streams in stream systems containing lakes
4 Redds built at short distances from the sea in stream systems with or without lakes
5 Redds built at long distances from the sea in stream systems with or without lakes
6 Redds built in intertidal gravels off the mouths of streams entering the sea in stream systems with or without lakes
7 Without building redds on the hard surface or rubble of lake bottoms

The following describes spawning areas utilized by the various species, the numbers referring to the types just having been listed; preferences and exceptions are indicated.

Oncorhynchus
  nerka
  1 This is true especially toward southern extremity of range and in smaller streams.
  2 This occurs chiefly in larger streams or streams with poor lake inlet areas, e.g., below Chilko Lake and Shuswap Lake on the Fraser River and to a lesser extent below Babine Lake on the Skeena River and Karluk Lake on the Karluk River.
  3 In some small lakes such as Cultus Lake on the Fraser. Toward the north this tendency increases, amounting to about 25% in Karluk Lake. However, in Bristol Bay it varies between river systems.
  7 In Iliamna Lake large numbers spawn on island lake beaches on broken rubble with little or no attempt at nest building (Kerns and Donaldson, 1968). EXCEPTIONS: A few small streams without lakes on the British Columbia coast have small runs of "creek" sockeye that go to sea after emerging. Another race spawns in the Harrison River rapids of the Fraser River, the young proceeding immediately to the sea.
  gorbuscha
  4 This category includes the majority of the pink salmon.
  5 The pink salmon spawning above Hell's Gate Canyon (250 miles up the Fraser River) were the largest contributors to the huge odd-year pink salmon runs in northern Puget Sound that fell to about one third of their size following the disastrous rock slide of 1913 that barred their passage through the canyon (Rounsefell and Kelez, 1938).
  6 This habit of intertidal spawning is characteristic of several races of pink salmon in southeastern Alaska and Prince William Sound. EXCEPTIONS: Pink salmon under the pressure of large populations

tend to proceed farther upstream and in years of big runs many spawn in tributary streams of Karluk Lake. Gilbert and Rich (1927) mention them even spawning in beach gravels of the lake during the huge run of 1924.

keta

4   The majority of chum salmon spawn at short distances from the sea.

5   A large run of chums enters the Yukon, some ascending as far as 2000 miles (Gilbert, 1922).

6   Intertidal spawning of chum salmon is less usual than in pink salmon.

kisutch

4   Coho or silver salmon spawn chiefly in lower tributaries of large rivers or in short coastal streams.

5   In the Yukon River cohos ascend more than 800 miles to tributaries of the Tanana. EXCEPTIONS: Cohos will spawn in streams entering lakes, and the young cohos will frequent both streams and lakes.

tshawytscha

4, 5   King salmon prefer large streams, short or long. In many of the larger rivers the early-running salmon press on to the upper reaches to spawn and the young reside for one or more seasons in the stream. In many streams the late-running stocks of king salmon spawn in the lower portions of the streams. In these areas it is quite usual for the majority of the young to descend to the sea after emerging in the same manner as the pinks and chums.

Salmo

salar, gairdneri, clarki, trutta

4, 5   These species of *Salmo* will spawn on suitable riffle areas in any stream. The landlocked races often spawn in lake outlet streams from which the young and adults return to the lake, but they usually spawn in inlet streams if available.

Salvelinus

fontinalis, alpinus, malma, oquassa

4   The anadromous races of *fontinalis, alpinus,* and *malma* usually spawn in shorter coastal streams.

7   The subspecies *alpinus aureolus* spawns without nest building on bottom rubble or gravel; it is not anadromous. *S. oquassa,* the blueback charr, likewise not anadromous, spawns in lake tributaries (Everhart, 1950).

Cristivomer

namaycush

7   The lake trout, *namaycush,* spawns on the hard or rough bottom of lakes without building a nest (Royce, 1951).

The substrate utilized for spawning varies somewhat with the size of the fish, since all North American Salmonidae, except the lake trout and the golden charr, usually dig nests. King salmon can spawn in large rubble and may dig a redd 18 inches deep, but the smaller charrs will spawn in pea gravel. One usual requirement is the sufficient seepage of water through the gravel to furnish oxygen for the eggs. For this reason the favored nest location is close to the upper end of riffle areas, but in crowded streams fish will spawn in poor locations. In lakes aeration depends on seepage, wave action, and currents generated by wind or seiches.

The female salmon digs the nest. Turning on her side, facing upstream, she vigorously thrashes the gravel. In doing this the whole body moves; the head and tail move up and down describing two arcs; the center of the body is relatively motionless; and the head is held slightly above the bottom so that the tail and caudal peduncle do the actual moving of the rubble. After several vigorous thrashings the female will rest for a short time and then return to her labors. When she is satisfied with her excavation she sinks deep into the hole and extrudes the ova. During this period the male presses close to her side, extruding the milt.

After this rapid extrusion of eggs the female will return to her labor, which results in burying the eggs in the egg pit and at the same time in enlarging the redd in an upstream direction. A pair of salmon may deposit eggs in two to several egg pits in the same redd.

Spawning seasons. The spawning season varies over a wide range, depending on latitude, distance of spawning areas from the sea, and age composition of the spawning stocks. To the Fraser River sockeyes, with a preponderance of 4-year-old adults, distance from the sea is the dominating factor. Those fish destined for the farthest upriver lakes run early; those spawning in the lower lakes tend to enter the river much later. At Karluk, with an extremely varied lake and marine sojourn, the age of the fish, especially the marine age, is dominant. The earliest spawners enter the lake tributaries and commence spawning by the last week in June (Gilbert and Rich, 1927). Waves of new arrivals enter the river, and spawning continues until very late in the fall. Chamberlain (1907) mentions reports of spawning late in the winter, even under the ice. This is corroborated by Bean (1891), who reports natives taking salmon through the ice during the winter.

The progression through the season of the spawning runs of the five species of *Oncorhynchus* in the Puget Sound–Fraser River area is shown in Fig. 3-9 (p. 57).

Spawning changes in color and morphometry. Most of the Salmonidae exhibit changes in color and often shape during the breeding season. The morphometric characteristics, such as the male hump and the great prolongation of the upper jaw, are most pronounced in the genus *Oncorhynchus* and least noticeable in the genus *Cristivomer*. This is not unexpected; *Cristivomer* lives in a very stable environment and does not leave it to spawn, whereas *Oncorhynchus* battles vast differences in environment, and so rigorous has been the evolution that the struggle has demanded the very life of the spawning individual.

The sockeye changes only slightly in body form, chiefly in the development of the hooked upper jaw, or kype, in the male. Since sockeye are lacustrine anadromous, the adults are predisposed to spending a longer time in fresh water before spawning. Consequently, one never sees a sockeye in breeding colors in salt water. The change occurs gradually, or faster for those arriving at the streams in the late fall. In full breeding color both sexes have a red back, a dull green head (on top), and creamy white underparts.

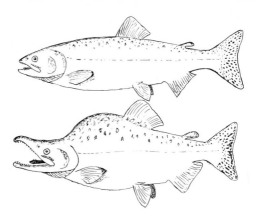

Fig. 18-6. Adult pink salmon as it approaches the coast (upper) and the breeding male pink salmon showing the great changes in the male with the onset of maturity, including the very pronounced hump, the great prolongation of the jaws (and the rest of the head) and the prominent teeth. (Modified from Evermann, B. W., and E. L. Goldsborough. 1907. U. S. Bur. Fish. **26:**219-360.)

The greatest breeding change occurs in the pink salmon, *O. gorbuscha*, long known as the humpback salmon until the canners decided that the name might retard sales. As with the other species only slight changes occur in the female, but the very striking change in the male is depicted in Fig. 18-6. The pink does not acquire bright colors. The silvery blue marine coloration gradually changes to a dark brown or black along the back, including the hump and the top of the head, and to a dirty, creamy white below.

Almost as startling as the bright red of the sockeye is the breeding color of the chum salmon. On the sides the chum acquires a wide jagged line of red and black that resembles a surrealistic painting of a thunderbolt. The anterior portion of this jagged band is usually a bright purplish red, and the posterior portion shades into a deep black.

The coho turns from its metallic silvery sea colors to a dark greenish brown, but on the sides a very broad bright red stripe appears that runs the entire length from the caudal peduncle to the preopercle. The upper jaw of the male does not become quite as elongated as in the pink salmon.

The king salmon shows the least change in color of the five species of *Oncorhynchus*. The silvery hue becomes dull, and the sides take on a dull reddish tinge.

The rainbow steelhead, *S. gairdneri*, acquires a wide bright iridescent stripe along the sides and extending onto the sides of the head. The cutthroat steelhead, *S. clarki*, in breeding color has orange-red suffused over the belly and lower fins. There may also be a pinkish stripe along the sides, less bright than in the rainbow and without clear-cut edges.

All of the charrs, except *Cristivomer*, tend toward reddish hues on the bellies and lower fins in spawning season.

Development. The period of time required for hatching and the dates of emergence from the spawning gravels are virtually controlled by the water temperature. Proceeding northward, the time becomes longer. The first to emerge in the spring are probably those that were spawned earliest the preceding summer. Gilbert and Rich (1927)

mention that in western Alaska, sockeye fry of the previous season's spawning, with the yolk sac still attached, can be found in the gravels at the very end of the season, doubtless from the latest eggs to be laid the preceding fall.

From 17 determinations of the length of time for hatching in British Columbia hatcheries, Foerster (1968) calculated the mean time to be 107 days, ranging from 57 to 171 days. The degree-days varied from 697 to 1333 F (359 to 741 degree-days C). This period does not include the time the fry remains in the stream gravels while the yolk sac is being absorbed.

The young of Pacific salmon (except the pink salmon) are marked on the sides with vertical black bars, or parr marks. They are especially large and oval in the coho and chinook salmons and narrower and chiefly above the lateral line in sockeye and chum salmons. These parr marks are covered with silver when the parr reach the smolt stage preparatory to migrating sea-

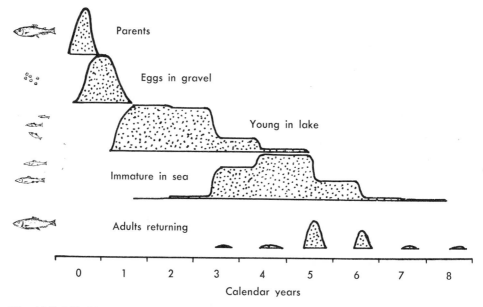

Fig. 18-7. Life history stages of one generation of sockeye salmon at Karluk Lake, Alaska. The parent salmon (one season's spawning of salmon of mixed ages) die after they deposit their eggs in the gravel. As shown, 8 years elapse before all of the progeny return to Karluk to spawn and die. (Modified from Rounsefell, G. A. 1958. U. S. Fish Wildl. Serv., Fish. Bull. **58**:83-169.)

ward. The pink salmon, which migrate to the sea immediately on emerging from the gravel (and therefore already in the smolt stage), do not have parr marks. On the chum salmon, which usually migrate to sea fairly soon after emergence, the parr marks are not pronounced and soon start to fade.

Age and growth. All *Oncorhynchus* die after spawning; therefore of chief interest is the age of maturity, which varies markedly with latitude and with the length of freshwater residence.

On the Fraser River the vast majority of the sockeye, especially those from upriver areas, leave their nursery lake in the spring of their second year (counting from the time of egg deposition), and return during their second year at sea, toward the end of their fourth year after egg deposition. In the lower river tributaries (below Hell's Gate Canyon) there are some that mature in their fifth year. In addition, there are a few precocious males in both areas that mature in their third year. Large numbers of precocious males (jacks) are considered as presaging a large run of normal-aged fish in the following year.

In the Columbia River four-year-olds are also predominant, but there are significant numbers maturing at 3 years of age.

As one proceeds to the northwest there is a very significant increase in the length of both freshwater and marine residences. At Karluk over 80% of the sockeye normally mature in the fifth year, but many mature at age 6 years, a few at 7 years of age, and occasionally individuals mature at 8 years of age. A time diagram of life history stages of sockeye at Karluk is shown in Fig. 18-7 (Rounsefell, 1958). In several of the Bristol Bay rivers the majority mature in their sixth year.

The pink salmon, *O. gorbuscha,* invariably matures in the second year. This causes the interesting circumstance that those runs of pinks spawning in odd-numbered years are not related, even in the same stream, to those spawning in even-numbered years.

Suggested readings

Barnaby, J. T. 1944. Fluctuations in abundance of red salmon, Oncorhynchus nerka (Walbaum), of the Karluk River, Alaska. U. S. Fish Wildl. Serv., Fish. Bull. **50:**237-295.

DeLacy, A. C., and W. M. Morton. 1943. Taxonomy and habits of the charrs, Salvelinus malma and Salvelinus alpinus of the Karluk drainage system. Trans. Amer. Fish. Soc. **72:** 79-91.

Dodimead, A. J., F. Favorite, and T. Hirano. 1963. Review of oceanography of the subarctic Pacific Region. Int. N. Pac. Fish. Comm. Bull. **13:**1-193.

Favorite, F. 1969. Fishery oceanography. III. Ocean temperature and distribution of Pacific salmon. Comm. Fish. Rev. **31:**34-40.

Foerster, R. E. 1968. The sockeye salmon, Oncorhynchus nerka. Fish. Res. Bd. Canada, Bull. 162. 422 pp.

Hanavan, M. G., and B. E. Skud. 1954. Intertidal spawning of pink salmon. U. S. Fish Wildl. Serv., Fish. Bull. **56:**167-185.

Kerns, O. E., Jr., and J. R. Donaldson. 1968. Behavior and distribution of spawning sockeye salmon on island beaches in Iliamna Lake, Alaska, 1965. J. Fish. Res. Bd. Canada **25:** 485-494.

Rounsefell, G. A. 1957a. Fecundity of North American Salmonidae. U. S. Fish Wildl. Serv., Fish. Bull. **57:**451-468.

Rounsefell, G. A. 1962. Relationships among North American Salmonidae. U. S. Fish Wildl. Serv., Fish. Bull. **62:**235-270.

Royce, W. F. 1951. Breeding habits of lake trout in New York, U. S. Fish Wildl. Serv., Fish. Bull. **52:**59-76.

chapter 19

✖ Life histories of codlike fishes

The order Gadiformes, according to the classification of Greenwood et al. (1966) contains five suborders and 10 families. This chapter will discuss chiefly the families Gadidae (the cods) and Merlucciidae (the hakes), the most important fish used directly for human consumption. In the northern North Atlantic, including Europe, the cod is paramount (Fig. 19-1), but in the United States the haddock is of greater importance on the East Coast. The hakes, family Merlucciidae, resemble the Gadidae in many respects but have softer flesh and therefore are not as highly regarded for tablefish. In Chapter 6 on world fisheries all of the gadoids have been considered together (Table 6-2, p. 90), and this arrangement will be continued.

Distribution

Hakes, genus *Merluccius,* are distributed worldwide both north and south of the equator (Table 19-1 and Fig. 19-2). The genus *Merluccius* differs in distribution from the other gadoids chiefly in the temperature of the waters inhabited (Table 19-2).

Table 19-2 shows that the hakes are predominantly cool-water fish in sharp contrast to the other gadoids. Even where their range extends into cold waters, they are

Table 19-1. Chief species of hake *(Merluccius)*

Species	Common name	Occurrence (Fig. 19-2)
M. merluccius	European hake	Europe, North Africa, Mediterranean and adjacent waters
M. productus	Pacific hake	Western Alaska to Baja California
M. bilinearis	Silver hake (whiting)	Atlantic coast of United States and Canada
M. albidus	Offshore hake	Atlantic coast of United States
M. magnoculus	—	Gulf of Mexico
M. augustimanus	Panamanian hake	Southern California to Panama
M. capensis	Cape hake (stockfish)	Southern Gulf of Guinea to South Africa
M. hubbsi	Argentine hake (merluza)	Southeast Brazil to southern Argentina
M. gayi	Chilean hake	Peru and Chile
M. polylepis	—	Tierra del Fuego and vicinity
M. australis	New Zealand hake	New Zealand

Fig. 19-1. Dories landing their catch of gutted codfish at Pirate Cove in the Shumagin Islands. In 1916 a Shumagin Island cod fisherman sailed one of these dories over 2100 miles (3885 km) across the open Pacific to the Panama Pacific Exposition in San Francisco. (Photo taken in 1913 by John N. Cobb.)

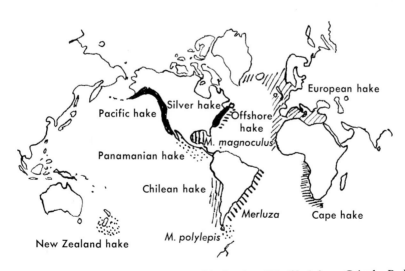

Fig. 19-2. World distribution of hake, genus *Merluccius*. (Modified from Grinols, R. B., and M. F. Tillman. 1970. In Pacific hake. U. S. Fish Wildl. Serv., Bur. Comm. Fish Circ. **332**: 1-21.)

Table 19-2. Distribution of hake *(Merluccius)* as compared to other gadoids*

Temperature zones	Metric tons in 1968 (thousands)		% Hake	% Other gadoids
	Hake	Other gadoids		
Cold	293	6,901	22.4	85.5
Cool	974	1,164	74.4	14.4
Warm to tropical	42	8	3.2	0.1
TOTAL	1,309	8,073	100.0	100.0

*Based on Table 6-2, p. 90.

Table 19-3. Chief species of Gadidae

Species	Common name(s)	Chief areas of occurrence
Gadus morhua and subspecies	Cod (Atlantic)	New Jersey to Davis Strait, Spitzbergen, Barents Sea to Bay of Biscay, White Sea, and Baltic Sea
Gadus ogac	Greenland cod	Point Barrow to southern Greenland, south to Gulf of St. Lawrence
Gadus macrocephalus	Cod (Pacific)	Southern Japan to Bering Strait, south to northern California
Gadus merlangus and subspecies	European whiting	Northwestern Europe to Black Sea
Melanogrammus aeglefinus	Haddock	Maryland to southern Grand Banks, Iceland, western Barents Sea to English Channel
Boreogadus saida	Arctic cod	Circumpolar
Pollachius virens	Pollock, coalfish, saithe	New Jersey to southern Grand Banks, western Greenland, Iceland, Spitzbergen, northwestern Europe to Bay of Biscay
Pollachius pollachius	Pollack	Western Europe
Urophycis tenuis	White hake, ling	Mid-Atlantic states to Gulf of St. Lawrence and southern Grand Banks
Urophycis chuss	Red or squirrel hake	Mid-Atlantic states to Gulf of St. Lawrence and southern Grand Banks
Theragra chalcogramma	Alaska pollock or walleye pollock	Japan, Okhotsk, and Bering Seas to California
Micromesistius potassou	Blue whiting, potassou	Northern Norway to Mediterranean
Trisopterus esmarkii	Norway pout	Barents Sea to southern Iceland, south of Iceland 100 to 200 fm
Brosme brosme	Cusk	Cape Cod to Strait of Belle Isle, Murman coast to northern North Sea, Iceland
Molva molva	European ling	Murman coast to Iceland, western Baltic, south to Bay of Biscay
Eleginus navaga	Navaga cod	White Sea to Kola Bay and east to Bay of Ob
Eleginus gracilis	Saffron cod	Chukchi Sea to Korea
Microgadus tomcod	Tomcod (Atlantic)	Virginia to northern Newfoundland
Microgadus proximus	Tomcod (Pacific)	Northern California to Gulf of Alaska

taken chiefly in the cool rather than the cold portions. The European hake is taken chiefly in southeast Europe, and the Chilean hake is taken in southern Peru and northernmost Chile.

The remaining codlike fishes of any economic importance are listed in Table 19-3. Among related families of slight economic importance I should mention the Macrouridae, or grenadiers, which are fishes of worldwide distribution usually taken in rather deep water. Some rock (or round-nose) grenadier, *Macrurus (= Coryphaen-oides) rupestris,* are being taken by the U.S.S.R. in the North Atlantic, and quantities of the roughhead grenadier, *Macrurus berglax,* are thought to occur at 320 to 360 m in the Labrador Sea. Templeman (1966) reports great quantities of the first species and lesser quantities of the latter in deep water off Labrador and Baffin Island. He states that the roughhead grenadier was

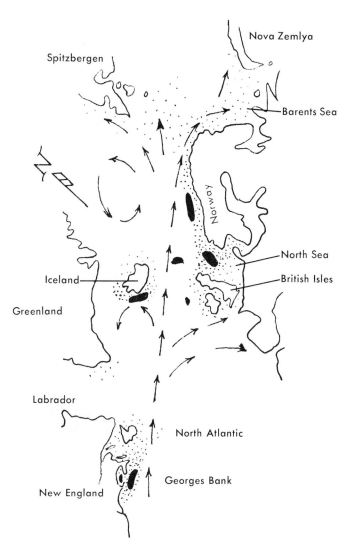

Fig. 19-3. Distribution of haddock, *Melanogrammus aeglefinus.* Arrows indicate the surface currents; black indicates abundance of haddock; and stippled areas indicate occurrence at low levels of abundance.

found to be almost as acceptable as cod on their ship's table.

The Japanese and Russians have found large concentrations of grenadiers on the slope in the central and northwestern Bering Sea, and Suda (1973) reports that experimental trawling off southern Chile shows grenadiers to be the dominant species south of 43° S lat.

Among the Gadidae, there are distinct differences in distribution that appear to be closely linked with temperature. In the Arctic Sea beyond the influence of the Gulf Stream are found *Boreogadus, Eleginus,* and *Gadus ogac,* the Greenland cod. *Gadus morhua* frequents the colder waters in the Atlantic boreal region. The haddock prefers slightly less cold water, being scarce on the Grand Banks and off northeast Iceland. On the European side of the Atlantic the blue whiting, *Micromesistius potassou,* ranges from northern Norway into the Mediterranean as far as the Adriatic. On the American side the white and red hakes, *Urophycis* spp., range from the southern Grand Banks to the mid-Atlantic states, and one species, *U. floridanus,* occurs in the Gulf of Mexico.

The most important gadoid fish in U. S. catches is the haddock, and it is used as the typical example of the group. As shown in Fig. 19-3, the haddock occurs only in the North Atlantic boreal region. It is perhaps the most representative example available since it avoids both the extreme cold (as shown by its great scarcity around Newfoundland, northeast Iceland, and the northeast Barents Sea) and the slightly milder waters of the southern North Sea, English Channel, and Chesapeake Bay areas.

Habitat

Haddock are a bank fish and rarely come close to shore. On the other hand, cod are taken in numbers in pound nets; young pollock abound in shoal harbors; and the silver hake will pursue small fish along the shore, sometimes becoming stranded as the tide falls. Haddock will sometimes pursue small fish but never come to the surface.

As a general rule haddock avoid water below 2° C or above 11° C. They withdraw from the shallow portions of the banks in winter and again in late summer. They appear to be stenohaline, as they never enter estuaries.

Haddock avoid the ledges and rocky ground preferred by cod and the soft oozy mud sought by the white hake. They are caught chiefly on gravel, pebbles, clay, smooth sand, and areas of broken shells.

Although they are caught as deep as 150 fm, haddock are more abundant between 20 and 60 fm, the younger haddock tending to inhabit the shallower water. They are abundant on Georges Bank, becoming progressively less abundant as one moves northeastward along the Nova Scotia coast. From tagging and from studies of growth rate and meristic characters, there appear to be at least three subpopulations. The most abundant and fastest growing inhabits Georges Bank and makes early summer incursions into the Gulf of Maine, at least as far as Mount Desert Island. The slower growing Nova Scotia population, with the center of abundance on Browns Bank, is separated from the Georges Bank population by the deep (over 100 fm) Fundian Channel. The scarce Newfoundland population is separated from the Nova Scotia group by the deep Laurentian Channel.

Description

Physical characteristics. The haddock is a typical Gadidae with three dorsal and two anal fins (Table 19-4). It differs from the cod, *Gadus morhua,* by having a black rather than a pale lateral line, by the higher falcate first dorsal fin, by the presence of a dusky blotch on each side over the middle of the pectoral fin, and by a slightly more concave caudal fin. The haddock is slimmer than the cod and more compressed laterally. The lower jaw is shorter than in the cod.

The chief gadoid species taken by U. S.

Table 19-4. Physical characteristics of gadoids important to U. S. fisheries

| | No. of dorsal fins | No. of anal fins | Maximum size | | Average size | | Chin barbel | Relation of lower jaw to upper jaw | Flesh |
			Length (inches)	Weight (lb)	Length (inches)	Weight (lb)			
Haddock	3	2	44	37	14-23	1-5	Yes	Shorter	Firm
Cod	3	2	72	211	—	6-12	Yes	Shorter	Firm
Pollock	3	2	42	35	24-36	4-15	Very small	Longer	Firm
Alaska pollock	3	2	36	—	—	—	Absent or minute	Longer	Firm
Atlantic tomcod	3	2	15	1¼	9-12	—	Yes	Shorter	Firm
Pacific tomcod	3	2	12	—	—	—	Yes	Shorter	Firm
White hake	2	1	48	40	—	8	Yes	Shorter	Soft
Red hake	2	1	30	6-7	—	1-3	Yes	Shorter	Soft
Silver hake	2	1	30	5	12	½	No	Longer	Soft
Pacific hake	2	1	32	—	20	2⅕	No	Longer	Soft
Cusk	1	1	40	27	18-30	5-10	Yes	Shorter	Firm

fishermen are given in Table 19-4, showing some of their physical characteristics.

All of the hakes have soft-textured flesh. However, when quick-frozen immediately after capture the silver hake has a pleasantly delicate flavor. The white hake also deteriorates rapidly, but I have found it excellent when fresh. The Pacific hake taken by U. S. fishermen have been used principally as industrial fish. The red hake have been used extensively for reduction, but some are being utilized directly.

The most prized fish is the haddock. Young haddock appear as broiled scrod throughout New England, and larger sizes provide frozen fillets; in Britain "finnan haddie" (lightly smoked fillets) is a favorite dish. The cod, cusk, and pollock have firm white flesh and are excellent market fish. The Pacific cod is fully as good as the Atlantic cod. The tomcods are too small for filleting and are seldom seen in the market. I have caught and eaten the Pacific species with enjoyment.

The presence or absence of a chin barbel and the length of the lower jaw in relation to the upper (Table 19-4) seem to be related to the habitat and feeding habits. The species with a short lower jaw and a chin barbel are more inclined to be benthic and

to feed chiefly on the bottom. The pollocks and the silver and Pacific hakes do feed on the bottom, but often they also feed far off the bottom, even schooling at the surface.

Color. When haddock are caught the head, back, and sides are dark purplish gray, fading below the lateral line to silvery gray with pinkish reflections and a distinct black lateral line and the dark to sooty black shoulder patch, known as the "devil's mark" or the "mark of St. Peter's thumb." The belly and lower side of the head are white. The dorsal, pectoral, and caudal fins are dark gray; the anal fins are pale with black speckling at the base. The ventral fins are white.

Cod differ from haddock by the pale lateral line, gray-green or reddish back, and thick speckling with small, round spots. Pollock are deep olive to brownish green above paling to yellowish or to smoky gray on the sides below the lateral line and silvery gray on the belly. All fins are olive, except for the white ventrals.

Cusk vary considerably in color, but the long dorsal and anal fins and the caudal fins have the general body tint, except for a distinct black margin narrowly edged with white.

Table 19-5. Percent of haddock mature
at each age

	Age (yr)				
	2	*3*	*4*	*5*	*6*
Males					
Georges Bank[1]	40	98	100	—	—
Browns Bank[1]	0	100	100	—	—
North Sea[2]	60	95	99	100	100
Females					
Georges Bank	0	77	100	—	—
Browns Bank	0	0	60	100	—
North Sea	10	75	95	99	100
Males and females					
Georges Bank	20	88	100	—	—
Browns Bank	0	0	80	100	—
North Sea	35	85	97	100	100
Newfound- land[3]	0	16	45	95	100

[1]Colton, 1955.
[2]Raitt, 1936.
[3]Thompson, 1939.

Reproduction

Age at maturity. The percent of haddock
maturing at each age is shown in Table
19-5. The males tend to mature earlier than
the females. There is only a slight difference
between the Georges Bank and the North
Sea haddock. However, the Browns Bank
haddock are about 1 year behind those of
Georges Bank, and the Newfoundland fish
are even slower in maturing.

Fecundity. Information on fecundity is
sparse, but the number of eggs varies with
size from about 100,000 to more than 2
million. The buoyant eggs lack an oil globule
and are about 1.19 to 1.72 mm in diameter,
slightly larger than those of the cod. The
eggs of the haddock and cod are indistin-
guishable and may be confused with those
of the witch in early stages, until the cod
and/or haddock eggs form black pigment.

Spawning habits and seasons. Haddock
spawn near the bottom; the eggs, after fertilization, rise and float on the surface.
Hatching requires about 14 days. The three-
sixteenth–inch (4.7 mm) larvae drift with
the current. In about 10 days the larvae

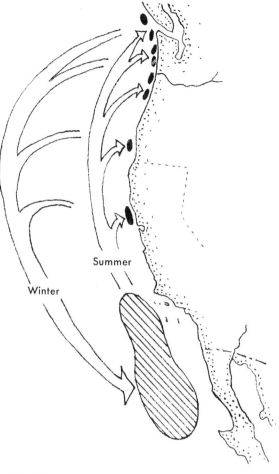

Fig. 19-4. Hypothesized migrations and seasonal
distribution of Pacific hake, *Merluccius productus.* (From Alverson, D. L. 1969. FAO Fish.
Rep. 2:1-461.)

absorb their yolk sac and then commence
feeding on zooplankton. During these
pelagic stages many young are carried off the
bank and perish because they are over too
deep water when they are ready to seek the
bottom. The larvae continue to grow, reaching 1 inch (25 mm) in about 60 days.

The peak of spawning occurs in March
and April on Georges Bank. The young
pelagic fish, up to 3 inches (7.5 cm) in
length, are often found during summer
closely associated with the red jellyfish,
Cyanea, living under its tentacles. These
young haddock usually seek the bottom

from September to October, having grown to about 5½ inches (14 cm) in length.

Migrations. Most gadoids perform short migrations, partially for feeding and partially to avoid unfavorable water temperatures. Georges Bank haddock move inshore along the Gulf of Maine in spring, returning to the bank in summer. The silver hake moves offshore in winter but returns to the shoal water in spring.

The Pacific hake, *Merluccius productus,* occurs from the Gulf of Alaska to the tip of Baja California but is only commercially abundant from Vancouver Island to about Cedros Island. Alverson (1969) states that the hake is abundant in the feeding areas off Vancouver Island to northern California during the summer but moves south of Point Conception in winter (Fig. 19-4). From midspring to late summer hake feed on the offshore banks at a depth of about 200 m but in the fall and winter may be found at about 350 to 400 m.

Suggested readings

Blacker, R. W. 1971. Synopsis of biological data on haddock. FAO Fish. Synopsis 84.

Grinols, R. B., and M. F. Tillman. 1970. Importance of the worldwide hake, Merluccius, resource. In Pacific hake, U. S. Fish Wildl. Serv., Bur. Comm. Fish. Circ. **332:**1-21.

chapter 20

❧ Life histories of shrimps and prawns

The shrimps and prawns comprise a large number of species of many genera scattered throughout the world. There is no definition separating the terms "shrimp" and "prawn." As a rough rule of thumb larger species are more apt to be called prawns, but there are numerous exceptions. In the United States all species are usually called shrimp; *Pandalus borealis* is a pink shrimp in Alaska and a deep water prawn in Europe.

Shrimps, as well as all insects, belong to the phylum Arthropoda, with jointed appendages and a chitinous exoskeleton. They fall in the large class Crustacea, which includes crabs, lobsters, barnacles, and mysids, and are in the subclass Malacostraca. This in itself is a large group with about 10 orders. Shrimp are in the order Decapoda and in the suborder Natantia. This suborder includes animals with slender, laterally compressed bodies and a full complement of well-developed pleopods for swimming.

The suborder Natantia is further subdivided into two sections: the Penaeidea and the Caridea. The penaeidean shrimps release their eggs directly into the water, and the large number of tiny eggs each hatch quickly into a nauplius larva. These larvae go through a number of molts. The total number of molts varies with the species,

as there may be several molts during one stage. Each succeeding stage may bear little resemblance to the former. From the nauplius stage they become protozoea, then zoea. The number of stages varies somewhat between species before reaching the mysis stage, which is the final stage before becoming a postmysis or postlarva.

The section Caridea, although containing several families, is much less important commercially than the Penaeidea. The caridean shrimp carry the eggs on the pleopods of the female for several months. The larvae that finally hatch bear only a slight resemblance to an adult and during a 2- to 3-month planktonic existence must undergo several molts (about six in *Pandalus borealis*) before they closely resemble an adult.

In general the penaeid shrimps occur in tropical and subtropical seas and the carid shrimps inhabit boreal seas. The nine species of caridean shrimp caught in Alaska all reproduce in a manner similar to that described for *Pandalus borealis,* which is the same species important in New England and is the deep water prawn of Europe. Similarly, *Pandalus montagui,* known as the pink shrimp in Britain, occurs in Alaska. Some pandalid shrimps do occur farther south, e.g., the bay shrimp, *Crago franciscorum,* of

Table 20-1. Life histories of penaeid and caridean shrimps

	Penaeus aztecus	*Pandalus borealis*
Eggs extruded	Directly into the sea	Attached to abdomen and pleopods of female
Eggs hatch	Almost immediately	In about 6 months
Planktonic life	2 to 3 weeks	3 months
Elapsed time to the juvenile stage	About 3 to 5 weeks	About 9 months
Sexes present	Both	All males for 3 to 4 years from larval stage
Female ratio	Remains about equal	All change to female during fourth and fifth year
Commercial size reached	About 4 to 5 months	2 to 3 years (all males)
Age of females at first spawning	About 8 to 11 months	4 to 5 years
Vertical diel migrations	No, but burrows into substrate during day	Yes, most abundant at night in midwater

San Francisco Bay and the ocean shrimp, *Pandalus jordani,* off the cost of northern California.

The most abundant penaeid shrimps are closely associated with brackish shallow water environments (Kutkuhn, 1966) during larval and/or juvenile stages. Penaeid shrimps are caught throughout the world along tropical and subtropical coasts with estuarine environments.

That the penaeid shrimps are more closely associated with estuaries than the caridean shrimps may be more apparent than real. The Penaeidea include such genera as *Sicyonia, Plesiopenaeus,* and *Xiphopenaeus* that certainly are not estuarine dependent. On the other hand the caridean shrimps include *Macrobrachium,* which spawns in fresh water, the larvae *descending* into brackish water and later *reascending* the stream.

Concerning the common shrimp, *Crangon vulgaris,* in the Bosphorus and the Black Sea Devedjian states:

La crevette se trouve répandue dans la plupart des mers. Elle fréquente les eaux côtières et se tient ordinairement sous les plantes aquatiques. Bien qu'animal marin, elle entre pârfois, au printemps, dans l'embrouchure des fleuves; il lui arrive même de remonter les courants d'eau saumâtre.*

---

*From Devedjian, K. 1926. Pêche et pêcheries en Turquie. Administration de la Dette Publique Ottomane, Constantinople. 649 pp.

The life histories of the penaeid and caridean shrimps are so strikingly different that I summarize them, selecting two species as examples, in Table 20-1.

The distribution of shrimps is partially related to the type of bottom sediments. Williams (1958) ran experiments with three penaeid shrimps, *Penaeus duorarum, P. aztecus,* and *P. setiferus,* using five substrates ranging from a broken shell–sand mixture to sandy mud. The pink shrimp, *P. duorarum,* preferred the shell–sand mixture; the other two more frequently chose the softer, muddier substrates. Grady (1971) compared the distribution of catches of pink shrimp on the Tortugas fishing grounds with the organic content of the sediments inside and outside the areas fished. The preferred areas appear to have a relatively high content of organic matter.

More is known of shrimp migrations in the Gulf of Mexico than elsewhere because of the many marking experiments carried out using vital stains supplemented at times with fluorescein dyes (Fig. 20-1). Costello and Allen (1966) describe in detail the migrations of two populations of pink shrimp, *P. duorarum.* One stock is caught on the Tortugas grounds from a short distance due west of Key West, Florida, extending about 75 nautical miles (134 km) in a westerly direction and about 50 nautical miles (90 km) in a north-south direction.

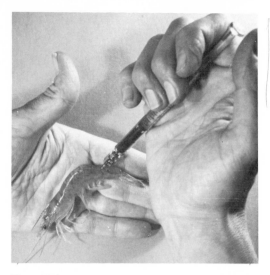

Fig. 20-1. Injecting a shrimp by hypodermic needle with a colored vital stain so that its migration may be traced.

The second stock is fished on the Sanibel grounds, which lie just offshore to about 30 miles (54 km) out, paralleling the coast from Naples, Florida, to north of the entrance to Charlotte Harbor, a distance of about 60 miles (108 km).

By marking juvenile shrimp at 15 locations from Biscayne Bay along the coast to Pine Island Sound, including the marking of some older juveniles on the fishing grounds themselves, it was discovered that the nursery grounds of the Tortugas stock include all of Florida Bay and the estuaries extending northward along the west coast at least as far as Indian Key. In traveling from their nursery grounds to the fishing area some shrimp travel at least 150 nautical miles (270 km). The Sanibel nursery grounds extend from Indian Key 55 miles (99 km) northeast to Pine Island Sound.

The Tortugas pink shrimp spawn on the western part of the Tortugas grounds so that the postlarval shrimp (about 10 to 14 mm in length) must on the average perform a journey of not less than 100 nautical miles (180 km) to reach their nursery estuaries in Florida Bay and the Everglades. Studies of the currents of the area by Koczy et al.

(1960) to determine how these tiny organisms could make such a trip show that the residual currents cannot possibly be the mechanism for their 100-mile transport. They did suggest that by remaining on the bottom during unfavorable portions of each tidal cycle and drifting with tidal currents flowing in a favorable direction, they could perform the journey in about 4 days.

The white shrimp, *Penaeus setiferus,* remains in the shallow brackish salt marshes longer than either the brown or pink shrimps, *P. aztecus* and *P. duorarum.* Consequently, they are larger before they leave the estuary. The white shrimp are seldom taken on the shelf in water over 15 fm (27 m), but brown and pink shrimp are taken out to 60 fm (110 m).

Another penaeid taken both in the Gulf and in the southern part of the U. S. Atlantic coast is the royal red shrimp, *Hymenopenaeus robustus.* In the Atlantic it ranges from the U. S. East Coast well down the east coast of South America. It is caught chiefly in depths of 140 to 300 fm (256 to 549 m). Anderson and Lindner (1971) state that it is taken in commercial quantities in three places: off the Mississippi River delta, off the Dry Tortugas, and off St. Augustine, Florida. They found that males mature at about 125 mm and females at about 155 mm total length. They had no information on developmental stages but stated that spawning, although occurring throughout the year, was at a peak from January to May. Unlike their shallow water cousins, they appear to not reach maturity until about the third year, and the minimum life span appears to be about 5 years.

Suggested readings

Anderson, W. W., and M. J. Lindner. 1971. Contributions to the biology of the royal red shrimp, Hymenopenaeus robustus Smith. U. S. Fish Wildl. Serv., Fish. Bull. **69**:313-336.

Barr, L. 1970a. Diel vertical migration of Pandalus borealis in Kachemak Bay, Alaska. J. Fish. Res. Bd. Canada 27:669-676.

Costello, T. J., and D. M. Allen. 1966. Migrations and geographic distribution of pink shrimp, Penaeus duorarum, of the Tortugas and Sanibel grounds, Florida. U. S. Fish Wildl. Serv., Fish. Bull. **65**:449-459.

Gotshall, D. W. 1972. Population size, mortality rates, and growth rates of northern California ocean shrimp, Pandalus jordani, 1965 through 1968. Calif. Fish Game, Fish Bull. **155**:1-47.

Grady, J. R. 1971. The distribution of sediment properties and shrimp catch on two shrimping grounds on the continental shelf of the Gulf of Mexico. In Proceedings of the Gulf and Caribbean Fisheries Institute, twenty-third annual session. pp. 139-148.

Holthuis, L. B., and H. Rosa, Jr. 1965. List of species of shrimps and prawns of economic value. FAO Fish. Tech. Pap. **52**:1-21.

Koczy, F. F., M. O. Rinkel, and S. J. Niskin. 1960. The current patterns on the Tortugas shrimp grounds. In Proceedings of the Gulf and Caribbean Fisheries Institute, twelfth annual session. pp. 112-125.

Kutkuhn, J. H. 1966. The role of estuaries in the development and perpetuation of commercial shrimp resources. In A symposium of estuarine fisheries. Amer. Fish. Soc., Spec. Publ. No. 3. pp. 16-36.

chapter 21

🌿 Life histories of herringlike fishes

Following Greenwood et al. (1966) I will consider clupeoid fishes as those of the order Clupeiformes belonging to the suborder Clupeoidei, i.e., the three families Clupeidae, Engraulidae, and Chirocentridae. The latter family, the wolf herrings, is of very minor commercial importance and will not be extensively discussed.

The 1970 landings of the clupeoids as reported by the FAO are shown in Table 21-1, the total being 21,358,000 metric tons. The wolf herrings contributed only 14,000 metric tons. The landings for the Clupeidae were 7,017,000 metric tons as compared to 14,341,000 metric tons for the Engraulidae. This is hardly a fair comparison because 91% of the Engraulidae landings were of only one species—the Peruvian anchoveta, *Engraulis ringens*—leaving only 1,288,000 tons of all other engraulids.

In considering their life histories it is necessary to discuss the environments occupied. As with most groups of worldwide occurrence, there are only a few species adapted to rigorous boreal conditions. The chief boreal species is *Clupea harengus,* with both Atlantic and Pacific subspecies penetrating into the Arctic Sea. Probably *Clupeonella,* with species in both the Black and Caspian Seas, should also be considered

boreal. The sprat, *Sprattus sprattus,* ranging from the Black Sea through the Mediterranean and north to Norway and the Baltic Sea, would seem to be both boreal and subtropical in distribution. However, Demir (1965) considers the north European sprats to be races distinct from those in the Mediterranean basin. This is analogous to the Pacific herring, *Clupea harengus pallasi,* which has local populations extending down the Pacific coast as far as San Diego, just north of the Mexican border. Furthermore, Demir states that the sprat lives in the northern portions of the Mediterranean and cannot tolerate temperatures above 24° C and is uncomfortable at temperatures above 19° C.

Nikol'skii (1954) states that the northern races of sprat are larger, the North Sea sprat attaining a length of 17 cm. This compares with about 12 cm for Bulgarian sprats in the Black Sea and about the same for sprats off the Spanish Mediterranean coast (Demir, 1965). As in the Pacific herring, the southern races are distinctly smaller in size. Both are boreal species that appear to be under environmental stress toward the south.

A second type of environment is offered by the coastal areas of strong upwelling.

Table 21-1. Landings of clupeoid fishes by species and area in 1970

Species	Common name	Metric tons (thousands)	Area taken
Clupea			
harengus harengus	Atlantic herring	469.7	Northwestern Atlantic, by Canada
		30.3	Northwestern Atlantic, by U. S.
		300.3	Chiefly Georges Bank, by U.S.S.R.
		1,426.0	Northeastern Atlantic
harengus pallasi	Pacific herring	350.5	Northwestern Pacific, by U.S.S.R.
		117.2	East Bering Sea, by U.S.S.R.
		98.1	Japan (0.7 Korea)
		11.0	U. S. and Canada
Sardinella			
aurita	African sardine	636.5	Gibraltar south to Angola
		110.1	Brazil
		6.0	Mediterranean, Black Sea
		3.6	Southeastern Atlantic
longiceps	Indian oil sardine	229.1	West coast of India, Pakistan
		69.7	Philippines
		1.0	Bangladesh
anchovia	Spanish sardine	41.5	Venezuela
cameronensis		0.7	Angola
spp.		1.5	Red Sea (Egypt)
Sardinops			
ocellata	South African sardine	554.9	South Africa and Namibia
		118.4	Angola
sagax sagax	Chilean sardine	68.0	Chile (0.5 Peru)
sagax caerulea	California sardine	30.1	Mexico (Pacific)
melanosticta	Japanese sardine	16.9	Japan
Sardina pilchardus	European sardine, or pilchard	171.8	Northeastern Atlantic
		156.9	Morocco
		156.7	Mediterranean
Sprattus sprattus	Sprat	147.1	Baltic Sea
		77.2	Norway to Gibraltar
		7.3	Mediterranean, Black Sea
Brevoortia			
patronus	Gulf menhaden	559.0	Gulf of Mexico, by U. S.
tyrannus	Atlantic menhaden	264.0	Maine to Florida
spp.	Menhadens	1.9	Brazil, Argentina
Ethmidium maculatus	Peruvian menhaden	19.8	Peru
Etrumeus micropus	Round herring	34.1	Japan, Taiwan, Hong Kong
		2.9	South Africa (Atlantic)
Ethmalosa fimbriata	Bonga	59.8	Gulf of Guinea
Opisthonema			
libertate	Thread herring	35.0	Ecuador
		6.0	Panama (Pacific)
oglinum	Thread herring	6.6	Venezuela
		1.1	U. S. and Cuba
Harengula spp.	Scaled sardines	3.1	Philippines
		2.1	Cuba
		1.7	Taiwan

Continued.

Table 21-1. Landings of clupeoid fishes by species and area in 1970—cont'd

Species	Common name	Metric tons (thousands)	Area taken
Alosa			
pseudoharengus	Alewife	39.2	U. S. (Atlantic)
		5.2	Canada (Atlantic)
		19.1	Off U. S. Atlantic coast by U.S.S.R.
sapidissima	American shad	3.1	U. S. (0.3 Pacific)
spp.	Various shads	4.0	France to Morocco and Turkey
Caspialosa	Shads	1.8	Caspian Sea, U.S.S.R.
		1.3	Black Sea
Paralosa, Ilisha	Hilsalike shads	22.9	Iraq to Bangladesh
		3.5	Korea
Clupanodon spp.	Short-nosed shads	7.9	Korea
		0.6	West Malaysia
Clupeonella			
deliculata deliculata	"Tyulka"	129.7	Black Sea, U.S.S.R.
deliculata caspia	"Kilka"	423.2	Caspian Sea, U.S.S.R.
Engraulis			
ringens	Peruvian anchoveta	12,277.0	Peru
		776.0	Chile
japonica	Japanese anchovy	419.5	Japan, Korea
		10.4	Taiwan (0.8 Hong Kong)
capensis	Cape anchovy	404.0	South Africa, Namibia
encrasicholus	European anchovy	180.9	Black Sea
		81.7	Mediterranean
		51.9	France to Morocco
mordax	Northern anchovy	87.5	California
anchoita	Argentine anchovy	13.6	Argentina
Cetengraulis			
mysticetus	Panamanian anchoveta	28.6	Panama (Pacific)
		3.9	Mexico (Pacific)
edentulus	Anchoveta	3.9	Venezuela
Anchoa compressa	Deepbody anchovy	0.1	Grenada
Unidentified anchovies		78.0	Chiefly Indo-Pacific
Chirocentrus dorab, C. nudus	Wolf herrings	9.4	India (both coasts)
		4.8	Malaysia
Unidentified Clupeoidei[1]		90.5	Japan to Malaysia
		92.0	India and Sri Lanka
		87.8	Yemen
		26.7	Gulf of Guinea
		14.5	All others

[1]FAO includes some fishes I omit from Clupeoidei.

Here, although the water is usually cool, the rigors of winter are absent and plankton are abundant. The species most abundant in the upwelling areas belong to the genera *Sardinella, Sardinops,* and *Engraulis.* Some members of the same genera inhabit tropical waters, but those in the upwelling areas are rather intolerant of high temperatures.

A third type of environment is offered by the estuaries. The menhadens, *Brevoortia,* thrive along the western Atlantic from New England to Texas and in much lesser abundance along the Brazilian and Argentine coasts. Two other genera, *Ethmidium* and *Ethmalosa,* are closely related to the Atlantic coast menhadens. *Ethmalosa* is the abundant bonga of the Gulf of Guinea. *Ethmidium,* not abundant, is the Peruvian menhaden,

Table 21-2. Temperatures encountered by anchovies of the genus *Engraulis**

Species	Summer (°C)	Winter (°C)	Area
mordax	10-25	5-20	West coast of United States
ringens	16-23	10-18	Peru and northern Chile
anchoita	15-25	7-20	Argentina and Brazil
capensis	15-24	15-18	Southwestern Africa
japonicus	18-27	0-20	Japan, winters in southern part of range
encrasicholus	12-17	2-10	Southern Baltic, leaves in winter
encrasicholus	12-17		North Sea, leaves in winter
encrasicholus	21-25		Sea of Azov, leaves in winter
encrasicholus	23-25	0-8	Black Sea
encrasicholus	22-28	10-17	Mediterranean
encrasicholus	22-27	16-26	Atlantic off northwest Africa
encrasicholus	16-21	10-15	Off France and Iberia
australis	15-26	12-21	Australia

*Modified from Reid, J. L. 1967. Calif. Mar. Res. Comm., CalCOFI Rep. **9**:29-33.

occurring not in the estuaries but in the upwelling area.

The fourth type of clupeoid life history is exemplified by the anadromous clupeids —the shads and river herrings. The most important U. S. genus is *Alosa,* containing the American shad, *A. sapidissima,* the alewife, *A. pseudoharengus,* and the summer (blueback) herring, *A. aestivalis.* Small numbers of twaite and Allis shad, *A. fallax* and *A. finta,* are taken from France to Morocco and in the Mediterranean. In the Black and Caspian Seas the genus *Caspialosa,* related to *Alosa* and placed in *Alosa* by Svetovidov (1952), contains both marine and anadromous species, of which some are called shad and others herring without regard to whether or not they are anadromous.

The fifth type of environment is offered by warm tropical waters. Typical genera are *Opisthonema, Etrumeus, Harengula,* and *Cetengraulis.*

The reality of these different environments is indicated by the summer and winter temperatures encountered by the anchovies of the genus *Engraulis* (Table 21-2). The closest these temperatures approach tropical temperatures is in the Mediterranean in midsummer, but this elevated temperature (less than in tropical waters) is only present in the thin surface layer. In winter the anchovies migrate away from the cold shallow waters of the southern Baltic and North Sea to the waters off France and Iberia. Similarly, they desert the cold Sea of Azov for the deeper waters of the Black Sea. The Japanese anchovy spends the winter in the southern part of its range.

Note that *Engraulis* does not choose to inhabit tropical areas except where upwelling keeps the temperature moderate. *Engraulis* is neither boreal nor tropical, avoiding both temperature extremes.

Cetengraulis, the Panamanian anchoveta that ranges from San Diego, California, to northern Peru, inhabits waters of mean monthly temperatures ranging from a low of 18° C to a high of 31° C and is obviously a tropical species.

Table 21-3 lists certain facts concerning examples from each of the five types of environment discussed.

The three examples from the family Clupeidae in Table 21-3 have a much higher ultimate age than the two from the family Engraulidae. Also, the average weight of the two anchovies was about 30 g (a little over an ounce). The smallest of the three clupeids averages about 150 g, (⅓ pound), although the largest herring I collected in Cook Inlet weighed 1 pound, and Dutch

Table 21-3. Examples of clupeoids from five environments showing features of their life histories

Item	Boreal seas	Upwelling areas	Estuaries	Fresh-salt waters	Tropical seas
Species	*Clupea harengus pallasi*	*Engraulis mordax*	*Brevoortia tyrannus*	*Alosa sapidis- sima*	*Cetengraulis mysticetus*
Common name	Pacific herring	Northern anchovy	Atlantic menhaden	American shad	Panamanian anchoveta
Range	North Pacific	California Current	Maine to Florida	Maritimes to Florida	San Diego to northern Peru
Egg type	Adhesive	Pelagic	Pelagic	Semibuoyant	Pelagic
No. of eggs (thousands)	20-60	20-30	40-60	100-600	25-50
Spawnings per year	1	2-3	1	1	1
Days to hatch	12-20	2-4	4	4-6	1
Age at ma- turity (yr)	3-4	2-3	2-3	3-6	1
Average age	5-7	2-3	3	4	Less than 1
Ultimate age	15+	4	10	7	3
Average weight (g)	150	30	460	1,000-1,800	32
Average weight (lb)	$\frac{1}{3}$	$\frac{1}{15}$	1	2-4	$\frac{1}{15}$

Harbor herring at 6 years of age were 19% heavier than those from Cook Inlet.

The majority of the Clupeoidei have pelagic eggs, but the herring has adhesive eggs that stick to whatever they come in contact with as they are extruded. The Atlantic herring usually spawns on the off-shore banks or the shelf on shingle, shells, or other hard surfaces, sometimes at a depth of as much as 200 to 250 m. The Pacific herring, on the contrary, spawns in the littoral zone, including the intertidal zone, and not much below tide level. The eggs are preferably extruded onto *Zostera* (eel-grass), *Fucus* (rockweed), *Laminaria,* or the fronds of the giant kelp, *Macrocystis,* but when vegetation is scarce they may be attached to bare rocks. That the difference in spawning habits between Atlantic and Pacific herrings is not always clear is indi-cated by Nikol'skii. Speaking of the White Sea herring, *Clupea harengus maris-alba,* he says:

The small herring spawns in the littoral zone at a water temperature ranging from 0 to 6° C.

The large herring also spawns close to the shores but at a higher water temperature (5 to 15° C). The eggs are deposited either on subaquatic vege-tation or on stones.*

He also describes the Kanin-Pechora herring, *Clupea harengus suworowi,* which occurs east of the White Sea as far as the Kara Sea, as spawning in the littoral zone.

The alewife, *Alosa pseudoharengus,* also has adherent eggs that stick to stones, sticks, and gravel. It spawns chiefly in ponds or lakes but sometimes in the quiet stretches of a stream. Its cousin, the shad, *Alosa sapidissima,* has semibuoyant eggs that a slight current will keep moving along the bottom, preventing their suffocation by sedi-ment. The black-spined shad of the Caspian Sea, *Caspialosa kessleri,* is about the same size as the American shad, reaching a weight of 1.8 kg (4 pounds). Nikol'skii (1954)

*From Nikol'skii, G. V. 1954. Special ichthyology, ed. 2. (Translated from Russian in 1961.) IPST Cat. No. 233, OTS 60-21817. Office of Technical Services, U. S. Department of Commerce, Spring-field, Va. 538 pp.

asserts that as with all herrings and shads of the genus *Caspialosa* the eggs are pelagic. However, from his description it would seem that their eggs are semibuoyant. He states that the eggs ". . . undergo development usually in the benthopelagic layers of the water while carried downstream."

For most of the Clupeoidei the eggs are pelagic and are usually found in the surface layers.

One notable feature of the clupeoids is the tendency for wide fluctuations in the success of reproduction of consecutive annual broods. This tendency is not quite so evident in those stocks inhabiting upwelling areas, which should be expected, since these areas exhibit less divergence in oceanographic conditions from year to year. Dominant year classes are more or less the rule for both Atlantic and Pacific herrings. This causes management difficulties, since fluctuations in available raw material impose an economic hardship on the fishing industry. Such hardships can be allayed to an extent by keeping fishing pressure low enough to permit maintenance of an adult population consisting of several age groups. Such an adult reservoir cushions the economic effect of dominant year classes while aiding in maintaining a large enough spawning reserve to allow the population to take full advantage of years in which conditions are favorable for successful reproduction.

It is important to consider the uses for which various species are employed. Among the Engraulidae most of the world catch is used in the manufacture of oil and fish meal. The Peruvian catch in 1970 was 97% anchovy, *Engraulis ringens,* and all were used for making fish meal for export. In a few countries a small proportion of the catch of the European anchovy, *E. encrasicholus,* is consumed fresh. In Turkey fish peddlers with baskets of anchovies going from house to house crying "hamsi hamsi" are a common sight. In some countries certain gourmet items such as anchovy paste or small cans of anchovy fillets in oil are prepared, but the great bulk of the catch is used as industrial fish. The term "industrial fish" also applies to *E. capensis, E. mordax,* and *E. japonicus.* Some of the latter species are used along with *Ammodytes* in the mariculture industry to feed yellowtail, *Seriola quinqueradiata,* raised in floating net enclosures.

In the Philippines the catch of anchovies (1970 catch of 20,000 metric tons was not identified by species) is used largely for sun-dried fish, for a salted fish paste, and for a fish sauce.

The Panamanian anchoveta, *Cetengraulis mysticetus,* is used chiefly for reduction into oil and fish meal, but some quantity is seined by the tuna clippers and kept alive in bait tanks. This species is esteemed as bait because of its hardiness, which is probably related to its tolerance for extremely high temperatures as compared with anchovies living all year in upwelling areas.

The statistics for clupeoids in tropical waters are quite inadequate because of the multiplicity of species landed by numerous small vessels. Dutt (1969) states that the landings of the oil sardine, *Sardinella longiceps,* along the west coast of India actually are normally about half those of other common clupeoids of over 20 species. He also states that the most abundant engraulids are *Stolephorus* and *Thryssa.* The 1970 FAO statistics for India showed 17,600 metric tons of unidentified anchovies.

Canned sardines may be young herring, *Clupea harengus,* of which large quantities are lightly smoked and canned (usually in oil) in small tins, principally in Canada, Maine, and Norway. The Norwegians also use sprats (labeled "brisling sardines"). French and Portuguese canned sardines are a true sardine (or pilchard), *Sardina pilchardus.* Herring are used in diverse ways —as canned fillets, salted and spiced herrings, and smoked kippers.

The menhadens, *Brevoortia,* of the U. S. Atlantic and Gulf coasts are, similar to the Peruvian anchoveta, used exclusively for reduction, since they are too bony and too oily for direct consumption.

The clupeoid fishes are the principal converters of plankton into usable protein. They are found in all seas and all environments from Arctic waters to the tropics. For instance, many biologists believe that the small anchovies of the genus *Anchoa* are the most abundant species in the estuaries and neritic waters of the Gulf of Mexico. Although not commercially fished they are an extremely important link in the food chain.

Suggested readings

Demir, M. 1965. Synopsis of biological data on sprat Sprattus sprattus (Linnaeus) 1758, rev. 1. FAO Fish. Synopsis 27.

Kinnear, B. S., and C. M. Fuss, Jr. 1971. Thread herring distribution off Florida's west coast. Comm. Fish. Rev. 33:27-39.

Reid, J. L., Jr. 1967. Oceanic environments of the genus Engraulis around the world. Calif. Mar. Res. Comm., CalCOFI Rep. 9:29-33.

Reintjes, J. W. 1969. Synopsis of biological data on the Atlantic menhaden, Brevoortia tyrannus. FAO Fish. Synopsis 42, U. S. Fish Wildl. Serv., Circ. 320:1-30.

Rounsefell, G. A. 1930a. Contribution to the biology of the Pacific herring, Clupea pallasii, and the condition of the fishery in Alaska. Doc. 1080. Bull. U. S. Bur. Fish. 45:227-320.

Rounsefell, G. A., and E. H. Dahlgren. 1935. Races of herring, Clupea pallasii, in southeastern Alaska. Bull. U. S. Bur. Fish. 48:119-141.

Warburg, C. H., and P. R. Nichols. 1967. Biology and management of the American shad and status of the fisheries, Atlantic coast of the United States, 1960. U. S. Fish Wildl. Serv., Spec. Sci. Rep. Fish. 550:1-105.

chapter 22

❧ Life histories of mackerels and tunas

This chapter on the mackerels and tunas will be confined strictly to the family Scombridae, thus omitting the Gempylidae, or snake mackerels; the Trichiuridae, or cutlass fishes; the Xiphiidae, or swordfishes; the Luvaridae, or louvars; and the Istiophoridae, or billfishes.

The family Scombridae can be conveniently divided into four subfamilies. The subfamily Gasterochismatinae is the little known group of butterfly mackerels, probably so named for the large ventral fins of the young. Whitley (1964) describes the species *Gasterochisma melampus* as lacking caudal keels. It is reported to occur in southern Australia, New Zealand, South America, South Africa, and the Falkland Islands. He states that it is probably a swift migrant, as it takes a trolled lure and is said to reach 5½ feet in length and 200 pounds in weight. Jones and Silas (1964) also state that the butterfly mackerel is an excellent sport fish. It is otherwise of very minor importance.

The other three subfamilies are the Scombrinae, or mackerels; the Thunninae, or tunas; and the Scomberomorinae, or Spanish mackerels and seerfishes. The relative commercial importance and the distribution of each major species is indicated in Table 22-1, showing both the quantity and area of capture.

Table 22-1 showes that almost two-thirds of the landings are mackerels, less than 30% are tunas, and only about 2% are Spanish mackerels.

Table 22-2 is an attempt to show the considerable differences in the areas preferred by different groups. The approximate boundaries of the areas shown in the table are as follows: central Atlantic, Gibraltar to the Congo River on the east and Cape Hatteras to Brazil on the south; and Central Pacific, the Oregon-California border to the Ecuador-Peru border on the east and from between Taiwan and the Philippines to south of Indonesia on the west. The central Atlantic, central Pacific, and Indian Ocean regions are warm seas; the remainder, except for the Mediterranean proper, are cool seas.

It is apparent that the two principal species of *Scomber* prefer cool waters. This is especially true of the Atlantic mackerel, *S. scombrus,* which ranges from Norway to Spain and into the Black Sea and from the Gulf of St. Lawrence to the mid-Atlantic states. The chub or Pacific mackerel, *Scomber japonicus,* tolerates warmer water than the Atlantic mackerel.

Text continued on p. 362.

357

Table 22-1. Mackerel and tuna landings by species and area in 1970[1]

Species	Common name	Metric tons (thousands)	Area taken
Scombrinae			
Scomber			
japonicus	Chub mackerel (Atlantic)	4.1	Mediterranean and Black Sea
	or Pacific mackerel	189.5	East Central Atlantic (139.7
	(Pacific)		U.S.S.R.)
		102.2	Southeastern Atlantic
		0.5	Caribbean
		12.0	Argentina, Brazil
		0.6	Pacific (U. S. and Mexico)
		8.8	Peru
		1,400.0	Northwestern Pacific (1,301.9
			Japan)
		1,708.6	
scombrus	Atlantic mackerel	460.2	Norway to Spain
		21.6	Mediterranean and Black Seas
		217.9	Northwestern Atlantic (128.5
			U.S.S.R.)
		699.7	
Rastrelliger			
kanagurta and	Indian mackerel and	191.9	Indian Ocean (44.9 Thailand)
brachysoma	short-bodied mackerel	176.1	Western Pacific, Thailand to
			Philippines
		368.0	
Thunninae			
Thunnus			
albacares	Yellowfin tuna	78.3	Eastern Atlantic (1.5 south-
			eastern Atlantic)
		7.9	Western Atlantic
		35.5	Indian Ocean
		88.0	East central Pacific (2.2
			northeastern Pacific)
		14.5	Southeastern Pacific
		55.3	Japan to Taiwan
		6.0	Southwestern Pacific
		285.5	
thynnus thynnus	Atlantic bluefin tuna	9.7	Mediterranean and Black Sea
		6.1	Norway to Gibraltar
		4.9	East central Atlantic
		7.1	Northwestern Atlantic (0.4
			west central Atlantic)
		27.8	
thynnus orientalis	Pacific bluefin tuna	15.2	Japan to Taiwan
		4.9	East central Pacific
		20.1	
maccoyi	Southern bluefin tuna	15.1	Southeastern Atlanic
		0.3	Southwestern Atlantic
		19.6	Indian Ocean (Japan)
		14.9	Southwestern Pacific (Japan)
		49.9	

[1]The totals for each species are not always correct because of the rounding off of many entries and the inclusion in the total of FAO estimates.

Table 22-1. Mackerel and tuna landings by species and area in 1970—cont'd

Species	Common name	Metric tons (thousands)	Area taken
obesus	Bigeye tuna	9.9	East Atlantic (3.1 southeastern Atlantic)
		1.8	West central Atlantic
		4.6	Southwestern Atlantic
		28.8	Indian Ocean
		39.2	East central Pacific (38.7 Japan)
		6.1	Southeastern Pacific (Japan)
		26.7	Japan to Taiwan
		5.8	Southwestern Pacific
		122.9	
alalunga	Albacore	33.5	Northeastern Atlantic (23.5 Spain)
		19.7	East central Atlantic
		7.9	Southeastern Atlantic (Taiwan)
		9.3	West central Atlantic (0.5 northwestern Atlantic)
		9.5	Southwestern Atlantic
		16.9	Indian Ocean
		30.6	Northeastern and east central Pacific
		0.4	Southeastern Pacific
		66.9	Japan to Taiwan
		12.6	Southwestern Pacific (0.4 Philippines)
		207.3	
Euthynnus alletteratus	Atlantic little tuna	0.6	Mediterranean
		5.9	East central Atlantic
		6.2	Angola
		0.2	Venezuela
		12.9	
affinis	Eastern little tuna	16.4	Philippines (0.4 Sarawak)
pelamis	Skipjack tuna	33.8	Morocco to Ivory Coast
		1.0	Angola
		1.8	Cuba and Brazil
		0.1	Indian Ocean
		56.0	U. S. to Ecuador
		8.7	Peru
		219.6	Japan (14.9 Taiwan)
		1.7	Southwestern Pacific
		322.7	
Auxis thazard	Frigate mackerel	17.8	Spain to Ghana (3.0 Mediterranean)
		0.5	Angola
		0.7	Venezuela
		26.7	Japan (0.8 Taiwan)
		45.7	

Continued.

Table 22-1. Mackerel and tuna landings by species and area in 1970—cont'd

Species	Common name	Metric tons (thousands)	Area taken
Sarda			
sarda	Atlantic bonito	55.2	Mediterranean, Black Sea (50.1 Turkey)
		4.8	East Atlantic (0.9 Angola)
		0.9	U. S. to Venezuela
		7.2	Argentina-Brazil
		68.1	
orientalis	Striped or oriental bonito	18.4	
chiliensis	Pacific bonito	4.2	U. S. and Mexico
		61.3	Peru (3.0 Chile)
		65.5	
Scomberomorinae			
Acanthocybium solandri	Wahoo	1.2	Mexico (Atlantic [0.1 Venezuela])
Scomberomorus			
cavalla and *regalis*	King mackerel and cero	3.2	U. S. Atlantic to Gulf of Mexico
		5.7	Mexico to Venezuela
		1.6	Brazil
		10.5	
maculatus	Spanish mackerel	5.0	U. S. Atlantic
		1.9	Cuba to Venezuela
		6.9	
tritor	West African Spanish mackerel	3.5	Ghana
sierra	Sierra	1.7	Mexico (0.4 Peru)
commerson	Seerfish	0.7	Australia[2]
		17.7	India (4.5 U.S.S.R.)[3]
niphonius	Japanese Spanish mackerel	12.3	Japan to Taiwan
spp.		26.0	Malaysia and southwestern Pacific
Various Scombroidei, Thunniformes		179.5	Worldwide

Summary

Subfamily	Common name	Metric tons (thousands)	Percent
Scombrinae	Mackerels	2,776.3	64.6
Thunninae	Tunas	1,263.2	29.4
Scomberomorinae	Spanish mackerels	80.5	1.8
Various		179.5	4.2
GRAND TOTAL		4,299.5	100.0

[2]Contains some *S. queenlandicus.*
[3]Contains some *S. guttatus,* the spotted seerfish, and *S. lineolatus,* the streaked Spanish mackerel.

Table 22-2. Distribution of landings of certain groups of Scombridae between warm and cool seas

Species or group	Landings (thousands of metric tons)			Percent		
	Mediterranean and Black Sea	North and South Atlantic and Pacific	Central Atlantic and Pacific and Indian Ocean	Mediterranean and Black Sea	North and South Atlantic and Pacific	Central Atlantic and Pacific and Indian Ocean
Scomber						
scombrus	22	678		3.1	96.9	
japonicus	4	1,529	192	0.3	88.6	11.1
Rastrelliger			560			100.0
Thunnus						
thynnus and *alalunga*	10	162	85	3.9	63.0	33.1
albacares and *obesus*		127	277		31.4	68.6
maccoyi		30	20		60.0	40.0
Euthynnus	1	239	115	0.3	67.3	32.4
Sarda	55	69	27	36.4	45.7	15.8
Auxis	3	28	16	6.4	59.6	34.0
Scomberomorus		30	50		37.5	62.5

Fig. 22-1. Pound net (dalian) for capturing bluefin tuna migrating through the Bosporus between the Black Sea and the Sea of Marmara. Note the lookout on a high platform and the two boats on the inshore side awaiting his signal to drop an apron of webbing across the entrance to prevent escape of the tuna.

The Indian mackerels, *Rastrelliger kanagurta* and *R. brachysoma,* are not separated in the statistics. In sharp contrast to the boreal *S. scombrus,* they occur wholly in warm seas throughout the Indo–west Pacific region.

Among species of the genus *Thunnus,* the bluefin tuna, *T. thynnus* (Fig. 22-1), and the albacore, *T. alalunga,* seem to prefer subtropical and even boreal waters. In summer the bluefin visits Nova Scotia, Norway, and the Black Sea, and the albacore ranges far into the north Pacific. The yellowfin tuna, *T. albacares,* and the bigeye tuna, *T. obesus,* obviously prefer tropical waters.

In the genus *Euthynnus* the principal species is the skipjack tuna, *E. pelamis,* which has a worldwide distribution in all tropical and subtropical seas but does not penetrate into water as cool as that sometimes frequented by the bluefin or albacore.

The bonitos, *Sarda,* are chiefly neritic species of both upwelling and other areas. They enter the Black Sea in large numbers and are also abundant in the Peruvian area of upwelling.

The seerfishes, king mackerels, and Spanish mackerels, subfamily Scomberomorinae, vary in size from the smaller Spanish mackerels, usually weighing only a few pounds, to the large seerfishes, e.g., the wahoo, *Acanthocybium solandri,* weighing up to 90 pounds (Beardsley and Richards, 1970). They are chiefly neritic fishes but occur around oceanic islands.

Whereas the tunas are oceanic in nature, the mackerels are not so widespread. Concerning *Scomber scombrus,* Bigelow and Schroeder state:

The mackerel is a fish of the open sea; while numbers of them, small ones especially, often enter estuaries and harbors in search of food, they never run up into fresh water. Neither are they directly dependent either on the coastline or on the bottom in any way at any stage of their lives. They are often encountered far out over the outer part of the shelf of the continent. But they are most numerous within the inner half of the continental shelf during the fishing season, and their normal range seems not to extend ocean-ward beyond the upper part of the continental slope, in which they contrast with their relatives the tunas, the bonitos, and the albacores.*

Another noteworthy difference between the mackerels and the tunas is that the ubiquitous tunas avoid waters below their preferred temperature range by performing long seasonal migrations, always remaining in near-surface waters. The Atlantic mackerels, on the other hand, avoid the cold winter temperatures on the shallower nearshore portions of the continental shelf by moving onto the deeper part of the shelf. Here the mackerel schools congregate on the bottom, as evidenced by large winter catches by the bottom-fishing otter trawls.

Reproduction is rather similar among the scombroids. They all spawn during the warmer season of the year (in their respective hemispheres) in the near-surface waters. They all appear to spawn several times during the season, as only a portion of the ova ripen at one time. The pelagic eggs hatch within about 2 days or more.

Information concerning their reproduction is summarized in Table 22-3. Information on many aspects is scanty, and it is difficult to vouch for the reliability of some of the figures given because some are based on few data. The figures on total fecundity, for instance, may be too high, as some believe that later spawnings in the same season contain fewer eggs.

Although the number of eggs per gram of fish weight is quite similar between fish of different size, it is impossible to state how many eggs are spawned by the *average* fish unless the size of the average fish is known; in several cases I have had to give merely the range of the number of eggs presumably spawned by the smallest and largest fish covered by the data, knowing that the average lies somewhere between.

The food of Scombridae is largely dependent on size. *Rastrelliger brachysoma*

---

*From Bigelow, H. B., and W. C. Schroeder. 1953. Fishes of the Gulf of Maine. U. S. Fish Wildl. Serv., Fish. Bull. **53:**1-577.

Table 22-3. Reproduction in Scombridae

Species	Maturity data						Ova data			Spawning season
	Minimum			Average			Diameter (mm)	Number spawned (thousands)		
	Age (yr)	Length (cm)	Weight (kg)	Age (yr)	Length (cm)	Weight (kg)		One time	Total	
Scomber										
scombrus (northwestern Atlantic)	2	30		3	35		1.0-1.4		400-500	May-July
japonicus (northeastern Pacific)	2	30			30-32		1.06-1.14	90		May-Aug.
Rastrelliger										
kanagurta	3	21-22			23-24		0.6-0.8	94		May-Sept.
brachysoma		15-16			16-17					
Thunnus										
alalunga	2-3	90					0.8-0.9	900-1,800		Summer (Hawaii)
albacares		90	25			47-88	0.70-1.24	1,100-6,600		May-Oct.
thynnus (Mediterranean)			15				1.05-1.12			June-July
Euthynnus										
pelamis (Atlantic)		40-45			47-81			262-1,331		Feb.-June
pelamis (India)		42			40-45			220-900		April-Sept.
affinis								210-680	800-2,500	
Sarda										
sarda								210-280	910-1,150	April-Sept.
orientalis							1.3	80-150	240-640	April-Sept.
Auxis thazard								280	1,370	April-Sept.
Scomberomorus maculatus	2	25		2-3	30	0.3	1.0	300-1,500		July-Sept.

feeds mainly on microplankton (chiefly phytoplankton), but the somewhat larger *R. kanagurta* feeds on copepods, larvae of fishes and invertebrates, and a little phytoplankton. *Scomber scombrus* appears to largely eschew phytoplankton in favor of zooplankton and even small fishes. *S. japonicus* of the northeast Pacific favors anchovies, squids, and copepods.

The Spanish mackerels are larger than the species just discussed. *Scomberomorus maculatus* feeds extensively on menhaden, alewives, herrings, and shrimp.

The tunas feed voraciously. In the northwest Atlantic the bluefin, *Thunnus thynnus,* the largest of the tunas, takes mackerel, herring, silver hake, menhaden, squid, euphausiids, and even the spiny dogfish.

The food of the skipjack tuna, *Euthynnus pelamis,* and yellowfin tuna, *Thunnus albacares,* was studied (Dragovich, 1971) for three Atlantic Ocean areas: (1) the northwestern Atlantic north of 30° N lat., (2) from the Amazon River north to the coast of Venezuela, including the West Indies from Puerto Rico south, and (3) the west coast of Africa from the Congo River north to about Sierra Leone.

For yellowfin tuna, fishes were the most important item in all three areas, about 75% by overall volume. For skipjack, fishes comprised more than 50% overall, but they were only about 25% in the first area and a little over 30% in the third area. It is noted that the yellowfin apparently tended to capture larger fishes than the skipjack, as shown by the fact that for the combined areas, the skipjack took about 25% fish by number and about 55% fish by volume, whereas the yellowfin only took about 5% fish by number yet about 75% by volume.

Other important items were crustaceans and cephalopods, which were chiefly squids.

The food of yellowfin and bigeye tunas in the Pacific was studied by King and Ikehara (1956). Although most of Dragovich's specimens of yellowfin and skipjack ranged from 40 to 60 cm in fork length, their specimens of yellowfin and bigeye were much larger, falling chiefly between 100 and 175 cm in fork length. Both species consumed by volume 62% fishes and about 30% squids, the remainder being chiefly other mollusks and a few crustaceans.

Suggested readings

Dragovich, A. 1971. The food of skipjack and yellowfin tunas in the Atlantic Ocean. NOAA, Nat. Mar. Fish. Serv., Fish. Bull. 68:445-460.

Jones, S., and H. Rosa, Jr. 1965. Synopsis of biological data on Indian mackerel Rastrelliger kanagurta (Cuvier) 1817 and short bodied mackerel Rastrelliger brachysoma (Bleeker) 1851. FAO Fish. Synopsis 29.

Jones, S., and E. G. Silas. 1964. A systematic review of the scombroid fishes of India. In Symposium on scombroid fishes, I. Marine Biological Association of India. pp. 28-105.

King, J. E., and I. I. Ikehara. 1956. Comparative study of food of bigeye and yellowfin tuna in the central Pacific. U. S. Fish Wildl. Serv., Fish. Bull. 57:61-85.

Klima, E. F. 1959. Aspects of the biology and the fishery for Spanish mackerel, Scomberomorus maculatus (Mitchill), of southern Florida. Fla. St. Bd. Conserv. Tech. Ser. 27: 1-39.

Kramer, D. 1969. Synopsis of biological data on the Pacific mackerel, Scomber japonicus Houttuyn (northeast Pacific). FAO Fish. Synopsis 40.

Raju, G. 1964. Studies of the spawning of the oceanic skipjack Katsuwonus pelamis (Linnaeus) in Minicoy waters. In Symposium on scombroid fishes, II. Marine Biological Association of India. pp. 744-768.

Silas, E. G. 1964. Aspects of the taxonomy and biology of the oriental bonito Sarda orientalis (Temminck and Schlegel). In Symposium on scombroid fishes, II. Marine Biological Association of India. pp. 283-308.

Whitley, G. P. 1964. Scombroid fishes of Australia and New Zealand. In Symposium on scombroid fishes, I. Marine Biological Association of India. pp. 221-254.

chapter 23

🌿 Life histories of bivalve mollusks

The bivalve mollusks, class Pelecypoda, embrace the oysters, mussels, clams, and scallops. Many species are considered delicacies and command very high prices, as shown in Table 6-4. In Table 23-1 I show the world production of bivalve mollusks for 1970 from the FAO statistics. Surprisingly few species of bivalves are sufficiently abundant to support a commercial fishery. However, this is not so different from man's dependence for heavy meat on cattle, sheep, and swine. Abbott and Zim (1962) estimate that the pelecypods, or lamellibranchs, the second largest class of mollusks, contain about 10,000 species, of which two thirds are marine. That is not to say that there are not a great many more noncommercial species that are captured and used for food, much as man harvests wild game. Undoubtedly a great many species were once very abundant in a restricted area but were unable to sustain a fishery of any size.

A case in point is the Pismo clam, *Tivela stultorum*. This very large and very delicious clam ranges from Santa Cruz, California (a few specimens have been taken as far north as Halfmoon Bay south of San Francisco), to Socorro Island (one of the Revillagigedo group) off the west coast of Mexico. It was so abundant on a few beaches in San Luis

Obispo County that farmers ploughed them out at low tide, using some for chicken feed. Over a 6-year period from 1916 through 1921 the *recorded* catch averaged 377,000 pounds (Weymouth, 1923). Today it is wholly a sport fishery for tourists and vacationers, kept alive only by stringent supervision. This is a fine example of a species adapted to a very narrow range of conditions; this clam lives only on unprotected beaches swept by heavy surf.

The same commentary could be made concerning the razor clams, which also inhabit only surf-swept beaches, but they prefer beaches broader and flatter than does the Pismo clam. In central Alaska they are taken at Hallo Bay and Swickshak Bay on Shelikof Strait and east of Cordova along the northern Gulf of Alaska. In a 20-year period from 1941 through 1960 the catch fell below 400,000 pounds in only 5 years. From 445,000 pounds in 1960 the catch fell in 5 years to 88,000 pounds and as late as 1969 it was still only 86,000 pounds. The same story is true of the razor clam fishery along the ocean coast of Washington. From 1926 through 1929 it produced an average of 1,435,000 pounds of clam meats; today it has difficulty exceeding 100,000 pounds. McMillin (1928) estimated the productive

Table 23-1. World production of bivalve mollusks in 1970 (thousands of metric tons, live weight)[1]

Item	Species	Weight	Source
Oysters, cupped			
Japanese (Pacific) oyster	*Crassostrea gigas*	246.5	Japan, Korea, Taiwan
		35.8	U. S.-Canada, Pacific
American oyster	*Crassostrea virginica*	312.8	U. S. Atlantic
		41.1	Mexico, Gulf
		1.2	Eastern Canada
Portuguese oyster	*Crassostrea (= Gryphaea) angulata*	48.9	Northeastern Atlantic
		0.5	Mediterranean (France)
		0.2	Senegal
Caribbean oyster	*Crassostrea rhizophora*	4.1	Cuba to Venezuela
Various	*Crassostrea* spp.	9.6	Australia–New Zealand
		0.4	Brazil
Oysters, flat			
European oyster	*Ostrea edulis*	21.2	Northeastern Atlantic
		0.1	Mediterranean and Black Seas
Chilean oyster	*Ostrea chilensis*	1.3	Mexico
		0.4	Peru and Chile
Western (Olympia) oyster	*Ostrea lurida*	0.1	Northwestern U. S.
Various	*Ostrea* spp.	5.3	Australia–New Zealand
Clams, venus			
Manila clam	*Venerupis japonica*	153.0	Japan and Korea
Grooved carpet shell	*Venerupis decussatus*	1.0	Northeastern Atlantic
Quahaug or hard clam	*Mercenaria mercenaria*	53.0	Northwestern Atlantic
Striped venus	*Venus gallina*	18.0	Northeastern Atlantic
Ocean quahaug	*Arctica islandica*	1.2	Northwestern Atlantic
Clams, surf	*Spisula solidissima*	141.5	U. S. Atlantic
Clams, *Anadara*			
"Blood" clam	*Anadara granosa*	32.0	Malaysia
"Mogai" clam	*Anadara subcrenata*	28.3	Japan
Clams, soft-shell	*Mya arenaria*	31.1	Northwestern Atlantic
Clams, razor (Solenidae)	*Siliqua patula*	0.1	Northeastern Pacific
	Ensis directus	0.2	Northeastern Atlantic
Mussels			
Edible (Europe)	*Mytilus edulis*	266.2	Northeastern Atlantic
		15.8	Mediterranean and Black Seas
		1.8	U. S. Atlantic
Bay or blue (U. S.)	*Mytilus* spp.	10.8	Korea
		6.2	Argentina
		1.3	Australia–New Zealand
		0.6	Turkey
		0.1	Mexico, Pacific
Large mussels	*Perna perna*	1.0	Venezuela and Uruguay
Cholga mussels	*Aulacomya ater*	13.0	Chile
		0.1	Argentina
Choromya and *Modiolus*		17.2	Chile and Peru

[1]Pillay (1973) states, "Pearl culture is expanding and in Japan over 100 tons of pearls, valued at above $71.5 (US) million, were produced in 1969."

Table 23-1. World production of bivalve mollusks in 1970 (thousands of metric tons, live weight)—cont'd

Item	Species	Weight	Source
Scallops			
Sea scallops	*Placopecten magellanicus*	72.5	Northwestern Atlantic
Common scallops	*Pecten maximus*	18.9	Northeastern Atlantic
Japanese scallops	*Pecten yessoensis*	16.5	Japan
Weathervane scallops	*Patinopecten caurinus*	5.1	Northwestern U. S.
Bay scallops	*Aequipecten irradians*	1.7	Eastern U. S.
Calico scallops	*Argopecten gibbus*	1.2	Eastern U. S.
Various scallops	Various	14.0	Argentina
		6.1	Australia–New Zealand
		0.5	Northeastern Atlantic
Cockles			
Common	*Cardium edule*	33.0	Northeastern Atlantic
Various	Various	3.6	Korea
		0.5	New Zealand
Arkshells	*Arca* (= *Anadara*) spp.	5.4	Venezuela

beach (35 miles long by 150 yards wide) at 2080 acres, so that the former production was 690 pounds of clam meats per acre.

Another clam, *Donax variabilis,* the coquina (one of the wedge clams, family Donacidae), was the object of a fishery in Florida that produced 54,000 pounds in 1945 but has not appeared in the catches since. This very small clam, usually not over ½ inch (12 mm) in length, is at times tremendously abundant on sandy beaches, but its abundance is so variable as to discourage a continuous commercial fishery. They are steamed for their delicious broth.

The world production of bivalves in 1970 is summarized in Table 23-2. The leading group is oysters with 41% of the total, followed by clams with 26%, mussels with 20%, scallops with 8%, cockles with 2%, and arkshells with only 0.3%. These figures from FAO are not comparable with those given in U. S. summaries because they include the weight of the shell. The shell weight itself varies considerably between species—oyster meats recovered vary from 4½ to 7½ pounds/U. S. standard bushel; soft-shell clam meats run over 12 pounds/ bushel; surf clams run about 17 pounds/ bushel; and for the ocean quahaug with its heavy shell the meats run only 10 pounds/ bushel.

Table 23-2. Summary of 1970 world production of bivalve mollusks (thousands of metric tons, live weight)

Item	Weight
Oysters	
Cupped	701.1
Flat	28.4
TOTAL	729.5
Clams	
Venus	226.2
Surf	141.5
Anadara (western Pacific)	60.3
Soft-shell	31.1
Razor	0.3
TOTAL	459.4
Mussels	
Mytilus	302.8
Other genera	31.3
TOTAL	334.1
Scallops	136.5
Cockles	37.1
Arkshells	5.4
GRAND TOTAL	1,702.0

Table 23-3. Live weight vs weight of edible portion for selected species in United States*

Species	Ratio of live weight to edible meats
Oysters	14.2
Clams	
Rangia	11.2
Hard clams	7.5
Ocean quahaugs	8.0
Surf clams	5.1
Soft-shell clams	5.0
Razor clams	2.4
Scallops	
Calico scallops	14.0
Bay scallops	9.3
Sea scallops	8.6
Mussels	5.4

*Data from FAO and 1969 Fishery statistics of the United States.

Perhaps the best idea of the difference between live weight, which includes the shell, and the weight of the edible portion can be gained by noting the figures given in the U. S. catch statistics and the live weight as transmitted to the FAO (Table 23-3).

As expected, the oysters with a ratio of 14.2:1 reflect the weight of the heavy shell. The rather high ratios of live weight to meats in the scallops is caused largely by the fact that only the adductor muscle is retained. Outside of rangia, for which the data are scanty, the clams have fairly low ratios; the highest are for the heavily shelled hard clams and ocean quahaugs. The razor clams with their thin fragile shells have by far the lowest ratio.

The species that appear in the U. S. statistics for 1969 are shown in Table 23-4. It is at once apparent that the North Atlantic (Chesapeake Bay to New England) produces the preponderance of our bivalves. In seeking the reason it is necessary to examine the environmental requirements of the various species. This is partially determined by their physical characteristics.

Both oysters and scallops have only one large adductor muscle for closing the shell; the clams, cockles, and mussels have both posterior and anterior adductors. In the clams and cockles the two are about equal, but in the mussels the anterior adductor is smaller. Scallops are easily distinguished by a lateral projection of shell on either side of the umbo.

An important factor in distribution and habitat is the mobility of the species. For example, oysters attach to hard surfaces via their left valve and, having no foot in the adult, they cannot move about even when detached from the substrate.

Mussels attach to hard objects (sometimes they attach to sand grains) by byssal threads. A few noncommercial species can exercise exceedingly slow movement by breaking off byssal threads and putting out new ones in the direction they desire to move, but the commercial species are, similar to the oyster, sessile. The clams usually have a well-developed foot by which most species can dig rapidly through soft substrate. A very few noncommercial species (family Chamidae) attach one valve to a rock or solid object. The cockles are similar to the clams but have a very highly developed foot by which they can move about rather freely, even leaping a short distance off the surface.

Adult scallops are not attached; they can move about with a flitting motion by clapping the valves together, sending out a jet of water. A few species of noncommercial scallops, *Hinnites,* sometimes called "rock oysters," attach by their right valve to hard objects.

Bearing the chief physical limitations of various groups in mind, the range and distribution of the major U. S. bivalves are shown in Table 23-5.

In Table 23-5 I attempt to clarify the discussion of habitats by breaking them into seven major divisions; the divisions may intergrade in a few instances. Rangia is a brackish water clam abundant at very low salinities. Although edible, it has been scarcely exploited except for large deposits of dead shell. One factor is its occurrence in the extreme upper portions of the estuaries,

Table 23-4. U. S. production of bivalve mollusks in 1969 (thousands of pounds of meats)

Item	Species	North Atlantic	South Atlantic	Gulf of Mexico	California	Northwest	Alaska	Total
American oyster	*Crassostrea virginica*	23,631	1,830	19,765	17			45,243
Pacific oyster	*Crassostrea gigas*				696	6,220		6,916
Western oyster	*Ostrea lurida*					40		40
Hard clams	*Mercenaria mercenaria*	15,315	383	11				15,709
Hard-shell clams	*Saxidomus giganteus*[1] and *Protothaca staminea*[2]					445		445
Manila clams	*Venerupis japonica*[3]							
Ocean quahaug	*Arctica islandica*	639						639
Sunray venus	*Macrocallista nimbosa*			636				636
Surf clam	*Spisula solidissima*	49,575						49,575
Soft-shell clam	*Mya arenaria*	13,481						13,481
Rangia	*Rangia cuneata*		40					40
Razor clams	*Siliqua patula*					117	86	203
	Ensis directus	2						2
Mixed clams						15		15
Sea mussels	*Mytilus edulis*	1,113						1,113
Sea scallops	*Placopecten magellanicus*	7,397	13					7,410
Weathervane scallop	*Patinopecten caurinus*					14	1,888	1,902
Bay scallops	*Aequipecten irradians*	1,421	613	80				2,114
Calico scallops	*Argopecten gibbus*		183	16				199
Cockles (Cardiidae)[5]		43[4]						43
GRAND TOTAL		112,617	3,062	20,508	713	6,851	1,974	145,725

[1]Butter clams.
[2]Little-neck clams.
[3]Included in hard-shell clams.
[4]Includes periwinkles.
[5]A Pacific coast species, *Clinocardium nuttalli*, although noncommercial, is sought after by sportsmen.

Table 23-5. Distribution and habitat of chief U. S. commercial bivalves

Species	Range	Habitat
Brackish water		
Rangia cuneata	Potomac River to Campeche	Low salinity (0.2 to 10.8 °/$_{00}$ in Louisiana) bays and lagoons, sand and mud
Upper estuary		
Mya arenaria	Labrador to Cape Hatteras; north Norway to Bay of Biscay; Alaska to Monterey, California; Kamchatka to south Japan	Intertidal flats protected from surf, mud or fine gravel; prefers upper estuary; rare below low tide
Venerupis japonica	Southern British Columbia to San Francisco (introduced); northwestern Pacific	Above half tide to 1 m, rarely subtidal, protected mud-gravel beach; remains close to surface; cannot withstand cold
Lower estuary		
Crassostrea virginica	Gulf of St. Lawrence; Massachusetts to Mexico; British Columbia to Morro Bay, California (introduced)	Optimum salinity 10 to 28 °/$_{00}$; firm bottom in lower estuary; lower intertidal to 10 m
Crassostrea gigas	British Columbia to Morro Bay, California (introduced); northwestern Pacific	Similar to above but can spawn successfully at much lower temperature
Ostrea lurida	Sitka to Cape San Lucas; Baja California	Chiefly firm bottom covered by water in shallow bays; only slightly subtidal but to 3 to 17 m in Yaquina Bay, Oregon; can reproduce in cooler water than either of the above
Mytilus edulis	Arctic Sea to North Carolina; Arctic Sea to Cape San Lucas, Baja, California; northeastern Atlantic	Dense beds near low tide level in sheltered waters; attached by byssal threads to rocks or hard objects; prefers strong currents
Surf-swept beach		
Siliqua patula	Bering Sea to Pismo Beach, California	Broad, flat, sandy beaches swept by surf; vertical in sand with hinge toward surf; burrows very rapidly
Tivela stultorum	Halfmoon Bay, California, to Socorro Island, Mexico	Sandy surf-swept beaches from low tide level to several meters; young use intertidal zone; near the surface with hinge toward surf

Exposed rocky shores		
Mytilus californianus	Aleutian Islands to Socorro Island, Mexico	Between tide lines; attached by byssal threads to rocks where surf is present; in summer may cause shellfish poisoning from ingested protista
Beach and shoal subtidal		
Mercenaria mercenaria[1]	Maine to Florida, abundant Massachusetts to Virginia	From high tide to 12 m in various bottoms, prefers the lower estuary
Saxidomus giganteus	Aleutian Islands to northern California	Lower third of tidal zone to 10 m on sand, gravel, or broken shell
Protothaca staminea	Aleutian Islands to Baja California	Prefers more gravel, firmer beach than *S. giganteus*
Macrocallista nimbosa	Southeastern U. S., abundant on Florida west coast	Low tide to several meters
Aequipecten irradians	Cape Cod to Texas	Lower estuaries and adjacent waters to several meters, often in eelgrass beds
Clinocardium nuttalli	Bering Sea to southern California	Sand-mud, often in eelgrass beds; does not bury deeply and moves actively; subtidal populations found in Puget Sound
Offshore		
Arctica islandica	Arctic Circle to mid-Atlantic, abundant off Long Island and New Jersey	20 to 50 m in sticky mud bottom
Spisula solidissima[2]	Gulf of St. Lawrence to Cape Hatteras	Near ocean salinities, low tide to 150 m, coarse sand and gravel; uncommon in shoal water south of Chesapeake Bay
Placopecten magellanicus	Strait of Belle Isle to Cape Hatteras	4 to 40 m in Newfoundland, to 55 m farther south; firm sand or gravel
Patinopecten caurinus	Wrangell, Alaska, to Eureka, California	Deep water, 60 to 90 m off northern California
Argopecten gibbus	South Atlantic and Gulf of Mexico, most abundant off Cape Canaveral	30 to 200 m on firm bottom

[1] May be *M. campechiensis* in south, which extends into Texas.
[2] A smaller form, *S. solidissima raveneli*, from Cape Hatteras to northern Mexico.

which are the areas most often subject to gross pollution.

The soft-shell clam, *Mya arenaria,* is most abundant on the intertidal flats of the upper estuary. In a survey of subtidal waters in Washington (Goodwin, 1973) the soft-shell clam seldom appeared in the subtidal samples. Similarly, the manila clam, *Venerupis japonica,* although abundant intertidally, was virtually absent from subtidal samples.

The lower estuary is the domain of the oyster. Although there are many other bivalves present, most of the others make more extensive use of the adjacent subtidal waters. Such bivalves I place in a different category. The bay (or blue) mussel, *Mytilus edulis,* shares the lower estuary with the oysters. Although mussels attach chiefly to hard objects, mussel beds are often established on any firm bottom, and once established the larvae can settle on the older mussels. Such beds often densely line the edges of tidal channels, where the mussels strain plentiful supplies of food from the strong current. Scattergood and Taylor (1950) state that the mussel beds in New Brunswick, Maine, New Hampshire, and part of Massachusetts are located near the low tide mark. In the Nantucket Island area the beds were not fully exposed at low tide but were in depths of about 2 to 4 m. They also mention small-sized mussels in Chatham Harbor; I have personally observed them just above and extending below low tide level. In Cape Cod Bay they indicate that the fishermen dredge for mussels at a depth of 9 to 12 m.

The confinement of oysters to the estuaries is partially dictated by the abundance of oyster drills in water of high salinity. When salinity drops, the oyster closes his shell and can endure very low salinity, especially in cool weather, for many days, but under these conditions the oyster drill's exposed foot swells and it dies. In Chapter 3 I mentioned that oyster larvae develop normally within the salinity range of 10 to 27 $^0/_{00}$, which suggests their need for the conditions usually found in the lower reaches of a typical estuary.

The third type of environment is the exposed shore of the outer coast. Here two types of conditions are involved. The sandy beach constantly swept by surf requires special adaptations for survival. The Pismo clam, *Tivela stultorum,* has short siphons, so it must remain close to the surface. However, it has a very heavy shell to resist wave action and a very strong foot to permit it to dig in quickly if exposed, or alternately, to permit it to dig out if buried, for these beaches present a very dynamic situation. The razor clam, *Siliqua patula,* also has short siphons but a very thin shell; however, its narrow elongated shape permits rapid progress through wet sand. Weymouth (1920) states that a small razor clam placed on wet sand will entirely bury itself in as little as 7 seconds.

Although only marginally commercial, a third clam that inhabits the sandy surf beaches belongs to the *Donax* genus and is called a wedge clam or bean clam. Weymouth (1920) states that *Donax gouldi,* found from Pismo Beach, California, to Cape San Lucas, Baja California, and apparently synonymous with his *Donax laevigata,* occurs from midtide to low water lying on the surface or only slightly buried. A very small clam measuring less than an inch (25 mm), it is occasionally tremendously abundant so that great numbers are easily sifted from the sand. Although abundant on exposed sand beaches, it appears at times to prefer some slight protection from the surf, such as a promontory or a sand bar. This clam is related to the coquina, *Donax variabilis,* already mentioned as being taken in Florida.

On the West Coast the exposed rocky shores subject to constant wave motion and pounding surf are the chosen habitat of the sea mussel, *Mytilus californianus* (not to be confused with the bay or blue mussel, *Mytilus edulis,* which on the Atlantic coast is sometimes also called the sea mussel to distinguish it from the freshwater mussel).

Mytilus californianus forms dense beds over the rocks from high tide to the level of the lowest ebb tide. These large mussels reach 8 inches (16 cm), in contrast to about 2 inches (4 cm) for the bay mussel, which is found on both coasts.

The sixth category of habitats I term beach and shoal subtidal. The chief difference between this category and that of the lower estuary is the greater use of areas outside of the estuary proper and the increased use of subtidal areas. The hard clams, *Mercenaria mercenaria, Saxidomus giganteus,* and *Protothaca staminea,* all inhabitat a portion of the tidal zone to several meters below low tide. Recent studies in Washington (Goodwin, 1973) show the heaviest subtidal populations of both *Saxidomus* and *Protothaca* to lie between 10 and 30 feet (3 and 9 m) below low tide, with some as deep as 50 to 70 feet (15 to 21 m).

The bay scallop, *Aequepecten irradians,* is taken in shoal water and often frequents beds of eelgrass. Gutsell (1931) states that it is found in a foot or so of water at low tide to as deep as 60 feet (18 m). The basket cockle, *Clinocardium nuttalli,* also frequents eelgrass beds, often lying only partially buried on the surface of exposed beaches, but it is also quite abundant below low tide level, being taken in over 25% of the Washington subtidal samples referred to previously (Goodwin, 1973).

Offshore bivalves (Table 23-5) include the ocean quahaug, the surf clam, and three species of scallops. These offshore species have withstood intensive fishing far better than the species confined to very specialized habitats or to a narrow fringe of coast.

Generally among bivalves the sexes are separate, but there are other possibilities. The basket cockle is hermaphroditic, simultaneously producing eggs and sperm. At a few months of age the quahaug is male, but later individuals are about evenly divided between male and female. The eastern or American oyster is protandric and functions first as a male, but there may be a few females. After the second spawning the sexes are about evenly divided. This is similar to the Pacific or Japanese oyster, *Crassostrea gigas,* the Australian oyster, *C. commercialis,* and the Portuguese oyster, *C. angulata.*

The western (Olympia) oyster, *Ostrea lurida,* is hermaphroditic and viviparous as is the European oyster, *O. edulis,* or the noncommercial *O. equestris* of the Atlantic coast. It also is protandric, maturing first as a male. Hopkins (1937) states that the sperm are ejected in balls of 250 to 2000 from the cloaca; the matrix of the ball disintegrates in seawater to free the sperm. The eggs, held in the anterior end of the mantle or branchial chamber adjacent to the gills and labial palps, are fertilized by sperm brought into the chamber with water pumped by the gills. Self-fertilization appears improbable but possible.

In *O. lurida* the period of development within the "brood chamber" is about 16½ days or less in British Columbia and about 10 to 12 days in southern California. Although the European oyster, *O. edulis,* is estimated to have about 1 million larvae in the average brood, the smaller *O. lurida* averages only 215,000 (70,000 to 355,000 in 25 broods). Hopkins (1937) states that these were below-average–sized oysters and suggests that 250,000 to 300,000 larvae is a closer estimate for the western oyster.

O. lurida spawns (releases larvae) from about mid-May through July at water temperatures of at least 14° to 16° C. In California the spawning period lasts for about 7 months. The eggs are 100 to 105 μ in diameter when discharged from the gonad. In about 3 days they have developed the swimming organ, or prototrich, and are actively swimming trochophore larvae. About the fourth day the larvae start developing small valves. This is the first conchiferous stage. The free-swimming veliger larvae are about 180 to 185 μ and are enclosed in a shell at the time of discharge.

After discharge these larvae are free swimming for about 1 month, during which time they grow from 180 μ to a size of 320

μ, which is the minimum size of newly set spat. In experiments with spat collectors Hopkins (1937) found a very great preference for setting on the undersurfaces of the collectors. He ascribed this as possibly because the larvae are in an inverted position, with the velum projecting through the valves as a flattened ciliated swimming organ whereas the heavier shell hangs downward.

The oviparous American oyster, *Crassostrea virginica,* has an enormous fecundity. Galtsoff (1930) found that one female spawns 15 to 114 million ova in a single spawning period. The Pacific oyster, *C. gigas,* discharged about 92 million eggs in three periods of spawning. It has been found that ova from oysters ranging from 2 years to 30 or 40 years of age are equally viable.

Ova of *C. virginica* usually range from 50 to 55 μ in diameter. Spawning takes place for about 2½ months in New England but extends over a protracted period in Florida. At 72° F (22.2° C) larvae will attain a size of 75 × 67 μ within 48 hours and be in the veliger stage with a straight hinge. Most larvae set between 275 and 315 μ. Larvae of the same age may begin to set as early as 18 days after fertilization and continue to set heavily for over 2 weeks.

The reproduction of the pearl oyster, *Pinctada,* is similar to that of *C. virginica.* For *P. martensi,* the principal pearl oyster of the main islands of Japan, the trochophore larva develops in a little over 4 hours, the veliger larva in 24 hours, and the straight-hinge larva (as in *C. virginica*) in 2 days at a size of 80 × 63 μ (Cahn, 1949). Cahn gives the time from fertilization to attachment of the larva at 25 days, which is roughly equivalent to the 18 days for the onset of attaching plus a setting period of 2 weeks for *C. virginica.* As in the American oyster, the pearl oyster is able to change from male to female or from female to male.

Suggested readings

Fitch, J. E. 1953. Common marine bivalves of California. Calif. Fish Game, Fish Bull. **90:** 1-102.

Galtsoff, P. S. 1964. The American oyster, Crassostrea virginica Gmelin. U. S. Fish Wildl. Serv., Fish. Bull. **64:**1-480.

Gutsell, J. S. 1931. The natural history of the bay scallop. Doc. 1100. Bull. U. S. Bur. Fish. **46:**569-632.

Hanks, R. W. 1963. The soft-shell clam. U. S. Fish Wildl. Serv., Circ. **162:**1-16.

Hopkins, A. E. 1937. Experimental observations on spawning, larval development, and setting in the Olympia oyster Ostrea lurida. Bull. U. S. Bur. Fish. **48:**439-503.

Loosanoff, V. L., and H. C. Davis. 1963. Rearing of bivalve mollusks. (Reprint.) Adv. Mar. Biol. **1:**1-136.

Quayle, D. B., and N. Bourne. 1972. The clam fisheries of British Columbia. Fish. Res. Bd. Canada, Bull. **179:**1-70.

Tarver, J. W., and R. J. Dugas. 1973. A study of the clam, Rangia cuneata, in Lake Pontchartrain and Lake Maurepas, Louisiana. Louisiana Wild Life. Fish. Comm., Tech. Bull. **5:**1-97.

Turner, H. J., Jr. 1953. A review of the biology of some commercial molluscs of the east coast of North America. In Sixth report on investigations of the shellfisheries of Massachusetts. Division of Marine Fisheries, Massachusetts. pp. 39-74.

Weymouth, F. W. 1923. The life-history and growth of the Pismo clam (Tivela stultorum Mawe). Calif. Fish Game, Fish Bull. **7:**1-120.

Weymouth, F. W., and S. H. Thompson. 1931. The age and growth of the Pacific cockle (Cardium corbis Martyn). Bull. U. S. Bur. Fish. **46:**633-641.

chapter 24

❧ Life histories of crabs

Crabs belong to the order Decapoda, which includes the shrimps. The shrimps are in the suborder Natantia; the crabs are in the suborder Reptantia. The United States, Japan, and Indochina account for about 75% of the world crab production (Table 24-1), the United States leading with 34% of the total.

Although a number of species contribute small amounts, 98% of the U. S. landings in 1969 came from four species: the blue crab, the king crab, the Dungeness crab, and the snow (tanner) crab (Tables 24-2 and 24-3).

The blue crab, *Callinectes sapidus,* ranges from Cape Cod to northern South America. The juvenile crabs inhabit the shallow estuaries, often in very low salinities. They are most numerous in the estuaries from the late autumn through the spring, moving into tidal marshes, secondary bays, and areas adjacent to streams. They mature in about 12 to 14 months.

In the spring the mature males molt first; soon afterward the females molt and during the soft-shell period are inseminated. The females now move toward deeper (and higher salinity) water. Along most of the Atlantic and Gulf coast this will be outside of the estuary or in the deeper portions of the larger bodies of water such as Chesapeake Bay, as at this time the females are seeking a salinity of over 20 $^o/_{oo}$. During this period the males remain in the estuary.

The females now extrude their eggs, which are fertilized by the sperm already stored in their sperm sacs. About 1½ to 2 million small eggs are deposited on the fringes of hair on the swimmerets between the abdomen and the body, forming a "sponge" about one third the size of the crab. The eggs are carried about by the female until they hatch in about 15 days. They hatch chiefly while the female is outside of the estuary, only occasionally in the bays. The eggs hatch into a larval stage called a zoea (about 1 mm in length) which is free swimming in the plankton.

Molting may occur as many as seven times during the zoeal stage. The zoea then change to megalops larvae, which can either swim or crawl. This stage molts only once. The megalops larvae (and some zoea larvae) enter the estuaries in spring, usually with a second influx in July. The megalops next molt into a stage (about 2.5 mm) recognizable as a small crab. When about 8 to 30 mm, these small crabs move into the shallow and brackish estuaries.

There is some disagreement as to the

Table 24-1. World production of crabs in 1970 (thousands of metric tons, live weight)

Item	Species	Weight	Source
King crab	*Paralithodes camtschatica*	24.2	Northwestern Pacific–U.S.S.R.
		7.2	Alaska-U.S.S.R.
		23.5	Alaska-U. S.
		17.8	Japan (0.2 Korea)
Southern king crab	*Lithodes antarcticus*	0.5	Southern Chile
		0.2	Southern Argentina
Snow (tanner) crab	*Chionoecetes bairdi*	7.0	Alaska-U. S.
Queen crab	*Chionoecetes* spp.	53.3	Japan[1]
Spinous spider crab	*Maia squinada*	11.7	Northeastern Atlantic
		0.1	Mediterranean–Black Sea
Blue crab	*Callinectes sapidus*	64.6	Western Atlantic–U. S.
		7.9	Northwestern Atlantic–Canada
Edible crab	*Cancer pagurus*	9.6	Northeastern Atlantic
Dungeness crab	*Cancer magister*	28.3	Northeastern Pacific
Rock crab	*Cancer irroratus*[2]	0.7	Northwestern Atlantic–U. S.
Rock crab	*Cancer* spp.[3]	0.7	California-Mexico
Stone crab	*Menippe mercenaria*	0.6	Florida
		0.2	Cuba
Green shore crab	*Carcinus maenas*	0.7	Spain
Sand (mud) crab		0.5	Australia
Miscellaneous marine crabs		66.7	Thailand-Vietnam
		33.3	Japan, Taiwan, Korea
		5.8	Philippines
		2.2	Malaysia
		0.7	Indian Ocean–Thailand
		0.4	Northeastern Atlantic–Spain
		0.8	Mediterranean–Black Sea
		3.4	Cuba to Venezuela
		19.1	Brazil
		1.8	Chile-Peru
		1.5	Africa
TOTAL		395.0	

[1]Includes Bering Sea catches.
[2]May include some Jonah crab, *C. borealis.*
[3]Probably rock crab, *C. antennarius,* with some rock (red) crab, *C. productus.*
NOTE: The 7.9 thousand tons of blue crab listed by FAO for Canada is undoubtedly an error; it is more likely the rock crab, *Cancer irroratus.*

number of molts during the zoeal stage, which is partially caused by the occurrence in the plankton of zoea larvae of smaller noncommercial species of *Callinectes.* Nichols and Keney (1963) state that along the Atlantic coast from North Carolina to Florida early stage *Callinectes* zoeae were more common than the advanced stage zoeae, although all eight stages and the megalops were present. In general, larger numbers of early stage zoeae were collected near the

Table 24-2. Percent of U. S. crabs by principal species in 1969

Species	U. S. catch (%)
Blue crab	53
King crab	22
Dungeness crab	19
Snow (tanner) crab	4
Other	2

beaches, with a progression to advanced stage zoeae occurring 20 to 40 miles off-shore; the megalops in greatest numbers were 40 or more miles offshore.

A preponderance of early stage zoeal larvae indicates a heavy natural mortality in the first stage. Adkins (1972) indicates that whereas the eggs normally hatch in shallow oceanic waters in salinity exceeding 20 $^0/_{00}$, some females may spawn in bays during times of high salinity. In this situation survival rates may be higher, as the larvae are not as dependent on wind and tidal action to transport them to a favorable environment.

The first zoeal stage may be the most critical for survival. Darnell (1959) stated that although zoea larvae consume a number of microscopic forms they grow successfully only when fed yellow dinoflagellates.

More (1969) found that blue crab catches along the Gulf side of Galveston Island contained only 3% males. Tagging studies showed that the males tend to remain in the brackish areas. These studies also showed that most of the females reached the higher salinity waters of the Gulf before forming a sponge. A few female crabs live to form a second sponge, but sampling in the Gulf surf showed these were never over 12% of the females. Very few second sponge females were caught inside the bay.

There is some question as to whether and how many times female crabs reenter the bay after hatching the eggs. More (1969) believes that most spent crabs that have spawned twice die soon afterward, but there is some evidence of an inward migration of spent female crabs in some localities.

The average weight of blue crabs from Matagorda Bay, Texas, was 255 g for males and 198 g for females. The heaviest male crab was 566 g, the heaviest female 340 g. The carapace width of commercial crabs ranged from 95 to 228 mm.

The Dungeness crab, *Cancer magister,* also called the market crab in California, ranges from Amchitka to Magdalena Bay,

Table 24-3. Distribution of U. S. production of crabs in 1969 (thousands of pounds, live weight)

Item	Species	North Atlantic	South Atlantic	Gulf of Mexico	California	Northwest	Alaska	Species total
Blue crab	*Callinectes sapidus*	62,020	41,373	33,386				136,779
Green crab	*Carcinus maenas*	54						54
Rock crab	*Cancer irroratus*[1]	1,575						1,575
Rock crab	*Cancer antennarius*[2]				500			500
Stone crab	*Menippe mercenaria*		108	1,258				1,366
Dungeness crab	*Cancer magister*				7,939	28,812	11,304	48,055
King crab	*Paralithodes camtschatica*						57,730	57,730
Snow crab	*Chionoecetes bairdi*						11,207	11,207
Red crab[3]	*Geryon quinquedens*							
Kona crab[4]	*Ranina ranina*							
GRAND TOTAL		63,649	41,481	34,644	8,439	28,812	80,241	257,266

[1] May include some Jonah crab, *C. borealis.*
[2] Probably rock crab, *C. antennarius,* with some rock (red) crab, *C. productus.*
[3] A deep water crab off U. S. Atlantic coast being developed.
[4] An Hawaiian crab.

Mexico, and is abundant from Monterey Bay to central Alaska. It has been reported to be found only in water at least 4 m deep in California, but Weymouth (1915) attributes this to the intensive fishing and quotes from an 1880 publication which stated that in years preceding 1880 immense numbers could be seined on the beaches just south of the Golden Gate on the ocean side. Weymouth states that in 1915 none could be taken there with seines. Similarly, in Humboldt Bay they could once fill a skiff in shallow water by using a pitchfork. While stormbound during the summer of 1931 in St. Mary Bay on the outside of Kruzof Island near Sitka, I quickly filled a large washtub with crabs from a shallow eelgrass bed using only a straightened fish hook lashed to a short pole. Dungeness crabs have a delicate flavor; I prefer them to lobster.

Dungeness crabs prefer sandy bottom; they are found on gravel but never on rocks. This is attributed by Weymouth (1915) to their habit of lying almost entirely buried in sand with only their stalked eyes, antennules, and antennae visible. He states that at such times they strain the oxygenated water needed for respiration from the sand. It is pulled in between the shell and the large pincers; when folded, the pincers closely fit the contour of the sides of the body and are covered with a dense plushlike coat of hair that acts as a very efficient strainer. Weymouth further states that *Cancer productus,* a much smaller crab called a rock crab or red crab in California, is not so endowed and as a result is restricted to rocky or gravelly bottom.

The male Dungeness crab in northern British Columbia reaches maturity at about 140 mm in carapace width at 3 years of age; some mature at a slightly smaller size (Butler, 1960). Females are about 100 mm in carapace width and are an estimated 2 years of age at spawning time, which of course is some time after mating. These crabs are polygamous, which is important to the management of the fishery, since in

these northern waters only the males attain the size legally permitted in the landings. In this area breeding occurs from May to September, but the ova do not mature until several months later in the autumn. The breeding usually takes place in shoal water.

The ova may number 1½ million. Extrusion (and fertilization) of the eggs takes place in the fall. The eggs hatch in the spring after being carried by the female for 7 to 10 months. After going through the zoea and megalops stages the young crabs are ready, after 3 to 4 months in the plankton, to settle on the bottom. Male crabs may reach 8 years of age and 10 inches (25 cm) in carapace width; females are much smaller.

Dungeness crabs are usually fished in 4 to 40 m of water, not in the shallow estuaries. They are reported to reach a weight of 3¾ pounds (1.7 kg), but the average crab is much smaller.

The king crab, *Paralithodes camtschatica,* belongs to the group Anomura whereas the blue and Dungeness crabs just discussed belong to the group Brachyura, or true crabs. The anomuran crabs are called lithode or "stone" crabs because of the roughness of their shell. Although the brachyuran crabs have five sets of well-developed legs (one pair is the large chelae or pincers), the anomurans have only four sets (the fifth set is extremely small) and the chelae are also quite small. In the blue crab the posterior set have flattened ends or paddles that enable it to swim with great facility.

The king crab ranges from southeastern Alaska to the northern Bering Sea and down the Asiatic coast to the Okhotsk Sea. It is a very large crab; Rees (1963) states that male crabs with an overall spread of 4 to 5 feet and weighing 15 pounds or more are not uncommon. The much smaller purple king crab, *Paralithodes platypus,* ranges from St. Lawrence Island to Icy Strait but is apparently not sufficiently numerous to support a fishery.

The king crab is not a shoal water species; in the Bering Sea they mate in 33 to 46 m and in north Pacific waters in 9 to 36 m. The males molt during the winter and are thus hard-shelled when the females molt in the spring.

The female king crab carries the 150,000 to 400,000 fertilized eggs for nearly a year. In the spring the eggs hatch into free-swimming zoea larvae. Immediately after the eggs hatch the female crab molts and then mates again before the shell hardens. Soon the female extrudes another batch of eggs, so that there is only a period of about 2 weeks or so during the year when the female king crab is not carrying eggs.

Very young king crabs up to about 12 cm in carapace width tend to inhabit shoal water (27 to 55 m) and to be very unevenly distributed as they congregate in "pods" of thousands of small crabs. The larger crabs are distributed from 9 to 183 m and perhaps deeper. King crabs prefer a substrate of mud or sand and mud but are sometimes found on broken shell.

The canning of king crab commenced near Otaru, Hokkaidō, about 1892 (Japan Times, 1935). It languished until about 1908 when several canneries operated in Hokkaidō and Karafuto. After the great earthquake and fire of 1923 it expanded rapidly, and floating crab canneries (the first experimental cannery sailed in 1916) began exploiting the Kamchatka fishing grounds; there were 15 floating crab canneries by 1923. In 1930 the Japanese production of canned king crab reached 580,000 cases, of which 226,000 cases was sold in the United States.

The American king crab industry got off to a very slow start. A salmon cannery in Seldovia canned 70 cases in 1920 and continued producing a few cases; their last recorded pack was 87 cases in 1925. In the summer of 1925 I observed a few king crabs in floating live cars alongside the cannery wharf in Seldovia. This was the end of the king crab fishery until a small pack by a floating cannery in the Bering Sea in 1938; the venture was unprofitable. Ten years later the government-sponsored

Pacific Explorer packed crabs taken by 10 boats using tangle nets and otter trawls in the Bering Sea north of Amak Island and in Pavlof Bay; this also was not a signal success. King crab production first exceeded 5 million pounds in 1954; by 1961 it was 43 million pounds. Presently the greatest production is from Kodiak, Cook Inlet, and south of the Alaska Peninsula. Tangle nets were outlawed in 1955, and otter trawling was excluded from inside waters; the present catch is taken by huge pots.

The snow crabs (once called "tanner" crabs), *Chionoecetes bairdi, C. opilio,* and *C. tanneri,* belong to the superfamily Oxyrhyncha or "sharp-nosed" crabs, usually called spider crabs because of the long slender legs in proportion to the body.

For many years *Chionoecetes* was generally referred to as deep water species, but *C. bairdi* is also abundant on the flats of the southeastern Bering Sea and makes up about 95% of the U. S. snow crab landings from Alaska. According to Hosie and Gaumer (1974) *C. bairdi* occurs sparsely as far south as Oregon in 125 to 190 fm (229 to 347 m). The original tanner crab, *C. tanneri,* often confused with *C. bairdi,* occurs in deeper water than *C. bairdi.* For example, off Oregon it occurs on the middle and lower continental shelf at 226 to 1050 fm (413 to 1920 m). A third closely related species, *C. opilio,* occurs in the Bering Sea, and according to Zahn (1970) it is not differentiated from *C. bairdi* in the Japanese crab pack, which FAO lists as queen crab, an apparently meaningless appellation.

The Japanese began fishing snow crabs in the Olyutorshiy Zaliv (Gulf) on the northern Kamchatka coast of the western Bering Sea (60° N lat.) due west of Nunivak Island. Finding spider crabs in abundance near the Pribilof Islands and just north of the Alaska Peninsula, they fished them to compensate for a declining abundance of king crabs, especially following the 1965 United States–Japan King Crab Agreement that placed a quota on the Japanese eastern Bering Sea crab catch.

The special pots and fishing methods they developed are discussed in Chapter 8.

The snow crab may reach 5 to 6 inches (13 to 15 cm) across the carapace with a stretch of 2½ feet (0.75 m) between the tips of the legs; they may reach a weight of 2¼ pounds. Most of the fishing is between 30 and 50 fm (55 and 91 m).

Several other crabs along the U. S. coast support minor fisheries. The green crab, *Carcinus maenas,* occurs in Europe and also along the Atlantic Coast north of New Jersey. Although formerly occurring northward only as far as Cape Cod, it has spread through New England where it is very destructive to soft-shell clams and is even entering the Maritimes. A few are caught in New England in small pots and sold chiefly as sport fishery bait.

The stone crab, *Menippe mercenaria,* ranges from Cape Lookout, North Carolina, to Yucatan, the Bahamas, Cuba, and Jamaica. Although not sufficiently abundant in the United States, except in Florida, to support a regular commercial fishery, they are very destructive to oysters. Menzel and Hopkins (1956) found while experimenting with oysters in Louisiana that stone crabs could break the shell and kill the largest oysters they could find, and that even small 2-inch (5 cm) stone crabs could kill market-size oysters. Averaged over an entire year, a stone crab would kill about 0.6 oysters/day.

The stone crab is caught for its large claws, which I have enjoyed as a gourmet item in Florida. The fishermen usually break off the claws and release the crabs to regenerate new claws, since there is little meat in the body. The very young crabs live in the deeper, saltier channels of the estuaries, moving to shallower water when about ½ inch (12 mm) in width; they hide among shells and rocks or around pilings. When nearly full size they make burrows just below the tide level that are about 6 inches in diameter and 12 to 20 inches long.

The rock crab, *Cancer irroratus,* ranges from the Maritimes to the south Atlantic states but is not very abundant south of New England. The Jonah crab, *C. borealis,* occupies the same range. Both reach up to 6 inches (15 cm) in width and are caught principally in modified lobster pots. The abundance of lobsters in the same area has discouraged full use of these crabs, even though they yield as much meat of as high a quality as the blue crab. The statistics of catch are probably too low because these crabs are often picked by families of lobstermen and the meat sold locally. Both crabs are found at depths from low tide to several hundred feet. The rock crab is more often taken in bays, the Jonah crab preferring the outer coast.

The deep-sea red crab, *Geryon quinquedens,* ranges from Nova Scotia to Brazil. South of New England it is rare in less than 170 fm (310 m), with most found between 250 and 300 fm (457 and 548 m). In the Gulf of Mexico and off Brazil it has been taken in 700 fm (2508 m). It is about twice as large as the blue crab and reaches 2¼ pounds. Although the meat is of good quality, the depth at which it lives has discouraged commercial use in the past.

The occurrence of red crabs in the deep water catches of the offshore lobster trawlers since the 1950's stimulated interest. In 1973 two plants—one in New Bedford, Massachusetts, and the other at Point Judith, Rhode Island—started processing them, paying the fishermen up to 30 cents a pound. In the north they are most abundant at depths of 1200 to 2000 feet (366 to 610 m) and temperatures of 38° to 43° F (3.3° to 6.1° C), so they can be classified as a mesobenthic species (University of Rhode Island, 1974).

Suggested readings

Adkins, G. 1972. A study of the blue crab fishery in Louisiana. Louisiana Wild Life Fish. Comm., Tech. Bull. 3:1-57.

Butler, T. H. 1960. Maturity and breeding of the Pacific edible crab, Cancer magister Dana. J. Fish. Res. Bd. Canada 17:641-646.

Leary, S. P. 1964. The crabs of Texas. Texas Parks Wildl. Dept., Bull. 43:1-57.

More, W. R. 1969. A contribution to the biology of the blue crab (Callinectes sapidus Rathbun) in Texas, with a description of the fishery. Texas Parks Wildl. Dept., Tech. Ser. **1:**1-31.

Pearson, J. C. 1948. Fluctuations in the abundance of the blue crab in Chesapeake Bay. U. S. Fish Wildl. Serv., Res. Rep. **14:**1-26.

Rees, G. H. 1963. Edible crabs of the United States. U. S. Fish Wildl. Serv., Fish. Leaf. **550:** 1-18.

Turner, H. J., Jr. 1953a. The edible crab fishery of Massachusetts. In Sixth report on investigations of the shellfisheries of Massachusetts, Division of Marine Fisheries, Massachusetts. pp. 25-28.

Wallace, M. M., C. J. Pertuit, and A. R. Hvatum. 1949. Contribution to the biology of the king crab (Paralithodes camtschatica Tilesius). U. S. Fish Wildl. Serv., Fish. Leaf. **340:**1-50.

Weymouth, F. W. 1915. Contributions to the life-history of the Pacific coast edible crab (Cancer magister). In Report of the British Columbia Commissioner of Fisheries for 1914 (1915). pp. 123-129.

Williams, A. B. 1965. Marine decapod crustaceans of the Carolinas. U. S. Fish Wildl. Serv., Fish. Bull. **65:**1-298.

chapter 25

❧ Life histories of flatfishes

Following Greenwood et al. (1966), I consider the flatfishes, order Pleuronectiformes (Heterosomata), to belong to three suborders—Psettodoidei, Pleuronectoidei, and Soloidei.

The first suborder, Psettodoidei, is distinguished from the other flatfishes by a dorsal fin that does not reach the head, by spines in the fins, and by the left eye migrating only to the edge of the head (forehead). There are only two noncommercial species; one extends from the Red Sea and Indian Ocean to the Indo-Malayan Archipelago; the other is found on the coast of tropical West Africa. They show no recorded landings in the summary of world flatfish catches (Table 25-1).

The suborder Soleoidei is somewhat more important because it includes two families—the Soleidae, or true soles, and the Cynoglossidae, or tonguefishes. In this suborder the edge of the preoperculum is not free and is covered with skin and scales, the eyes are small and close together, the mouth is very small and twisted, and teeth are rudimentary or lacking. The Cynoglossidae (tonguefishes) are easily distinguished from the Soleidae by the dorsal and anal fins being confluent with the caudal fin.

The tonguefishes consist of many species distributed worldwide in tropical seas. They are small fishes and thus seldom fished, contributing only about 0.5% of the world flatfish landings. The Soleidae are more important; the common sole, *Solea solea* comprises 4.1% of the world landings. The soles are represented on the American Atlantic coast by the hogchoker, *Trinectes maculatus,* and a few other small soles, the maximum length being 6 inches (15 cm).

The third suborder, Pleuronectoidei, accounts for about 95.4% of the world landings of identified flatfishes. This suborder can be divided into two to several families according to inclination. The most usual division is into the lefteye flounders, or Bothidae, and the righteye flounders, or Pleuronectidae, an obviously artificial division. The American Fisheries Society (Committee on Names of Fishes, 1970) places all flatfishes of the United States and Canada in only four families. Since the tropical Psettodidae do not occur in this region, I assume that they may recognize five families of flatfishes. However, Lagler et al. (1962) give only four families of world flatfishes, but their list is titled "List of Common and Representative Families

Table 25-1. Estimate of world production of flatfishes (thousands of metric tons, live weight)*

Item	Species	Weight	Source
Psettodoidei			
Psettodidae	*Psettodes erumei*	0.0	Red Sea, Indian Ocean, and Indo-Malayan Archipelago
	Psettodes belcheri	0.0	Tropical west Africa
Soleoidei			
Soleidae (true soles)			
Common sole	*Solea solea*	25.4	Denmark to France
		1.6	Southern British Isles
		3.1	Spain-Portugal
		3.9	Mediterranean–Black Sea
West coast sole	*Austroglossus microlepis*	1.1	Angola to South Africa
Agulhas sole	*Austroglossus pectoralis*	1.1	Agulhas Bank
Cynoglossidae (tonguefishes)		1.5	Tropical east Atlantic
		0.4	Eastern Indian Ocean
		2.7	Sarawak to Korea
Pleuronectoidei			
Bothidae (lefteye flounders, turbots, flukes)			
European turbot	*Rhombus maximus*	3.6	Denmark to France
		1.4	British Isles
		0.1	Mediterranean-France
Black Sea turbot	*Rhombus maeoticus*	2.8	Turkey (0.1 Romania)
Megrim	*Lepidorhombus whiffiagonis*	0.1	Iceland
		8.4	Belgium to France
		1.4	British Isles
		11.1	Spain[1]
Brill	*Scophthalmus rhombus*	0.8	Denmark to Belgium
		0.3	Southern British Isles
		0.1	Spain
Northern fluke (summer flounder)	*Paralichthys dentatus*	0.1	New England[2]
		0.9	Middle Atlantic[2]
		0.7	Chesapeake[2]
Southern fluke (southern flounder)	*Paralichthys lethostigma*	1.3	South Atlantic[2]
		0.7	Gulf of Mexico by U. S.[2]
California halibut	*Paralichthys californicus*	1.3	California[2]
Bastard halibut	*Paralichthys olivaceous*	7.2	Japan
		3.1	Korea
Sand dab	*Citharichthys sordidus*	0.3	California[2]
Pleuronectidae (righteye flounders, halibuts, "soles")			
Atlantic halibut	*Hippoglossus hippoglossus*	1.7	Iceland–Faroe Islands
		2.7	Norway
		0.7	Denmark to Belgium
		1.5	British Isles
		2.1	Northwestern Atlantic by Canada
		0.5	Northwestern Atlantic (0.1 U. S.)

*Data From FAO except where otherwise indicated. *Continued.*
[1]Includes some *L. bosci.*
[2]Year 1969 from National Marine Fisheries Service. 1972. Stat. Digest **63**:1-474.

Table 25-1. Estimate of world production of flatfishes (thousands of metric tons, live weight)—cont'd

Item	Species	Weight	Source
Pacific halibut	*Hippoglossus stenolepis*	0.3	Bering Sea (Japan)[3]
		17.6	Northeastern Pacific–Bering Sea (Canada)
		15.7	Northeastern Pacific–Bering Sea (U. S.)
		26.1	North Pacific–U.S.S.R. (FAO reports northeastern Pacific)
		—	Northwestern Pacific (Japan)
Greenland halibut	*Reinhardtius hippoglossoides*	11.5	Iceland–Faroe Islands
		75.7	Barents-Norwegian Seas
		1.2	Greenland
		12.9	Northwestern Atlantic by Canada
		16.5	Northwestern Atlantic by Europeans
Arrowtooth halibut	*Atherestes stomias*	6.6	Bering Sea–Japan[3]
		2.1	Northeastern Pacific–Japan[3]
Kamchatka flounder	*Atherestes evermanni*	31.5	Northwestern Pacific–Japan
American plaice (dab)	*Hippogossoides platessoides*	87.1	Northwestern Atlantic–Canada[4]
		3.5	Northwestern Atlantic–U. S.
		2.5	Northwestern Atlantic–Europe
Flathead sole	*Hippoglossoides elassodon*	6.6	Japan (FAO reports *H. dubius*)
		18.1	Bering Sea–Japan[3]
		0.1	Northeastern Pacific–Japan[3]
European plaice	*Pleuronectes platessa*	8.5	Iceland–Faroe Islands
		1.7	Sweden–Norway
		108.9	Denmark to Belgium
		51.4	British Isles
		4.9	France (0.1 Mediterranean)
Yellowtail flounder	*Limanda ferruginea*	20.0	Newfoundland
		4.3	Maritimes[4]
		0.2	Northwestern Atlantic by Europeans
		29.5	New England[2]
		2.3	Middle Atlantic[2]
Common dab	*Limanda limanda*	10.4	Sweden to France
		1.5	British Isles
Yellowfin sole	*Limanda aspera*	46.5	Bering Sea–Japan
		—	Bering Sea–U.S.S.R.
Winter flounder	*Pseudopleuronectes americanus*	3.4	Maritimes
		10.3	New England[2]
		0.8	Middle Atlantic[2]
		0.2	Chesapeake[2]
Yellow striped flounder	*Pseudopleuronectes herzensteini*	11.5	Japan
		21.6	Korea
Gray sole (witch)	*Glyptocephalus cynoglossus*	0.2	Iceland
		0.6	Sweden to Belgium
		0.8	British Isles
		9.1	Newfoundland

[3]Year 1970 from International North Pacific Fisheries Commission. 1972. Annual report, 1970. Vancouver, Canada. pp. 1-120.
[4]Includes landings of St.-Pierre and Miquelon.

Table 25-1. Estimate of world production of flatfishes (thousands of metric tons, live weight)—cont'd

Item	Species	Weight	Source
		7.6	Maritimes[1]
		3.6	Northwestern Atlantic by Poland
		2.5	New England
Rex sole	*Glyptocephalus zachirus*	1.0	California[2]
		0.1	Northeastern Pacific[6]
Hireguro fluke	*Glyptocephalus stelleri*	11.9	Japan[5]
Lemon sole	*Microstomus kitt*	0.3	Iceland
		1.6	Sweden to Belgium
		4.3	British Isles
Dover sole	*Microstomus pacificus*	3.0	British Columbia[7]
		6.9	Washington-Oregon[7]
		14.2	California[7]
Slime flounder	*Microstomus achne*	6.1	Japan[5]
European flounder	*Platichthys flesus*	4.7	Sweden to Belgium
		0.2	Southern England
Starry flounder	*Platichthys stellatus*	0.1	British Columbia
Petrale sole	*Eopsetta jordani*	0.5	British Columbia[7]
		1.5	Washington-Oregon[7]
		1.7	California[7]
Roundnosed flounder	*Eopsetta grigorjewi*	2.7	Japan[5]
Frog flounder	*Pleuronichthys cornutus*	2.0	Japan[5]
Hornyhead turbot	*Pleuronichthys verticalis*	1.1	Northeastern Pacific[6]
Sohachi flounder (pointed head flounder)	*Cleisthenes herzensteini*	20.3	Japan[5]
English sole	*Parophrys vetulus*	0.7	British Columbia[7]
		1.4	Washington-Oregon[7]
		1.4	California[7]
		0.2	Northeastern Pacific[6]
Rock sole	*Lepidopsetta bilineata*	8.3	Bering Sea by Japan[3]
		2.0	British Columbia[7]
		0.3	Washington-Oregon[7]
Sand sole	*Psettichthys melanostictus*	0.1	California[2]
Sand flounder	*Rhombosolea* spp.	0.1	Australia
		1.1	New Zealand
Miscellaneous unidentified flatfishes		197.3	U.S.S.R.
		120.4	Japan
		137.9	Other countries
TOTAL		1,348.9	

[5]Year 1967, which was latest Japanese report on this species in FAO reports.
[6]Year 1965; used for fur farm food mixed with other species (Niska, 1969).
[7]Year 1971 from Pacific Marine Fisheries Commission. 1972. Twenty-fourth annual report for 1971. Portland, Ore. pp. 1-44.

of Living Fishes." Assuming that they considered Psettodidae to be an uncommon family, they may recognize five families. This appears likely, since Reeve M. Bailey, chairman of the American Fisheries Society committee, states that there are six families of Pleuronectiformes (Bailey and Cavender, 1971). This is only one short of the seven families recognized by Greenwood et al. (1966). I do not attempt to divide the Pleuronectoidei into several families, even though the division into only two families is ill adapted to explaining such a diverse group.

Table 25-2. Percent of identified flatfishes of each family landed

Family	Identified flatfishes (%)
Psettodidae	0.0
Cynoglossidae	0.5
Soleidae	4.1
Bothidae	5.1
Pleuronectidae	90.3
TOTAL	100.0

The relative commercial importance of the flatfish groups is apparent if the percent each group forms of the identified flatfishes listed in Table 25-1 is determined (Table 25-2).

Because they remain on or close to the bottom, depth is one of the chief factors in the distribution and abundance of the flatfishes. This was recognized by Moiseev (1946), Nikol'skii (1954), and Alverson et al. (1964). Alverson et al. divide the flatfishes into three habitat groups that they define as:

1. Coastal (inner sublittoral), with the maximum density of the fish at depths less than 20 fm (55 m)
2. Shallow water (outer sublittoral), for fish living on the continental shelf and at times on the upper slope down to 100 to 149 fm (183 to 274 m), with their maximum density on the shelf at depths over 20 fm (55 m)
3. Deep water (bathyl), for fish most abundant on the outer shelf and continental slopes to 500 fm (914 m)

Their third category fits into my mesobenthic habitat (Chapter 6). However, the deep-sea sole, *Embassichthys bathybius,* which they caught only at depths greater than 400 fm (732 m), I classify as archibenthic. The first of their categories is closely akin to what I define as shore species except that, unlike pelagic species, the chief constraint for flatfishes is depth rather than proximity to land.

A few flatfishes habitually enter streams.

Nikol'skii (1954) reports a sole, *Achirus achirus,* that migrates 1000 km up the Amazon River. He mentions the turbot, *Rhombus maximus,* and the brill, *Rhombus rhombus,* entering the fresh water above estuarine areas of rivers. He states that the starry flounder, *Platichthys stellatus,* ascends the Amur River as far as Nikolaevsk, about 30 km upriver. The European flounder, *Platichthys flesus* (he calls it the river flounder), he reports as occasionally ascending considerable distances up rivers, adding that the young ascend farther upriver than the adults. Nikol'skii further states that the circumpolar Arctic flounder, *Liopsetta glacialis,* usually lives in the coastal zone and ascends rivers; it ascends far up the North Dvina and Vyga rivers. The winter flounder, *Pseudopleuronectes americanus,* also enters fresh water. Bigelow and Schroeder (1953) mention catching them in the Susquehanna River where the water was fresh enough to drink. The hogchoker, *Trinectes maculatus,* is also reported by them as frequenting brackish waters and sometimes running up into fresh water.

The habitats of a number of flatfishes are shown in Table 25-3. I have indicated with asterisks several species that enter streams. Probably there are additional epibenthic species that either enter streams or tarry in brackish waters. On the other hand a few epibenthic species such as the yellowtail flounder, *Limanda ferruginea,* while very scarce below 100 m, do not like to venture into shoal water; Bigelow and Schroeder (1953) give 5 to 7 fm (9 to 13 m) as the upper limit of the preferred habitat.

The halibut may spend time on the continental slope, but it also spends time in very shoal water. At Seldovia I observed very large halibut among wharf pilings in a couple of feet (⅔ m) of water feasting on salmon offal, and it is well known that large halibut congregate about the mouths of salmon streams to catch any unwary migrant. They are very fast, predacious

Table 25-3. Habitat classification of certain flatfishes

Epibenthic	Mesobenthic	Archibenthic
*Rhombus maximus[2]	Hippoglossus hippoglossus[4]	Embassichthys bathybius[3]
*Scophthalmus rhombus[2]	Hippoglossus stenolepis[3]	
*Pseudopleuronectes americanus[4, 5]	Reinhardtius hippoglossoides[2]	
*Platichthys stellatus[2, 3]	Reinhardtius hippoglossoides	
*Platichthys flesus[2]	matsuurae[2]	
*Paralichthys lethostigma	Atherester stomias[2, 3]	
*Liopsetta glacialis[2]	Atherester evermanni[2]	
*Trinectes maculatus[4]	Hippoglossoides elassodon[3]	
Solea solea[2]	Hippoglossoides platessoides[2, 4, 5]	
Psettodes erumei[2]	Glyptocephalus zachirus[3]	
Psettodes belcheri[2]	Glyptocephalus cynoglossus[4, 5]	
Rhombus maeoticus[2]	Glyptocephalus stelleri[1]	
Paralichthys dentatus[4]	Microstomus pacificus[3, 6]	
Citharichthys sordidus[3]	Eopsetta jordani[3]	
Pleuronectes platessa[2]	Cleisthenes herzensteini[1, 2]	
Pleuronectes quadrituberculatus[2, 3]	Parophrys vetulus[3]	
Limanda aspera[1, 2, 3]		
Limanda ferruginea[5]		
Lepidopsetta bilineata[3]		
Liopsetta putnami[4]		
Scophthalmus aquosus[4]		
Psettichthys melanostictus[7]		

*Flatfishes known to enter streams.
[1]Moiseev, 1946; northwestern Pacific.
[2]Nikol'skii, 1954; waters fished by U.S.S.R.
[3]Alverson et. al., 1964; northeastern Pacific.
[4]Bigelow and Schroeder, 1953; northwestern Atlantic.
[5]Rounsefell, 1957; New England banks.
[6]Hagerman, 1952; California.
[7]Hart, 1973; western Canada.
NOTE: *Parophrys vetulus* is shown as mesobenthic in Fig. 40 but epibenthic in Fig. 3 of Alverson et al. (1964).

fish that do not mind leaving the bottom in search of prey. Similarly, in New England the northern fluke, *Paralichthys dentatus,* will follow the offered bait or lure to the surface without the slightest hesitation.

It may be noted that all but four of the mesobenthic species listed in Table 25-3 are from the Pacific coast. This is perhaps influenced by the narrow shelf and paucity of shallow estuarine waters along the North Pacific coast. Only in the Bering Sea are there extensive shallow flats.

Flatfish vary greatly in size from the halibut, exceeded by few fishes, to some tiny soles rarely more than 6 inches (15 cm). Size is a large factor in commercial value because of the great waste of both labor and raw material in filleting very small fish. A few species such as the arrowtooth flounder, *Atherester stomias,* are a desirable size but the flesh is too soft; consequently, they are used principally for mink feed.

Table 25-4 offers some data on size. Sizes are difficult to compare because of differences in shape. A gray sole is very thin and weighs much less for its length than the winter flounder. Thin compressed species are always less valuable because only skilled filleters can process them without excessive waste.

For delicious eating, I cannot decide whether to plump for broiled southern fluke, *Paralichthys lethostigma,* or baked steaks

Table 25-4. Size of certain flatfishes

Species	Average		Maximum		Greatest age attained	Where
	kg	cm	kg	cm		
Hippoglossus						
hippoglossus	2.3		317.5	274		
stenolepis	13.6-15.9		230.0	267	42 (female)	Pacific
					27 (male)	Pacific
Reinhardtius hippoglossoides			11.3	102		Atlantic
	2-4	60-80				Barents Sea
Rhombus						
maximus				100		
maeoticus			15.0	85		Black Sea
Paralichthys			16.0	100		
californicus						
dentatus	0.9-2.3		11.8	94		Northwestern Atlantic
lethostigma			11.8			Texas
Platichthys						
stellatus	2-4	60	9.1	91		Northeastern Pacific
flesus				40-48	12	
Atherestes stomias				84		
Hippoglossoides platessoides			6.4	83	24-30	Northwestern Atlantic
Pleuronectes						
platessa		35-40		80	20	Barents Sea
quadrituberculatus	1.0	39	3.0	60		West Kamchatka
	0.55	36				Tatar Strait
Psettodes spp.				70		
Microstomus pacificus		39-46		71	15+	
Eopsetta jordani				70	25	
Pseudopleuronectes americanus	0.7-0.9	31-38	3.6	64		
Glyptocephalus						
cynoglossus			1.8	64		
zachirus		28		59	24	
Psettichthys melanostictus				63		
Solea solea				61		
Lepidopsetta bilineata		33		60		
Parophrys vetulus		30		57		
Hippoglossoides platessoides				52	19	Barents Sea
Embassichthys bathybius				47		
Isopsetta isolepis				46	11	
Limanda						
aspera		29		45		East Bering Sea
	0.35			40		Kamchatka
limanda			0.7	40		

of "kalkan," the large, juicy, Black Sea turbot, *Rhombus maeoticus*. My judgment might be warped by atmosphere, but it is not easy to choose between a bayou lined with huge live oaks festooned with Spanish moss or a shady hillside grape arbor overlooking the cliffs of the Bosphorus. For my taste halibut is a mite too dry and does not possess the delicate flavor of some of the lesser known flounders.

In describing the life histories of flatfishes I start with fecundity and spawning (Table 25-5). The age at maturity of flatfishes averages somewhat higher than for roundfishes of comparable weight. The age at maturity varies considerably for the same species from one area to another, so that all averages are generalizations.

The majority of the flatfishes that spawn off the shelf (in general over 200 m) spawn during the winter months. Most of the spawning in water of a depth less than 200 m occurs from late winter to late spring or summer. An exception is the Arctic flounder, *Liopsetta glacialis,* which spawns in shoal water in the Kara Inlet in late winter at subzero temperatures. After reaching maturity this flounder is reported to spawn only every other year. Most flatfish eggs are planktonic, but those of the winter flounder, *Pseudopleuronectes americanus,* are adherent.

The larvae of all the flatfishes and the eggs of all but a few are part of the zooplankton. Although the eggs of some species float in surface or near-surface layers, most flatfish eggs control their specific gravity so as to float somewhat below the surface.

The halibut, the most thoroughly studied North American flatfish, exemplifies flatfish biology. Thompson and Van Cleve (1936) show in their Fig. 4 (which is based on Fig. 6 of Broch, 1933) the boreal regions of the North Atlantic. These areas correspond well with the commercial distribution of Atlantic halibut, *Hippoglossus hippoglossus.* The Atlantic halibut is found on the southern and western Icelandic banks, avoiding the colder northeastern coast. Halibut are taken around the Faroe Islands, on Rockall Bank, and along the edge of the European continental shelf from just northwest of Ireland to Finmarken. They occur in low abundance in the southern Barents Sea off the Murman and White Sea coasts and along the edge of the Barents Sea shelf from Bear Island to Spitzbergen. They do not occur on the cold coast of East Greenland but are found along the coast of West Greenland as far as Davis Strait. They occur in light abundance along the edge of the southern Labrador coast, in the Gulf of St. Lawrence, and along the edges of the Grand Bank. They are taken in some quantity on rough ground all along the edges of the Nova Scotia banks and in lesser quantities in the Gulf of Maine and on Georges Bank.

The Pacific halibut, *Hippoglossus stenolepis,* which many consider to be a subspecies of the Atlantic halibut, is similarly boreal in its distribution. It is taken in commercial quantities from the banks off the Oregon and Washington coast northward to Unimak Pass and from there northwestward along the deeper portions of the eastern Bering Sea shelf to about 57.5° N lat., northwest of the Pribilof Islands. On the Asiatic coast it is taken commercially along the southeastern and northeastern coasts of Hokkaidō, on the southeastern coast of Sakhalin Island, and northward around the southern half of the Kurile Island chain. Halibut occur in low abundance along the Asiatic coast north to the southern Gulf of Anadyr and from there southeast toward the Pribilof Islands. They also occur around Nunivak Island but not as far north as St. Lawrence Island.

Female halibut reach maturity at 8 to 16 years of age, averaging about age 12 years. Males mature earlier; their average age at maturity is about 7 to 8 years. The eggs are spawned in deep water off the edge of the shelf, the season varying with the area from November to March. The eggs, fertilized after extrusion, hatch in about 15 days. The eggs and larvae during their long sojourn in the plankton are often carried hundreds of miles from the spawning site. The mature halibut must therefore perform a long contranatant migration to ensure proper distribution of the young.

The newly hatched larvae soon absorb the remaining yolk sac and become postlarvae. These postlarvae may float freely in the plankton for as long as 6 months. At first the post-larval halibut resemble those of roundfishes with an eye on each side of the head, and they swim with the dorsal side on top. At about 16 mm in length the left eye is slightly higher than the right. By 20 mm about half the left eye is visible above the profile and the right eye has started to descend ventrally. By 26 mm the postlarvae can be identified by adult characteristics.

Before hatching the ova float between about 125 and 700 m, with the greatest concentration between about 150 to 200

Table 25-5. Fecundity and spawning in certain flatfishes

Species	Maturity[1] Age (yr)	Maturity[1] Length (cm)	Spawning depth (m)	Spawning season	Egg diam. (mm)	Fecundity (thousands)	Where
Reinhardtius hippoglossoides	9+		Deep	April-July	4.0-4.5		
Hippoglossus							
hippoglossus	7-8		300-700	Nov.-March	3.5-4.2	2,000-3,500	Barents Sea
stenolepis	12		230-460		3.0-3.5	2,000-3,000	Georges Bank
Hippoglossoides							
platessoides	10-12		150-200	March-July	2.5	250-300	Northwestern Atlantic
			Above 91	March-May		30-60	East Bering Sea
				March-June		72-600	West Bering Sea
elassodon	4		40-70	May-June	2.75-3.75	228	Barents Sea
Microstomus pacificus	5	35	Below 256	Dec.-Jan.	2.05-2.57	37-230	California
		38-40		Nov.-Feb.			British Columbia
Eopsetta jordani	8			Jan.-April	1.3	400-1,200	
Solea solea		44	366	Feb.	1.3-1.5	150	Mediterranean
				April-Aug.			North Sea
Glyptocephalus cynoglossus			Deep	July-Aug.	1.07-1.25		Georges Bank
				Jan.-April			
Platichthys flesus	3-5			Jan.-Feb.	0.82-1.38	400-2,000	Black Sea
				Feb.-March			North Sea
				April-June			Murman coast
Rhombus maximus		17	10-40	April-Aug.	1.0	1,000-9,000	Sweden
Lepidopsetta bilineata				Feb.-April	0.92	400-1,300	
Limanda							
ferruginea			36-91	March-Aug.	0.87-0.94		
limanda	4-5	22-24		May-July		80-150	
				June-July			
aspera	6-7	23-24		May-Aug.		1,089	
Parophrys vetulus		29.5		Jan.-March	0.89-0.93	150-1,900	Georges Bank

Species	Average age and size of females at maturity[1]	Number of eggs	Egg diameter (mm)	Spawning season	Locality
Pleuronectes platessa	6; 11-13	160-200		Jan.-March; April	200; 50-520 — North Sea; Barents Sea
quadrituberculatus	3	100+		March-April	500 — West Kamchatka
Pseudopleuronectes americanus[2]		2-73		Jan.-May	52-200
Liopsetta glacialis	4-5		0.74-0.85	Jan.-Feb.[4]; May	Kara Inlet; White Sea
Trinectes maculatus	11.4	Shoal[3]; Coast		June-Aug.	0.3
Paralichthys californicus		3-10		Feb.-July	54 — California

[1]Average age and size of females at maturity.
[2]Eggs adherent.
[3]Spawning at subzero temperatures.
[4]Spawning only every other year.

m. After hatching the first stage larvae float a little deeper. As the postlarvae develop they approach closer to the surface. After passing 20 mm in length the postlarvae are mostly between the surface and 50 m. At about 3.5 cm they are ready to settle on the bottom. Here they remain in the shallower bays, gradually moving into a little deeper water as they grow. When they reach maturity they annually perform long contranatant migrations to their spawning grounds.

The food habits of flatfishes in general are well summarized by Ketchen and Forrester:

> The flounder family may be divided into two groups based on mouth size and dentition. Small-mouthed flounders have relatively weak dentition and, with a few notable exceptions, prey largely on small invertebrates such as annelid worms, clams, and brittle stars. The large-mouthed flounders, to which group belongs the petrale sole, have strong dentition and feed predominantly on fish and pelagic or semi-pelagic invertebrates.*

The breakdown into only two categories is, however, somewhat difficult. Halibut above about 70 cm turn wholly to fish; at the opposite end of the spectrum the Dover sole, *Microstomus pacificus,* eats no vertebrates. In the following list I attempt to divide those flatfishes on which I have a modicum of information into four diet categories, knowing that any species may be shifted into another category with more information, and that some species may fit a different category in a locality other than that from which information has been obtained.

Food habit categories of certain adult flatfishes
Piscivorous
  Hippoglossus hippoglossus
  Hippoglossus stenolepis
  Reinhardtius hippoglossoides
  Reinhardtius hippoglossoides matsuurae
  Paralichthys dentatus

*From Ketchen, K. S., and C. R. Forrester. 1966. Population dynamics of the petrale sole, Eopsetta jordani, in waters off western Canada. Fish. Res. Bd. Canada, Bull. **153**:1-195.

Rhombus maximus
Rhombus maeoticus
Atherestes stomias
Partially piscivorous
  Scophthalmus rhombus
  Hippoglossoides platessoides
  Eopsetta jordani
  Psettichthys melanostictus
Slightly piscivorous
  Limanda limanda
  Solea solea
  Isopsetta isolepis
  Platichthys flesus
  Platichthys stellatus
  Cleisthenes herzensteini
Fish absent or very minor
  Microstomus pacificus
  Parophrys vetulus
  Lepidopsetta bilineata
  Limanda ferruginea
  Limanda aspera
  Pseudopleuronectes americanus
  Glyptocephalus cynoglossus
  Liopsetta glacialis
  Pleuronectes quadrituberculatus
  Pleuronectes platessa

Those listed as piscivorous actively pursue sizeable fishes; some authors refer to them as predacious. They take such active fishes as cod, haddock, cusk, sculpins, herring, skates, wolffish, mackerel, and silver hake. The Atlantic halibut is even credited with capturing sea birds. One strange item of food common in many flounders is the tips of clam siphons, which they apparently snip off where they protrude through the bottom. Individual rock sole, *Lepidopsetta bilineata*, in Puget Sound are sometimes filled with these clam siphons to the exclusion of any other food.

Suggested readings

Alverson, D. L., A. T. Pruter, and L. L. Ronholt. 1964. A study of demersal fishes and fisheries of the northeastern Pacific Ocean. H. R. MacMillan lectures in fisheries, University of British Columbia, Vancouver, Canada. 190 pp.

Bell, F. H., and G. St.-Pierre. 1970. The Pacific halibut. Int. Pac. Halibut Comm., Tech. Rep. **6**:1-24.

Bigelow, H. B., and W. C. Schroeder. 1953. Fishes of the Gulf of Maine. U. S. Fish Wildl. Serv., Fish. Bull. **53**:1-577.

Hagerman, F. B. 1952. The biology of the Dover sole, Microstomus pacificus (Lockington). Calif. Fish Game, Fish Bull. **85**:1-48.

Ketchen, K. S., and C. R. Forrester. 1966. Population dynamics of the petrale sole, Eopsetta jordani, in waters off western Canada. Fish. Res. Bd. Canada, Bull. **153**:1-195.

Leim, A. H., and W. B. Scott. 1966. Fishes of the Atlantic coast of Canada. Fish. Res. Bd. Canada, Bull. **155**:1-485.

Nikol'skii, G. V. 1954. Special ichthyology, ed. 2. (Translated from Russian in 1961.) IPST Cat. No. 233, OTS 60-21817. Office of Technical Services, U. S. Department of Commerce, Springfield, Va. pp. 1-538.

Rounsefell, G. A. 1957. A method of estimating abundance of groundfish on Georges Bank. U. S. Fish Wildl. Serv., Fish. Bull. **57**:265-278.

Thompson, W. F., and R. Van Cleve. 1936. Early life history of the Pacific halibut. 2. Distribution and early life history. Rep. Int. Fish. Comm. **9**: 1-184.

✥ Appendices

appendix A

References

Abbott, R. T., and H. S. Zim. 1962. Sea shells of the world. Golden Press, New York. 160 pp.

Adkins, G. 1972. A study of the blue crab fishery in Louisiana. Louisiana Wild Life Fish. Comm., Tech. Bull. **3:**1-57.

Adler, C. 1970. The prospect of building and stabilizing dunes by using waste sludge. Mar. Tech. **1:**329-336.

Ahlstrom, E. H. 1953. Pilchard eggs and larvae and other fish larvae, Pacific Coast—1951. U. S. Fish Wildl. Serv., Spec. Sci. Rep. Fish. **102:**1-55.

Ahlstrom, E. H. 1966. Distribution and abundance of sardine and anchovy larvae in the California Current Region off California and Baja California, 1951-64: a summary. U. S. Fish Wildl. Serv., Spec. Sci. Rep. Fish. **534:**1-71.

Alekin, O. A. 1966. Earth that flows into the ocean. Geomar. Tech. **2:**1-11.

Alekseev, A. P., editor. 1968. Fish behavior and fishing techniques. All-Union Conference, Murmansk, U.S.S.R. (Translated from Russian in 1971.) IPST Cat. No. 5938, TT 71-50010. Office of Technical Services, U. S. Department of Commerce, Springfield, Va. pp. 1-192.

Alverson, D. L. 1960. A study of annual and seasonal bathymetric catch patterns for commercially important groundfishes of the Pacific northwest coast of North America. Pac. Mar. Fish. Comm. Bull. **4:**1-66.

Alverson, D. L. 1968. Fisheries resources in the northeastern Pacific Ocean. In fishery resources of the world. University of Washington, Publ. in Fisheries, New Ser. **4:**86-100.

Alverson, D. L. 1969. Distribution and behavior of Pacific hake as related to design of fishing strategy and harvest rationale. FAO Fish. Rep. **2:**1-461.

Alverson, D. L., A. T. Pruter, and L. L. Ronholt. 1964. A study of demersal fishes and fisheries of the northeastern Pacific Ocean. H. R. MacMillan lectures in fisheries, University of British Columbia, Vancouver, Canada. 190 pp.

Anderson, J. H. 1967. Ocean power generation. Oceanol. Int. **1:**65-66.

Anderson, W. W., and M. J. Lindner. 1971. Contributions to the biology of the royal red shrimp, Hymenopenaeus robustus Smith. U. S. Fish Wildl. Serv., Fish. Bull. **69:**313-336.

Ansell, A. D. 1969. Thermal releases and shellfish culture: possibilities and limitations. Chesapeake Sci. **10:**256-257.

Aplin, J. A. 1947. The effect of explosives on marine life. Calif. Fish Game **33:**23-30.

Asada, Y. 1973. License limitation regulations: the Japanese system. J. Fish. Res. Bd. Canada **30:** 2085-2095.

Atkins, C. G. 1887. The river fisheries of Maine. In Goode, G. B., editor. The fisheries and fishery industries of the United States. U. S. Commission of Fish and Fisheries, section V. **1:**673-728.

Bader, R. G. 1954. The role of organic matter in determining the distribution of bivalves in sediments. J. Mar. Res. **13:**32-47.

Bailey, R. M., and T. M. Cavender. 1971. Fishes, ed. 3 (Reprint.) In Encyclopedia of science and technology. McGraw-Hill Book Co., New York. 34 pp.

Baker, R. C., F. Wilke, and C. H. Baltzo. 1970. The northern fur seal. U. S. Fish Wildl. Serv., Circ. **336:**1-21.

Banse, K. 1968. Hydrography of the Arabian Sea

shelf of India and Pakistan and effects on demersal fishes. Deep-Sea Res. **15**:45-79.

Bardach, J. E., J. H. Ryther, and W. O. McLarney. 1972. Aquaculture: the farming and husbandry of freshwater and marine organisms. Wiley-Interscience, Div. John Wiley & Sons, Inc., New York. 868 pp.

Barnaby, J. T. 1944. Fluctuations in abundance of red salmon, Oncorhynchus nerka (Walbaum), of the Karluk River, Alaska. U. S. Fish Wildl. Serv., Fish. Bull. **50**:237-295.

Barnes, H. 1957. Nutrient elements. In Hedgpeth, J., editor. Treatise on marine ecology and paleoecology, memoir 67, vol. 1, chap. 11. Geological Society of America, National Research Council, Washington, D. C. pp. 297-343.

Barr, L. 1970. Alaska's fishery resources—the shrimps. U. S. Fish Wildl. Serv., Fish. Leaf. **631**:1-10.

Barr, L. 1970a. Diel vertical migration of Pandalus borealis in Kachemak Bay, Alaska. J. Fish. Res. Bd. Canada **27**:669-676.

Bates, D. W., and J. G. Vanderwalker. 1970. Traveling screens, for collection of juvenile salmon (models I and II). In Preliminary designs of traveling screens to collect juvenile fish. U. S. Fish Wildl. Serv., Spec. Sci. Rep. Fish. **608**:1-5.

Bates, D. W., E. W. Murphey, and M. G. Beam. 1971. Traveling screen for removal of debris from rivers. NOAA Tech. Rep., Nat. Mar. Fish. Serv., Spec. Sci. Rep. Fish. **645**:1-6.

Baylor, E. R., and W. H. Sutcliffe, Jr. 1963. Dissolved organic matter in sea water as a source of particulate food. Limnol. Oceanog. **8**:369-371.

Bean, T. H. 1891. Report of the salmon and salmon rivers of Alaska, with notes on the conditions, methods, and needs of the salmon fisheries. Bull. U. S. Fish. Comm. **9**:165-208.

Beardsley, A. J. 1971. "Bêche-de-mer" fishery for Truk? Comm. Fish. Rev. **33**:64-66.

Beardsley, G. L., Jr., and W. J. Richards. 1970. Size, seasonal abundance and length-weight relation of some scombrid fishes from southeast Florida. U. S. Fish Wildl. Serv., Spec. Sci. Rep. Fish. **595**:1-6.

Beaufort, R. 1970. World fisheries still expanding. Hydrospace **11**:1-8.

Beaufort, R. 1971. Egypt and the Aswan High Dam. Undersea Tech. **12**:1-17.

Bell, F. H., and A. T. Pruter. 1958. Climatic temperature changes and commercial yields of some marine fisheries. J. Fish. Res. Bd. Canada **15**:625-683.

Bell, F. H., and G. St.-Pierre. 1970. The Pacific halibut. Int. Pac. Halibut Comm., Tech. Rep. **6**:1-24.

Bell, M. C., and C. H. Clay. 1960. Facilities for anadromous fish passage, Passamaquoddy Project. J. Fish. Res. Bd. Canada **17**:507-516.

Belyanina, T. N. 1969. Synopsis of biological data on smelt, Osmerus eperlanus (Linnaeus) 1758. FAO Fish. Synopsis 78.

Berg, L. S. 1940. Classification of fishes both recent and fossil. (Reprinted by J. W. Edwards, Ann Arbor, Mich., 1947.) Trans. Inst. Zool. Acad. Sci. U.S.S.R. **5**:87-517.

Bergman, P. K., K. B. Jefferts, H. F. Fiscus, and R. C. Hager. 1968. A preliminary evaluation of an implanted coded wire fish tag. Wash. Dept. Fish., Fish. Res. Pap. **3**:63-84.

Beverton, R. J. H., and S. J. Holt. 1957. On the dynamics of exploited fish populations. Ministry of Agriculture, Fisheries, and Food, Fisheries Investigations, United Kingdom, Ser. II. **19**:1-533.

Bieri, R. 1966. Pelagic distribution. In Fairbridge, R. W., editor. The encyclopaedia of oceanography. Van Nostrand Reinhold Co., New York. pp. 684-688.

Bigelow, H. B., and W. C. Schroeder. 1953. Fishes of the Gulf of Maine. U. S. Fish Wildl. Serv., Fish. Bull. **53**:1-577.

Blackburn, M. 1966. Biological oceanography of the eastern tropical Pacific: summary of existing information. U. S. Fish Wildl. Serv., Spec. Sci. Rep. Fish. **540**:1-18.

Blacker, R. W. 1971. Synopsis of biological data on haddock. FAO Fish. Synopsis 84.

Boerema, L. K., and J. A. Gulland. 1973. Stock assessment of the Peruvian anchovy (Engraulis ringens) and management of the fishery. J. Fish. Res. Bd. Canada **30**:2226-2235.

Borgstrom, G. 1961. The Atlantic fisheries of the U.S.S.R. In Borgstrom, G., and A. J. Heighway, editors: Atlantic Ocean fisheries. Fishing News (Books), Ltd., London. 335 pp.

Borgstrom, G., and A. J. Heighway, editors. 1961. Atlantic Ocean fisheries. Fishing News (Books), Ltd., London. 335 pp.

Brandhorst, W. 1958. Thermocline topography, zooplankton standing crop, and mechanisms of fertilization in the eastern tropical Pacific. J. Conseil **24**:16-31.

Brenko, M. H., and A. Calabrese. 1969. The combined effects of salinity and temperature on larvae of the mussel Mytilus edulis. Mar. Biol. **4**:224-226.

Brett, J. R., and D. F. Alderice. 1958. Research on guiding young salmon at two British Columbia field stations. Fish. Res. Bd. Canada, Bull. **117**:1-75.

Broch, H. 1933. Einige probleme der biogeographischen abgrenzung der arktischen region. Berlin. Universität. K. Zoologishes Museum. Mitteilungen **19**:1-20.

Brongersma-Sanders, M. 1957. Mass mortality in the sea. In Hedgpeth, J., editor. Treatise on marine ecology and paleoecology, memoir 67, vol. 1, chap. 29. Geological Society of America, National Research Council, Washington, D. C. pp. 941-1010.

Broom, J. 1971. Shrimp cuulture. In Avault, J. W., Jr., E. Boudreaux, and E. Jaspers, editors. Proceedings of the first annual workshop, World Mariculture Society. pp. 63-68.

Brown, R. P. 1969. An inventory of ocean dumping. Oceanol. Int. **4**:1-23.

Bruun, A. F. 1957. Deep sea and abyssal depths. In Hedgpeth, J., editor. Treatise on marine ecology and paleoecology, memoir 67, vol. 1, chap. 22. Geological Society of America, National Research Council, Washington, D. C. pp. 641-672.

Buck, D. H. 1956. Effects of turbidity on fish and fishing. Trans. N. Amer. Wildl. Conf. **21**:249-261.

Bull, H. O. 1952. An evaluation of our knowledge of fish behavior in relation to hydrography. Rapp. Proc. Verb., Cons. Perm. Int. Explor. Mer **131**:8-23.

Bullis, H. R., Jr., and J. R. Thompson. 1968. Harvesting the ocean in the decade ahead. Ocean Ind. **3**:52-60.

Bureau of Sport Fisheries and Wildlife. 1962. A detailed report on Hurricane Study Area No. 1, Lake Pontchartrain and vicinity, Louisiana. U. S. Fish Wildl. Serv., Bur. Sport Fish. Wildl., Region 4, Atlanta. 32 pp.

Butler, P. A. 1965. Reaction of estuarine mollusks to some environmental factors. Biological problems in water pollution. Third seminar, 1962. Publ. No. 999-WP-25. U. S. Public Health Service, Cincinnati. pp. 92-104.

Butler, T. H. 1960. Maturity and breeding of the Pacific edible crab, Cancer magister Dana. J. Fish. Res. Bd. Canada **17**:641-646.

Cahn, A. R. 1949. Pearl culture in Japan. U. S. Fish Wildl. Serv., Fish. Leaf. **357**:1-91.

Calabrese, A. 1969. Individual and combined effects of salinity and temperature on embryos and larvae of the coot clam, Mulinia lateralis (Say). Biol. Bull. Woods Hole **137**:417-428.

Calhoun, A. J., D. H. Fry, Jr., and E. P. Hughes. 1951. Plastic deterioration and metal corrosion in Petersen disk fish tags. Calif. Fish Game **37**:301-314.

California Department of Fish and Game. 1960. California ocean fisheries resources to the year 1960. Calif. Fish Game. 79 pp.

Campbell, B. A. 1973. License limitation regulations: Canada's experience. J. Fish. Res. Bd. Canada **30**:2070-2076.

Carlisle, J. G., Jr., C. H. Turner, and E. E. Ebert. 1964. Artificial habitat in the marine environment. Calif. Fish Game, Fish Bull. **124**:1-93.

Carruthers, N., and A. L. Sawfort. 1952. Nature (London) **169**:601.

Caspers, H. 1957. Black Sea and Sea of Azov. In Hedgpeth, J., editor. Treatise on marine ecology and paleoecology, memoir 67, vol. 1, chap. 25. Geological Society of America, National Research Council, Washington, D. C. pp. 801-889.

Chamberlain, F. M. 1907. Some observations on salmon and trout in Alaska. Report of the Commissioner of Fisheries for 1906. Bur. Fish. Doc. **627**:1-112.

Chapman, C. 1968. Channelization and spoiling Gulf Coast and South Atlantic estuaries. In Proceedings of the Marsh and Estuary Management Symposium held July, 1967, in Baton Rouge, La. pp. 93-106.

Chapman, W. M. 1936. The pilchard fishery of the state of Washington in 1936 with notes on the food of the silver and chinook salmon of the Washington coast. Dept. Fish. Wash., Biol. Rep. **36C**:1-30.

Chapman, W. M. 1969. Setting up an overseas fishing industry. Hydrospace **2**:36-38.

Chapman, W. M., M. Katz, and D. W. Erickson. 1941. The races of herring in the state of Washington. Dept. Fish. Wash., Biol. Rep. **38A**:1-36.

Chesapeake Biological Laboratory. 1948. Effects of underwater explosions on oysters, crabs and fish. Chesapeake Biol. Lab., Publ. **70**:1-43.

Christy, F. T., Jr., and A. Scott. 1965. The common wealth in ocean fisheries. The Johns Hopkins University Press, Baltimore. 281 pp.

Clarke, F. W. 1916. The data of geochemistry. U. S. Geol. Surv. Bull. No. 616. 821 pp.

Clemens, H. B., and W. L. Craig. 1965. An analysis of California's albacore fishery. Calif. Fish Game, Fish Bull. **128**:1-301.

Clemens, W. A., and G. V. Wilby. 1961. Fishes of the Pacific coast of Canada. Fish. Res. Bd. Canada, Bull. **68**:1-443.

Cobb, J. N. 1930. Pacific salmon fisheries. Report of the Commissioner of Fisheries for 1930. Bur. Fish. Doc. **1092**:409-704.

Coker, C. M. 1949. Maryland's commercial fishing gears. I. The fin-fish gears. Dept. Res. Educ., Maryland, Educ. Ser. **18**:1-37.

Collin, A. E. 1966. Canadian Arctic Archipelago and Baffin Bay. A. Introduction and oceanography. In Fairbridge, R. W., editor. The encyclopaedia of oceanography. Van Nostrand Reinhold Co., New York. pp. 157-160.

Colton, J. B., Jr. 1955. Spring and summer distribution of haddock on Georges Bank. U. S. Fish. Wildl. Serv., Spec. Sci. Rep. Fish. **156**:1-65.

Colton, J. B., Jr., and R. F. Temple. 1961. The enigma of Georges Bank spawning. Limnol. Oceanog. **6**:280-291.

Commercial Fisheries Review editorials:
1968. A salmon you can call your own. Comm. Fish. Rev. **30**:23.
1969. Florida University plants artificial sea grass. Comm. Fish. Rev. **31**(7):30-31.
1969a. Blanket of plastic balls speeds growth rate of young fish at Hunterston. Comm. Fish. Rev. **31**(5):41.
1970. Antarctic krill fishery is considered. Comm. Fish. Rev. **32**(1):79.
1970a. Fisheries affected by Aswan Dam. Comm. Fish. Rev. **32**(4):64.
1970b. Underwater power plants studied. Comm. Fish. Rev. **32**(7):20-21.
1970c. Hard clam culture method developed at VIMS. Comm. Fish. Rev. **32**(8-9) 22.
1971. Peru's anchoveta fishery. Comm. Fish. Rev. **33**:57-60.

Commission on Marine Science, Engineering, and Resources. 1969. Panel reports. Report of the Commission. Washington, D. C. vol. 1-3.

Commission on Marine Science, Engineering, and Resources. 1969a. Our nation and the sea. Report of the Commission. Washington, D. C. 305 pp.

Committee on Names of Fishes. 1970. A list of the common and scientific names of fishes from the United States and Canada, ed. 3. Amer. Fish. Soc., Spec. Publ. 6. 149 pp.

Copeland, B. J., and H. D. Hoese. 1966. Growth and maturity of the American oyster, Crassostrea virginica, in high salinity shallow bays in central Texas. Publ. Inst. Mar. Sci., Texas **11**:149-158.

Costello, T. J. 1959. Marking shrimp with biological stains. In Proceedings of the Gulf and Caribbean Fisheries Institute, eleventh annual session. pp. 1-6.

Costello, T. J., and D. M. Allen. 1966. Migrations and geographic distribution of pink shrimp, Penaeus duorarum, of the Tortugas and Sanibel grounds, Florida. U. S. Fish Wildl. Serv., Fish. Bull. **65**:449-459.

Cottam, C., and D. A. Munro. 1954. Eelgrass status and environmental relations. J. Wildl. Mgt. **18**:449-460.

Cox, K. W. 1948. Sablefish run at Monterey Bay. Calif. Fish Game **34**:1-37.

Cox, K. W. 1962. California abalones, family Haliotidae. Calif. Fish Game, Fish Bull. **118**:1-133.

Craig, J. A., and R. L. Hacker. 1940. The history and development of the fisheries of the Columbia River. Bull. U. S. Bur. Fish. **49**:132-216.

Cromwell, T. 1953. Circulation in a meridional plane in the central equatorial Pacific. J. Mar. Res. **12**:196-213.

Crutchfield, J. A. 1969. Effects of mineral and petroleum extraction on living resources of continental shelf waters. In Proceedings of the Gulf and Caribbean Fisheries Institute, twenty-first annual session. pp. 20-36.

Crutchfield, J. A., and D. MacFarlane. 1968. Economic evaluation of the 1965-66 salt-water fisheries of Washington. Wash. Dept. Fish., Res. Bull. **8**:1-57.

Cushing, D. H. 1958. Some experiments using the ^{14}C technique. Rapp. Proc. Verb., Cons. Perm. Int. Explor. Mer **144**:73-75.

Cushing, D. H. 1968. Fisheries biology. University of Wisconsin Press, Madison, Wis. 200 pp.

Cushing, D. H. 1969. Upwelling and fish production. FAO Fish. Tech. Pap. **84**:1-40.

Cushing, D. H. 1973. Dependence of recruitment on parent stock. J. Fish. Res. Bd. Canada **30**:1965-1976.

Cushing, J. E. 1956. Observations on serology of tuna. U. S. Fish Wildl. Serv., Spec. Sci. Rep. Fish. **183**:1-14.

Dahlstrom, W. A., and D. W. Gotshall. 1969. Will the shrimp boats keep a comin'? Comm. Fish. Rev. **31**:20-25.

Darnell, R. M. 1959. Studies of the life history of the blue crab (Callinectes sapidus Rathbun) in Louisiana waters. Trans. Amer. Fish. Soc. **88**:294-304.

Davidson, F. A. 1933. Temporary high carbon dioxide content in an Alaskan stream at sunset. Ecology **14**:238-240.

Davis, H. C., and A. Calabrese. 1964. Combined effects of temperature and salinity on development of eggs and growth of larvae of M. mercenaria and C. virginica. U. S. Fish Wildl. Serv., Fish. Bull. **63**:643-655.

Davis, J. H. 1957. Dune formation and stabilization by vegetation and plantings. U. S. Army Corps of Engineers, Beach Erosion Board. Tech. Mem. **101**:1-47.

Davison, R. C., W. P. Breese, C. E. Warren, and P. Doudoroff. 1959. Experiments on the dissolved oxygen requirements of cold-water fishes. Sewage Ind. Wastes. August, pp. 950-966.

Dawson, C. E. 1957. Studies on the marking of commercial shrimp with biological stains. U. S. Fish Wildl. Serv., Spec. Sci. Rep. Fish. **231**:1-24.

Defant, A. 1961. Physical oceanography, vol. 1. Pergamon Press, Inc., New York. 727 pp.

DeLacy, A. C., and W. M. Morton. 1943. Taxonomy and habits of the charrs, Salvelinus malma and Salvelinus alpinus of the Karluk drainage system. Trans. Amer. Fish. Soc. **72:** 79-91.

de Loture, R. 1949. History of the great fishery of Newfoundland. (Translated from French by Clyde C. Taylor in 1957.) U. S. Fish Wildl. Serv., Spec. Sci. Rep. Fish. **213:**1-147.

Demel, K., and S. Rutkowicz. 1958. The Barents Sea. Wydawnictwo Morskie, Gdynia. (Translated from Polish in 1966.) TT 63-11393. Office of Technical Services, U. S. Department of Commerce, Springfield, Va. 301 pp.

Demir, M. 1965. Synopsis of biological data on sprat Sprattus sprattus (Linnaeus) 1758, rev. 1. FAO Fish. Synopsis 27.

deSylva, D. P. 1969. The unseen problems of thermal pollution. Oceans **1:**37-41.

Devedjian, K. 1926. Pêche et pêcheries en Turquie. Administration de la Dette Publique Ottomane, Constantinople. 649 pp.

DeWitt, J. W., Jr. 1954. A survey of the coast cutthroat trout, Salmo clarki clarki Richardson, in California. Calif. Fish Game **40:**329-335.

Dickie, L. M. 1959. Water temperature and survival of giant scallop. Trans. Amer. Fish. Soc. **88:**1-73.

Dickie, L. M. 1959a. Effects of high temperature on survival of the giant scallop. J. Fish. Res. Bd. Canada **15:**1189-1211.

Dietrich, G. 1957. General oceanography. (Translated from German in 1963.) John Wiley & Sons, Inc., New York. 588 pp.

Dodimead, A. J., F. Favorite, and T. Hirano. 1963. Review of oceanography of the subarctic Pacific region. Int. N. Pac. Fish. Comm. Bull. **13:**1-193.

Donaldson, L. R. 1971. Selective breeding of salmonid fishes. In Avault, J. W., Jr., E. Boudreaux, and E. Jaspers, editors. Proceedings of the second annual workshop, World Mariculture Society. pp. 75-83.

Donaldson, L. R., and F. J. Foster. 1941. Experimental study of the effect of various water temperatures on the growth, food utilization, and mortality rates of fingerling sockeye salmon. Trans. Amer. Fish. Soc. **70:**339-346.

Dragovich, A. 1969. Review of studies of tuna food in the Atlantic Ocean. U. S. Fish Wildl. Serv., Spec. Sci. Rep. Fish. **593:**1-20.

Dragovich, A. 1971. The food of skipjack and yellowfin tunas in the Atlantic Ocean. NOAA, Nat. Mar. Fish. Serv., Fish. Bull. **68:**445-460.

Dutt, S. 1969. Indian fisheries. In Firth, F. E., editor: The encyclopedia of marine resources. Van Nostrand Reinhold, New York. pp. 315-319.

Dymond, J. R. 1940. Pacific salmon in the Arctic Ocean. In Proceedings of the sixth Pacific Science Congress, vol. 3. pp. 1-435.

Ebel, W. J. 1971. Dissolved nitrogen concentrations in the Columbia and Snake Rivers in 1970 and their effect on chinook salmon and steelhead trout. NOAA Tech. Rep., Nat. Mar. Fish. Serv., Spec. Sci. Rep. Fish. **646:**1-7.

Eberman, J. W. 1956. Disposal of wastes at sea. Sewage Ind. Wastes **28:**1365-1370.

Editorial. 1961. The sea fishing industry of the Argentine. In Borgstrom, G., and A. J. Heighway, editors. Atlantic Ocean fisheries. Fishing News (Books), Ltd., London. 335 pp.

Edwards, R. L. 1968. Fishery resources of the North Atlantic area. In Fishery resources of the world. University of Washington, Publ. in Fisheries, New Ser. **4:**52-60.

Eicher, G. J., and G. A. Rounsefell. 1957. Effects of lake fertilization by volcanic activity on abundance of salmon. Limnol. Oceanog. **2:** 70-76.

Elling, C. H. 1960. Further experiments in fishway capacity, 1957. U. S. Fish Wildl. Serv., Spec. Sci. Rep. Fish. **340:**1-16.

Evans, G. 1966. Persian Gulf. In Fairbridge, R. W., editor. The encyclopaedia of oceanography. Van Nostrand Reinhold Co., New York. p. 689.

Everhart, W. H. 1950. Fishes of Maine. Inland Fish Game, Maine. pp. 1-53.

Evermann, B. W., and E. L. Goldsborough. 1907. The fishes of Alaska. Doc. 624. U. S. Bur. Fish. Bull. **26:**219-360.

Fairbridge, R. W., editor. 1966. The encyclopaedia of oceanography. Van Nostrand Reinhold Co., New York. 1021 pp.

Fairbridge, R. W. 1966a. Andaman Sea. In Fairbridge, R. W., editor. The encyclopaedia of oceanography. Van Nostrand Reinhold Co., New York. pp. 32-35.

Farris, D. A. 1957. A review of paper chromatography as used in systematics. U. S. Fish Wildl. Serv., Spec. Sci. Rep. Fish. **208:**35-38.

Favorite, F. 1969. Fishery oceanography. III. Ocean temperature and distribution of Pacific salmon. Comm. Fish. Rev. **31:**34-40.

Fedosov, M. V. 1962. Investigation of formation conditions of primary productivity in the northwest Atlantic. In Marti, Y. Y., editor. Soviet fisheries investigations in the northwest Atlantic. (Translated from Russian in 1963.) IPST Cat. No. 944, OTS 63-11102. Office of Technical Services, U. S. Department of Commerce, Springfield, Va. pp. 125-135.

Filice, F. P. 1958. Invertebrates from the estuarine portion of San Francisco Bay and some factors influencing their distributions. Wasmann J. Biol. **16:**159-211.

Firth, F. E., editor. 1969. The encyclopedia of marine resources. Van Nostrand Reinhold Co. New York. 740 pp.

Fisher, R. A. 1930. Statistical methods for research workers, ed. 3. Oliver & Boyd, Ltd., Edinburgh. 283 pp.

Fiske, J. D., C. E. Watson, and P. G. Coates. 1966. A study of the marine resources of the North River. Mass. Div. Mar. Fish., Monogr. Ser. **3**:1-53.

Fiske, J. D., C. E. Watson, and P. G. Coates. 1967. A study of the marine resources of Pleasant Bay. Mass. Div. Mar. Fish., Monogr. Ser. **5**:1-56.

Fitch, J. E. 1953. Common marine bivalves of California. Calif. Fish Game, Fish Bull. **90**:1-102.

Fitch, J. E., and P. H. Young. 1948. Use and effect of explosives in California coastal waters. Calif. Fish Game **34**:53-70.

Fleming, R. H. 1955. Review of the oceanography of the Northern Pacific. Int. N. Pac. Fish. Comm., Bull. **2**:1-43.

Fleming, R. H. 1957. General features of the oceans. In Hedgpeth, J., editor. Treatise on marine ecology and paleoecology, memoir 67, vol. 1, chap. 5. Geological Society of America, National Research Council, Washington, D. C. pp. 87-107.

Fleming, R. H., and R. Revelle. 1939. Physical processes in the ocean. In Trask, editor. Recent marine sediments. American Association of Petroleum Geologists, Tulsa, Okla. pp. 48-141.

Flores, L. A. 1967. Informe preliminar del crucero 6611 de la primavera de 1966 (Cabo Blanco–Punta Coles). Infme. Inst. Mar. Peru **17**:1-16.

Flores, L. A., and L. A. P. Elias. 1967. Informe preliminar del crucero 6608-9 de invierno 1966 (Manora-Ilo). Infme. Inst. Mar. Peru **16**:1-24.

Florida Conservation News. 1972. Shrimp rearing studies conducted at Crystal River power plant. Fla. Cons. News **7**:5.

Foerster, R. E. 1968. The sockeye salmon, Oncorhynchus nerka. Fish. Res. Bd. Canada, Bull. 162. 422 pp.

Food and Agriculture Organization. 1969. Yearbook of fishery statistics for 1968, vol. 26. 320 pp.

Food and Agriculture Organization. 1971. Yearbook of fishery statistics for 1970. **30**:1-476.

Food and Agriculture Organization, Fisheries Division. 1953. Improving the fisheries contribution to world food supplies. FAO Fish. Bull. **6**:159-191.

Forbes, S. T., and O. Nakken, editors. 1972. Manual of methods for fisheries resource survey and appraisal. II. The use of acoustic instruments for fish detection and abundance estimation. FAO Man. Fish. Sci. **5**:1-138.

Fraser, C. M. 1916. On Clupea pallasii Cuvier and Valenciennes. Trans. Royal Can. Inst. **11**:97-108.

Fritz, R. L. 1962. Silver hake. U. S. Fish Wildl. Serv., Fish. Leaf. **538**:1-7.

Gage, B. O. 1970. Experimental dunes of the Texas coast. U. S. Army Corps of Engineers, Coastal Engineering Research Center, Misc. Pap. **1-70**:1-34.

Galtsoff, P. S. 1930. The fecundity of the oyster. Science **72**:97-98.

Galtsoff, P. S. 1962. The story of the Bureau of Commercial Fisheries Biological Laboratory, Woods Hole, Massachusetts. U. S. Fish Wildl. Serv., Circ. **145**:1-121.

Galtsoff, P. S. 1964. The American oyster, Crassostrea virginica Gmelin. U. S. Fish Wildl. Serv., Fish. Bull. **64**:1-480.

Garrey, W. C. 1916. The resistance of fresh water fish to changes of osmotic and chemical conditions. Amer. J. Physiol. **39**:313-329.

Garside, E. T., and C. M. Jordan. 1968. Upper lethal temperatures at various levels of salinity in the euryhaline cyprinodontids Fundulus heteroclitus and F. diaphanus after isosmotic acclimation. J. Fish. Res. Bd. Canada **25**:2717-2720.

Gaudet, J. L. 1967. The status of warm-water pond fish culture in Europe. FAO Fish. Rep. **44**:70-87.

Gaul, R. D., and N. G. Vick. 1964. Sessile organism accumulation in a nearshore water column during a one year period. Texas A. & M. University, Department of Oceanography and Meteorology, Project 286-D, Reference 64-10T. 16 pp.

Gauley, J. R. 1960. Effect of fishway slope on rate of passage of salmonids. U. S. Fish Wildl. Serv., Spec. Sci. Rep. Fish. **350**:1-23.

Gibbs, R. H., Jr., and B. B. Collette. 1966. Comparative anatomy and systematics of the tunas, genus Thunnus. U. S. Fish Wildl. Serv., Fish. Bull. **66**:65-130.

Gilbert, C. H. 1922. The salmon of the Yukon River. Doc. 928. Bull. U. S. Bur. Fish. **38**:317-332.

Gilbert, C. H., and W. H. Rich. 1927. Investigations concerning the red-salmon runs to the Karluk River, Alaska. Doc. 1021. Bull. U. S. Bur. Fish. **43**(pt. II):1-69.

Gilmore, R. M. 1969. Ambergris. In Firth, F. E., editor. The encyclopedia of marine resources. Van Nostrand Reinhold Co., New York. pp. 23-24.

Glanville, A. 1956. The Larsen mid-water trawl. FAO Fish. Bull. **9**:113-129.

Glude, J. B. 1951. The effect of man on shellfish

populations. Trans. N. Amer. Wildl. Conf. **16**:397-403.

Godfrey, H. 1965. Salmon of the North Pacific Ocean. IX. Coho, chinook and masu salmon in offshore waters. 1. Coho salmon in offshore waters. Int. N. Pac. Fish. Comm., Bull. **16**:1-39.

Goldman, C. R. 1968. The use of absolute activity for eliminating serious errors on the measurement of primary productivity with ^{14}C. J. Conseil **32**:172-179.

Goodwin, C. L. 1973. Distribution and abundance of subtidal hard-shell clams in Puget Sound, Washington. Wash. Dept. Fish., Tech. Rep. **14**:1-81.

Gordon, A. 1966. Caribbean Sea—oceanography. In Fairbridge, R. W., editor. The encyclopaedia of oceanography. Van Nostrand Reinhold Co., New York. p. 689.

Gotshall, D. W. 1972. Population size, mortality rates, and growth rates of northern California ocean shrimp, Pandalus jordani, 1965 through 1968. Calif. Fish Game, Fish Bull. **155**:1-47.

Gowanloch, J. N., and J. E. McDougall. 1945. Effects from the detonation of explosives on certain marine life. Oil **4**:13-16.

Grady, J. R. 1971. The distribution of sediment properties and shrimp catch on two shrimping grounds on the continental shelf of the Gulf of Mexico. In Proceedings of the Gulf and Caribbean Fisheries Institute, twenty-third annual session. pp. 139-148.

Graham, H. W., and N. Bronikovsky. 1944. The genus Ceratium in the Pacific and North Atlantic Oceans. Carnegie Institute, Washington, D. C. Publ. **565**:1-209.

Graham, H. W., and R. L. Edwards. 1962. The world biomass of marine fishes. (FAO report of the international conference on fish in nutrition. Washington, D. C., Sept. 19-27, 1961. pp. 3-8.) In Fish in nutrition. Fishing News (Books), Ltd., London. 447 pp.

Greenwood, P. H., D. E. Rosen, S. H. Weitzman, and G. S. Myers. 1966. Phyletic studies of teleostean fishes, with a provisional classification of living forms. Bull. Amer. Mus. Nat. Hist. **131**:341-455.

Griggs, R. F. 1920. The recovery of vegetation at Kodiak. Ohio State Univ. Bull. **24**:1-57.

Grinols, R. B., and M. F. Tillman. 1970. Importance of the worldwide hake, Merluccius, resource. In Pacific hake, U. S. Fish Wildl. Serv., Bur. Comm. Fish. Circ. **332**:1-21.

Guillen, O., and L. A. Flores. 1967. Informe preliminar del crucero 6702 del verano de 1967 (Cabo Blanco–Arica). Infme. Inst. Mar. Peru **18**:1-17.

Gulland, J. A. 1969. Manual of methods for fish stock assessment. I. Fish population analysis. FAO Man. Fish. Sci. **4**:1-154.

Gunter, G. 1957. Predominance of the young among marine fishes found in fresh water. Copeia, No. 1. pp. 13-16.

Gunter, G. 1957a. Temperature. In Hedgpeth, J., editor. Treatise on marine ecology and paleoecology, memoir 67, vol. 1, chap. 8. Geological Society of America, National Research Council, Washington, D. C. pp. 159-184.

Gutsell, J. S. 1931. The natural history of the bay scallop. Doc. 1100. Bull. U. S. Bur. Fish. **46**:569-632.

Hachey, H. B. 1961. Oceanography and Canadian Atlantic waters. Fish. Res. Bd. Canada, Bull. **134**:1-120.

Hagerman, F. B. 1952. The biology of the Dover sole, Microstomus pacificus (Lockington). Calif. Fish Game, Fish Bull. **85**:1-48.

Hall, F. G. 1929. The influence of varying oxygen tensions upon the rate of oxygen consumption in marine fishes. Amer. J. Physiol. **88**:212-218.

Hanamura, N. 1966. Salmon of the North Pacific Ocean. III. A review of the life history of North Pacific salmon. 1. Sockeye salmon in the Far East. Int. N. Pac. Fish. Comm., Bull. **18**:1-27.

Hanavan, M. G., and B. E. Skud. 1954. Intertidal spawning of pink salmon. U. S. Fish Wildl. Serv., Fish. Bull. **56**:167-185.

Hand, C. H., and L. Berner, Jr. 1959. Food of the Pacific sardine (Sardinops caerulea). U. S. Fish Wildl. Serv., Fish. Bull. **60**:175-184.

Hanks, R. W. 1963. The soft-shell clam. U. S. Fish Wildl. Serv., Circ. **162**:1-16.

Hanks, R. W. 1968. Benthic community formation in a "new" environment. Chesapeake Sci. **9**:163-172.

Harleman, D. R. F., and A. T. Ippen. 1969. Salinity intrusion effects in estuary shoaling. American Society of Civil Engineers, Hydraulics Division J. Hyd. **95**:9-27.

Hart, J. L. 1973. Pacific fishes of Canada. Fish. Res. Bd. Canada, Bull. **180**:1-740.

Hart, J. L., and J. L. McHugh. 1944. The smelts (Osmeridae) of British Columbia. Fish. Res. Bd. Canada, Bull. **64**:1-27.

Hart, J. L., and D. L. McKernan. 1960. International Passamaquoddy Fisheries Board fisheries investigations 1956-59. Introductory account. J. Fish. Res. Bd. Canada **17**:127-131.

Hartt, A. C. 1961. Problems in tagging salmon at sea. ICNAF North Atlantic Fish Marking Symposium, May, 1961. Contribution No. 24. p. 29.

Hassler, W. W. 1958. The striped bass in relation to the multiple use of the Roanoke River, North Carolina. Trans. N. Amer. Wildl. Conf. **23**:378-391.

Hastings, W. H. 1971. Fish feeds. In Avault, J. W., Jr., E. Boudreaux, and E. Jaspers, editors.

Proceedings of the first annual workshop, World Mariculture Society. pp. 118-126.

Hedgpeth, J. W., editor. 1957. Treatise on marine ecology and paleocology, memoir 67, vol. 1. Geological Society of America, National Research Council, Washington, D. C. pp. 1-1296.

Hedgpeth, J. W. 1964. Man and the sea. (Series of lectures given over KPFA, Berkeley, Calif., April 7-13, 1964.) Pacific Marine Station, Dillon Beach, Calif.

Hela, I., and T. Laevastu. 1961. Fisheries hydrography. Fishing News (Books), Ltd., London. 137 pp.

Herlinveaux, R. H. 1962. Oceanography of Saanich Inlet in Vancouver Island, British Columbia. J. Fish. Res. Bd. Canada 19:1-37.

Herrington, W. C. 1943. Some methods of fishery management and their usefulness in a management program. U. S. Fish Wildl. Serv., Spec. Sci. Rep. 18:3-22, 55-59.

Herrington, W. C., and G. A. Rounsefell. 1940. Restoration of the Atlantic salmon in New England. Trans. Amer. Fish. Soc. 70:123-127.

Heselton, L. R., Jr. 1969. The continental shelf. Center for Naval Analyses, Doc. AD686 703. Office of Technical Services, U. S. Department of Commerce, Springfield, Va. 44 pp.

Hewatt, W. G. 1935. Ecological succession in the Mytilus californianus habitat as observed in Monterey Bay, California. Ecology 16:244-251.

Hildebrand, H. H., and G. Gunter. 1953. Correlation of rainfall with the Texas catch of white shrimp, Penaeus setiferus (Linnaeus). Trans. Amer. Fish. Soc. 82:151-155.

Hildebrand, S. F. 1929. Review of experiments on artificial culture of diamond-back terrapin. Doc. 1060. Bull. U. S. Bur. Fish. 45:25-70.

Hildebrand, S. F., and L. E. Cable. 1930. Development and life history of fourteen teleostean fishes at Beaufort, N. C. Doc. 1093. Bull. U. S. Bur. Fish. 46:383-488.

Hildebrand, S. F., and L. E. Cable. 1938. Further notes on the development and life history of some teleosts at Beaufort, N. C. Bull. U. S. Bur. Fish. 48:505-642.

Hildebrand, S. F., and W. C. Schroeder. 1928. Fishes of Chesapeake Bay. Doc. 1024. Bull. U. S. Bur. Fish. 43:1-366.

Holden, M. J. 1967. Fishing: the next ten years. Hydrospace 1:54-59.

Holthius, L. B., and H. Rosa, Jr. 1965. List of species of shrimps and prawns of economic value. FAO Fish. Tech. Pap. 52:1-21.

Hopkins, A. E. 1937. Experimental observations on spawning, larval development, and setting in the Olympia oyster Ostrea lurida. Bull. U. S. Bur. Fish. 48:439-503.

Hosie, M. J., and T. F. Gaumer. 1974. Southern range extension of the Baird crab, (Chionoecetes bairdi Rathbun). Calif. Fish Game 60: 44-47.

Hubbs, C. L., and A. B. Rechnitzer. 1952. Report on experiments designed to determine effects of underwater explosions on fish life. Calif. Fish Game 38:333-366.

Hublou, W. F. 1963. Oregon pellets. Prog. Fish-Cult. 25:175-180.

Huet, M. 1959. Profiles and biology of western European streams as related to fish management. Trans. Amer. Fish. Soc. 88:155-163.

Hughes, J. T. 1968. Biologists breed lobsters selectively. Comm. Fish. Rev. 30:20.

Hutchinson, G. E. 1957. A treatise on limnology. I. Geography, physics, and chemistry. John Wiley & Sons, Inc., New York. 1015 pp.

Idler, D. R., and P. M. Jangaard. 1969. Cod fishery. In Firth, F. E., editor. The encyclopedia of marine resources. Van Nostrand Reinhold Co., New York. pp. 129-135.

Idyll, C. P. 1973. Marine aquaculture: problems and prospects. J. Fish Res. Bd. Canada 30: 2178-2183.

International North Pacific Fisheries Commission. 1955. On the salmon in waters adjacent to Japan. Int. N. Pac. Fish. Comm. Bull. 1:57-92.

International North Pacific Fisheries Commission. 1972. Annual report 1970. Vancouver, Canada. pp. 1-120.

Isaacs, J. D., and W. R. Schmitt. 1969. Stimulation of marine productivity with waste heat and mechanical power. J. Conseil 33:20-29.

Ishida, T. 1960. Salmon of the North Pacific Ocean. III. A review of the life history of North Pacific salmons. 2. Pink salmon in the Far East. Int. N. Pac. Fish. Comm. Bull. 18: 29-39.

Iversen, E. S., and C. P. Idyll. 1960. Aspects of the biology of the Tortugas pink shrimp, Penaeus duorarum. Trans. Amer. Fish. Soc. 89:1-8.

Izhevskii, G. K. 1961. Oceanological principles as related to the fishery productivity of the seas. (Translated from Russian in 1964.) IPST Cat. No. 917, OTS 63-11120. Office of Technical Services, U. S. Department of Commerce, Springfield, Va. 186 pp.

Izhevskii, G. K. 1964. Forecasting of oceanological conditions and the reproduction of commercial fish. (Translated from Russian in 1966.) IPST Cat. No. 1854. TT 67-51264. Office of Technical Services, U. S. Department of Commerce, Springfield, Va. 95 pp.

Japan Times. 1935. The canning industry. The Japan Times and Mail, Aquatic Industry number, February, pp. 2-7.

Jerome, W. C., Jr., A. P. Chesmore, and C. O.

Anderson, Jr. 1966. A study of the marine resources of Quincy Bay. Mass. Div. Mar. Fish., Monogr. Ser. **2**:1-62.

Jerome, W. C., Jr., A. P. Chesmore, and C. O. Anderson. 1967. A study of the marine resources of Beverly-Salem Harbor. Mass. Div. Mar. Fish., Monogr. Ser. **4**:1-74.

Jerome, W. C., A. P. Chesmore, C. O. Anderson, Jr., and F. Grice. 1965. A study of the marine resources of the Merrimack River estuary. Mass. Div. Mar. Fish., Monogr. Ser. **1**:1-90.

Jhingran, V. G., and V. Gopalakrishnan. 1973. Prospects for the development of brackish-water fish and shrimp culture in India. J. Fish. Res. Bd. Canada **30**:2341-2345.

Johnson, L. J., and W. L. High. 1970. Midwater trawling equipment and fishing technique for capturing hake off the coast of Washington and Oregon. In Pacific hake. U. S. Fish Wildl. Serv. Circ. **332**:77-101.

Jones, J. R. E. 1964. Fish and river pollution. Butterworth & Co. (Publishers), Ltd., London. 203 pp.

Jones, N. W. 1950. Marine bottom communities. Biol. Rev. **25**:283-313.

Jones, S., and H. Rosa, Jr. 1965. Synopsis of biological data on Indian mackerel Rastrelliger kanagurta (Cuvier) 1817 and short bodied mackerel Rastrelliger brachysoma (Bleeker) 1851. FAO Fish. Synopsis **29**.

Jones, S., and E. G. Silas. 1964. A systematic review of the scombroid fishes of India. In Symposium on scombroid fishes, I. Marine Biological Association of India. pp. 28-105.

Jorgensen, C. B. 1949. The rate of feeding by Mytilus in different kinds of suspensions. J. Mar. Biol. Assoc. U. K. **28**:333-344.

Jorgensen, C. B. 1955. Quantitative aspects of filter feeding in invertebrates. Biol. Rev. **30**:391-454.

Joseph, J. 1973. Scientific management of the world stocks of tunas, billfishes, and related species. J. Fish. Res. Bd. Canada **30**:2471-2482.

Juhl, R. 1971. Status and potential of the fishery in the Caribbean. In Proceedings of the Gulf and Caribbean Fisheries Institute, twenty-third annual session. pp. 175-183.

June, F. C. 1953. Spawning of yellowfin tuna in Hawaiian waters. U. S. Fish Wildl. Serv. **54**:47-64.

Kask, J. L. 1936. The experimental marking of halibut. Science, N. S. **83**:435-436.

Kask, J. L., and Y. Hiyama. 1947. Japanese fishing gear. U. S. Fish Wildl. Serv., Fish. Leaf. **234**:1-107.

Kelley, J. W. 1968. Effects of incubation temperature on survival of largemouth bass eggs. Prog. Fish-Cult. **30**:159-163.

Kendall, W. C. 1914. The fishes of New England. The salmon family. I. The trouts or charrs. Mem., Boston Soc. Nat. Hist. **8**:1-103.

Kendall, W. C. 1918. The Rangeley Lakes, Maine: with special reference to the habits of the fishes, fish culture, and angling. Doc. 861. Bull. U. S. Bur. Fish. **35**:489-594.

Kendall, W. C. 1927. The smelts. Doc. 1015. Bull. U. S. Bur. Fish. **42**:217-375.

Kendall, W. C. 1935. The fishes of New England. The salmon family. II. The salmons. Mem., Boston Soc. Nat. Hist. **9**:1-166.

Kennedy, W. A. 1953. The morphometry of the Coregonine fishes of Great Bear Lake, N. W. T. J. Fish. Res. Bd. Canada **10**:51-61.

Kenny, R. 1969. Effects of temperature, salinity and substrate on distribution of Clymenella torquata (Leidy) (Polychaeta). Ecology **50**:624-631.

Kerns, O. E., Jr., and J. R. Donaldson. 1968. Behavior and distribution of spawning sockeye salmon on island beaches in Iliamna Lake, Alaska, 1965. J. Fish. Res. Bd. Canada **25**:485-494.

Kerswill, C. J., and J. G. Hunter. 1970. FRB studies in Canada's Arctic. Fish. Res. Bd. Canada, Misc. Spec. Publ. **13**:1-16.

Ketchen, K. S. 1956. Climatic trends and fluctuations in yield of marine fisheries of the northeast Pacific. J. Fish. Res. Bd. Canada **13**:357-374.

Ketchen, K. S., and C. R. Forrester. 1966. Population dynamics of the petrale sole, Eopsetta jordani, in waters off western Canada. Fish. Res. Bd. Canada, Bull. **153**:1-195.

Ketchum, B. H. 1951. The flushing of tidal estuaries. Sewage Ind. Wastes **23**:198-209.

Ketchum, B. H. 1969. Productivity of marine communities. In Firth, F. E., editor. The encyclopedia of marine resources. Van Nostrand Reinhold Co., New York. pp. 553-559.

Khlebovich, V. V. 1968. Some peculiar features of the hydrochemical regime and the fauna of mesohaline waters. Mar. Biol. **2**:47-49.

King, C. A. M. 1962. An introduction to oceanography. McGraw-Hill Book Co., New York. 337 pp.

King, J. E., and I. I. Ikehara. 1956. Comparative study of food of bigeye and yellowfin tuna in the central Pacific. U. S. Fish Wildl. Serv., Fish. Bull. **57**:61-85.

Kinnear, B. S., and C. M. Fuss, Jr. 1971. Thread herring distribution off Florida's west coast. Comm. Fish. Rev. **33**:27-39.

Kirsch, M. 1956. Ionic ratios of some of the major components in river-diluted sea water in Bute and Knight Inlets, British Columbia. J. Fish. Res. Bd. Canada **13**:273-289.

Klima, E. F. 1959. Aspects of the biology and the fishery for Spanish mackerel, Scomberomorus maculatus (Mitchill), of southern Florida. Fla. St. Bd. Conserv. Tech. Ser. **27**:1-39.

Klima, E. F. 1971. Distribution of some coastal pelagic fishes in the western Atlantic. Comm. Fish. Rev. **33**:21-34.

Koczy, F. F., M. O. Rinkel, and S. J. Niskin. 1960. The current patterns on the Tortugas shrimp grounds. In Proceedings of the Gulf and Caribbean Fisheries Institute, twelfth annual session. pp. 112-125.

Kolhonen, J. 1974. Fish meal: international market situation and the future. Mar. Fish. Rev. **36**:36-40.

Kolpack, R. L. editor. 1971. Biological and oceanographical survey of the Santa Barbara oil spill 1969-1970. II. Physical, chemical and geological studies. Allan Hancock Foundation, University of Southern California, Los Angeles. 477 pp.

Korringa, P. 1957. Lunar periodicity. In Hedgpeth, J., editor. Treatise on marine ecology and paleoecology, memoir 67, vol. 1, chap. 27. Geological Society of America, National Research Council, Washington, D. C. pp. 917-934.

Kossinna, E. 1921. Die Tiefen des Weltmeeres. Berlin Universität Institut für Meereskunde, Veroff, N. F., A. Geogr.-Naturwiss. **9**:1-70.

Kramer, D. 1969. Synopsis of biological data on the Pacific mackerel, Scomber japonicus Houttuyn (northeast Pacific). FAO Fish. Synopsis 40.

Kulp, J. L. 1953. Carbon-14 measurements on geological samples. Atomics. April, vol. 4.

Kuo, C., Z. E. Shehadeh, and C. E. Nash. 1973. Induced spawning of captive grey mullet (Mugil cephalus L.) females by injection of human chorionic gonadotropin (HCG). Aquaculture **1**:429-432.

Kutkuhn, J. H. 1966. The role of estuaries in the development and perpetuation of commercial shrimp resources. In A symposium on estuarine fisheries. Amer. Fish. Soc. Spec. Publ. No. 3. pp. 16-36.

Laevastu, T. 1961. Natural bases of fisheries in the Atlantic Ocean: their past and present characteristics and possibilities for future expansion. In Atlantic ocean fisheries. Fishing News (Books), London. pp. 18-39.

Lagler, K. F., J. E. Bardach, and R. R. Miller. 1962. Ichthyology. John Wiley & Sons, New York. 545 pp.

Landis, A. T., Jr. 1970. Eelgrass grows under Arctic ice. Undersea Tech. **11**(1):17.

Landis, A. T., Jr. 1970a. Turnover time in the Mediterranean. Undersea Tech. **11**(5):23.

Landis, A. T., Jr. 1970b. Artificial fishing reef. Undersea Tech. **11**(7):15.

Landis, A. T., Jr. 1970c. Solid waste disposal at sea. Undersea Tech. **11**(12):12.

Landis, A. T., Jr. 1971. Hazards of deep water. Undersea Tech. **12**(1):14.

Leary, S. P. 1964. The crabs of Texas. Texas Parks Wildl. Dept., Bull. **43**:1-57.

Legendre, V., and R. Lagueux. 1948. The tomcod (Microgadus tomcod) as a permanent freshwater resident of Lake St. John, P. Q. Can. Field-Naturalist **62**:157.

Leim, A. H., and W. B. Scott. 1966. Fishes of the Atlantic coast of Canada. Fish. Res. Bd. Canada, Bull. **155**:1-485.

Leppakoski, E. 1969. Transitory return of the benthic fauna of the Bornholm Basin after extermination by oxygen insufficiency. Cah. Biol. Mar. **10**:162-172.

Lewis, R. M., and W. F. Hettler, Jr. 1968. Effect of temperature and salinity on the survival of young Atlantic menhaden, Brevoortia tyrannus. Trans. Amer. Fish. Soc. **97**:344-349.

Liao, P. B., and R. D. Mayo. 1972. Salmonid hatchery water reuse systems. Aquaculture **1**: 317-335.

Lindner, M. J., and J. S. Bailey. 1968. Distribution of brown shrimp (Penaeus aztecus aztecus Ives) as related to turbid water photographed from space. U. S. Fish Wildl. Serv., Fish. Bull. **67**: 289-294.

Loosanoff, V. L. 1937. Use of nile blue sulfate in marking starfish. Science **86**:64.

Loosanoff, V. L. 1965. The American or eastern oyster. U. S. Fish Wildl. Serv., Circ. **205**:1-36.

Loosanoff, V. L., and H. C. Davis. 1963. Rearing of bivalve mollusks. (Reprint.) Adv. Mar. Biol. **1**:1-136.

Loosanoff, V. L., and F. D. Tommers. 1948. Effect of suspended silt and other substances on rate of feeding of oysters. Science **107**:69-70.

Lucas, C. E. 1949. External metabolites and ecological adaptation. In Symposium of the Society for Experimental Biology. III. Selective toxicity and antibiotics. Academic Press, Inc., New York. pp. 336-356.

Lyles, C. H. 1969. Historical catch statistics (shellfish). U. S. Fish Wildl. Serv., Curr. Fish. Statistics **5007**:1-116.

Lyles, C. H. 1969a. Fishery statistics of the United States, 1967. Bureau of Commercial Fisheries. pp. 1-489.

Lynch, S. A. 1954. Geology of the Gulf of Mexico. In Galtsoff, P. A., editor. Gulf of Mexico, its origin, waters, and marine life. U. S. Fish Wildl. Serv., Fish. Bull. **55**:67-86.

MacGinitie, G. E. 1939. Littoral marine communities. Amer. Midl. Nat. **21**:28-55.

MacGinitie, G. E., and N. MacGinitie. 1968. Natural history of marine animals, ed. 2. McGraw-Hill Book Co., New York. 523 pp.

MacGregor, J. S. 1964. Relation between spawning-stock size and year-class size for the Pacific sardine Sardinops caerulea (Girard). U. S. Fish Wildl. Serv., Fish. Bull. **63**:477-491.

MacGregor, J. S. 1966. Synopsis on the biology of the jack mackerel (Trachurus symmetricus). U. S. Fish Wildl. Serv., Spec. Sci. Rep. Fish. **526**:1-16.

Major, R. D., and H. H. Shippen. 1970. Synopsis of biological data on Pacific ocean perch, Sebastes alutus. FAO Species Synopsis 79, NOAA, Nat. Mar. Fish. Serv., Circ. **347**:1-38.

Manar, T. A. 1969. Pacific fisheries. In Firth, F. E., editor. The encyclopedia of marine resources. Van Nostrand Reinhold Co., New York. pp. 477-483.

Margolis, L. 1963. Parasites as indicators of the geographical origin of sockeye salmon, Oncorhynchus nerka (Walbaum), occurring in the North Pacific Ocean and adjacent seas. Int. N. Pac. Fish. Comm., Bull. **11**:101-156.

Margolis, L., F. C. Cleaver, Y. Fukuda, and H. Godfrey. 1966. Salmon of the North Pacific Ocean. VI. Sockeye salmon in offshore waters. Int. N. Pac. Fish. Comm., Bull. **20**:1-70.

Marine Fisheries Review editorials:
1973. Soviets build machine to produce krill paste. Mar. Fish. Rev. **35**:42.
1973a. Norway's fish farming grows. Mar. Fish. Rev. **35**:44.

Marr, J. C. 1961. Note on the recovery rate of tagged skipjack, Katsuwonus pelamis, and the effects of handling. ICNAF North Atlantic Fish Marking Symposium, May, 1961, Contribution No. 1. pp. 1-2.

Martin, W. R. 1960. Predicted effects of proposed tidal power structures on groundfish catches in Charlotte County, N. B. J. Fish. Res. Bd. Canada **17**:169-173.

Martino, P. A., and J. M. Marchello. 1968. Using waste heat for fish farming. Ocean Ind. **3**:37-39.

Maxfield, G. H., R. H. Lander, and C. D. Volz. 1970. Laboratory tests of an electrical barrier for controlling predation by northern squawfish. U. S. Fish Wildl. Serv., Spec. Sci. Rep. Fish. **611**:1-8.

May, R. C. 1971. An annotated bibliography of attempts to rear the larvae of marine fishes in the laboratory. NOAA Tech. Rep., Nat. Mar. Fish. Serv., Spec. Sci. Rep. Fish. **632**:1-24.

Mayer, A. G. 1914. The effects of temperature upon tropical marine animals. Pap. Tortugas Lab. **6**:1-24.

McClendon, R. I. 1968. Detection of fish schools by radar. Comm. Fish. Rev. **30**(4):26-29.

McConnaughey, B. H. 1970. Introduction to marine biology. The C. V. Mosby Co. St. Louis. 449 pp.

McEwen, G. F. 1912. The distribution of ocean temperatures along the coast of North America deduced from Ekman's theory of the upwelling of cold waters from the adjacent ocean depths. Int. Rev. Geo. Hydrobiol. W. Hydrog. Bd. **5**:243-286.

McLaughlin, P. A., and J. F. Hebard. 1961. Stomach contents of the Bering Sea king crab. Int. N. Pac. Fish. Comm., Bull. **5**:5-8.

McLean, J. 1932. Notes of a twenty-five years' service in the Hudson's Bay Territory. The Champlain Society, Toronto.

McLeese, D. W. 1956. Effects of temperature, salinity and oxygen on the survival of the American lobster. J. Fish. Res. Bd. Canada **13**:247-272.

McMillin, H. C. 1928. Condition of the razor-clam fishery of Washington. U. S. Bur. Fish., Econ. Circ. **64**:1-7.

McNeil, W. J. 1966. Effect of the spawning bed environment on reproduction of pink and chum salmon. U. S. Fish Wildl. Serv., Fish. Bull. **65**:495-523.

McNulty, J. K., R. C. Work, and B. Moore. 1962. Some relationships between the infauna of the level bottom and the sediment in south Florida. Bull. Mar. Sci., Gulf Carib. **12**:322-332.

McVay, S. 1966. The last of the great whales. Sci. Amer. **215**:13-21.

Medcof, J. C. 1962. Possible effects of Passamaquoddy power project on clams, scallops and shipworms in Canadian waters. J. Fish. Res. Bd. Canada **19**:877-889.

Menard, H. W. 1969. The deep-ocean floor. Sci. Amer. **221**:127-142.

Menzel, W. R., and S. H. Hopkins. 1956. Crabs as predators of oysters in Louisiana. In Proceedings of the National Shellfish Association, 1955 (1956). **46**:177-184.

Menzies, W. J. M. 1934. Salmon passes—their design and construction. Fisheries, Scotland, Salmon Fisheries, 1934, No. 1. pp. 1-29.

Mertz, E. T. 1969. Amino acid and protein requirements of fish. In Neuhaus, O., editor. Fish in research. Academic Press, Inc., New York. pp. 233-244.

Meseck, G. 1962. Importance of fisheries production and utilization in the food economy. (FAO report of the international conference on fish in nutrition. Washington, D. C., Sept. 19-27, 1961. pp. 23-27.) In Fish in nutrition. Fishing News (Books), Ltd., London. 447 pp.

Messersmith, J. D., J. L. Baxter, and P. M. Roedel. 1969. The anchovy resources of the California

Current Region off California and Baja California. Calif. Mar. Res. Comm., CalCOFI Rep. **13**:32-38.

Miller, D. J., and D. Gotshall. 1965. Ocean sport-fish catch and effort from Oregon to Point Arguello, California. Calif. Fish Game, Fish Bull. **130**:1-130.

Miller, D. J., and R. N. Lea. 1972. Guide to the coastal marine fishes of California. Calif. Fish Game, Fish Bull. **157**:1-235.

Miller, D. J., and J. Schmidtke. 1956. Report on the distribution and abundance of Pacific herring (Clupea pallasi) along the coast of central and southern California. Calif. Fish Game **42**: 161-187.

Mills, E. L. 1969. The community concept in marine zoology, with comments on continua and instability in some marine communities: a review. J. Fish Res. Bd. Canada **26**:1415-1428.

Milne, P. H. 1972. Fish and shellfish farming in coastal waters. Fishing News (Books), Ltd., London. 208 pp.

Mock, C. R. 1967. Natural and altered estuarine habitats of penaeid shrimp. In Proceedings of the Gulf and Caribbean Fisheries Institute, nineteenth annual session. pp. 86-98.

Mock, C. R. 1973. The culture of Penaeus japonicus in Japan. In Proceedings of the third annual workshop, World Mariculture Society. pp. 285-286.

Moiseev, P. A. 1946. Some data on the biology and fishery of flounders in the Bay of Peter the Great. Izvestiya TINRO. **22**:75-184.

Moiseev, P. A. 1953. Cod and flounder of the Far Eastern seas. Izvestia TINRO. **40**:277-287.

Moiseev, P. A. 1969. The living resources of the world ocean. (First published under the title Biologicheskie resursy Mirovogo okeana; translated from Russian in 1971.) IPST Cat. No. 5954, TT 71-50026. Published jointly by National Science Foundation and National Marine Fisheries Service. Nat. Tech. Inf. Serv., U. S. Department of Commerce, Springfield, Va. 334 pp.

More, W. R. 1969. A contribution to the biology of the blue crab (Callinectes sapidus Rathbun) in Texas, with a description of the fishery. Texas Parks Wildl. Dept., Tech. Ser. **1**:1-31.

Moser, J. F. 1899. The salmon and salmon fisheries of Alaska. Bull. U. S. Fish Comm. **18**: 1-178.

Muromtsev, A. M. 1958. The principal hydrological features of the Pacific Ocean. Main Administration of Hydrometeorological Service U.S.S.R., State Oceanographic Institute. IPST Cat. No. 753, OTS 63-11065. Office of Technical Services, U. S. Department of Commerce, Springfield, Va. 417 pp.

Murphy, G. I. 1965. Preliminary analysis of the population dynamics of the peruvian anchovy. (Mimeo.) Report to the Instituto del Mar del Peru.

Murphy, G. I. 1966. Population biology of the Pacific sardine (Sardinops caerulea.) Proc. Calif. Acad. Sci., Ser. 4. **34**:1-84.

Murray, J. 1913. The oceans. Henry Holt, New York. 256 pp.

Murray, J., and J. Hjort. 1912. The depths of the ocean. Macmillan International, Ltd., London. 821 pp.

Myklevoll, S. 1968. Basking shark fishery. Comm. Fish. Rev. **30**:59-63.

Nash, C. E. 1969. Thermal aquaculture. Sea Frontiers **15**:268-276.

National Council on Marine Resources and Engineering Development. 1969. Marine science affairs. 251 pp.

National Council on Marine Resources and Engineering Development. 1971. Marine science affairs. 114 pp.

National Marine Fisheries Service. 1972. Fishery statistics of the United States 1969. Stat. Digest **63**:1-474.

National Marine Fisheries Service. 1973. Fishery statistics of the United States 1970. Stat. Digest **64**:1-489.

Naylor, E. 1965. Effects of heated effluents upon marine and estuarine organisms. Adv. Mar. Biol. **3**:63-103.

Needham, P. R., and R. Gard. 1959. Rainbow trout in Mexico and California. Univ. Calif. Publ. Zoology **67**:1-124.

Nelson, E. W. 1887. Field notes on Alaskan fishes. In Henshaw, H. W., editor. Report upon natural history collections made in Alaska between the years 1877 and 1881. U. S. Army Signal Serv. Arctic Ser. 3, Washington, D. C. pp. 295-322.

Nelson, W. R. 1967. Studies on the croaker, Micropogon undulatus, Linnaeus and the spot, Leiostomus xanthurus, Lacepede in Mobile Bay, Alabama. J. Mar. Sci. Alabama **1**:4-92.

Nesbit, R. A. 1943. Biological and economic problems of fishery management. U. S. Fish Wildl. Serv., Spec. Sci. Rep. **18**:23-53, 61-68.

Neumann, A. C. 1966. Red Sea. In Fairbridge, R. W., editor. The encyclopaedia of oceanography. Van Nostrand Reinhold Co., New York. pp. 748-751.

Neumann, G. 1942. Die absolute topographie des physikalishen meeresniveaus und die oberflächenströmungen des Schwarzen Meeres. Ann. Hydro. Mar. Meteorol. **70**:1-265.

Neumann, G., and W. F. Pierson, Jr. 1966. Principles of physical oceanography. Prentice-Hall, Inc., New York. 545 pp.

New England Marine Resources. 1973. Commercial lobster farms still a long way off. Information No. 45. p. 2.

Nichols, P. R., and P. M. Keney. 1963. Crab larvae (Callinectes), in plankton collections from cruises of M/V Theodore M. Gill, south Atlantic coast of the United States, 1953-54. U. S. Fish Wildl. Serv., Spec. Sci. Rep. Fish. **448**:1-14.

Nicholson, N. L., and R. L. Cimberg. 1971. The Santa Barbara oil spills of 1969: a post-spill survey of the rocky intertidal. In Kolpack, R. L., editor. Biological and oceanographical survey of the Santa Barbara oil spill 1969-1970. I. Biology and bacteriology, chap. 17. Allan Hancock Foundation, University of Southern California, Los Angeles. pp. 325-400.

Nielsen, E. S. 1960. Productivity of the oceans. Ann. Rev. Plant Physiol. **11**:341-362.

Nielsen, E. S. 1964. On the determination of the activity in ^{14}C ampoules. (Mimeo.) ICES C.M. 1964, Plankton Committee Doc. 105. 2 pp.

Nigrelli, R. F., and F. E. Firth. 1939. On Sphyrion lumpi (Krøyer), a copepod parasite on the redfish, Sebastes marinus (Linnaeus), with special reference to the host-parasite relationships. Zoologica **24**:1-10.

Nikol'skii, G. V. 1954. Special ichthyology, ed. 2. (Translated from Russian in 1961.) IPST Cat. No. 233, OTS 60-21817. Office of Technical Services, U. S. Department of Commerce, Springfield, Va. pp. 1-538.

Niska, E. L. 1969. The Oregon trawl fishery for mink food, 1958-65. Pac. Mar. Fish. Comm., Bull. **7**:89-101.

Ocean Industry editorial. 1969. Plastic "seaweed" tested in fight against erosion. Ocean Ind. **4**:15.

Oceanology International editorials.
1969. Plastic seaweed barrier tested. Oceanol. Int. **4**:28.
1970. Mariculture experiment in progress at St. Croix. Oceanol. Int. **5**:8.
1971. Note on ocean dumping. Oceanol. Int. **6**:15.

Odum, H. T. 1959. Values and conflicts in the marine resources of Texas. (Mimeo.) Publications of the Institute for Marine Science, University of Texas. 12 pp.

Odum, H. T., and E. P. Odum. 1959. Principles and concepts pertaining to energy in ecological systems. In Odum, H. T., and E. P. Odum. Fundamentals of ecology. W. B. Saunders Co., Philadelphia. pp. 43-87.

O'Kelley, J. C. 1968. Mineral nutrition of algae. Ann. Rev. Plant Physiol. **19**:89-112.

Otsu, T., and R. N. Uchida. 1959. Sexual maturity and spawning of albacore in the Pacific Ocean. U. S. Fish Wildl. Serv., Fish. Bull. **59**:287-305.

Outram, D. N. 1955. Extent of herring spawning in British Columbia waters during 1955. Fish. Res. Bd. Canada, Circ. **37**:1-10.

Pacific Marine Fisheries Commission. 1960. The sport fisheries for salmon in Washington, Oregon and California. Pac. Mar. Fish. Comm., thirteenth annual report for 1960, appendix L. pp. 47-51.

Pacific Marine Fisheries Commission. 1966. Status report on the marine "non-salmon" sport fishery in Washington state. Pac. Mar. Fish. Comm., eighteenth annual report for 1965, appendix 2. p. 23.

Pacific Marine Fisheries Commission. 1972. Twenty-fourth annual report for 1971. Portland, Ore. pp. 1-44.

Painter, R. E. 1966. Zoobenthos of San Pablo and Suisin Bays. Calif. Fish Game, Fish Bull. **133**: 40-56.

Pariser, E. R. 1969. Fish protein concentrate. In Firth, F. J., editor. The encyclopedia of marine resources. Van Nostrand Reinhold Co., New York. pp. 265-272.

Parsons, T. R., R. J. LeBrasseur, and W. E. Barraclough. 1970. Levels of production in the pelagic environment of the Strait of Georgia, British Columbia: a review. J. Fish. Res. Bd. Canada **27**:1251-1264.

Pearse, A. S., and G. Gunter. 1957. Salinity. In Hedgpeth, J., editor. Treatise on marine ecology and paleocology, memoir 67, vol. 1. chap. 7. Geological Society of America, National Research Council, Washington, D. C. pp. 129-157.

Pearson, J. C. 1928. Natural history and conservation of the redfish and other commercial sciaenids on the Texas coast. Doc. 1046. Bull. U. S. Bur. Fish. **44**:129-214.

Pearson, J. C. 1939. The early life histories of some American Penaeidae, chiefly the commercial shrimp Penaeus setiferus (Linn.). Bull. U. S. Bur. Fish. **49**:1-73.

Pearson, J. C. 1948. Fluctuations in the abundance of the blue crab in Chesapeake Bay. U. S. Fish Wildl. Serv., Res. Rep. **14**:1-26.

Pequenat, J., S. W. Fowler, and L. F. Small. 1969. Estimates of the zinc requirements of marine organisms. J. Fish. Res. Bd. Canada **26**:145-150.

Petelin, V. P. 1966. Okhotsk Sea. In Fairbridge, R. W., editor. The encyclopaedia of oceanography. Van Nostrand Reinhold Co., New York. pp. 644-651.

Pew, P. 1954. Food and game fishes of the Texas coast. Texas Game Fish Comm., Bull. **33**:1-68.

Phillips, R. C. 1960. Observations on the ecology and distribution of Florida seagrasses. Fla. St. Bd. Conserv., Prof. Pap. Ser. **2**:1-72.

Phleger, C. F., N. Schultz, A. Soutar, and E.

Duffrin. 1970. Experimental sablefish fishing off San Diego. Comm. Fish. Rev. **32**:31-40.

Pickard, G. L. 1963. Descriptive physical oceanography. Pergamon Press, Inc., New York. 200 pp.

Pike, S. T., and A. Spilhaus. 1962. Marine resources, report to the Committee on Natural Resources. NAS/NRC Publ. 100-E. National Academy of Sciences–National Research Council, Washington, D. C., pp. 1-8.

Pillay, T. V. R. 1973. The role of aquaculture in fishery development and management. J. Fish. Res. Bd. Canada **30**:2202-2217.

Popiel, J., and J. Sosinski. 1973. Industrial fisheries and their influence on catches for human consumption. J. Fish. Res. Bd. Canada **30**: 2254-2259.

Pratt, D. M. 1953. Abundance and growth of Venus mercenaria and Callocardia morrhuana in relation to the character of bottom sediments. J. Mar. Res. **12**:60-74.

Pratt, D. M., and D. A. Campbell. 1956. Environmental factors affecting growth in Venus mercenaria in Narragansett Bay. Limnol. Oceanog. **1**:2-17.

Price, W. A., K. W. Tomlinson, and J. N. Junt. 1969. The effect of artificial seaweed in promoting the build-up of beaches. In Coastal engineering, eleventh conference proceedings **1**:570-578.

Provasoli, L. 1958. Nutrition and ecology of protozoa and algae. Ann. Rev. Microbiol. **12**: 279-308.

Quast, J. C., and E. L. Hall. 1972. List of fishes of Alaska and adjacent waters with a guide to some of their literature. NOAA Tech. Rep., Nat. Mar. Fish. Serv., Spec. Sci. Rep. Fish. **658**: 1-47.

Quayle, D. B. 1971. Pacific oyster raft culture in British Columbia. Fish. Res. Bd. Canada, Bull. **178**:1-34.

Quayle, D. B., and N. Bourne. 1972. The clam fisheries of British Columbia. Fish. Res. Bd. Canada, Bull. **179**:1-70.

Raitt, D. S. 1936. Stock replenishment and fishing intensity in the haddock of the North Sea. J. Conseil **11**:211-218.

Raju, G. 1964. Studies of the spawning of the oceanic skipjack Katsuwonus pelamis (Linnaeus) in Minicoy waters. In Symposium on scombroid fishes, II. Marine Biological Association of India. pp. 744-768.

Ralph M. Parsons Co. 1969. Evaluation of construction methods for offshore airports. Federal Aviation Administration, Systems Research and Development Service, final report RD-69-42. No. AD 693 185. Office of Technical Services,

U. S. Department of Commerce, Springfield, Va. 197 pp.

Rao, K. V. N. 1964. An account of the ripe ovaries of some Indian tunas. In Symposium on scombroid fishes, II. Marine Biological Association of India. pp. 733-743.

Rawson, D. S. 1946. Successful introduction of fish in a large saline lake. Can. Fish. Cult. **1**: 1-4.

Rawson, D. S. 1950. The physical limnology of Great Slave Lake. J. Fish. Res. Bd. Canada **8**:1-66.

Rawson, D. S., and J. E. Moore. 1944. The saline lakes of Saskatchewan. Can. J. Res., Sec. D. **22**:141-201.

Ray, S. M., and W. B. Wilson. 1957. Effects of unialgal and bacteria-free cultures of Gymnodinium brevis on fish, and notes on related studies with bacteria. U. S. Fish Wildl. Serv., Fish. Bull. **57**:469-496.

Rees, G. H. 1963. Edible crabs of the United States. U. S. Fish Wildl. Serv., Fish. Leaf. **550**: 1-18.

Reid, J. L., Jr. 1962. On circulation, phosphate-phosphorus content, and zooplankton volumes in the upper part of the Pacific Ocean. Limnol. Oceanog. **7**:287-306.

Reid, J. L., Jr. 1967. Oceanic environments of the genus Engraulis around the world. Calif. Mar. Res. Comm., CalCOFI Rep. **9**:29-33.

Reintjes, J. W. 1969. Synopsis of biological data on the Atlantic menhaden, Brevoortia tyrannus. FAO Fish. Synopsis 42, U. S. Fish Wildl. Serv., Circ. **320**:1-30.

Reintjes, J. W., and A. L. Pacheco. 1966. The relation of menhaden to estuaries. In A symposium on estuarine fisheries. Amer. Fish. Soc., Spec. Publ. 3. pp. 50-58.

Reish, D. J. 1961. A study of benthic fauna in a recently constructed boat harbor in southern California. Ecology **42**:84-91.

Reish, D. J. 1962. A study of succession in recently constructed marine harbors in southern California. In Gorsline, D. S., editor. Proceedings of the first national coastal and shallow water research conference, Tallahassee, Fla. pp. 73 (abstr.), 570-572.

Reish, D. J. 1963. Further studies on the benthic fauna in a recently constructed boat harbor in southern California. Bull. S. Calif. Acad. Sci. **62**:23-32.

Reish, D. J. 1964. Discussion of the Mytilus californianus community on newly constructed rock jetties in southern California. Veliger **7**: 95-101.

Reish, D. J. 1969. Discussion of the Mytilus californianus community on newly constructed rock jetties in southern California (Mollusca:

Bivalvia). In Reish, D. J., editor. Biology of the oceans. Dickenson Pub. Co., Inc., Encino, Calif. pp. 18-28.

Remane, A. 1958. Ökologie des Brackwassers. In Remane, A., and C. Schlieper, editors. Die Biologie des Brackwassers. Stuttgart-Schweizerbartsche Verlag, Binnengewasser. pp. 1-213.

Renfro, W. C. 1963. Gas-bubble mortality of fishes in Galveston Bay, Texas. Trans. Amer. Fish. Soc. **92:**320-322.

Rice, D. W. 1967. Cetaceans. In Anderson, S., and J. K. Jones, editors. Recent mammals of the world: a synopsis of families, chap. 15. The Ronald Press Co., New York. pp. 291-324.

Richards, F. A. 1957. Oxygen in the ocean. In Hedgpeth, J., editor. Treatise on marine ecology and paleoecology, memoir 67, vol. 1, chap. 9. Geological Society of America, National Research Council, Washington, D. C. pp. 185-238.

Ricker, W. E. 1934. A critical discussion of various measures of oxygen saturation in lakes. Ecology **15:**348-363.

Ricker, W. E. 1958. Handbook of computations for biological statistics of fish populations. Fish. Res. Bd. Canada, Bull. **119:**1-300.

Ridgway, G. J. 1957. The use of immunological techniques in racial studies. U. S. Fish Wildl. Serv., Spec. Sci. Rep. Fish. **208:**39-43.

Ridgway, G. J., J. E. Cushing, and G. L. Durall. 1961. Serological differentiation of populations of sockeye salmon, Oncorhynchus nerka. Int. N. Pac. Fish. Comm., Bull. **3:**5-10.

Rietze, H. L. 1972. Alaska fisheries. In Our changing fisheries. National Marine Fish Service, U. S. Department of Commerce, Washington, D. C. pp. 258-279.

Riley, G. A. 1951. Oxygen, phosphate and nitrate in the Atlantic Ocean. Bingham Oceanogr. Coll. Bull. **13:**1-26.

Rivas, L. R. 1970. Snappers of the western Atlantic. Comm. Fish. Rev. **32:**41-44.

Rivas, L. R. 1970a. The red grouper of the Gulf of Mexico. Comm. Fish. Rev. **32:**24-30.

Roden, G. I. 1961. On non-seasonal temperature and salinity variations along the west coast of the United States and Canada. Calif. Mar. Res. Comm., CalCOFI Rep. **8:**95-119.

Roe, T., Jr., J. S. Williams, and H. J. Migliore. 1970. Chemical overlays for seafloor sediments. Second annual Offshore Technical Conference. Preprints **1:**221-226.

Rostlund, E. 1952. Freshwater fish and fishing in native North America. Univ. Calif. Publ. Geography **9:**1-313.

Rounsefell, G. A. 1926. Report of progress in Alaska herring investigations. Pac. Fisherman **24:**20-21.

Rounsefell, G. A. 1930. The existence and causes of dominant year classes in the Alaska herring. In Contributions to marine biology. Stanford University Press, Stanford, Calif. pp. 260-270.

Rounsefell, G. A. 1930a. Contribution to the biology of the Pacific herring, Clupea pallasii, and the condition of the fishery in Alaska. Doc. 1080. Bull. U. S. Bur. Fish. **45:**227-320.

Rounsefell, G. A. 1942. Field experiments in selecting the most efficient tag for use in haddock studies. Trans. Amer. Fish. Soc. **71:**228-235.

Rounsefell, G. A. 1957. A method of estimating abundance of groundfish on Georges Bank. U. S. Fish Wildl. Serv., Fish. Bull. **57:**265-278.

Rounsefell, G. A. 1957a. Fecundity of North American Salmonidae. U. S. Fish Wildl. Serv., Fish. Bull. **57:**451-468.

Rounsefell, G. A. 1958. Factors causing decline in sockeye salmon of Karluk River, Alaska. U. S. Fish Wildl. Serv., Fish. Bull. **58:**83-169.

Rounsefell, G. A. 1958a. Anadromy in North American Salmonidae. U. S. Fish Wildl. Serv., Fish. Bull. **58:**171-185.

Rounsefell, G. A. 1962. Relationships among North American Salmonidae. U. S. Fish Wildl. Serv., Fish. Bull. **62:**235-270.

Rounsefell, G. A. 1963. Marking fish and invertebrates. U. S. Fish Wildl. Serv., Fish. Leaf. **549:**1-12.

Rounsefell, G. A. 1964. Preconstruction study of the fisheries of the estuarine areas traversed by the Mississippi River–Gulf Outlet Project. U. S. Fish Wildl. Serv., Fish. Bull. **63:**373-393.

Rounsefell, G. A. 1971. Potential food from the sea. J. Mar. Sci. Alabama **1:**1-82.

Rounsefell, G. A. 1972. Ecological effects of offshore construction. J. Mar. Sci. Alabama **2:**1-208.

Rounsefell, G. A., and L. H. Bond. 1949. Salmon restoration in Maine. Atlantic Sea-run Salmon Comm., Res. Rep. **1:**1-52.

Rounsefell, G. A., and E. H. Dahlgren. 1932. Fluctuations in the supply of herring, Clupea pallasii, in Prince William Sound, Alaska. Bull. U. S. Bur. Fish. **47:**263-291.

Rounsefell, G. A., and E. H. Dahlgren. 1935. Races of herring, Clupea pallasii, in southeastern Alaska. Bull. U. S. Bur. Fish. **48:**119-141.

Rounsefell, G. A., and A. Dragovich. 1966. Correlation between oceanographic factors and abundance of the Florida red tide (Gymnodinium breve Davis), 1954-61. Bull. Mar. Sci., Gulf Carib. **16:**404-422.

Rounsefell, G. A., and W. H. Everhart. 1953. Fishery science. John Wiley & Sons, Inc., New York. 444 pp.

Rounsefell, G. A., and J. L. Kask. 1945. How to mark fish. Trans. Amer. Fish. Soc. **73:**320-363.

Rounsefell, G. A., and G. B. Kelez. 1938. The salmon and salmon fisheries of Swiftsure Bank, Puget Sound, and the Fraser River. Bull. U. S. Bur. Fish. **49**:693-823.

Rounsefell, G. A., and W. R. Nelson. 1966. Red-tide research summarized to 1964 including an annotated bibliography. U. S. Fish Wildl. Serv., Spec. Sci. Rep. Fish. **535**:1-85.

Royce, W. F. 1951. Breeding habits of lake trout in New York. U. S. Fish Wildl. Serv., Fish. Bull. **52**:59-76.

Royce, W. F. 1957. Statistical comparison of morphological data. In Contributions to the study of subpopulations of fishes. U. S. Fish Wildl. Serv., Spec. Sci. Rep. Fish. **208**:7-28.

Royce, W. F. 1972. Introduction to the fishery sciences. Academic Press, Inc., New York. 351 pp.

Royce, W. F., L. S. Smith, and A. C. Hartt. 1968. Models of oceanic migrations of Pacific salmon and comments on guidance mechanisms. U. S. Fish Wildl. Serv., Fish. Bull. **66**:441-462.

Rupp, R. S. 1966. Generalized equation for the ratio method of estimating population abundance. J. Wildl. Mgt. **30**:523-526.

Ruttner, F. 1963. Fundamentals of limnology, ed. 3. (Translated from German in 1963.) University of Toronto Press, Toronto. 295 pp.

Ryan, W. B. F. 1966. Mediterranean Sea, introduction. In Fairbridge, R. W., editor. The encyclopaedia of oceanography. Van Nostrand Reinhold Co., New York. pp. 490-493.

Ryther, J. H. 1969. Photosynthesis and fish production in the sea. Science **166**:72-76.

Ryzhkov, Y. G. 1960. Role of vertical stability of layers in development of deep-sea upwelling phenomena. Akademiya Nauk SSSR, Trudy Morskogo Gidrofizicheskogo Instituta 20. IPST Cat. No. 932. Office of Technical Services, U. S. Department of Commerce, Springfield, Va. pp. 33-35.

Sakamoto, W. 1968. Study on the turbidity in an estuary. II. Observations on coagulation and settling processes of particles in the boundary of fresh and salt water. Bull. Fac. Fish., Hokkaidō Univ. **18**:317-327.

Sanders, H. L. 1960. Benthic studies in Buzzards Bay. III. The structure of the soft-bottom community. Limnol. Oceanog. **5**:138-153.

Sandoz, M., and R. Rogers. 1944. The effect of environmental factors on hatching, moulting, and survival of zoea larvae of the blue crab, Callinectes sapidus Rathbun. Ecology **25**:216-228.

Savage, R. P., and W. W. Woodhouse, Jr. 1969. Creation and stabilization of coastal barrier dunes. Coastal engineering, eleventh conference proceedings **1**:671-700.

Scarratt, D. J. 1968. An artificial reef for lobsters (Homarus americanus). J. Fish. Res. Bd. Canada **25**:2683-2690.

Scattergood, L. W., and C. C. Taylor. 1950. The mussel resources of the North Atlantic region. I. The survey to discover the locations and areas of the North Atlantic mussel-producing beds. U. S. Fish Wildl. Serv., Fish. Leaf. **364**:1-34.

Scattergood, L. W., C. J. Sindermann, and B. E. Skud. Spawning of North American herring. Trans. Amer. Fish. Soc. **88**:164-168.

Schaefer, M. B. 1965. The potential harvest of the sea. Trans. Amer. Fish. Soc. **94**:123-128.

Schaefer, M. B. 1967. Dynamics of the fishery for the anchoveta, Engraulis ringens, off Peru. Inst. Mar. Peru. Bol. **1**:189-304.

Scheffer, V. B., and D. W. Rice. 1963. A list of the marine mammals of the world. U. S. Fish Wildl. Serv., Spec. Sci. Rep. Fish. **431**:1-12.

Schuster, W. H. 1949. Fish-culture in brackish-water ponds of Java. (First published under the title De Viscultuur in de Kustvijers op Java as publication No. 2 of Inland Fisheries Division of the Agricultural Service of Department of Agriculture and Fisheries, Indonesia; translated from Dutch in 1952.) Published in English as Spec. Publ. No. 1, Indo-Pacific Fisheries Council. pp. 1-143.

Scientific Committee on Oceanic Research. 1970. Proceedings of the Scientific Committee on Research. **6**:54-93.

Segerstråle, S. G. 1957. Baltic Sea. In Hedgpeth, J., editor. Treatise on marine ecology and paleoecology, memoir 67, vol. 1, chap. 24. Geological Society of America, National Research Council, Washington, D. C. pp. 751-800.

Seki, H., J. Skelding, and T. R. Parsons. 1968. Observations on the decomposition of a marine sediment. Limnol. Oceanog. **13**:440-447.

Sette, O. E. 1961. Problems in fish population fluctuations. Calif. Mar. Res. Comm., CalCOFI Rep. **8**:21-24.

Sherman, K. 1969. Norwegian holding net tested in Maine sardine fishery. Comm. Fish. Rev. **31**:8-10.

Shuman, R. F. 1950. Bear depredations on red salmon spawning populations in the Karluk River system, 1947. J. Wildl. Mgt. **14**:1-9.

Shuster, C. N., Jr. 1959. A biological evaluation of the Delaware River estuary. University of Delaware Marine Laboratory, Inform. Ser. No. 3. 77 pp.

Sidel'nikov, I. I., and E. M. Izmest'ev. 1971. Peculiarities in the behavior of Pacific saury and squid with fishing at light. In Alekseev, A. P., editor. Fish behavior and fishing techniques. IPST Cat. No. 5938, TT 71-50010. Office of Technical Services, U. S. Department of Commerce, Springfield, Va. pp. 57-61.

Silas, E. G. 1964. Aspects of the taxonomy and biology of the oriental bonito Sarda orientalis (Temminck and Schlegel). In Symposium on scombroid fishes, II. Marine Biological Association of India. pp. 283-308.

Silliman, R. P. 1943. Studies on the Pacific pilchard or sardine (Sardinops caerulea). V. A method of computing mortalities and replacements. U. S. Fish Wildl. Serv., Spec. Sci. Rep. **24**:1-10.

Simmons, E. G. 1957. An ecological survey of the upper Laguna Madre of Texas. Publ. Inst. Mar. Sci., Texas **4**:156-200.

Skud, B. E. 1959. Herring spawning surveys in southeastern Alaska. U. S. Fish Wildl. Serv., Spec. Sci. Rep. Fish. **321**:1-16.

Slater, D. W. 1949. Re-formation of excised fins of king salmon fingerlings and its effect on recognition of marked adults. Trans. Amer. Fish. Soc. **77**:132-140.

Slatick, E. 1970. Passage of adult salmon and trout through pipes. U. S. Fish Wildl. Serv., Spec. Sci. Rep. Fish. **592**:1-18.

Small, G. L. 1971. The blue whale. Columbia University Press, New York. 248 pp.

Smith, O. R., and E. H. Ahlstrom. 1948. Echo-ranging for fish schools and observations on temperature and plankton in waters off central California in the spring of 1946. U. S. Fish Wildl. Serv., Spec. Sci. Rep. **44**:1-43.

Smith, T. G. 1973. Population dynamics of the ringed seal in the Canadian eastern Arctic. Fish. Res. Bd. Canada, Bull. **181**:1-55.

Snyder, G. R. 1970. Thermal pollution of Columbia River might threaten smelt. Comm. Fish. Rev. **32**:58-64.

Snyder, J. O. 1931. Salmon of the Klamath River, California. Calif. Fish Game, Fish Bull. **34**:1-130.

Snyder, J. O. 1940. The trouts of California. Calif. Fish Game **26**:96-138.

Solov'ev, Y. 1971. Results of experimental fishing of commercial items at light in the Atlantic. In Alekseev, A. P., editor. Fish behavior and fishing techniques. IPST Cat. No. 5938, TT 71-50010. Office of Technical Services, U. S. Department of Commerce, Springfield, Va. pp. 91-95.

Soutar, A., and J. D. Isaacs. 1969. History of fish populations inferred from fish scales in anaerobic sediments off California. Calif. Mar. Res. Comm., CalCOFI Rep. **13**:63-70.

Sport Fishing Institute editorials.

1971. Thermal pollution fish kill. Sport Fish. Inst., Bull. **223**:3-4.

1972. Atlantic salmon symposium. Sport Fish. Inst., Bull. **240**:6-8.

Stauffer, R. C. 1937. Changes in the invertebrate community of a lagoon after disappearance of the eelgrass. Ecology **18**:427-431.

Stephens, F., R. W. Sheldon, and T. R. Parsons. 1967. Seasonal variations in the availability of food for benthos in a coastal environment. Ecology **48**:852-855.

Stickney, A. P. 1968. Supersaturation of atmospheric gases in the coastal waters of the Gulf of Maine. U. S. Fish Wildl. Serv., Fish. Bull. **67**:117-123.

Stocks, T. 1938. Morphologie des Atlantischen Ozeans. "Meteor" Werk 3, 1, Berlin.

Stommel, H. 1949. Trajectories of small bodies sinking slowly through convection cells. J. Mar. Res. **8**:24-29.

Storr, J. F. 1964. Ecology of the Gulf of Mexico commercial sponges and its relation to the fishery. U. S. Fish Wildl. Serv., Spec. Sci. Rep. Fish. **466**:1-73.

Straughan, D. 1971. What has been the effect of the spill on the ecology in the Santa Barbara Channel? In Kolpack, R. L., editor. Biological and oceanographical survey of the Santa Barbara Channel oil spill 1969-1970. I. Biology and bacteriology, chap. 18. Allan Hancock Foundation, University of Southern California, Los Angeles. pp. 401-426.

Suda, A. 1973. Development of fisheries for nonconventional species. J. Fish. Res. Bd. Canada **30**:2121-2158.

Sundstrom, G. T. 1957. Commercial fishing vessels and gear. U. S. Fish Wildl. Serv., Circ. **48**:1-48.

Sverdrup, H. U., M. Johnson, and R. H. Fleming. 1942. The oceans. Prentice-Hall, Inc., New York. 1087 pp.

Svetovidov, A. N. 1952. Sel'devye (Clupeidae). (Cited by Nikol'skii, G. V.) Fauna SSSR, vol. 2, No. 1.

Sykes, J. E., and J. H. Finucane. 1966. Occurrence in Tampa Bay, Florida, of immature species dominant in Gulf of Mexico commercial fisheries. U. S. Fish Wildl. Serv., Fish. Bull. **65**:369-379.

Tamura, T. 1970. Marine aquaculture, ed. 2, (Translated from Japanese in 1966.) PB 194051 T in two parts. National Science Foundation, Office of Technical Services, U. S. Department of Commerce, Springfield, Va.

Tarver, J. W., and R. J. Dugas. 1973. A study of the clam, Rangia cuneata, in Lake Pontchartrain and Lake Maurepas, Louisiana. Louisiana Wild Life Fish. Comm., Tech. Bull. **5**:1-97.

Taylor, C. C., H. B. Bigelow, and H. W. Graham. 1957. Climatic trends and the distribution of marine animals in New England. U. S. Fish Wildl. Serv., Fish. Bull. **57**:293-345.

Taylor, F. H. C. 1955. The Pacific herring (Clupea pallasi) along the Pacific coast of Canada. Int. N. Pac. Fish. Comm. Bull. **1**: 105-128.

Taylor, J. L., and C. H. Saloman. 1968. Some effects of hydraulic dredging and coastal development in Boca Ciega Bay, Florida. U. S. Fish Wildl. Serv., Fish. Bull. **67**:213-241.

Templeman, W. 1966. Marine resources of Newfoundland. Fish. Res. Bd. Canada, Bull. **154**: 1-170.

Tester, A. L. 1937. Populations of herring (Clupea pallasii) in the coastal waters of British Columbia. J. Biol. Bd. Canada **3**:108-144.

Tester, A. L., and J. C. Stevenson. 1947. Results of the west coast of Vancouver Island herring investigation, 1946-47. British Columbia Dept. Fish., Rep. (1946). pp. M42-M71.

Thompson, H. 1939. The occurrence and biological features in the biology of the haddock of the Newfoundland area. Dept. Nat. Res. Newfoundland, Res. Bull. (Fish) **4**:1-160.

Thompson, H. 1951. Latent fishery resources and means for their development. In Proceedings of the United Nations Conference on Conservation and Utilization of Resources **7**:28-38.

Thompson, W. F., and W. C. Herrington. 1930. Life history of the Pacific halibut. I. Marking experiments. Rep. Int. Fish. Comm. **2**:1-137.

Thompson, W. F., and J. B. Thompson. 1919. The spawning of the grunion (Leuresthes tenuis). Calif. Fish Game, Fish Bull. **3**:1-29.

Thompson, W. F., and R. Van Cleve. 1936. Early life history of the Pacific halibut. 2. Distribution and early life history. Rep. Int. Fish. Comm. **9**:1-184.

Thomson, J. A. 1958. Biological effects of the Ripple Rock explosion. Fish. Res. Bd. Canada, Prog. Rep. Pac. Coast Sta. **111**:3-8.

Tilton, J. E., and J. E. Kelley. 1971. Experimental cage culture of channel catfish in heated discharge water. In Avault, J. W., Jr., E. Boudreaux, and E. Jaspers, editors. Proceedings of the first annual workshop, World Mariculture Society. pp. 73-87.

Travin, V. I., and L. N. Pechenik. 1962. Soviet fishery investigations and fishing in the northwest Atlantic. In Marti, Y. Y., editor. Soviet fishery investigations in the northwest Atlantic. IPST Cat. No. 994, OTS 63-11102. Office of Technical Services, U. S. Department of Commerce, Springfield, Va. pp. 4-54.

Tressler, D. K., and J. M. Lemon. 1951. Marine products of commerce, ed. 2. Van Nostrand Reinhold Co., New York. 782 pp.

Trites, R. W. 1961. Probable effects of proposed Passamaquoddy Power Project on oceanographic conditions. J. Fish. Res. Bd. Canada **18**:163-201.

Tubb, J. A. 1967. Status of fish culture in Asia and the far east. FAO Fish. Rep. **44**:45-53.

Tully, J. P., and A. J. Dodimead. 1957. Properties of the water in the Strait of Georgia, British Columbia. J. Fish. Res. Bd. Canada **14**:241-310.

Turner, C. H., E. E. Ebert, and R. R. Given. 1969. Man-made reef ecology. Calif. Fish Game, Fish Bull. **146**:1-210.

Turner, H. J., Jr. 1953. A review of the biology of some commercial molluscs of the east coast of North America. In Sixth report on investigations of the shellfisheries of Massachusetts. Division of Marine Fisheries, Massachusetts. pp. 39-74.

Turner, H. J., Jr. 1953a. The edible crab fishery of Massachusetts. In Sixth report on investigations of the shellfisheries of Massachusetts. Division of Marine Fisheries, Massachusetts. pp. 25-28.

Turner, H. J., Jr., and C. J. George. 1955. Some aspects of the behavior of the quahaug, Venus mercenaria, during the early stages. In Eighth report on investigations of the shellfisheries of Massachusetts. Division of Marine Fisheries, Massachusetts. pp. 5-14.

Turner, L. M. 1886. Contributions to the natural history of Alaska. IV. Fishes. U. S. Army Signal Serv. Arctic Ser. **2**:87-113.

Uda, M. 1957. A consideration on the long years' trend of the fisheries fluctuation in relation to sea conditions. Bull. Jap. Soc. Sci. Fish. **23**:7-8.

Uda, M. 1961. Fisheries oceanography in Japan, especially on the principles of fish distribution, concentration, dispersal and fluctuation. Calif. Mar. Res. Comm. CalCOFI Rep. **8**:25-31.

Ullyott, P. 1953. Conditions of flow in the Bosphorus. Univ. Istanbul, Hydrobiol. Res. Inst., Ser. B. **1**:199-215.

Ullyott, P., and H. Pektaş. 1952. A note on the yearly temperature and salinity cycle in the Dardanelles. Univ. Istanbul, Hydrobiol. Res. Inst., Ser. B. **1**:133-147.

Umali, A. F. 1950. Guide to the classification of fishing gear in the Philippines. U. S. Fish Wildl. Serv., Res. Rep. **17**:1-165. (Illustrations by S. G. Duran.)

United States Department of Commerce. 1973. Marine sport fisheries. In National Marine Fisheries Service. Fisheries of the United States, 1972. Curr. Fish. Stat. **6100**:87.

University of Rhode Island. 1974. Lobster scarce? Try red crab. University of Rhode Island, New England Marine Resources, Information No. 58.

Van Andel, T. H. 1966. Gulf of California. In

Fairbridge, R. W., editor. The encyclopaedia of oceanography. Van Nostrand Reinhold Co., New York. pp. 312-315.

Van Andel, T. H., and H. D. Tjia. 1966. Timor Sea. In Fairbridge, R. W., editor. The encyclopaedia of oceanography. Van Nostrand Reinhold Co., New York. pp. 923-927.

Van Oosten, J. 1944. Lake trout. U. S. Fish Wildl. Serv., Fish. Leaf. **15**:1-8.

Vodyanitskii, V. A. 1954. Biological productivity of bodies of water, particularly the Black Sea. Trudy Severo-Kaspiiskoi Biololicheskoi Stantsii 8.

Voipio, A. 1962. Some notes on recent studies of chemical oceanography in Finland. In Gorsline, D. S., editor. Proceedings of the first coastal and shallow water conference, Tallahassee, Fla. pp. 785-800.

Vrooman, A. M., and P. E. Smith. 1971. Biomass of the subpopulations of northern anchovy Engraulis mordax Girard. Calif. Mar. Res. Comm., CalCOFI Rep. **15**:49-51.

Waldichuk, M. 1957. Physical oceanography of the Strait of Georgia, British Columbia. J. Fish. Res. Bd. Canada **14**:321-486.

Wallace, M. M., C. J. Pertuit, and A. R. Hvatum. 1949. Contribution to the biology of the king crab (Paralithodes camtschatica Tilesius). U. S. Fish Wildl. Serv., Fish. Leaf. **340**:1-50.

Warburg, C. H., and P. R. Nichols. 1967. Biology and management of the American shad and status of the fisheries, Atlantic coast of the United States, 1960. U. S. Fish Wildl. Serv., Spec. Sci. Rep. Fish. **550**:1-105.

Watson, J. E. 1961. The branding of sea herring as a short-term mark. Progr. Fish-Cult. **23**: 105.

Wenk, E., Jr. 1969. The physical resources of the sea. Sci. Amer. **221**:167-176.

Weymouth, F. W. 1915. Contributions to the life-history of the Pacific coast edible crab (Cancer magister). Report of the British Columbia Commissioner of Fisheries for 1914 (1915). pp. 123-129.

Weymouth, F. W. 1920. The edible clams, mussels and scallops of California. Calif. Fish Game, Fish Bull. **4**:1-74.

Weymouth, F. W. 1923. The life-history and growth of the Pismo clam (Tivela stultorum Mawe). Calif. Fish Game, Fish Bull. **7**:1-120.

Weymouth, F. W., and H. C. McMillin. 1931. The relative growth and mortality of the Pacific razor clam (Siliqua patula, Dixon), and their bearing on the commercial fishery, Doc. 1099. Bull. U. S. Bur. Fish. **46**:543-567.

Weymouth, F. W., and S. H. Thompson. 1931. The age and growth of the Pacific cockle (Cardium corbis Martyn). Bull. U. S. Bur. Fish. **46**:633-641.

Whitley, G. P. 1964. Scombroid fishes of Australia and New Zealand. In Symposium on scombroid fishes, I. Marine Biological Association of India. pp. 221-254.

Whitworth, W. R., and W. H. Irwin. 1961. The minimum oxygen requirements of five species of fish under quiescent conditions. In Proceedings of the fifteenth annual conference of the Southeastern Association of Game and Fish Commissioners. pp. 226-235.

Widrig, T. M. 1954. Method of estimating fish populations, with application to Pacific sardine. U. S. Fish Wildl. Serv., Fish. Bull. **56**:141-166.

Wilder, D. G. 1960. Possible effects of Passamaquoddy tidal power structures on the Canadian lobster industry. J. Fish. Res. Bd. Canada **17**: 553-563.

Williams, A. B. 1958. Substrates as a factor in shrimp distribution. Limnol. Oceanog. **3**:283-290.

Williams, A. B. 1965. Marine decapod crustaceans of the Carolinas. U. S. Fish Wildl. Serv., Fish. Bull. **65**:1-298.

Wilson, J. 1959. The effects of erosion, silt, and other inert materials on aquatic life. Water Poll. Abstr. **34**:1948.

Wilson, J. T.: 1963. Continental drift. Sci. Amer. Reprint No. 868. pp. 1-16.

Woodard, D. W., B. E. Dahl, R. L. Baker, and D. E. Feray. 1970. The use of grasses for dune stabilization along the Gulf coast with initial emphasis on the Texas coast. Gulf Univ. Res. Corp., Final Rep. 1969-1970. pp. 1-63.

Woodhouse, W. W., Jr., and R. E. Hanes. 1967. Dune stabilization with vegetation on the Outer Banks of North Carolina. U. S. Army Corps of Engineers, Coastal Engineering Research Center, Tech. Mem. **22**:1-43.

Wooster, W. S., M. B. Schaefer, and M. K. Robinson. 1967. Atlas of the Arabian Sea for fishery oceanography. IMR 67-12. Institute of Marine Resources, University of California.

World Fishing. 1969. 'Tsukiisos' and 'Gyoshos.' A review of artificial reefs research. World Fish. **18**:62.

Worthington, L. V. 1954. A preliminary note on the time scale in North Atlantic circulation. Deep-Sea Res. **1**:244-251.

Wynne-Edwards, V. C. 1952. Freshwater vertebrates of the Arctic and subarctic. Fish. Res. Bd. Canada, Bull. **94**:1-28.

Wyrtki, K. 1962. The oxygen minima in relation to ocean circulation. Deep-Sea Res. **9**:11-23.

Wyrtki, K. 1964. Upwelling in the Costa Rica Dome. U. S. Fish Wildl. Serv., Fish. Bull. **63**: 355-372.

Young, P. H. 1969. The California partyboat fishery, 1947-1967. Calif. Fish Game, Fish Bull. **145:**1-91.

Zahn, M. C. 1970. Japanese tanner crab fishery in eastern Bering Sea. Comm. Fish. Rev. **32:**52-56.

Zein-Eldin, Z. P., and D. V. Aldrich. 1965. Growth and survival of post-larval Penaeus aztecus under controlled conditions of temperature and salinity. Biol. Bull. Woods Hole **129:**199-216.

Zeitoun, M. A., E. F. Mandelli, W. F. McIlhenny, and R. O. Reid. 1969. Disposal of the effluents from desalination plants: the effects of copper content, heat and salinity. U. S. Office of Saline Water, Res. Dev. Prog. Rep. **437:**1-203.

Zenkevich, L. A. 1957. Caspian and Aral Seas. In Hedgpeth, J., editor. Treatise on marine ecology and paleoecology, memoir 67, vol. 1, chap. 26. Geological Society of America, National Research Council, Washington, D. C. pp. 891-916.

Zenkevich, L. A. 1963. Biology of the seas of the USSR. Wiley-Interscience Div., John Wiley & Sons, Inc., New York.

Zenkovitch, V. P. 1966. Black Sea. In Fairbridge, R. W., editor. The encyclopaedia of oceanography, Van Nostrand Reinhold Co., New York. pp. 145-151.

Znamierowska-Prüffer, M. 1957. Thrusting implements for fishing in Poland and neighboring countries. Studia Societatis Scientiarum Torunensis, Suppl. IV, 1957. (Translated from Polish in 1966.) TT 61-11367. Office of Technical Services, U. S. Department of Commerce, Springfield, Va.

Zobell, C. E. 1954. Marine bacteria and fungi in the Gulf of Mexico. In Galtsoff, P. S., editor. Gulf of Mexico: its origins, waters, and marine life, U. S. Fish Wildl. Serv., Fish. Bull. **55:**217-222.

Zobell, C. E., and C. B. Feltham. 1938. Bacteria as food for certain marine invertebrates. J. Mar. Res. **1:**312-327.

appendix B

🦐 Common and scientific names of organisms

This list of common and scientific names of organisms mentioned in the text requires some explanation. Many organisms are known by two or more common names; e.g., the sand lance is also known as the sand eel, although the fish is definitely not an eel. Sand lance is the preferred common name so it is followed by sand eel in parentheses: Sand lance (sand eel). Under the entry "sand eel" the reader is referred to "sand lance." Many common names are misleading; Bombay duck is not a duck but a large fish common in India, so after the entry "Bombay duck" "(a fish)" is added to so inform the reader. Similarly, after "Wahoo" the reader is referred to the Spanish mackerels by "*see* Spanish mackerel."

Many fish have the same common name in different localities but do not use a geographic name as part of the common name. Other fish have different common names in different localities; the spiny dogfish, which is common on both the Atlantic and Pacific coasts of the United States, is called the picked dogfish in Europe, so the common name is entered as "Dogfish, spiny (picked in Europe)."

In the distribution column the ranges are intended to include areas in which the species is common. A dash between two localities indicates a continuous range between the localities. The term "Indo-Pacific" includes a large tropical area of the eastern Indian Ocean, the East Indies, and the southwest Pacific and is a zoogeographic region.

In a few of the scientific names the genus or species is followed by a word in parentheses. This word is usually preceded by an equal sign. The equal sign indicates that the second word is an older generic or species name that has been replaced by the first word or that the new generic or species name may still be in some doubt. In many cases there is no doubt, but the change has occurred so recently that the older name is the one best known among scientists. The entry for the sea catfish is therefore *Arius (= Galeichthys) felis*. If the equal sign is missing after the generic name, it indicates a subgenus. A subspecies name is indicated by a generic name followed by two more words without parentheses.

Abalone	Pacific and Indian Oceans	*Haliotis* spp.
Acanthocybium solandri	Tropical seas	Wahoo (a Spanish mackerel)
Achirus		
achirus	E. South America	Sole
lineatus	Tropical W. Atlantic	Striped or lined sole
Acipenser		
oxyrhynchus	W. Atlantic	Atlantic sturgeon
transmontanus	N.E. Pacific	White sturgeon
Actinopyga nobilis	S.W. Pacific	Black teatfish (a sea cucumber)
Aequepecten irradians	Cape Cod–Texas	Bay scallop
Albula vulpes	Warm seas	Bonefish
Alewife (river herring); *see also* Blueback	Nova Scotia–North Carolina	*Alosa pseudoharengus*
Alga; *see* Bluegreen alga		
Alosa		
aestivalis	Maine-Florida	Blueback (summer herring)
fallax	N.E. Atlantic-Mediterranean	Twaite shad
finta	N.E. Atlantic-Mediterranean	Allis shad
pseudoharengus	Nova Scotia–North Carolina	Alewife (river herring)
sapidissima	Gulf of St. Lawrence–Florida; Central California–British Columbia	American shad
Amberjack, greater	Florida-Brazil	*Seriola dumerili*
Ammodytes		
americanus	Cape Hatteras–Labrador; Newfoundland–Grand Banks	American sand lance (sand eel)
cicerellus	Black Sea	Black Sea sand lance (sand eel)
dubius	Finmarken-Spain-Iceland; Newfoundland–Grand Banks	Northern sand lance (sand eel)
hexapterus	Murman coast–Chukchi Sea–Hudson Bay; N. California–Bering Sea–Japan	Pacific sand lance (sand eel)
Anadara		
granosa	Malaysia	"Blood" clam
subcrenata	Japan	"Mogai" clam
Anarhichas lupus	Spitzbergen-France; Labrador–Cape Cod	Atlantic wolffish (ocean catfish)
Anchoa		
compressa	California–Baja California	Deepbody anchovy
hepsetus	Cape Cod–Uruguay	Striped anchovy
mitchilli	Cape Cod–Texas	Bay anchovy
Anchoveta		
anchoveta	Tropical W. Atlantic	*Cetengraulis edentulus*
anchovetas	Indo-Pacific	*Stolephorus* and *Thryssa*
Panamanian anchoveta	Tropical E. Pacific	*Cetengraulis mysticetus*
Peruvian anchoveta	Peru Current	*Engraulis ringens*
Anchovy; *see also* Anchoveta		
anchovy	Black Sea	*Engraulis encrasicholus ponticus*
anchovy	N.E. Atlantic-Mediterranean	*Engraulis encrasicholus encrasicholus*
Argentine anchovy	S.W. Atlantic	*Engraulis anchoita*
Australian anchovy	S.W. Pacific	*Engraulis australis*
bay anchovy	Cape Cod–Texas	*Anchoa mitchilli*
Cape anchovy	South Africa	*Engraulis capensis*
deepbody anchovy	California–Baja California	*Anchoa compressa*
Japanese anchovy	N.W. Pacific	*Engraulis japonicus*
northern anchovy	Baja California–British Columbia	*Engraulis mordax*
striped anchovy	Cape Cod–Uruguay	*Anchoa hepsetus*

Angler

deepsea angler	Cosmopolitan in deep water	*Ceratias holboelli*
goosefish, monkfish	N.W. Atlantic	*Lophius americanus*
monkfish	N.E. Atlantic	*Lophius piscatorius*
Anguilla spp.		Common eel
Anoplopoma fimbria	California–Bering Sea–Hokkaidō	Sablefish (black cod)
Apolectus niger	Philippines	Pomfret
Arca spp.		Arkshell
Archosargus probatocephalus	Cape Cod–Texas	Sheepshead
Arctica islandica	Arctic Circle–Chesapeake Bay	Ocean quahaug (a clam)
Arctocephalus		
australis	S. South America	South American fur seal
pusillus	South Africa	South African fur seal
Argopecten gibbus	S. Atlantic–Gulf of Mexico	Calico scallop
Arius (= *Galeichthys*) *felis*	U. S. Atlantic–Gulf of Mexico	Sea catfish
Arkshell		*Arca* spp.
Artemia salina		Brine shrimp
Asterias rubens	Atlantic	Starfish
Atherestes		
evermanni	N.W. Pacific	Kamchatka flounder
stomias	Oregon–E. Bering Sea	Arrowtooth halibut
Atherinidae		Silversides
Atherinops affinis	Gulf of California–British Columbia	Topsmelt (a silverside)
Atherinopsis californiensis	California–Oregon	Jacksmelt (a silverside)
Atka mackerel (a greenling)	Japan–Bering Sea–Monterey	*Pleurogrammus monopterygius*
Aulacomya ater	Chile-Argentina	Cholga mussel
Austroglossus		
microlepis	S.W. Africa	West coast sole
pectoralis	Agulhas Bank	Agulhas sole
Auxis thazard	Atlantic-Pacific	Frigate mackerel (a tuna)
Bagre marinus	Panama–Cape Cod	Gaff-topsail catfish
Bairdiella chrysura	New York–Texas	Silver perch
Balaena mysticetus	Northern seas–Arctic	Greenland right (bowhead) whale
Balaenoptera		
acutorostrata	All oceans	Minke whale
borealis	All oceans	Sei whale
edeni	Warm seas	Bryde whale
musculus	All oceans	Blue whale
physalus	All oceans	Finback whale
Balanus amphitrite		Barnacle
Barnacle		*Balanus amphitrite*
Barracouta; *see* Snoek		
Barracuda		
California barracuda; *see* Barracuda, Pacific		
Pacific barracuda	Baja California–British Columbia	*Sphyraena argentea*
Bass; *see also* Sea bass; Striped bass; White perch		
largemouth (freshwater)		*Micropterus salmoides*
Basses, temperate		Percichthyidae
Bathylagus		Blacksmelt or deepsea smelt
Belone belone	Europe	Garfish or needlefish
Beluga; *see* Whale		
Billfishes		Istiophoridae
Black cod; *see* Sablefish		
Blackfish; *see* Whale, pilot		

Blackfish, Alaska (freshwater) (a mudminnow)	N. Alaska	*Dallia pectoralis*
Blacksmelt or deepsea smelt		*Bathylagus*
Bloodworm		*Glycera dibranchiata*
Blueback; *see* Salmon, sockeye		
Blueback (summer herring)	Maine-Florida	*Alosa aestivalis*
Bluefish	Warm Atlantic–Mediterranean–Indian Ocean	*Pomatomus saltatrix*
Bluegreen alga (nitrogen-fixing)	Gulf of Mexico	*Oscillatoria* (= *Skujaella*) (= *Trichodesmium*)
Blue runner	Warm Atlantic	*Caranx crysos*
Blue whiting; *see* Cod		
Bombay duck (a fish)	India	*Harpodon nehereus*
Bonefish	Warm seas	*Albula vulpes*
Bonga (related to menhaden)	Guinea	*Ethmalosa fimbriata*
Bonito		
Atlantic bonito	Atlantic	*Sarda sarda*
Pacific bonito	Pacific	*Sarda chiliensis*
striped or oriental bonito	Indo-W. Pacific	*Sarda orientalis*
Boreogadus saida	Circumpolar	Arctic cod
Bothidae		Lefteye flounders, turbots, flukes
Brachymystax lenok	Siberia; Amur River; Japan; W. Okhotsk Sea–Korea	Lenok (a freshwater salmonid)
Brevoortia		
gunteri	Gulf of Mexico	Fine-scale menhaden
patronus	Gulf of Mexico	Gulf menhaden
tyrannus	Maine-E. Florida	Atlantic menhaden
Brill; *see* Flatfishes		
Brosme brosme	Cape Cod–Iceland–Murman coast	Cusk (saithe in Europe)
Buccinum undatum	N.E. Atlantic	Whelk
Burbot (freshwater)		*Lota lota*
Butterfish	Nova Scotia–Cape Hatteras	*Peprilus triacanthus*
Butterfly mackerel	New Zealand–South Africa	*Gasterochisma melampus*
Butterfly mackerels		Gasterochismatinae
Busycon and *Strombus*		Conchs
Cabezon (a sculpin)	Baja California–Sitka	*Scorpaenichthys marmoratus*
Callinectes sapidus	Cape Cod–N. South America	Blue crab
Callorhinus ursinus	N. Pacific–Bering Sea	Northern fur seal
Cancer		
antennarius	California	Rock crab
borealis	Maritimes–New England	Jonah crab
irroratus	Maritimes–New England	Rock crab
magister	Monterey–central Alaska	Dungeness crab
pagurus	Europe	Edible crab
productus	California	Rock (or red) crab
Candlefish; *see* Smelt, eulachon		
Capelin; *see* Smelt		
Caranx		
crysos	Warm Atlantic	Blue runner
hippos	Tropical seas	Crevalle
Carassius; see also Cyprinus		Asian carp
Carcinus maenas	Maine–New Jersey; Europe	Green crab
Cardium edule	N.E. Atlantic	Common cockle
Caretta caretta	Atlantic	Loggerhead turtle
Carp		
Asian		*Carassius*
common		*Cyprinus carpio*
Caspialosa kessleri	Caspian Sea	Black-spined shad

Caspialosa spp.	Black and Caspian Seas	Herrings and shads
Catfish		
freshwater		*Ictalurus* spp.
blue catfish		*Ictalurus furcatus*
marine		
gaff-topsail catfish	Panama–Cape Cod	*Bagre marinus*
ocean catfish; *see* Wolffish		
sea catfish	U. S. Atlantic–Gulf of Mexico	*Arius (= Galeichthys) felis*
Catostomus		Sucker (freshwater)
Centropristis striata	Cape Cod–Cape Hatteras	Black sea bass
Ceratias holboelli	Cosmopolitan in deep water	Deepsea angler
Cero; *see* Spanish mackerel		
Cetengraulis		
edentulus	Tropical W. Atlantic	Anchoveta
mysticetus	Tropical E. Pacific	Panamanian anchoveta
Cetorhinus maximus	Circumpolar	Basking shark
Chaetodipterus faber	Cape Cod–Brazil	Spadefish
Chamidae	Tropical seas	Attached clams (noncommercial)
Channel bass; *see* Drum, red		
Chanos chanos	Indo-Pacific	Milkfish
Charr; *see also* Trout		
alpine; *see* Charr, arctic		
arctic charr	Circumpolar	*Salvelinus alpinus*
blueback charr (freshwater)	Maine	*Salvelinus oquassa*
Dolly Varden charr	N. California–arctic Alaska–Kamchatka–Japan–Korea	*Salvelinus malma*
eastern brook charr	Hudson Bay–Cape Cod	*Salvelinus fontinalis*
golden charr (freshwater)	New England	*Salvelinus alpinus aureolus*
red Quebec charr (freshwater)	Quebec	*Salvelinus oquassa marstoni*
Chelonia mydas		Green turtle
Cherrystone; *see* Clam, hard		
Chimaera		
Atlantic chimaera	Banquereau-Portugal	*Hydrolagus affinus*
Pacific chimaera	California-Alaska	*Hydrolagus colliei*
Chionoecetes		
bairdi	Columbia River–E. Bering Sea	Snow (tanner) crab
opilio	Bering Sea–W. North Atlantic	Snow (tanner) crab (queen crab in Canada)
tanneri	Oregon-Alaska (in deep water)	Tanner crab
Chirocentrus		
dorab	Indo-Pacific	Wolf herring
nudus	Indo-Pacific	Wolf herring
Chlamys islandicus	Newfoundland-Norway	Iceland scallop
Chondrus crispus	Atlantic	Irish moss
Choromya and *Modiolus*	Chile and Peru	Mussels
Chrysophrys major	Japan	Red sea bream
Citharichthys		
sordidus	California–British Columbia	Sand dab
spilopterus	Warm W. Atlantic	Spotfin (bay) whiff
Clam; *see also* Cockle		
attached (noncommercial)	Tropical seas	Chamidae
bean clam; *see* Clam, wedge		
"blood" clam	Malaysia	*Anadara granosa*
butter clam	N. California–Aleutian Islands	*Saxidomus giganteus*
cherrystone clam; *see* Clam, hard		
coot clam	W. Atlantic	*Mulinia lateralis*
coquina clam; *see* Clam, wedge		
geoduck	California-Alaska	*Panope generosa*

Clam—cont'd

grooved carpet shell clam	N.E. Atlantic	*Venerupis decussatus*
hard clam		
hard clam	Maine-Florida	*Mercenaria mercenaria*
southern hard clam	South of Cape Hatteras	*Mercenaria campechiensis*
littleneck clam	California-S.E. Alaska	*Protothaca staminea*
manila clam	Japan; Korea; Washington– British Columbia	*Venerupis japonica*
"mogai" clam	Japan	*Anadara subcrenata*
ocean quahaug	Arctic Circle–Chesapeake Bay	*Arctica islandica*
Pismo clam	Magdalena Bay–Halfmoon Bay	*Tivela stultorum*
quahaug; *see* Clam, hard		
rangia	Potomac River–Campeche	*Rangia cuneata*
razor clam		
Atlantic razor clam	U. S. North Atlantic	*Ensis directus*
Pacific razor clam	Oregon–western end of Alaska Peninsula	*Siliqua patula*
soft (soft-shell) clam	N.W. Atlantic; California– British Columbia	*Mya arenaria*
surf clam		
southern surf clam	S.E. United States	*Spisula solidissima raveneli*
surf clam	Gulf of St. Lawrence–Cape Hatteras	*Spisula solidissima*
venus clam		
striped venus clam	N.E. Atlantic	*Venus gallina*
sunray venus clam	S.E. United States	*Macrocallista nimbosa*
wedge clam		
bean (wedge) clam	Baja California–Pismo Beach	*Donax gouldi*
coquina (wedge) clam	Florida	*Donax variabilis*
Cleisthenes herzensteini	Japan	Sohachi (pointed head) flounder
Clinocardium nuttalli	California–Bering Sea	Basket cockle
Clupanodon	Indo-Pacific	Short-nosed shads
Clupea		
harengus harengus	New England–Newfoundland– Iceland–Norway–Baltic Sea– Gibraltar	Atlantic herring
harengus maris-alba	White Sea	White Sea herring
harengus pallasi	San Diego–arctic Alaska– Kamchatka–Japan	Pacific herring
harengus suworowi	S.E. Barents Sea	Kanin-Pechora herring
Clupeonella		
deliculata caspia	Caspian Sea	"Kilka"
deliculata deliculata	Black Sea	"Tyulka"
Cockle		
basket cockle	California–Bering Sea	*Clinocardium nuttalli*
common cockle	N.E. Atlantic	*Cardium edule*
Cod		
Atlantic cod	New York–W. Greenland; Bay of Biscay–Barents Sea	*Gadus morhua*
arctic cod	Circumpolar	*Boreogadus saida*
black cod; *see* Sablefish		
blue whiting; *see* Cod, potassou		
burbot (ling) (freshwater)		*Lota lota*
Greenland cod	Cape Breton Island–W. Green- land–Point Barrow	*Gadus ogac*
navaga cod	Arctic	*Eleginus navaga*
Pacific cod	California–Bering Sea–Japan	*Gadus macrocephalus*
potassou (blue whiting)	N.E. Atlantic	*Micromesistius* (= *Gadus*) *potassou*

Cod—cont'd		
saffron cod	N. Pacific	*Eleginus gracilis*
tomcod		
Atlantic tomcod	Virginia–S. Labrador	*Microgadus tomcod*
Pacific tomcod	N.E. Pacific	*Microgadus proximus*
Cods (and hakes)		Gadidae
Cololabis saira	California–Gulf of Alaska–Japan	Pacific saury
Conchs		*Strombus* and *Busycon*
Conger eels		Congridae
Congridae		Conger eels
Corbina, California	California	*Menticirrhus undulatus*
Coregonus clupeaformis		Whitefish (freshwater)
Coryphaena hippurus	Cosmopolitan in warm seas	Dolphin (a fish)
Coryphaenidae		Dolphins (fish)
Cottidae		Sculpins
Crab		
blue crab	Cape Cod–N. South America	*Callinectes sapidus*
Dungeness crab	Monterey–central Alaska	*Cancer magister*
edible crab	Europe	*Cancer pagurus*
green crab	Maine–New Jersey; Europe	*Carcinus maenas*
horseshoe crab; *see* Horseshoe (king) crab		
Jonah crab	New England–Maritimes	*Cancer borealis*
king crab; *see also* Horseshoe (king) crab		
king crab	S.E. Alaska–N. Bering Sea	*Paralithodes camtschatica*
purple king crab	Icy Strait–St. Lawrence Island	*Paralithodes platypus*
southern king crab	S. South America	*Lithodes antarcticus*
kona crab	Hawaii	*Ranina ranina*
queen crab; *see* Crab, snow		
red crab; *see* Crab, rock		
red crab, deepsea	W. Atlantic	*Geryon quinquedens*
rock crab		
rock crab	New England–Maritimes	*Cancer irroratus*
rock crab	California	*Cancer antennarius*
rock (red) crab	California	*Cancer productus*
snow crab		
snow (tanner) crab	Columbia River–E. Bering Sea	*Chionoecetes bairdi*
snow (tanner) crab (queen crab in Canada)	Bering Sea–W. North Atlantic	*Chionoecetes opilio*
tanner crab	Oregon-Alaska	*Chionoecetes tanneri*
spinous spider crab	N.E. Atlantic-Mediterranean	*Maia squinada*
stone crab	Warm W. Atlantic–Gulf of Mexico	*Menippe mercenaria*
Crago franciscorum	California	Bay shrimp
Crangon vulgaris	N.E. Atlantic-Mediterranean	Common shrimp
Crassostrea		
(= *Gryphaea*) *angulata*	S.E. Europe-Mediterranean	Portuguese oyster
commercialis	Australia	Australian oyster
gigas	N.W. Pacific; Washington–British Columbia	Pacific (Japanese) oyster
rhizophora	Caribbean	Caribbean oyster
virginica	Maritimes-Mexico; west coast of United States	American (eastern) oyster
Crevalle	Tropical seas	*Caranx hippos*
Cristivomer namaycush	N. North American lakes	Lake trout (freshwater) (togue in Maine)

Croaker
  Atlantic croaker   New York–Texas   *Micropogon undulatus*
  king croaker; *see* Croaker, white
  white (king) croaker   Baja California–Vancouver Island   *Genyonemus lineatus*
Cusk (saithe in Europe)   Cape Cod–Iceland–Murman   *Brosme brosme*
                          coast
Cusk-eels   Ophidiidae
Cutlassfish, Atlantic   Warm Atlantic   *Trichiurus lepturus*
Cuttlefish   *Sepia*
Cyanea   Red jellyfish
Cyclopterus lumpus   New Jersey–Hudson Bay; Ice-   Lumpfish
                           land; British Isles–Murman
                           coast
Cymatogaster aggregata   California-S.E. Alaska   Shiner perch (shiner sea perch)
Cynoglossidae   Tonguefishes
Cynoscion   Weakfishes (sea trouts)
  nebulosis   New York–Texas   Spotted or speckled sea trout
  nobilis   Baja California–San Francisco   White sea bass
  nothus   Gulf of Mexico   Silver (white) sea trout
  regalis   Cape Cod–Florida   Weakfish
Cyprinodon variegatus   Sheepshead minnow
Cyprinus carpio   Common carp
Cystophora cristata   N. Atlantic   Hooded seal
Dab; *see* Flatfish
Dace, longnose (freshwater)   *Rhinichthys cataractae*
Dallia pectoralis   N. Alaska   Alaska blackfish (freshwater)
                                          (a mudminnow)
Decapterus and other genera   Scads
Deepsea smelt; *see* Blacksmelt
  or deepsea smelt
Delphinapterus leucas   Arctic-boreal   Beluga (white) whale
Dogfish, spiny (picked in   Temperate and warm Atlantic   *Squalus acanthias*
  Europe)   and Pacific
Dolly Varden; *see* Charr
Dolphin (a fish)   Cosmopolitan in warm seas   *Coryphaena hippurus*
Dolphin (harbor porpoise)
  dolphin   Black Sea   *Phocoena phocoena relicta*
  dolphin   Seas other than Black Sea   *Phocoena phocoena phocoena*
Dolphins (fish)   Coryphaenidae
Donax
  gouldi   Baja California–Pismo Beach   Bean (wedge) clam
  variabilis   Florida   Coquina (wedge) clam
Drill
  oyster drill   Gulf of Mexico   *Thais haemostoma*
  oyster drill   N.W. Atlantic   *Urosalpinx cinerea*
Drum
  black drum   New York–E. South America   *Pogonias cromis*
  channel bass; *see* Drum, red
  red drum   New York–Texas   *Sciaenops ocellata*
Eel
  common eel   *Anguilla* spp.
  conger eels   Congridae
  moray eels   Muraenidae
Eelgrass   Atlantic and Pacific   *Zostera*
Eleginus
  gracilis   N. Pacific   Saffron cod
  navaga   Arctic   Navaga cod or navaga
Elops saurus   Warm seas   Ladyfish or tenpounder
Embassichthys bathybius   N.E. Pacific   Deepsea sole

Embiotocidae	E. Pacific	Surfperches
Engraulis		
anchoita	S.W. Atlantic	Argentine anchovy
australis	S.W. Pacific	Australian anchovy
capensis	South Africa	Cape anchovy
encrasicholus encrasicholus	N.E. Atlantic-Mediterranean	Anchovy
encrasicholus ponticus	Black Sea	Anchovy
japonicus	N.W. Pacific	Japanese anchovy
mordax	Baja California–British Columbia	Northern anchovy
ringens	Peru Current	Peruvian anchoveta
Enhydra lutris	California–Gulf of Alaska–Aleutian Islands–Commander Islands–Kurile Islands	Sea otter
Ensis directus	U. S. North Atlantic	Atlantic razor clam
Entosphenus tridentatus	Baja California–Bering Sea–Japan	Pacific lamprey
Eopsetta		
grigorjewi	Japan	Roundnosed flounder
jordani	Baja California–Gulf of Alaska	Petrale sole
Epinephalus		
itajara	Gulf of Mexico	Jewfish (grouper)
morio	Gulf of Mexico	Red grouper
nigritus	Warm W. Atlantic	Warsaw grouper (warsaw)
Epinephalus and *Mycteroperca*		Groupers
Eretmochelys imbricata	Atlantic	Hawksbill turtle
Erignathus barbatus	Circumboreal; Atlantic and Pacific	Bearded seal
Eschrichtius gibbosus	N. Pacific	Gray whale
Ethmalosa fimbriata	Guinea	Bonga (related to menhaden)
Ethmidium maculatus	Peru	Peruvian menhaden
Etropus crossotus	Virginia-Brazil; Baja California–Panama	Fringed flounder
Etrumeus microps	Indo-Pacific	Round herring
Eulachon; *see* Smelt		
Eumetopias jubata	California-Alaska-Japan	Steller sea lion
Eunice viridis	S.W. Pacific	Palolo worm
Euthynnus		
affinis	Philippines	Eastern little tuna
alletteratus		Atlantic little tuna
pelamis		Skipjack tuna (skipjack)
Exocoetidae		Flying fishes
Flatfishes		
brill (a bothid flounder)	S. North Sea–Spain	*Scophthalmus rhombus*
dab; *see also* Flatfishes, plaice		
common dab	Sweden-France	*Limanda limanda*
sand dab	California–British Columbia	*Citharichthys sordidus*
flatfish (Psettodidae)	Central W. Africa	*Psettodes belcheri*
flatfish (Psettodidae)	Red Sea–Malaya–Philippines	*Psettodes erumei*
flounder		
arctic flounder	Arctic	*Liopsetta glacialis*
European flounder	Europe	*Platichthys flesus*
fringed flounder	Virginia-Brazil; Baja California–Panama	*Etropus crossotus*
frog flounder	Japan	*Pleuronichthys cornutus*
Kamchatka flounder	N.W. Pacific	*Atherestes evermanni*
roundnosed flounder	Japan	*Eopsetta grigorjewi*
sand flounder	S.W. Pacific	*Rhombosolea* spp.

Flatfishes—cont'd

slime flounder	Japan	*Microstomus achne*
smooth flounder	Rhode Island–Ungava	*Liopsetta putnami*
sohachi (pointed head) flounder	Japan	*Cleisthenes herzensteini*
starry flounder	California–Bering Sea–Sea of Japan	*Platichthys stellatus*
summer flounder; *see* Flatfishes, fluke, northern		
winter (blackback) flounder (lemon sole on Georges Bank)	Chesapeake Bay–Maritimes	*Pseudopleuronectes americanus*
yellow striped flounder	N.W. Pacific	*Pseudopleuronectes herzensteini*
yellowtail flounder	Chesapeake Bay–Strait of Belle Isle	*Limanda ferruginea*

fluke

hireguro fluke	Japan	*Glyptocephalus stelleri*
northern fluke	Cape Cod–South Carolina	*Paralichthys dentatus*
southern fluke	Middle Atlantic–Texas	*Paralichthys lethostigma*
summer flounder; *see* Flatfishes, fluke, northern		

halibut

arrowtooth halibut	Oregon–E. Bering Sea	*Atherestes stomias*
Atlantic halibut	Boreal N. Atlantic	*Hippoglossus hippoglossus*
bastard halibut	Japan	*Paralichthys olivaceous*
California halibut	Baja California–British Columbia	*Paralichthys californicus*
Greenland halibut (turbot)	W. Barents Sea–Norwegian Sea–Iceland–W. Greenland–Newfoundland–Grand Banks–E. Bering Sea	*Reinhardtius hippoglossoides*
Greenland halibut (turbot)	W. Bering Sea–Japan	*Reinhardtius hippoglossoides matsuurae*
Pacific halibut	Oregon–Bering Sea–Japan	*Hippoglossus stenolepis*
hogchoker	Cape Cod–Gulf of Mexico	*Trinectes maculatus*
megrim	N.E. Atlantic	*Lepidorhombus whiffiagonis*

plaice

Alaska plaice	Bering Sea	*Pleuronectes quadrituberculatus*
American plaice (dab)	Cape Cod–Grand Banks–Iceland–Barents Sea (few)	*Hippoglossoides platessoides*
plaice	N.E. Atlantic	*Pleuronectes platessa*

sole

Agulhas sole	Agulhas Bank	*Austroglossus pectoralis*
butter sole	S. California–S.E. Alaska	*Isopsetta isolepis*
deepsea sole	N.E. Pacific	*Embassichthys bathybius*
Dover sole	N. Baja California–Bering Sea	*Microstomus pacificus*
common sole	North Sea–Mediterranean–Black Sea	*Solea solea*
English sole	California–British Columbia	*Parophrys vetulus*
flathead sole	Japan	*Hippoglossoides elassodon dubius*
flathead sole	N.E. Pacific	*Hippoglossoides elassodon*
gray sole (witch)	Cape Cod–Newfoundland–Iceland–Sweden–France	*Glyptocephalus cynoglossus*
lemon sole	N.E. Atlantic	*Microstomus kitt*
petrale sole	Baja California–Gulf of Alaska	*Eopsetta jordani*
rex sole	N.E. Pacific	*Glyptocephalus zachirus*
rock sole	California–Bering Sea–Japan	*Lepidopsetta bilineata*
sand sole	N. California–Gulf of Alaska	*Psettichthys melanostictus*

Goby, naked	U. S. Atlantic coast; Gulf of Mexico	*Gobiosoma bosci*
Gonyaulax spp.		Group of dinoflagellates causing paralytic shellfish poisoning
Goosefish; *see* Angler		
Grayling (freshwater)		*Thymallus*
Greenlings		Hexagrammidae
Green turtle		*Chelonia mydas*
Grenadier		
rock (roundnose) grenadier	N. Atlantic	*Macrurus* (= *Coryphaenoides*) *rupestris*
roughhead grenadier	N. Atlantic	*Macrurus berglax*
Grenadiers		Macrouridae
Ground mullet; *see* Kingfish, Gulf		
Grouper		
jewfish	Gulf of Mexico	*Epinephalus itajara*
red grouper	Gulf of Mexico	*Epinephalus morio*
warsaw grouper (warsaw)	Warm W. Atlantic–Gulf of Mexico	*Epinephalus nigritus*
Groupers		*Epinephalus* and *Mycteroperca*
Grunion (a silverside)	Baja California–San Francisco	*Leuresthes tenuis*
Grunts		Pomadasyidae
Gurnards		Triglidae
Gymnodinium breve	Gulf of Mexico–W. Atlantic–Caribbean	Florida red tide
Haddock	S. Georges Bank–Strait of Belle Isle; Iceland–British Isles–Barents Sea	*Melanogrammus aeglefinus*
Hake		
Argentine hake	S.E. Brazil-S. Argentina	*Merluccius hubbsi*
Cape hake (stockfish)	S. Gulf of Guinea–South Africa	*Merluccius capensis*
Chilean hake	Peru-Chile	*Merluccius gayi*
European hake	Central Norway–Dakar–Mediterranean	*Merluccius merluccius*
hake	Tierra del Fuego	*Merluccius polylepis*
New Zealand hake	New Zealand	*Merluccius australis*
offshore hake	U. S. Atlantic coast–Gulf of Mexico	*Merluccius albidus* (= *magnocolus*)
Pacific hake	Central Baja California–Gulf of Alaska	*Merluccius productus*
Panamanian hake	Panama-S. California	*Merluccius augustimanus*
silver hake (whiting)	New York–S. Grand Banks	*Merluccius bilinearis*
"Hake" (ling)		
longfin hake	N.W. Atlantic	*Phycis chesteri*
red hake	U. S. mid-Atlantic–Gulf of St. Lawrence	*Urophycis chuss*
southern hake	S.E. United States–Gulf of Mexico	*Urophycis floridanus*
white hake	U. S. mid-Atlantic–Gulf of St. Lawrence	*Urophycis tenuis*
Halibut; *see* Flatfishes		
Haliotis spp.	Pacific and Indian Oceans	Abalone
Harengula		Scaled sardines
Harpodon nehereus	India	Bombay duck (a fish)
Hawksbill turtle	Atlantic	*Eretmochelys imbricata*
Herring; *see also* Wolf herring		
Caspian herring	Caspian and Black Seas	*Caspialosa* spp.
river herring; *see Alosa pseudoharengus*		

Herring—cont'd
round herring | Indo-Pacific | *Etrumeus microps*
sea herring
   Atlantic herring | New England–Newfoundland–Iceland–Norway–Baltic Sea–Gibraltar | *Clupea harengus harengus*

   Kanin-Pechora herring | S.E. Barents Sea | *Clupea harengus suworowi*
   Pacific herring | San Diego–Arctic Alaska–Kamchatka–Japan | *Clupea harengus pallasi*

   White Sea herring | White Sea | *Clupea harengus maris-alba*
summer herring; *see Alosa aestivalis*
thread herring
   Atlantic thread herring | U. S. mid-Atlantic–Gulf of Mexico–Brazil | *Opisthonema oglinum*

   middling thread herring; *see* Herring, thread, Pacific
   Pacific thread herring | California-Peru | *Opisthonema medirastre*
Herrings and shads | Black and Caspian Seas | *Caspiolosa* spp.
Hexagrammidae | | Greenlings
Hinnites | | "Rock oysters" (attached scallops)

Hippiospongia and *Spongia* | | Sponges
Hippoglossoides
   elassodon | N.E. Pacific | Flathead sole
   elassodon dubius | Japan | Flathead sole
   platessoides | Cape Cod–Grand Banks–Iceland–Barents Sea | American plaice (dab)

Hippoglossus
   hippoglossus | Boreal N. Atlantic | Atlantic halibut
   stenolepis | Oregon–Bering Sea–Japan | Pacific halibut
Histrio | Atlantic | Sargassumfish
Hogchoker; *see* Flatfishes
Holothuria argus | S.W. Pacific | Tigerfish (a sea cucumber)
Homarus
   americanus | New Jersey-Gulf of St. Lawrence | Lobster
   vulgaris | Europe; E. Mediterranean–Black Sea | Lobster

Horse mackerel, Atlantic (a carangid) | Germany–Spain–Mediterranean–Black Sea | *Trachurus trachurus*
Horseshoe (king) crab | W. Atlantic–Gulf of Mexico | *Limulus polyphemus*
Hucho
   hucho | Danube River | Danube salmon (freshwater)
   perryi | Japan Sea | Sakhalin taimen (anadromous)
   taimen | Siberian rivers | Siberian taimen
Hydrodamalis gigas | Commander Islands | Steller sea cow (extinct)
Hydrolagus
   affinis | Banquereau-Portugal | Chimaera or ratfish
   colliei | California-Alaska | Chimaera or ratfish
Hymenopenaeus robustus | U. S. South Atlantic–Gulf of Mexico–Brazil | Royal red shrimp

Hyperoodon ampullatus | Atlantic | Bottlenosed whale
Hypomesus pretiosus | California-Chignik | Surf (silver) smelt
Ictalurus furcatus | | Blue catfish (freshwater)
Ictalurus spp. | | Freshwater catfishes
Ilisha | Indo-Pacific | Hilsalike shads
Irish moss | Atlantic | *Chondrus crispus*
Isopsetta isolepis | S. California-S.E. Alaska | Butter sole
Istiophoridae | | Billfishes
Jack mackerel (a carangid) | Baja California–S.E. Alaska | *Trachurus symmetricus*

Jacksmelt (a silverside)	Baja California–Oregon	*Atherinopsis californiensis*
Jellyfish, red		*Cyanea*
Jewfish; *see* Grouper		
Kelp		
giant kelp		*Macrocystis*
other kelps		*Laminaria*
Kelp bass; *see* Sea bass		
"Kilka"	Caspian Sea	*Clupeonella deliculata caspia*
Killifish		
banded killifish		*Fundulus diaphanus*
Gulf killifish		*Fundulus grandis*
mummichog		*Fundulus heteroclitus*
sheepshead minnow		*Cyprinodon variegatus*
King croaker; *see* Croaker, white		
Kingfish		
Gulf kingfish (ground mullet)	Gulf of Mexico	*Menticirrhus littoralis*
southern kingfish	Gulf of Mexico	*Menticirrhus americanus*
Ladyfish or tenpounder	Warm seas	*Elops saurus*
Lagodon rhomboides	Cape Cod–Cuba–Gulf of Mexico	Pinfish
Laminaria		Kelp
Lamna nasus	N. Atlantic	Porbeagle (mackerel shark)
Lamprey		
sea lamprey	Florida–Gulf of St. Lawrence; Norway–Baltic Sea–Mediterranean	*Petromyzon marinus*
Pacific lamprey	Baja California–Bering Sea–Japan	*Entosphenus tridentatus*
Lanternfishes		Myctophidae
Lates calcarifer	Indo-Pacific	Slipmouth (giant perch)
Laticauda calubrina	Philippines	Sea snake
Leatherjacket (a carangid)	Peru–S. California; West Indies–New York	*Oligoplites saurus*
Lefteye flounders, turbots, flukes		Bothidae
Leiognathidae		Slipmouths
Leiostomus xanthurus	Cape Cod–Texas	Spot
Lenok (a freshwater salmonid)	Siberia; Amur River; Japan; W. Okhotsk Sea–Korea	*Brachymystax lenok*
Lepidopsetta bilineata	California–Bering Sea–Japan	Rock sole
Lepidorhombus whiffiagonis	N.E. Atlantic	Megrim (a flatfish)
Lepomis		Sunfish (freshwater)
Leuresthes tenuis	Baja California–San Francisco	Grunion (a silverside)
Limanda		
aspera	Hecate Strait–Bering Sea–Japan	Yellowfin sole
ferruginea	Chesapeake Bay–Strait of Belle Isle	Yellowtail flounder
limanda	Sweden-France	Common dab
Limulus polyphemus	W. Atlantic–Gulf of Mexico	Horseshoe (king) crab
Ling; *see also* "Hake"; Cod, burbot		
blue ling	N. Norway-Iceland-Kattegat	*Molva dypterygia*
European ling	Murman coast–Iceland–Bay of Biscay	*Molva molva*
Lingcod	Ensenada–Shumagin Islands	*Ophiodon elongatus*
Liopsetta		
glacialis	Arctic	Arctic flounder
putnami	Rhode Island–Ungava	Smooth flounder
Lithodes antarcticus	S. South America	Southern king crab
Littorina		Periwinkle
Lizardfish	W. Pacific	*Saurida* spp.

Lizardfish, inshore	Carolinas–Brazil–Gulf of Mexico	*Synodus foetens*
Lobster		
lobster	Europe; E. Mediterranean–Black Sea	*Homarus vulgaris*
lobster	New Jersey–Gulf of St. Lawrence	*Homarus americanus*
Norway lobster	N.E. Atlantic	*Nephrops norvegicus*
spiny lobster	California	*Panulirus interruptus*
spiny lobster	Florida	*Panulirus argus*
squat lobster		Galatheidae
Loggerhead turtle	Atlantic	*Caretta caretta*
Loligo		Squid
Longfin hake	N.W. Atlantic	*Phycis chesteri*
Lophius		
americanus	N.W. Atlantic	Goosefish, monkfish (angler)
piscatorius	N.E. Atlantic	Monkfish (angler)
Lopholatilus chamaeleonticeps	Nova Scotia–Gulf of Mexico	Tilefish
Lota lota		Burbot (freshwater)
Loxechinus albus	Chile	Sea urchin
Lumpfish	New Jersey–Hudson Bay; Iceland–British Isles–Murman coast	*Cyclopterus lumpus*
Lutjanidae		Snappers
Lutjanus		
campechanus	Gulf of Mexico–West Indies	Red snapper
synagris	Warm W. Atlantic	Lane snapper
Mackerel; *see also* Atka mackerel; Butterfly mackerel; Spanish mackerel		
Atlantic mackerel	Cape Hatteras–Newfoundland; Norway–Spain–Mediterranean–Black Sea	*Scomber scombrus*
frigate mackerel (a tuna)	Atlantic and Pacific	*Auxis thazard*
horse mackerel, Atlantic (a carangid)	Germany–Spain–Mediterranean–Black Sea	*Trachurus trachurus*
Indian mackerels		
Indian mackerel	Indo-W. Pacific	*Rastrelliger kanagurta*
shortbodied mackerel	Indo-W. Pacific	*Rastrelliger brachysoma*
jack mackerel (a carangid)	Baja California–S.E. Alaska	*Trachurus symmetricus*
king mackerel; *see* Spanish mackerel		
Pacific mackerel (chub mackerel on Atlantic coast)	Mazatlan–Vancouver Island; Sakhalin–Taiwan; Virginia–Gulf of St. Lawrence; British Isles–Mediterranean–Black Sea	*Scomber japonicus*
shortbodied mackerel; *see* Mackerel, Indian		
Mackerel-like fishes		Scombridae
Mackerels		Scombrinae
Macrobrachium		Freshwater shrimp
Macrocallista nimbosa	S.E. United States	Sunray venus clam
Macrocystis	Pacific	Giant kelp
Macrouridae		Grenadiers
Macrozoarces americanus	New Jersey–Gulf of St. Lawrence	Ocean pout
Macrurus		
berglax	N. Atlantic	Roughhead grenadier
(= *Coryphaenoides*) *rupestris*	N. Atlantic	Rock (roundnose) grenadier
Maena maena or *M. smaris*	Meditarranean–Black Sea	Picarel
Maia squinada	N.E. Atlantic-Mediterranean	Spinous spider crab
Malaclemmys	W. Atlantic	Terrapin

Mallotus villosus	Arctic–adjacent Atlantic and Pacific	Capelin (a smelt)
Manatee		
Amazon manatee	Brazil–Amazon River–Orinoco River	*Trichecus inunguis*
Caribbean manatee	Gulf of Mexico–Caribbean	*Trichecus manatus*
Marlin, striped	Warm Pacific	*Tetrapterus audax*
Megalops atlantica	S.E. United States–Caribbean	Tarpon
Megaptera novaeangliae	All oceans	Humpback whale
Megrim; *see* Flatfishes		
Melanogrammus aeglefinnus	S. George Bank–Strait of Belle Isle–Iceland–British Isles– Barents Sea	Haddock
Menhaden		
Atlantic menhaden	Maine-E. Florida	*Brevoortia tyrannus*
bonga (related to menhaden)	Guinea	*Ethmalosa fimbriata*
fine-scale menhaden	Gulf of Mexico	*Brevoortia gunteri*
Gulf menhaden	Gulf of Mexico	*Brevoortia patronus*
Peruvian menhaden	Peru	*Ethmidium maculatus*
Menidia menidia	Cape May–Maritimes	Atlantic silverside
Menippe mercenaria	Warm W. Atlantic–Gulf of Mexico	Stone crab
Menticirrhus		
americanus	Gulf of Mexico	Southern kingfish
littoralis	Gulf of Mexico	Gulf kingfish (ground mullet)
undulatus	California	California corbina
Mercenaria		
campechiensis	U. S. Atlantic south of Cape Hatteras–Gulf of Mexico	Southern hard clam
mercenaria	Maine-Florida	Hard clam, quahaug, or cherrystone
Merlangus (= Gadus) merlangus	N.E. Atlantic	Whiting
Merluccius		
albidus (= magnocolus)	W. Atlantic–Gulf of Mexico	Offshore hake
augustimanus	S. California-Panama	Panamanian hake
australis	New Zealand	New Zealand hake
bilinearis	New York–S. Grand Banks	Silver hake (whiting)
capensis	South Africa	Cape hake (stockfish)
gayi	S.E. Pacific	Chilean hake
hubbsi	S.E. Brazil–S. Argentina	Argentine hake
merluccius	Central Norway–Dakar–Mediterranean	European hake
polylepis	Tierra del Fuego	Hake
productus	Central Baja California–Gulf of Alaska	Pacific hake
Microcosmus sulcatus	N.E. Atlantic	Grooved sea squirt
Microgadus		
proximus	N.E. Pacific	Pacific tomcod
tomcod	Virginia-S. Labrador	Atlantic tomcod
Micromesistius (= Gadus) potassou	N.E. Atlantic	Potassou (blue whiting)
Micropogon undulatus	New York–Texas	Atlantic croaker
Micropterus salmoides		Largemouth bass (freshwater)
Microstomus		
achne	Japan	Slime flounder
kitt	N.E. Atlantic	Lemon sole
pacificus	N. Baja California–Bering Sea	Dover sole

Ocean perch (redfish or rosefish)		
ocean perch	Georges Bank–Grand Banks	*Sebastes marinus*
Pacific ocean perch	S. California–Bering Sea–Japan	*Sebastes alutus*
redfish	Greenland–Iceland–Faroe Islands–Spitzbergen	*Sebastes mentella*
Ocean pout	New Jersey–Gulf of St. Lawrence	*Macrozoarces americanus*
Ocean quahaug; *see* Clam		
Ocean sunfish	Cosmopolitan, warm and temperate ocean	*Mola mola*
Ocean sunfishes		Molidae
Octopus		*Octopus* spp.
Octopus spp.		Octopus
Odobenus rosmarus	Arctic	Walrus
Oligoplites saurus	S. California-Peru; New York–West Indies	Leatherjacket (a carangid)
Oncorhynchus		
gorbuscha	Columbia River–arctic Alaska–Japan	Pink (humpback) salmon
keta	Columbia River–arctic Alaska–Japan	Chum (dog) salmon
kisutch	Monterey Bay–Yukon River–Kamchatka	Coho (silver) salmon
nerka	Columbia River–Yukon River–Okhotsk Sea	Sockeye (red or blueback) salmon
nerka kennerlyi	Washington–Cook Inlet	Kokanee (freshwater)
tshawytscha	Sacramento River–Yukon River–Kamchatka	Chinook (king) salmon
Ophidiidae		Cusk-eels
Ophiodon elongatus	Ensenada–Shumagin Islands	Lingcod
Opisthonema		
medirastre	California-Peru	Pacific (middling) thread herring
oglinum	U. S. mid-Atlantic–Gulf of Mexico–Brazil	Atlantic thread herring
Opsanus tau	Maine–Gulf of Mexico–Cuba	Toadfish
Orcinus orca	All seas	Killer whale
Oscillatoria (= *Skujaella*) (= *Trichodesmium*)	Gulf of Mexico	Bluegreen alga (nitrogen-fixing)
Osmerus		
eperlanus dentex	White Sea–Arctic–Bering Sea–British Columbia–Kamchatka–Korea	Rainbow smelt
eperlanus mordax	New Jersey–E. Labrador–Iceland–North Sea–Baltic	Common smelt
Ostrea		
chilensis	Mexico-Chile	Chilian oyster
edulis	N.E. Atlantic-Mediterranean	European oyster
lurida	N. California–British Columbia	Western (Olympia) oyster
Otario byronia	S. Atlantic	South American sea lion
Oyster; *see also* Pearl oysters; "Rock oysters"		
American (eastern) oyster	Maritimes-Mexico; U. S. Pacific coast	*Crassostrea virginica*
Australian oyster	Australia	*Crassostrea commercialis*
Caribbean oyster	Caribbean	*Crassostrea rhizophora*
Chilean oyster	Mexico-Chile	*Ostrea chilensis*
eastern oyster; *see* Oyster, American		
European oyster	N.E. Atlantic-Mediterranean	*Ostrea edulis*
Japanese oyster; *see* Oyster, Pacific		

Oyster—cont'd

Olympia oyster; *see* Oyster, western		
Pacific (Japanese) oyster	N.W. Pacific; Washington–British Columbia	*Crassostrea gigas*
Portuguese oyster	S.E. Europe-Mediterranean	*Crassostrea (= Gryphaea) angulata*
western oyster	N. California–British Columbia	*Ostrea lurida*
Pagophilus groenlandicus	N. Atlantic-Arctic	Harp seal
Palolo worm	S.W. Pacific	*Eunice viridis*
Pandalus		
borealis	N. Pacific-N. Atlantic	Deepwater prawn (in Europe) or pink shrimp (in Alaska)
jordani	N.E. Pacific	Ocean shrimp (ocean prawn)
montagui	Alaska; N.E. Atlantic	Pink shrimp (in Britain)
Panope generosa	California-Alaska	Geoduck (a clam)
Panulirus		
argus	Florida	Spiny lobster
interruptus	California	Spiny lobster
Paralabrax		
clathratus	Baja California–Oregon	Kelp bass (a sea bass)
maculatofasciatus	Monterey-Mazatlan	Spotted sand bass (a sea bass)
nebulifer	Monterey–Baja California	Barred sand bass (a sea bass)
Paralichthys		
californicus	Baja California–British Columbia	California halibut
dentatus	Cape Cod–South Carolina	Northern fluke (summer flounder)
lethostigma	U. S. mid-Atlantic–Texas	Southern fluke
olivaceous	Japan	Bastard halibut
Paralithodes		
camtschatica	S.E. Alaska–N. Bering Sea–Okhotsk Sea	King crab
platypus	Icy Strait–St. Lawrence Island	Purple king crab
Paralosa	Indo-Pacific	Hilsalike shads
Parophrys vetulus	California–British Columbia	English sole
Patinopecten caurinus	N.E. Pacific	Weathervane (sea) scallop
Pearl oyster, Japanese	Japan	*Pinctada martensi*
Pearl oysters	Warm seas	*Pinctada (= Margaritifera)*
Pecten		
maximus	N.E. Atlantic	Common scallop
yessoensis	Japan	Japanese scallop
Pelecypoda		Bivalve mollusks
Penaeus		
aztecus	Gulf of Mexico–S.E. United States	Brown shrimp
duorarum	Gulf of Mexico-Caribbean	Pink shrimp
setiferus	Gulf of Mexico–Carolinas–Florida	White shrimp
Peprilus		
simillimus	San Diego–Puget Sound	Pacific pompano
triacanthus	Cape Hatteras–Nova Scotia	Butterfish
Perch		
giant perch; *see* Slipmouth		
ocean perch; *see* Ocean perch		
shiner perch (shiner sea perch)	California-S.E. Alaska	*Cymatogaster aggregata*
silver perch; *see* Silver perch		
white perch; *see* White perch		
Percichthyidae		Temperate basses
Periwinkle		*Littorina*

Permit (a carangid)	Chesapeake Bay–Panama	*Trachinotus falcatus*
Perna perna	Venezuela-Uruguay	Large mussel
Petromyzon marinus	Florida–Gulf of St. Lawrence– Great Lakes; Baltic-Norway- Mediterranean	Sea lamprey
Phocoena		
phocoena phocoena	Other than Black Sea	Dolphin (harbor porpoise)
phocoena relicta	Black Sea	Dolphin (harbor porpoise)
Phycis chesteri	N.W. Atlantic	Longfin "hake" (ling)
Physeter catodon	All oceans	Sperm whale
Picarel	Mediterranean–Black Sea	*Maena maena* or *M. smaris*
Pike, blue; *see* Walleye		
Pike-perch; *see* Walleye		
Pilchard; *see also* Sardine		
European pilchard	N.E. Atlantic-Mediterranean	*Sardina pilchardus*
South African pilchard	South Africa	*Sardinops ocellata*
Pinctada (= *Margaritifera*)	Warm seas	Pearl oysters
martensi	Japan	Japanese pearl oyster
Pinfish	Cape Cod–Cuba–Gulf of Mexico	*Lagodon rhomboides*
Pipefish, northern	Gulf of Mexico	*Syngnathus fuscus*
Placopecten magellanicus	Cape Hatteras–Strait of Belle Isle	Sea (giant) scallop
Plaice; *see* Flatfishes		
Platichthys		
flesus	Europe	European flounder
stellatus	California–Bering Sea–Sea of Japan	Starry flounder
Plesiopenaeus edwardsianus	Gulf of Mexico	Scarlet prawn
Pleurogrammus monopterygius	Monterey–Bering Sea–Japan	Atka mackeral (a greenling)
Pleuronectes		
platessa	N.E. Atlantic	Plaice
quadrituberculatus	Bering Sea	Alaska plaice
Pleuronectidae		Righteye flounders, halibuts, "soles"
Pleuronichthys		
cornutus	Japan	Frog flounder
verticalis	N.E. Pacific	Hornyhead turbot
Pogonias cromis	New York–E. South America	Black drum
Pollachius		
pollachius	Europe	Pollack
virens	N. Atlantic	Pollock (saithe in Europe)
Pollack	Europe	*Pollachius pollachius*
Pollock (saithe in Europe)	N. Atlantic	*Pollachius virens*
Pollock, Alaska (walleye)	Alaska	*Theragra chalcogramma*
Polydactylus octonemus	Virginia–Rio Grande	Atlantic threadfin
Pomadasyidae		Grunts
Pomatomus saltatrix	Warm Atlantic–Mediterranean– Indian Ocean	Bluefish
Pomfret	Philippines	*Apolectus niger*
Pompano		
Florida pompano	Virginia–Gulf of Mexico– West Indies	*Trachinotus carolinus*
Pacific pompano	San Diego–Puget Sound	*Peprilus simillimus*
Paloma pompano	S. California-Peru	*Trachinotus paitensis*
Porbeagle (mackerel shark)	N. Atlantic	*Lamna nasus*
Porpoise; *see* Dolphin		
Potassou; *see* Cod		
Pout		
Norway pout	Barents Sea–Iceland	*Trisopterus esmarkii* (a Gadidae)
ocean pout	New Jersey–Gulf of St. Lawrence	*Macrozoarces americanus*

Prawn; *see also* Shrimp		
deepwater prawn (in Europe) or pink shrimp (in Alaska)	N. Pacific–N. Atlantic	*Pandalus borealis*
ocean prawn (ocean shrimp)	N.E. Pacific	*Pandalus jordani*
scarlet prawn	Gulf of Mexico	*Plesiopenaeus edwardsianus*
Prionotus tribulus	S.E. United States–Gulf of Mexico	Southern sea robin
Protothaca staminea	California–S.E. Alaska	Littleneck clam
Psettichthys melanostictus	N. California–Gulf of Alaska	Sand sole
Psettodes		
belcheri	Central W. Africa	Flatfish (Psettodidae)
erumei	Red Sea–Malaya–Philippines	Flatfish (Psettodidae)
Psettodidae		Small family of flatfishes
Pseudopleuronectes		
americanus	Chesapeake Bay–Maritimes	Winter (blackback) flounder (lemon sole on Georges Bank)
herzensteini	N.W. Pacific	Yellow striped flounder
Ptychocheilus oregonensis		Northern squawfish (freshwater)
Puffer		
least puffer	Warm W. Atlantic–Gulf of Mexico	*Sphoeroides parvus*
northern puffer (swellfish)	U. S. Atlantic coast	*Sphoeroides maculatus*
Pusa hispida	Arctic–adjacent seas	Ringed seal
Pyura chilensis	Chile	Edible sea squirt
Quahaug or quahog; *see* Clam, hard		
Quahaug, ocean; *see* Clam, ocean quahaug		
Raja		Skate
Rangia (a brackish water clam)	Potomac River–Campeche	*Rangia cuneata*
Rangia cuneata	Potomac River–Campeche	Rangia (a brackish water clam)
Ranina ranina	Hawaii	Kona crab
Rastrelliger		
brachysoma	E. Indo-Pacific	Shortbodied mackerel
kanagurta	Indo-Pacific	Indian mackerel
Ratfish; *see* Chimaera		
Redfish; *see* Ocean perch; Drum, red		
Redfish, prickly; *see* Sea cucumber		
Red tide, Florida	Gulf of Mexico–W. Atlantic–Caribbean	*Gymnodinium breve*
Reinhardtius		
hippoglossoides	W. Barents Sea–Norwegian Sea–Iceland–W. Greenland–Newfoundland–Grand Banks–E. Bering Sea	Greenland halibut (turbot)
hippoglossoides matsuurae	W. Bering Sea–Japan	Greenland halibut (turbot)
Rhinichthys cataractae		Longnose dace (freshwater)
Rhombosolea spp.	S.W. Pacific	Sand flounder
Rhombus		
maeoticus	Black Sea	Black Sea turbot
maximus	North Sea–W. Mediterranean	European turbot
Righteye flounders, halibuts, "soles"		Pleuronectidae
Rock; *see* Striped bass		
Rockfish, black	Santa Barbara–Gulf of Alaska	*Sebastes melanops*
Rockfishes		Scorpaenidae
Rockling, bearded	Mediterranean	*Motella*

"Rock oysters" (attached
  scallops)   *Hinnites*

Rockweed   *Fucus*

Rosefish; *see* Ocean perch

Runner, blue	Warm Atlantic	*Caranx crysos*
Sablefish (black cod)	California–Bering Sea– Hokkaidō	*Anoplopoma fimbria*
Saithe; *see* Cusk		
Salmo		
clarki clarki	N. California–S.E. Alaska	Cutthroat trout
clarki lewisi	W. United States	Blackspotted trout (freshwater)
gairdneri gairdneri	Monterey–Bristol Bay	Rainbow or steelhead trout
gairdneri kamloops	British Columbia	Kamloops trout (freshwater)
gairdneri nelsoni	Baja California mountains	Rainbow trout (freshwater)
levenensis; see Salmo *trutta trutta*		
salar	Norway–Portugal–Iceland– western tip of Greenland– Ungava–Maine	Atlantic salmon
salar sebago	E. North America	Landlocked salmon
trutta fario		Brown trout (freshwater)
trutta trutta (Salmo *levenensis)*	Europe; Maine; British Columbia	Brown trout (anadromous)
Salmon		
Atlantic salmon	Norway–Portugal–Iceland– western tip of Greenland– Ungava–Maine	*Salmo salar*
blueback salmon; *see* Salmon, sockeye		
chinook salmon	Sacramento River–Yukon River–Kamchatka	*Oncorhynchus tshawytscha*
chum salmon	Columbia River–arctic Alaska– Japan	*Oncorhynchus keta*
coho salmon	Monterey Bay–Yukon River– Kamchatka	*Oncorhynchus kisutch*
Danube salmon (freshwater)	Danube River	*Hucho hucho*
dog salmon; *see* Salmon, chum		
humpback salmon; *see* Salmon, pink		
king salmon; *see* Salmon, chinook		
kokanee (freshwater)	Washington–Cook Inlet	*Oncorhynchus nerka kennerlyi*
landlocked salmon	E. North America	*Salmo salar sebago*
pink salmon	Columbia River–arctic Alaska	*Oncorhynchus gorbuscha*
red salmon; *see* Salmon, sockeye		
silver salmon; *see* Salmon, coho		
sockeye salmon	Columbia River–Yukon River– Okhotsk Sea	*Oncorhynchus nerka*
Salvelinus		
alpinus	Circumpolar	Arctic (alpine) charr
alpinus aureolus	New England	Golden charr (freshwater)
fontinalis	Cape Cod–Hudson Bay	Eastern brook charr
malma	N. California–arctic Alaska; Kamchatka–Japan–Korea	Dolly Varden charr
oquassa	Maine	Blueback charr (freshwater)
oquassa marstoni	Quebec	Red Quebec charr (freshwater)
Sand bass; *see* Sea bass		
Sand eel; *see* Sand lance		

Sandfishes | | Trichodontidae
Sand lance (sand eel) | |
  American sand lance | Cape Hatteras–Newfoundland–Labrador–Grand Banks | *Ammodytes americanus*
  Black Sea sand lance | Black Sea | *Ammodytes cicerellus*
  northern sand lance | Finmarken-Spain-Iceland; Newfoundland–Grand Banks | *Ammodytes dubius*
  Pacific sand lance | Murman coast–Chukchi Sea–Hudson Bay; N. California–Bering Sea–Japan | *Ammodytes hexapterus*

Sand worm | | *Neanthes* (= *Nereis*)
Sarda | |
  chiliensis | Pacific | Pacific bonito
  orientalis | W. Indo-Pacific | Striped or oriental bonito
  sarda | Atlantic | Atlantic bonito
Sardina pilchardus | N.E. Atlantic-Mediterranean | European pilchard
Sardine | |
  African sardine | W. Africa-Mediterranean; Brazil | *Sardinella aurita*
  Chilean sardine | S.E. Pacific | *Sardinops sagax sagax*
  Japanese sardine | Japan | *Sardinops melanosticta*
  oil sardine | Indo-Pacific | *Sardinella longiceps*
  Pacific sardine (pilchard) | California | *Sardinops sagax caerulea*
  scaled sardine | | *Harengula*
  Spanish sardine | Warm Atlantic | *Sardinella anchovia*
  Spanish sardine | W. Africa | *Sardinella cameronensis*
  young herring | N. Atlantic | *Clupea harengus harengus* (canned as sardines)
  young sprat | Norway | *Sprattus sprattus* (canned as brisling sardines)

Sardinella | |
  anchovia | Warm Atlantic | Spanish sardine
  aurita | W. Africa-Mediterranean; Brazil | African sardine
  cameronensis | W. Africa | Spanish sardine
  longiceps | Indo-Pacific | Oil sardine
Sardines, scaled; *see* Scaled sardines | |
Sardinops | |
  melanosticta | Japan | Japanese sardine
  ocellata | South Africa | South African pilchard
  sagax caerulea | California | Pacific sardine (pilchard)
  sagax sagax | S.E. Pacific | Chilean sardine
Sargassumfish | Atlantic | *Histrio*
Saurida spp. | Atlantic | Lizardfish
Saury | |
  Atlantic saury | Atlantic | *Scomberesox saurus*
  Pacific saury | California–Gulf of Alaska–Japan | *Cololabis saira*
Saxidomus giganteus | N. California–Aleutian Islands | Butter clam
Scads | | *Decapterus* and other genera
Scaled sardines | | *Harengula*
Scallop | |
  bay scallop | Cape Cod–Texas | *Aequipecten irradians*
  calico scallop | U. S. South Atlantic–Gulf of Mexico | *Argopecten gibbus*
  common scallop | N.E. Atlantic | *Pecten maximus*
  giant sea scallop; *see* Scallop, sea | |
  Iceland scallop | Newfoundland-Norway | *Chlamys islandicus*
  Japanese scallop | Japan | *Pecten yessoensis*
  sea scallop | Cape Hatteras–Strait of Belle Isle | *Placopecten magellanicus*
  weathervane (sea) scallop | N.E. Pacific | *Patinopecten caurinus*

Sciaenops ocellata	New York–Texas	Red drum (channel bass)
Scomber		
japonicus	Mazatlan–Vancouver Island; Sakalin-Taiwan; Virginia–Gulf of St. Lawrence; British Isles–Mediterranean–Black Sea	Pacific mackerel (chub mackerel on Atlantic coast)
scombrus	Cape Hatteras–Newfoundland; Norway–Spain–Mediterranean–Black Sea	Atlantic mackerel
Scomberesox saurus	N. Atlantic	Atlantic saury
Scomberomorinae		Spanish mackerels
Scomberomorus		
cavalla	Warm Atlantic–Gulf of Mexico–Brazil	King mackerel
commerson	W. Indo-Pacific	Seerfish
guttatus	W. Indo-Pacific	Spotted seerfish
lineolatus	W. Indo-Pacific	Streaked Spanish mackerel
maculatus	New England–Brazil	Spanish mackerel
niphonius	N.W. Pacific	Japanese Spanish mackerel
queenlandicus	Australia	Australian Spanish mackerel
regalis	New England–Brazil	Cero
sierra	S. California-Peru	Sierra
tritor	Tropical E. Atlantic	West African Spanish mackerel
Scombridae		Mackerel-like fishes
Scombrinae		Mackerels
Scophthalmus		
aquosus	Chesapeake Bay–Maritimes	Windowpane (a bothid flounder)
rhombus	S. North Sea–Spain	Brill (a bothid flounder)
Scorpaenidae		Rockfishes
Scorpaenichthys marmoratus	Baja California–Sitka	Cabezon (a sculpin)
Sculpin; *see* Cabezon		
Sculpins		Cottidae
Scup	Cape Cod–Chesapeake Bay	*Stenotomus chrysops*
Sea bass		
black sea bass	Cape Cod–Cape Hatteras	*Centropristis striata*
giant sea bass	N. California–Gulf of California	*Stereolepis gigas*
kelp bass	Oregon–Baja California	*Paralabrax clathratus*
sand bass		
barred sand bass	Monterey–Baja California	*Paralabrax nebulifer*
spotted sand bass	Monterey-Mazatlan	*Paralabrax maculatofasciatus*
white sea bass; *see* Cynoscion		
Sea basses		Serranidae
Seabob; *see* Shrimp		
Sea bream, red	Japan	*Chrysophrys major*
Sea breams		Sparidae
Sea catfish; *see* Catfish, marine		
Sea cow, Steller (extinct)	Commander Islands	*Hydrodamalis gigas*
Sea cows		Sirenia
Sea cucumber		
black teatfish	S.W. Pacific	*Actinopyga nobilis*
prickly redfish	S.W. Pacific	*Thalenota aranas*
sea cucumber	N.W. Pacific	*Stichopus japonicus*
tigerfish	S.W. Pacific	*Holothuria argus*
Seal		
bearded seal	Circumboreal; Atlantic-Pacific	*Erignathus barbatus*
elephant seals	Pacific; Antarctic	*Mirounga*
fur seal; *see* Fur seal		
harp seal	N. Atlantic-Arctic	*Pagophilus groenlandicus*
hooded seal	N. Atlantic	*Cystophora cristata*
ringed seal	Arctic–adjacent seas	*Pusa hispida*

Sea lion		
South American sea lion	S. Atlantic	*Otario byronia*
Steller sea lion	California-Alaska-Japan	*Eumetopias jubata*
Sea otter	California–Gulf of Alaska– Aleutian Islands–Commander Islands–Kurile Islands	*Enhydra lutris*
Sea perch; *see* Surfperch		
Sea robin, southern	S.E. United States–Gulf of Mexico	*Prionotus tribulus*
Sea snake	Philippines	*Laticauda calubrina*
Sea squirt		
edible sea squirt	Chile	*Pyura chilensis*
grooved sea squirt	N.E. Atlantic	*Microcosmus sulcatus*
Sea trout; *see* Weakfish		
Sea urchin		
purple sea urchin	California	*Strongylocentrotus purpuratus*
red sea urchin	California	*Strongylocentrotus franciscanus*
sea urchin	Chile	*Loxechinus albus*
Sebastes		
alutus	California–Bering Sea–Japan	Pacific ocean perch
marinus	Georges Bank–Grand Banks	Ocean perch
melanops	Santa Barbara–Gulf of Alaska	Black rockfish
mentella	Greenland; Iceland–Faroe Islands– Spitzbergen	Ocean perch (redfish)
Seerfish; *see* Spanish mackerel		
Sepia		Cuttlefish
Seriola		
dorsalis	California-Chile	Yellowtail
dumerili	Florida-Brazil	Greater amberjack
quinqueradiata	Japan	Yellowtail
Serranidae		Sea basses
Shad		
allis shad	N.E. Atlantic-Mediterranean	*Alosa finta*
American shad	Florida–Gulf of St. Lawrence; Central California–British Columbia	*Alosa sapidissima*
black-spined shad	Caspian Sea	*Caspialosa kessleri*
twaite shad	N.E. Atlantic-Mediterranean	*Alosa fallax*
Shads		
hilsalike shads	Indo-Pacific	*Ilisha, Paralosa*
short-nosed shads	Indo-Pacific	*Clupanodon*
Shark		
basking shark	Circumpolar	*Cetorhinus maximus*
mackerel shark; *see* Porbeagle		
Sheepshead	Cape Cod-Texas	*Archosargus probatocephalus*
Sheepshead minnow		*Cyprinodon variegatus*
Shiner		
blacknose shiner (freshwater)		*Notropis heterolepis*
golden shiner (freshwater)		*Notemigonus crysoleucas*
Shipworms (teredos)		Teredinidae
Shrimp; *see also* Prawn		
bay shrimp	California	*Crago franciscorum*
brine shrimp		*Artemia salina*
brown shrimp	Gulf of Mexico	*Penaeus aztecus*
common shrimp	N.E. Atlantic-Mediterranean	*Crangon vulgaris*
freshwater shrimp		*Macrobrachium*
ocean shrimp (ocean prawn)	N.E. Pacific	*Pandalus jordani*
pink shrimp	Gulf of Mexico	*Penaeus duorarum*
pink shrimp (in Britain)	N.E. Atlantic-Alaska	*Pandalus montagui*

Shrimp—cont'd

pink shrimp (in Alaska) or deepwater prawn (in Europe)	N. Pacific; N. Atlantic	*Pandalus borealis*
rock shrimp	Gulf of Mexico–S.E. United States	*Sicyonia*
royal red shrimp	U. S. South Atlantic–Gulf of Mexico–Brazil	*Hymenopenaeus robustus*
seabob	Gulf of Mexico–S.E. United States–Brazil	*Xiphopenaeus*
white shrimp	Gulf of Mexico–S.E. United States	*Penaeus setiferus*
Sicyonia	Gulf of Mexico–S.E. United States	Rock shrimp
Sierra; *see* Spanish mackerel		
Siliqua patula	Oregon–western end of Alaska Peninsula	Pacific razor clam
Silver perch	New York–Texas	*Bairdiella chrysura*
Silverside		
Atlantic silverside	Cape May–Maritimes	*Menidia menidia*
grunion	Baja California–San Francisco	*Leuresthes tenuis*
jacksmelt	Baja California–Oregon	*Atherinopsis californiensis*
topsmelt	Gulf of California–British Columbia	*Atherinops affinis*
Silversides		Atherinidae
Sirenia		Sea cows
Skate		*Raja*
Slipmouth (giant perch)	Indo-Pacific	*Lates calcarifer*
Slipmouths		Leiognathidae
Smelt; *see also* Silverside; Blacksmelt		
candlefish; *see* Smelt, eulachon		
capelin	Arctic–adjacent Atlantic and Pacific	*Mallotus villosus*
common smelt	New Jersey–E. Labrador; Baltic–North Sea–Iceland	*Osmerus eperlanus mordax*
eulachon	N. California–Bering Sea	*Thaleichthys pacificus*
rainbow smelt	White Sea–Arctic–Bering Sea–British Columbia–Kamchatka–Korea	*Osmerus eperlanus dentex*
silver smelt; *see* Smelt, surf		
surf (silver) smelt	California–Chignik	*Hypomesus pretiosus*
Snapper		
lane snapper	Warm W. Atlantic	*Lutjanus synagris*
red snapper	Gulf of Mexico–West Indies	*Lutjanus campechanus*
Snappers		Lutjanidae
Snoek (barracouta)	South Africa–Indian Ocean	*Thyrsites atun*
Sole; *see* Flatfishes		
Solea solea	North Sea–Mediterranean–Black Sea	Sole
Soleidae		Soles (true soles)
Soles (true soles)		Soleidae
Spadefish	Cape Cod–Brazil	*Chaetodipterus faber*
Spanish mackerel		
Australian Spanish mackerel	Australia	*Scomberomorus queenlandicus*
cero	New England–Brazil	*Scomberomorus regalis*
Japanese Spanish mackerel	N.W. Pacific	*Scomberomorus niphonius*
king mackerel	Warm Atlantic–Gulf of Mexico–Brazil	*Scomberomorus cavalla*
seerfish	W. Indo-Pacific	*Scomberomorus commerson*
sierra	S. California–Peru	*Scomberomorus sierra*
Spanish mackerel	New England–Brazil	*Scomberomorus maculatus*
spotted seerfish	W. Indo-Pacific	*Scomberomorus guttatus*

Swordfish	Cosmopolitan in warm seas	*Xiphias gladius*
Symphurus plagiusa	Gulf of Mexico–U. S. South Atlantic coast	Tonguefish
Syngnathus fuscus	Gulf of Mexico	Northern pipefish
Synodus foetens	Carolinas–Brazil–Gulf of Mexico	Inshore lizardfish
Taimen		
Sakhalin taimen (anadromous)	Japan Sea	*Hucho perryi*
Siberian taimen	Siberian rivers	*Hucho taimen*
Tarpon	S.E. United States–Caribbean	*Megalops atlantica*
Tautog	Carolinas–New Brunswick	*Tautoga onitis*
Tautoga onitis	Carolinas–New Brunswick	Tautog
Teatfish; *see* Sea cucumber		
Temperate basses		Percichthyidae
Tenpounder or ladyfish	Warm seas	*Elops saurus*
Teredinidae		Shipworms (teredos)
Teredos (shipworms)		Teredinidae
Terrapin	W. Atlantic	*Malaclemmys*
Tetrapterus audax	Warm Pacific	Striped marlin
Thais haemostoma	Gulf of Mexico	Oyster drill
Thaleichthys pacificus	N. California–Bering Sea	Eulachon (a smelt)
Thalenota aranas	S.W. Pacific	Prickly redfish (a sea cucumber)
Theragra chalcogramma	Alaska	Alaska pollock (walleye)
Threadfin, Atlantic	Virginia–Rio Grande	*Polydactylus octonemus*
Thryssa	Indo-Pacific	Anchovy
Thunninae		Tunas
Thunnus		
alalunga		Albacore tuna (albacore)
albacares		Yellowfin tuna
maccoyi	S. Atlantic-W. Pacific	Southern bluefin tuna
obesus		Bigeye tuna
thynnus orientalis	Pacific	Pacific bluefin tuna
thynnus thynnus	Atlantic	Atlantic bluefin tuna
Thymallus		Grayling (freshwater)
Thyrsites atun	South Africa–Indian Ocean	Snoek (barracouta)
Tigerfish; *see* Sea cucumber		
Tilapia		*Tilapia mossambica* (and others)
Tilapia mossambica (and others)		Tilapia
Tilefish	Gulf of Mexico–Nova Scotia	*Lopholatilis chamaeleonticeps*
Tivela stultorum	Magdalena Bay–Halfmoon Bay	Pismo clam
Toadfish	Maine–Gulf of Mexico–Cuba	*Opsanus tau*
Togue; *see* Trout, lake		
Tomcod; *see* Cod		
Tonguefish; *see* Flatfishes		
Tonguefishes		Cynoglossidae
Topsmelt (a silverside)	Gulf of California–British Columbia	*Atherinops affinis*
Trachinotus		
carolinus	Virginia–Gulf of Mexico–West Indies	Florida pompano
falcatus	Chesapeake Bay–Panama	Permit
paitensis	S. California-Peru	Paloma pompano
Trachurus		
symmetricus	Baja California– southeastern Alaska	Jack mackerel
trachurus	Germany–Spain–Mediterranean– Black Sea	Atlantic horse mackerel
Trachurus spp.		Jack mackerels
Trichecus		
inunguis	Brazil–Amazon River–Orinoco River	Amazon manatee

Trichecus—cont'd		
manatus	Gulf of Mexico–Caribbean	Caribbean manatee
Trichiuris lepturus	Warm Atlantic	Atlantic cutlassfish
Trichodontidae		Sandfishes
Triglidae		Gurnards
Trinectes maculatus	Cape Cod–Gulf of Mexico	Hogchoker
Trisopterus esmarkii (a Gadidae)	Barents Sea–Iceland	Norway pout
Trout; *see also* Charr		
blackspotted trout (freshwater)	W. United States	*Salmo clarki lewisi*
blueback trout; *see* Charr		
brown trout (freshwater)		*Salmo trutta fario*
brown trout (anadromous)	Europe; Maine; British Columbia	*Salmo trutta trutta (Salmo levenensis)*
cutthroat trout	N. California–S.E. Alaska	*Salmo clarki clarki*
eastern brook trout; *see* Charr		
Kamloops trout (freshwater)	British Columbia	*Salmo gairdneri kamloops*
lake trout (freshwater)	N. North American lakes	*Cristivomer namaycush*
rainbow or steelhead trout	Monterey–Bristol Bay	*Salmo gairdneri gairdneri*
rainbow trout (freshwater)	Baja California mountains	*Salmo gairdneri nelsoni*
sea trout; *see* Trout, brown (sea) (anadromous)		
togue; *see* Trout, lake		
Tuna		
albacore tuna (albacore)		*Thunnus alalunga*
bigeye tuna		*Thunnus obesus*
bluefin tuna		
Atlantic	Atlantic	*Thunnus thynnus thynnus*
Pacific	Pacific	*Thunnus thynnus orientalis*
southern	S. Atlantic–W. Pacific	*Thunnus maccoyi*
frigate mackerel	Atlantic; Pacific	*Auxis thazard*
little tuna		
Atlantic		*Euthynnus alletteratus*
eastern	Philippines	*Euthynnus affinis*
skipjack tuna (skipjack)		*Euthynnus pelamis*
yellowfin tuna		*Thunnus albacares*
Tunas		Thunninae
Turbot; *see* Flatfishes		
Turtle		
green turtle		*Chelonia mydas*
hawksbill turtle	Atlantic	*Eretmochelys imbricata*
loggerhead turtle	Atlantic	*Caretta caretta*
terrapin	W. Atlantic	*Malaclemmys*
"Tyulka"	Black Sea	*Clupeonella deliculata deliculata*
Umbridae		Mudminnows
Urophycis		
chuss	U. S. mid-Atlantic–Gulf of St. Lawrence	Red "hake" (ling)
floridanus	S.E. United States–Gulf of Mexico	Southern "hake" (ling)
tenuis	U. S. mid-Atlantic–Gulf of Mexico	White "hake" (ling)
Urosalpinx cinerea	N.W. Atlantic	Oyster drill
Venerupis		
decussatus	N.E. Atlantic	Grooved carpet shell clam
japonica	Japan-Korea; Washington–British Columbia	Manila clam
Venus gallina	N.E. Atlantic	Striped venus clam
Wahoo; *see* Spanish mackerel		
Walleye; *see* Pollock, Alaska		
Walleye (blue pike) (freshwater)		*Stizostedion vitreum*
Walrus	Arctic	*Odobenus rosmarus*

Warsaw (warsaw grouper)	Warm W. Atlantic	*Epinephalus nigritus*
Weakfish		
silver (white) sea trout	Gulf of Mexico	*Cynoscion nothus*
spotted or speckled sea trout	New York–Texas	*Cynoscion nebulosis*
weakfish	Cape Cod–Florida	*Cynoscion regalis*
white sea bass	Baja California–San Francisco	*Cynoscion nobilis*
white sea trout; *see* Weakfish, silver (white) sea trout		
Weakfishes (sea trouts)		*Cynoscion*
Whale		
baleen whales		
bowhead whale; *see* Greenland right		
gray whale	N. Pacific	*Eschrichtius gibbosus*
Greenland right (bowhead) whale	Northern seas–Arctic	*Balaena mysticetus*
rorquals		
blue whale	All oceans	*Balaenoptera musculus*
Bryde whale	Warm seas	*Balaenoptera edeni*
finback whale	All oceans	*Balaenoptera physalus*
humpback whale	All oceans	*Megaptera novaeangliae*
minke whale	All oceans	*Balaenoptera acutorostrata*
sei whale	All oceans	*Balaenoptera borealis*
toothed whales		
beluga (white whale)	Arctic-boreal	*Delphinapterus leucas*
blackfish; *see* pilot whale		
bottlenosed whale	Atlantic	*Hyperoodon ampullatus*
killer whale	All oceans	*Orcinus orca*
narwhal	Arctic Atlantic	*Monodon monoceros*
pilot whale		*Globicephala melaena*
sperm whale	All oceans	*Physeter catodon*
white whale; *see* Whale, beluga		
Whelk	N.E. Atlantic	*Buccinum undatum*
Whiff; *see* Flatfishes		
Whitefish (freshwater)		*Coregonus clupeaformis*
White perch	Carolinas–Nova Scotia	*Morone americana*
Whiting; *see also* Hake, silver	N.E. Atlantic	*Merlangus (= Gadus) merlangus*
Windowpane; *see* Flatfishes		
Winkle; *see* Periwinkle		
Witch; *see* Flatfishes, sole, gray		
Wolffish, Atlantic (ocean catfish)	Cape Cod–Labrador; France-Spitzbergen	*Anarhichas lupus*
Wolf herring		
wolf herring	Indo-Pacific	*Chirocentrus dorab*
wolf herring	Indo-Pacific	*Chirocentrus nudus*
Xiphias gladius	Cosmopolitan in warm seas	Swordfish
Xiphopenaeus	Gulf of Mexico–S.E. United States–Brazil	Seabob (a shrimp)
Yellowtail		
yellowtail	California-Chile	*Seriola dorsalis*
yellowtail	Japan	*Seriola quinqueradiata*
Zostera	Atlantic; Pacific	Eelgrass

Suggested readings

Committee on Names of Fishes. 1970. A list of the common and scientific names of fishes from the United States and Canada, ed. 3. Amer. Fish. Soc., Spec. Publ. 6. 149 pp.

Hart, J. L. 1973. Pacific fishes of Canada. Fish. Res. Bd. Canada, Bull. **180**:1-740.

Leim, A. H., and W. B. Scott. 1966. Fishes of the Atlantic coast of Canada. Fish. Res. Bd. Canada, Bull. **155**:1-485.

Miller, D. J., and R. N. Lea. 1972. Guide to the coastal marine fishes of California. Calif. Fish Game, Fish Bull. **157**:1-235.

Quast, J. C., and E. L. Hall. 1972. List of fishes of Alaska and adjacent waters with a guide to some of their literature. NOAA Tech. Rep., Nat. Mar. Fish. Serv., Spec. Sci. Rep. Fish. **658**: 1-47.

Scheffer, V. B., and D. W. Rice. 1963. A list of the marine mammals of the world. U. S. Fish Wildl. Serv., Spec. Sci. Rep. Fish. **431**:1-12.

Templeman, W. 1966. Marine resources of Newfoundland. Fish. Res. Bd. Canada, Bull. **154**: 1-170.

❧ List of lesser known places

Aegean Sea Between Greece and Turkey.

Affleck Canal Deep bay on south side of Kuiu Island, southeastern Alaska.

Agulhas Bank Fishing bank off southeastern coast of South Africa.

Alabama River Flows through east central Alabama to Gulf of Mexico.

Alamitos Bay Small bay south of Long Beach, southern California.

Amak Island Small island close to north side of Alaska Peninsula just east of False Pass.

Amchitka One of the more distant islands of Aleutian chain, Alaska.

Amur River Large river emptying into western side of Sea of Okhotsk at about 53° N lat.

Andaman Sea Between Andaman Islands (Bay of Bengal) and southern Burma, from 10° to 15° N lat.

Arafura Sea Poorly defined area south of New Guinea and north of Australia lying between Torres Strait on east and Darwin, Australia, on west; included in what I call the North Australia Sea.

Aswan High Dam Recently constructed, very large hydroelectric dam on Nile in southern Egypt.

Auke Bay Important herring spawning area just north of Juneau, Alaska.

Babine Lake Sockeye nursery lake on Skeena River, British Columbia, where many sockeye spawn in outlet stream.

Baffin Bay Deep basin between Greenland and central Baffin Island with a sill in Davis Strait.

Bangladesh Formerly East Pakistan.

Bangor Pool Famous Atlantic salmon angling pool below first dam on Penobscot River in Maine where anglers fish from canoes; first salmon caught each spring is traditionally sent to the President.

Banquereau Quereau Bank, large fishing bank with rough bottom and variable depth off northern Nova Scotia.

Barents Sea Large sea on continental shelf bounded on south by northern Norway and Kola Peninsula, on east by Novaya Zemlya, on northeast by Zemlya Frantsa-Josifa, and on northwest by Spitzbergen.

Bass Strait Between Australia and Tasmania.

Bay of Bengal Between India and Burma.

Bay of Biscay Large open bight between Spain and France.

Bay of Fundy Funnel-shaped bay between New Brunswick and Nova Scotia famed for its tidal bore.

Bay of Izmir On eastern shore of Aegean Sea.

Bay of Ob Bay at mouth of Ob River, east side of Kara Sea, arctic U.S.S.R.

Bear Island Small island on west side of Barents Sea, between northern Norway and Spitzbergen.

Beaufort Site of biological station in North Carolina.

Behm Canal Channel on three sides of Revillagigedo Island, southeastern Alaska.

Bella Coola River	On midwest coast of British Columbia.
Bering Island	Westernmost of Commander Islands (fur seal islands) in western Bering Sea; once home of Steller sea cows, now extinct.
Beverley-Salem Harbor	Sheltered bay just north of Boston, Massachusetts.
Bimini	Very small Bahamian island 60 miles (97 km) due east of Miami; site of Lerner Marine Laboratory and also noted for sportfishing of bluefin tuna.
Biscayne Bay	At southeastern tip of Florida opening onto Atlantic.
Blue Nile	Nile tributary from Ethiopia; chief contributor of rich sediments brought by Nile floods.
Boca Ciega Bay	Behind barrier islands at St. Petersburg, Florida.
Bonneville Dam	Large dam nearest tidewater on Columbia River, Washington.
Bornholm Basin	Deepest portion of Baltic Sea.
Bosphorus	Connects Black Sea and Sea of Marmara.
Breton Sound	Shallow open bay north of Mississippi River delta.
Brooks Lake	Sockeye nursery lake flowing into Naknek Lake; located in Mount Katmai National Park and site of a biological field station.
Browns Bank	Fishing bank 100 miles (160 km) south of southern tip of Nova Scotia.
Burke Channel	Fjord in northern British Columbia.
Burwood Bank	Large bank about 200 miles (320 km) south of Falkland Islands.
Bute Inlet	Long fjord leaving northeastern corner of Strait of Georgia in a northerly direction.
Buzzards Bay	Bay just west of southern extension of Cape Cod, Massachusetts.
Cabo Blanco	Cape at 4° S lat. near northwestern extremity of Peru.
Cabo Frio	Cape just east of Rio de Janiero, Brazil, named from low temperature of upwelling waters caused by cape jutting into a current.
Calicut	City on southwestern Indian coast 190 nautical miles (342 km) northwest of southern tip of India.
Campeche	City on west shore of Yucatan Peninsula.
Campeche Banks	Large shoal banks north of Yucatan province noted for shrimp and red snappers.
Canadian Straits	Waterways between northern Canadian Islands from Hudson Bay to Beaufort Sea.
Cape Addington	Southwestern point of Noyes Island, southeastern Alaska; area just to north is heavily populated with immature halibut.
Cape Bendel	Northwestern tip of Kuiu Island where Frederick Sound joins Chatham Strait, southeastern Alaska.
Cape Breton Island	Large island forming northeastern portion of Nova Scotia and southeastern boundary of Gulf of St. Lawrence and separated from Newfoundland by narrow Cabot Strait.
Cape Canaveral	Middle of east coast of Florida.
Cape Cod	Long narrow curved peninsula in southeastern Massachusetts; waters to north of cape are cooler than those to south, cape acting as barrier to northward extension of many species.
Cape Flattery	Northwestern tip of Washington at southern entrance to Strait of Juan de Fuca.
Cape Hatteras	On outer barrier islands of North Carolina, where the Gulf Stream is deflected offshore; marks southern boundary for many northern species and northern boundary for many subtropical species.
Cape May	South end of New Jersey at northern entrance to Delaware Bay; long a rendezvous for vessels in the winter trawl fishery for scup and butterfish.
Cape Ommaney	South end of Baranof Island at entrance to Chatham Strait, southeastern Alaska.
Cape San Lazaro	About 150 miles (240 km) northwest of south end of Baja California.
Cape San Lucas	Southern end of Baja California.
Cape Spencer	At north entrance to Cross Sound, the northernmost entrance into southeastern Alaska waterways; point at which small vessels from Seattle must leave over 1000 miles (1600 km) of inland waterways to cross the stormy Gulf of Alaska.
Cariaco Trench	Trench 1400 m deep close to central coast of Venezuela on continental shelf with a sill depth of 146 m; below 200 m, water is devoid of oxygen.
Carquinez Strait	Entrance to Suisin Bay, San Francisco Bay, California.
Cedros Island	About center of outer coast of Baja California.
Celilo Falls	Falls on Columbia River once a favorite location for dipnetting salmon by the Indians; now drowned out by a power dam.

Charles River Flows through Boston, Massachusetts; site of prehistoric salmon weirs.

Charlotte Harbor Bay just north of Fort Myers, Florida.

Chatham Strait Channel over 100 miles (160 km) long east of Chichagof and Baranof Islands, southeastern Alaska.

Chef Menteur One of the two tidal entrances to Lake Pontchartrain, Louisiana; the other is the Rigolets.

Chesterfield Islands About 1000 miles (1600 km) off east coast of Australia.

Chickamon River Enters Behm Canal, southeastern Alaska.

Chignik River This very productive sockeye river enters ocean through Chignik Bay about 120 miles (192 km) southwest of Kodiak Island, on south side of Alaska Peninsula.

Chilko Lake In Fraser River system above Hell's Gate Canyon; the great majority of sockeye spawn in outlet stream.

Chukchi Sea Arctic sea just north of Bering Strait between northwestern Alaska and northeastern Siberia as far as Wrangell Island.

Clear Lake Tributary estuary on west shore of Galveston Bay, Texas.

Cobscook Bay Lower of two tidal basins of Passamaquoddy Power Project; receives Dennys River, famous Atlantic salmon stream.

Cochin City on southwestern Indian coast 120 nautical miles (216 km) northwest of southern tip of India.

Commander Islands Fur seal islands at Soviet end of Aleutian chain.

Cook Inlet Long, large inlet with extreme tides at head of Gulf of Alaska.

Copper Island Medny Island; easternmost of two Commander Islands (fur seal islands) in western Bering Sea; once home of Steller sea cows, now extinct.

Copper River flats Salmon gillnetting area, especially for sockeye, off mouth of Copper River, entering Gulf of Alaska just east of Prince William Sound.

Cordova City on east shore of Prince William Sound, Alaska.

Coronation Island Outer coast midway between Cape Ommaney and Noyes Island, southeastern Alaska.

Crescent City On California coast less than 20 miles (32 km) south of Oregon.

Crystal River Central west coast of Florida.

Cultus Lake Small lake tributary to Fraser River system below Hell's Gate; famous for sockeye salmon experiments.

Cumberland Sound Site of trading post on east side of Baffin Island, Canada.

Dakar City at westernmost point of Africa about 15° N lat., 17° 30′ W long.

Damariscotta Lake In central Maine; famed for its alewife run.

Dardanelles Connects Aegean Sea and Sea of Marmara.

Davis Strait Between Greenland and southern Baffin Island.

Dawson Capital of Yukon, Canada.

Departure Bay Near south end of Strait of Georgia, Vancouver Island, British Columbia.

Dixon Entrance Wide strait between southeastern Alaska and British Columbia.

Don River Enters Sea of Azov, U.S.S.R.

Douglas Island Summer herring area south of Douglas Island near Juneau, southeastern Alaska.

Drake Passage Between Cape Horn and Antarctica.

East Orland River North of mouth of Penobscot River, Maine.

Eastport City at northern tip of Maine noted for sardine canning.

Eel River Enters sea just south of Eureka, California.

Egegik Lake One of five large sockeye lakes tributary to Bristol Bay; lies just north of southernmost Ugashik Lake, Alaska.

Elrington Passage Summer herring area in southwestern Prince William Sound, central Alaska.

Ensenada City about 50 miles south of United States in Baja California.

Eureka City 80 miles south of California-Oregon border.

Falkland Islands British islands lying east of entrance to Straits of Magellan.

False Pass Isonotski Strait, very shallow pass between Unimak Island and west end of Alaska Peninsula.

Farallon Islands Group of small islands about 20 miles (32 km) west of San Francisco; long a favorite trawling ground for flatfish.

Faroe Islands	Danish islands between Scotland and Iceland.
Favorite Bay	Small bay, once a summer herring bay, near mouth of Kootznahoo Inlet, Chatham Strait, southeastern Alaska.
Finmarken	Northernmost part of Norway.
Florida Bay	Large shoal bay dotted with tiny islets and coral heads lying between Florida Keys and mainland; often has very high salinity.
Fort Ross	Former Russian fort north of San Francisco, California, established as base for hunting sea otter.
Foxe Basin	North of Hudson Bay between Baffin and Southampton Islands.
Fraser Lake	One of headwater lakes of Fraser River, British Columbia.
Frobisher Bay	Bay in southeastern part of Baffin Island, Canada.
Fundian Channel	Deep channel into Gulf of Maine between Georges and Browns Bank.

Galápagos Islands	On equator about 600 miles west of Ecuador.
Galveston Bay	Large estuary landward of Galveston, Texas.
George River	On east side of Ungava Bay, northern Quebec, Canada.
Georges Bank	Extensive bank east of New England.
Golden Gate	Deep channel between ocean and San Francisco Bay.
Grays Harbor	Large bay on outer coast of Washington.
Great Bear Lake	Lies on Arctic Circle in Northwest Territories of Canada and empties into Mackenzie River; mean depth 400 m, maximum depth not certain, but it has slight cryptodepression.
Great Slave Lake	Lies south of Arctic Circle in Northwest Territories of Canada and empties into Mackenzie River; world's fourth deepest freshwater lake (614 m) with cryptodepression of 464 m.
Greenland Sea	Opinion differs as to whether Greenland Sea exists or is merely part of Norwegian Sea; Dietrich (1957), for instance, calls West Spitzbergen at 79° N lat. the eastern side of Norwegian Sea; Heselton (1969) begs the question by entitling a figure of the area the "Norwegian-Greenland Sea"; in reality only one sea but western (Greenland) side is sometimes referred to as Greenland Sea as a matter of geographical convenience.
Grenada	West Indies island 130 km north of coast of Venezuela.
Guadalupe Island	Island at 29° N lat., 150 miles (241 km) west of Baja California; home of colony of fur seals.
Gulf Breeze	Seaside town with federal marine laboratory just south of Pensacola, Florida.
Gulf of Anadyr	Large open gulf on Siberian coast due west of St. Lawrence Island, about 63° N lat.
Gulf of Bothnia	Large northward-extending arm of Baltic Sea.
Gulf of Carpentaria	Large gulf open on north side of Australia to Arafura Sea, extending about 390 nautical miles (722 km) into Australian Continent, just west of Torres Strait; included in what I call the North Australia Sea.
Gulf of Georgia	Large strait open at either end lying between central Vancouver Island and mainland.
Gulf of Iskenderun	Named for Iskander, Alexander the Great; gulf on extreme southeastern coast of Turkey.
Gulf of Kara-Bogaz	Usually misspelled as "Bugaz" (translates as Black Strait Gulf or Gulf of the Black Strait); large body of water about 100 × 70 nautical miles (185 × 130 km) without entering streams, connected to middle of eastern shore of Caspian Sea by very long and shallow entrance channel so that high evaporation of arid area causes extremely high salinities.
Gulf of Maine	Between Nova Scotia and northern New England.
Gut Bay	Deep fjord on west side of southern Chatham Strait, southeastern Alaska; home of small, late-spawning herring.

Half Moon Bay	Small open bight 20 miles south of San Francisco.
Halibut Cove Lagoon	In upper Kachemak Bay, Cook Inlet, Alaska.
Hallo Bay	Shallow bay on north side of Shelikof Strait; razor clam flat.
Harbin	City in central Manchuria.
Hecate Strait	Large halibut bank between Queen Charlotte Islands and British Columbia mainland.
Hell's Gate Canyon	Narrow deep canyon of Fraser River 250 miles from sea.
Herschel Island	Small island in Arctic Sea just west of mouth of Mackenzie River; famed as overwintering area for whalers.
Hokkaidō Island	Northern island of Japan.

Holmes Harbor Bay on east shore of Whidbey Island, northern Puget Sound, Washington; well-known herring spawning area.

Home Bay Site of trading post on east side of Baffin Island, Canada.

Homestead Town near southern end of Florida.

Honshū Island Largest island of Japan, south of Hokkaidō Island.

Hopedale Village on Bayou La Loutre, Louisiana; data center base for studies of Mississippi River–Gulf Outlet Project.

Hudson Canyon Submarine canyon extending seaward off mouth of Hudson River.

Humboldt Bay About 90 miles south of Oregon-California border.

Hunterston Nuclear plant in Ayrshire, Scotland; site of rearing experiments on sole in heated effluent.

Iberia Spanish-Portuguese peninsula.

Icy Strait Northern entrance into southeastern Alaska from Cape Spencer (through Cross Sound) to Chatham Strait.

Iliamna Lake Large lake (90 × 40 miles) tributary to Kvichak River, Alaska.

Iliuk Arm Portion of Naknek Lake close to Mount Katmai volcano.

Indian Key Small key near north end of Everglades National Park.

Irminger Sea South of Iceland.

Ismailof Island Upper Kachemak Bay, Cook Inlet, Alaska.

Jones Sound Between Devon and Ellesmere Islands, about 75° N lat., in Canadian Arctic.

Juan de Fuca Strait Between Washington and Vancouver Island.

Kachemak Bay Large bay on east side of lower Cook Inlet, central Alaska.

Kamchatka Siberian peninsula between Okhotsk and Bering Seas.

Karachi Capital of Pakistan and important fishing port at head of Arabian Sea.

Karafuto Southern half of Sakhalin Island formerly held by Japan.

Kara Inlet Entrance to Kara Sea between Novaya Zemlya and mainland.

Kara Sea Semienclosed shallow arctic sea about 800 km long east of Novaya Zemlya.

Karluk Lake Famous sockeye lake on Kodiak Island, central Alaska, draining into Shelikof Strait.

Karta Bay Head of Skowl Arm, Clarence Strait, southeastern Alaska.

Kattegat Channel between Denmark and Sweden leading into Baltic Sea.

Kerguelen Islands About 50° S lat., 70° E long.

Ketchikan Creek At Ketchikan on Revillagigedo Island, southeastern Alaska.

Key West City almost at western end of Florida Keys and at end of "Overseas Highway."

Killisnoo Village and former herring plant on Admiralty Island, center of Chatham Strait, southeastern Alaska.

Klamath River Salmon river in northern California.

Knight Inlet Exceptionally long fjord in central British Columbia.

Kola Bay Bay on Kola Peninsula, arctic Russia.

Kootznahoo Inlet On Admiralty Island, central Chatham Strait, southeastern Alaska.

Kotzebue Sound Estuary north of Bering Strait, Alaska.

Kruzof Island Small wooded island just north of Sitka on outer coast.

Kurile Islands Chain of small islands from Kamchatka southwest to Hokkaidō Island across mouth of Okhotsk Sea.

Kuskokwim River Enters eastern Bering Sea north of Bristol Bay.

Labrador Sea Between Greenland and Labrador.

Lake Baikal World's deepest lake; in central Siberia.

Lake Balkhash Brackish inland sea in central Asia east of Aral Sea.

Lake Borgne Estuary at west end of Mississippi Sound.

Lake Ladoga Large lake in southeastern Finland.

Lake Nyasa East African rift valley lake 706 m deep with cryptodepression of 242 m lying between 9° and 15° S lat. (about due west of north end of Madagascar); about 350 miles (563 km) in length.

Lake Pontchartrain Large estuary bordering New Orleans on north.

Lake St. John In Quebec 100 miles (160 km) up Saguenay River, which empties into west side of lower St. Lawrence River; home of freshwater population of tomcod *(Microgadus tomcod).*

Lake Tanganyika African rift valley lake 1470 m deep with cryptodepression of 647 m; world's second deepest inland sea, lying between Zaire and Tanzania; over 400 miles (644 km) in length.

Lake Victoria East African lake lying on equator; although relatively shallow (40 m), one of world's largest inland seas (69,000 km²), 28% as large as all five Great Lakes of North America; because of great water loss from evaporation and transpiration in vegetation-clogged swamps, does not contribute as much water to White Nile as its water regime should furnish.

Lake Winnipeg Large shoal lake in southern Manitoba.

Larch Bay Small open bight on outer coast just north of Cape Ommaney, famed as heavy producer of summer herring.

Laurentian Channel Deep channel between Newfoundland and Nova Scotia fishing banks extending toward Gulf of St. Lawrence.

Lena River Large river arising near Lake Baikal in southern Siberia and flowing northward across central Siberia into Laptev Sea.

Levantine Basin Basin of Mediterranean Sea east of sill between Tunis and Sicily.

Liscombe Very small fishing bank off Nova Scotia.

Little Port Walter Chatham Strait, near south end of Baranof Island, Alaska.

Long Island Sound Between Long Island and New York–Connecticut.

Lopez Island Southernmost of San Juan Islands, Washington.

Machias River Atlantic salmon river in eastern Maine.

Mackenzie River Flows north through Yukon into Arctic Sea.

Magdalena Bay Bay behind Cape San Lazaro, Baja California.

Maritimes Canadian provinces of New Brunswick, Nova Scotia, and Prince Edward Island.

Martha's Vineyard Island south of Cape Cod, Massachusetts; site of lobster rearing experiments.

Matagorda Bay Large estuary on central Texas coast.

Mazatlán City on west coast of Mexico due east of south end of Baja California.

McClinton Creek Enters Masset Inlet, north end of Queen Charlotte Islands, British Columbia; site of pink salmon life history experiments.

Merrimack River Between Massachusetts and New Hampshire; once famous for Atlantic salmon.

Monhegan Island Small island off central coast of Maine used by precolonial fishermen for drying codfish.

Monterey Bay Large open bay about 70 miles (113 km) south of San Francisco.

Morro Bay (and Beach) 70 miles (113 km) north of Point Conception, California.

Mount Katmai Volcano on Alaska Peninsula opposite Kodiak Island; last large eruption in 1912.

Mt. Desert Island Pronounced "de zert'"; large island in northern Maine.

Mt. St. Augustine High volcano on small island on west side of lower Cook Inlet.

Mount Veniaminof Old crater, still smoking with fumaroles, just north of Chignik on Alaska Peninsula.

Murman coast Arctic coast of U.S.S.R. west of the White Sea.

Naknek Lake Large sockeye lake draining into Bristol Bay, Alaska.

Namibia Official United Nations name for former German Southwest Africa.

Naples Small city 35 miles (56 km) south of Fort Myers, Florida.

Narragansett Bay Chief bay in Rhode Island.

Nass River Salmon river in northern British Columbia.

Newport River Small coastal river and estuary, North Carolina.

New York Bight Open bight between Long Island and New Jersey.

Nikolaevsk Siberian city about 30 km up Amur River at about 53° N lat.

North Dvina River Enters White Sea at Archangel.

North River Small coastal stream in central Massachusetts.

Northumberland Strait Between Prince Edward Island and New Brunswick.

Norwegian Sea Area bounded on east by Norway, on northeast by Barents Sea, on north by Spitzbergen, on west by Greenland, and on south by ridges between Greenland, Iceland, Faroe Islands, and Shetland Islands.

Novaya Zemlaya "New Land"; large islands trending northeasterly from Siberia between Barents Sea and Kara Sea.

Noyes Island Summer feeding area for herring race that spawns near Klawak; lies off outer coast of

Prince of Wales Island, southeastern Alaska; also important location for trolling for salmon.

Nunivak Island Large island 30 miles (48 km) off Bering Sea coast of Alaska at 60° N lat. between mouths of Kuskokwim and Yukon Rivers.

Ocean Springs Central Mississippi coast on Mississippi Sound; noted for large modern marine research station.

Offats Bayou Deeply dredged bayou north of Galveston Island, Texas; haven for cold-sensitive fishes during winter northers.

Okhotsk Sea Large sea between Kamchatka and Siberian mainland.

Olive Cove (Stream) Stream on east side of Etolin Island south of Wrangell, Alaska, where early studies were made of pink salmon biology.

Olyutorshiy Zaliv (Gulf) Small gulf where Japanese commenced fishery for spider crabs (snow crabs); due west of Nunivak Island (60° N lat.) on northern coast of Kamchatka in western Bering Sea.

Orissa Area of seasonal upwelling off province of Orissa on northeastern coast of India in Bay of Bengal.

Otaru Fishing town on west shore of Hokkaidō; first king crab were canned there in 1892.

Otter Island One of smaller islands in Pribilof group.

Ozette Lake (and River) Small sockeye salmon stream south of Cape Flattery on outer coast of Washington.

Passamaquoddy Bay Large bay between Maine and New Brunswick selected as upper pool in huge tidal power project.

Patagonia Southern part of Argentina.

Pavlof Bay Small bay on south side of Alaska Peninsula near western end.

Pearl River Enters Lake Borgne between Louisiana and Mississippi.

Penobscot River Large river in northern Maine.

Petersburg City at north end of Wrangell Narrows, southeastern Alaska.

Pine Island Sound North-south channel behind barrier islands due west of Fort Myers, Florida.

Pismo Beach Sandy surf beach in central California.

Playa del Rey Small boat harbor on coast of southern California.

Pleasant Bay (Orleans) Sheltered bay, southeastern corner of Cape Cod, Massachusetts.

Point Adolphus Summer herring area south side of Icy Strait, southeastern Alaska.

Point Arguello North Santa Barbara County, California, just north of Point Conception.

Point Barrow Northernmost point in Alaska between Chukchi Sea and Beaufort Sea, about 156° W long.

Point Conception About one third of length of California coast from southern boundary; marks division between two habitats.

Point Gardner Southwestern tip of Admiralty Island, southeastern Alaska.

Point Hope On Alaska coast 150 nautical miles (270 km) north of Bering Strait.

Point Judith Fishing port at west entrance to Narragansett Bay, Rhode Island.

Point Wilson At Port Townsend, west entrance to lower Puget Sound.

Port Aransas Shrimp fishing port near Corpus Christi, Texas, and site of large marine biological laboratory.

Port Hobron Former whaling station on Sitkalidak Island just off east coast of Kodiak Island.

Portlock Bank East of Kodiak Island; largest halibut and king crab bank in Gulf of Alaska.

Pribilof Islands U. S. fur seal islands in eastern Bering Sea, 300 miles (483 km) from Alaska mainland.

Prince William Sound Large protected sound containing harbors of Cordova, Valdez, Whitney, and La Touche in northeastern Gulf of Alaska.

Provincetown Fishing town on northern tip of Cape Cod.

Quinault Lake (and River) Sockeye lake on outer Washington Coast noted for extremely early-running race of salmon. (I have seen records of salmon commencing to ascend the river in December.)

Quincy Bay Extensive clam flats adjoining Boston on south.

Redberry Lake Saline lake (one of many) in Saskatchewan.

Red Fox Bay Small bay on south side of Shuyak Strait on Afognak Island in central Alaska; once had abundance of very large herring (1924 through 1927) during summer months but fishery collapsed with end of Kachemak Bay winter fishery.

Revillagigedo Islands Group 600 miles (966 km) west of Mexico, 240 miles (386 km) south of Baja California.

Rigolets One of two tidal entrances to Lake Pontchartrain, Louisiana; the other is Chef Menteur.

Rio Grande Enters Gulf of Mexico between Texas and Mexico.

Ripple Rock Former rock about an acre in extent hazardous to navigation in Seymour Narrows at north end of Strait of Georgia. (I have piloted a small boat through these narrows with a 16-knot current.)

Roanoke River Enters Albemarle Sound, North Carolina; famed as spawning stream for striped bass.

Robben Island (Kaihyo To) Southernmost breeding island of northern fur seal on Asiatic coast; former Japanese island lies close to coast of southern Sakhalin Island.

Rockall Bank Small fishing bank about 400 km west of Scotland at 57° 30′ N lat., about 900 km due south of easternmost point of Iceland.

Roseway Bank Small fishing bank 35 miles (56 km) east of south end of Nova Scotia.

Sable Island Bank Large fishing bank surrounding Sable Island, about 90 miles (144 km) off coast of northern Nova Scotia.

Safety Lagoon Small coastal lagoon near Nome, Alaska.

St. Andrew Bay Large bay behind Panama City, northwestern Florida.

St. Augustine Small city 60 miles (96 km) south of Georgia-Florida border; founded by Spaniards in 1565.

St. George Island Southernmost of two principal islands of Pribilof group; about 20% of fur seal herd uses this island; St. Paul Island lies about 40 miles (64 km) to north.

St. Lawrence Island Large U. S. island 135 miles (216 km) south of Bering Strait between Alaska and Siberia; walrus is important to native economy.

St. Michael Very old Russian settlement just north of mouth of Yukon River.

St. Paul Island Northernmost of two principal islands of Pribilof group; used by about 80% of fur seal herd.

Saint Pierre Island Now part of French fishing colony of Saint Pierre and Miquelon just south of Newfoundland; used in precolonial times for drying codfish.

Sakhalin Island Very large north-south–oriented island close to Siberian coast just north of Hokkaidō.

Salinas River Small river, once with coho salmon run, entering central Monterey Bay, California.

Saltspring Island Island used by spawning herring in southern end of Gulf of Georgia, British Columbia.

San Juan Archipelago Islands north of Puget Sound between Vancouver Island and Washington.

San Miguel Island Westernmost of islands that form Santa Barbara Channel; lies 30 miles (48 km) south of Point Conception, California; colony of northern fur seals formed here in 1968.

Santa Barbara Channel Between mainland and three northernmost channel islands, southern California; oriented east and west.

Santa Cruz City on north end of Monterey Bay.

Santa Rosa Sound Long narrow bay south of Pensacola, Florida.

Santo Domingo River In Sierra San Pedro Mártir of Baja California.

Sarawak Portion of Malaysia on northwestern coast of Borneo.

Sargasso Sea Oceanic gyre of low fertility with little wind or current in North Atlantic; famed for sargassum weed.

Scammon Lagoon Shallow lagoon off Bahia Sebastion Vixcaino, central outer coast of Baja California; one of several lagoons used as breeding grounds by Pacific gray whales.

Scotia Sea Between Tierra del Fuego and Antarctica.

Sea Lion Rock Smallest of Pribilof Islands.

Sea of Azov Connected with northern Black Sea through Strait of Kerch.

Sea of Marmara Between Asia Minor and Europe.

Sevastopol City on Crimean peninsula, northern Black Sea.

Security Bay On Frederick Sound in northwestern corner of Kuiu Island, southeastern Alaska.

Seldovia From "seld," Russian for "herring"; small town on Seldovia Bay at south entrance to Cook Inlet; as late as 1925 I saw a few herring wintering in a very small lagoon back of town.

Sheepscot River Small river in central Maine.

Shelikof Strait Between Kodiak Island and Alaska peninsula.

Shetland Islands Small islands lying northeast of Scotland.

Shumagin Islands South of Alaska peninsula, near end of peninsula.

Shuswap Lake Fraser River lake below which late-running sockeye spawn.
Shuyak Island Adjacent to north side of Afognak Island, Gulf of Alaska.
Shuyak Strait Between Shuyak and Afognak Islands, Gulf of Alaska.
Sierra Leone Small country on west coast of Africa just west of Gulf of Guinea.
Sierra San Pedro Mártir High forested mountain range in Baja California.
Sitka Old Russian capital of Alaska on outer coast of Baranof Island.
Socorro Island *See* Revillagigedo Islands.
South Channel Deeper trawling ground between Georges Bank and Cape Cod.
South China Sea Between South China and Indochina on west and Philippines to Borneo on east.
South Georgia Islands About 54° S lat., 37° W long.
South Orkney Islands About 61° S lat., 45° W long.
Spitzbergen Islands northwest of Barents Sea belonging to Norway.
Sri Lanka Official United Nations name for what was formerly Ceylon.
Stikine flats Gill net fishing area for sockeye near Wrangell on flats off mouth of Stikine River in southeastern Alaska.
Strait of Belle Isle Narrow strait between Newfoundland and Labrador with very cold southward-flowing current.
Strait of Gibraltar Narrow passage between Atlantic Ocean and Mediterranean Sea.
Strait of Kerch Connects Sea of Azov with Black Sea.
Stuart Lake One of headwater lakes of Fraser River.
Sunda Shelf Very extensive continental shelf in South China Sea.
Susquehanna River Large river entering north end of Chesapeake Bay.
Swickshak Bay Small razor clam bay on north side of Shelikof Strait due west of Shuyak Island.

Tamgas Stream Stream with small-sized race of sockeye on Annette Island, southeastern Alaska.
Tampa Bay Large estuary on central west coast of Florida.
Tanana River Enters Yukon River 800 miles (1280 km) above its mouth.
Tarpon Springs Once important sponge fishing port on west coast of Florida.
Tatar Strait Narrow, shallow strait between northern Sakhalin Island and mainland connecting Sea of Okhotsk with Gulf of Tartary.
Terminal Island In Long Beach–Los Angeles Harbor.
Tierra del Fuego Large island separated from south end of South America by Straits of Magellan.
Timor Sea Wide open–ended body of water lying roughly between Australia (west of Darwin) and former Portuguese colony of Timor, now part of Indonesia; included in what I call the North Australia Sea.
Tomales Bay Bay just north of San Francisco; herring spawning area.
Tortugas grounds Tortuga, Spanish for "tortoise"; large shrimp fishing bank west of Key West, Florida, extending beyond Dry Tortugas Islands.
Trinity Bank Large fishing bank just south of Kodiak Island.
Truk Lagoon Complex coral atoll 30 to 40 miles (48 to 64 km) in diameter at 7° 25' N lat., 151° 45' E long. in the heart of Micronesia.
Tunk Stream Small river in northern Maine.
Tyrrhenian Sea Between Sardinia and Italy.

Ugashik Lake Southernmost of five large sockeye lakes flowing into Bristol Bay, Alaska.
Ungava Bay On south side of Hudson Strait in northern Quebec, Canada.
Unimak Pass Between Unimak Island and remainder of Aleutian Islands; first navigable pass into Bristol Bay west of Alaska Peninsula (except for shallow draft vessels at False Pass).
Unuk River Enters Behm Canal, southeastern Alaska.

Ventura County (and River) Just south of Santa Barbara, California.
Virginia Capes Cape Charles and Cape Henry at mouth of Chesapeake Bay.
Vistula River Flows through Poland to southern Baltic Sea.
Volga River Very large river flowing into Caspian Sea, U.S.S.R.
Vyga River Enters southwestern White Sea.

Waddell Creek Small stream in coastal redwood belt that enters Pacific Ocean just north of Monterey Bay; contains runs of both steelhead trout and coho salmon.

Walrus Island One of smaller islands of Pribilof group.

Weddell Sea Large bay in Atlantic sector of Antarctica; largest source of Deep Bottom Water.

West Bay West arm of St. Andrew Bay near Panama City, Florida; site of former shrimp farm.

Willapa Bay North of Columbia River on Washington coast; noted for oysters.

Wood Lakes Chain of several sockeye nursery lakes that flow into lower Nushagak River on north side.

Wrangell Fishing town near mouth of Stikine River; once Hudson Bay Company trading post.

Yakutat Large deep fjord about halfway between Cape Spencer and Prince William Sound.

Yaquina Bay Sheltered bay on Oregon coast 100 miles (160 km) south of Columbia River.

Yellow Sea Between Korea and China.

Yes Bay Very short stream near sea level with large lake on northwestern shore of Behm Canal, southeastern Alaska; once site of large sockeye salmon hatchery and noted for large-sized sockeye very low in fat.

Yumurtalik From "yumurta," Turkish for "eggs," means place of the eggs; bay on north side of Gulf of Iskenderun, Turkey, where mullet are fenced in while young and later taken chiefly for their roe.

appendix D

❧ Glossary

abyssal Refers to the deeper portions of the oceans.

abyssal plain More or less flat bottom of the deep ocean between the continental rise and mid-oceanic ridges; may be broken by abyssal hills.

abyssobenthic Bottom-dwelling species below 4000 m or the 4° C isotherm.

abyssopelagic Species in water column below 4000 m or the 4° C isotherm.

acclimation Holding of experimental animals for a specified period of time at a particular level of a variable prior to exposure to other levels of the variable. Acclimation is important because it usually extends the limits of the range of a variable tolerated by an organism. Animals held at low oxygen levels respond by a rise in hemoglobin content of the blood that permits them to withstand lower oxygen levels than animals not so acclimated.

acclimatization Adjustment of an organism to a new or strange environment.

adductor Muscle or muscles attached to both valves of a bivalve mollusk to control shell movements. Oysters and scallops possess only a posterior adductor muscle, which is the edible portion of a scallop. Clams and cockles have posterior and anterior adductor muscles of about equal size. In mussels the anterior adductor is much smaller than the posterior adductor. In the oyster the semitranslucent central portion of the adductor muscle closes the shell very quickly but soon relaxes (hence the name "quick" muscle). The opaque outer portion of the muscle (the "catch" muscle) contracts relatively slowly but can remain contracted for periods of several days or even weeks without relaxing, thus protecting the oyster against unfavorable conditions such as freshets or temporary pollution, since whenever the entire adductor muscle relaxes the ligament that joins the two valves together automatically forces the oyster to open.

adfluvial Applied to fishes descending to a lake instead of to the sea. *See* anadromous.

adiabatic Refers to a temperature change without exchange of heat, as water is warmed by compression and cooled by expansion.

adipose fin Small fleshy second dorsal fin lacking rays or spines occurring in Salmonidae and a few related families.

advection Movement of water masses in a horizontal plane.

aerobic Organisms requiring oxygen; usually applied to bacteria.

allochthonous Organisms or other material arising in another habitat.

ambergris Waxylike substance formed in the rectum or rectum and descending colon of male sperm whales. Usually it contains fragments of the chitinous beaks of squids and perhaps fragments of the calcareous skeleton or "pen bone" of certain species. It has a musky odor and is used as a fixative in expensive perfumes but has lost much of its former value owing to the synthesis of other fixatives.

ammocoete Wormlike larval stage of the lamprey. After living for a few years buried in the sandy mud of stream bottoms it transforms into the adult stage.

anadromous Species spawning in fresh water that make some or most of their growth during a visit or visits to the sea.

456

anaerobic Organisms able to live in the absence of oxygen; usually applied to bacteria.

annulus Mark on a scale, bone, fin ray, otolith, or shell formed once a year during a period when the rate of growth becomes slow.

anomaly Average deviation (plus or minus) of a set of values from an average curve.

antennae Paired preoral feelers. In Crustacea the first smaller pair are called antennules.

antennules First pair of feelers in Crustacea.

archibenthic Bottom-dwelling species on the continental slope below the edge of the shelf down to 4000 m or the 4° C isotherm.

autochthonous Organisms or material arising in the same habitat.

autolysis Process of organism's own enzymes breaking down the dead organism without the aid of bacteria.

autotomy Power of self-amputation whereby an organism, because of injury to a part or to escape from an enemy, can cast off an appendage or other part at a definite breaking point. The part is usually regenerated within one to several molts.

autotrophic Applied to plants and some protista (e.g., dinoflagellates) that can produce organic matter from inorganic matter in the presence of carbon dioxide, water, and light; called photosynthesis.

available *See* vulnerable.

axenic Axenic culture of an organism contains no other organisms. A unialgal culture containing bacteria is not axenic.

bacteria Very small unicellular fungilike organisms 1 to 5 μ in size, usually with a rigid cellulose cell wall. A very few have chlorophyll-like pigments and carry on photosynthesis. They do not liberate molecular oxygen in the process but release other substances. The great majority are heterotrophic; only a few are photosynthetic or chemotrophic.

baleen Whalebone; the horny plates attached to the upper jaw of baleen whales through which water is strained to capture krill or small fishes; once a very expensive product used principally in the manufacture of corsets.

barbel Fleshy, often elongated, projection(s) found in catfish, cods, sturgeon, etc., below the lower jaw, under the snout, or around the mouth.

bathypelagic Species living in the water column between about 1000 and 4000 m or the 4° C isotherm.

bathythermograph (BT) Oceanographic instrument to record temperature vs depth by tracing on a coated glass slide. Instrument can be used to record while a vessel is under way.

benthopelagic Species varying their habitat seasonally between the bottom and the near-surface portion of the water column, e.g., *Pollachius virens* and *Anoplopoma fimbria*.

benthos Bottom-dwelling (benthic) organisms.

berried *See* sponge.

bioassay Determination of the effect of varying concentrations of a substance or of varying physical conditions or stresses on living organisms by testing these materials or conditions against living organisms under standardized conditions.

biochemical oxygen demand (BOD) Decrease in oxygen content, measured in milligrams per liter of water, while held in the dark at a certain temperature over a certain period of time, caused by metabolism of organic matter.

biological indicators Organisms that by their presence or absence tend to indicate environmental conditions.

bioluminescence Light produced by living organisms. In fishes it is produced in two ways: (1) by photophores under nervous control of the fish and (2) by luminous bacteria living in pockets in the skin. Such fishes are principally deep- or midwater inhabitants. Many protista, e.g., *Noctiluca,* also produce bioluminescence that betrays the presence of surface-dwelling fish because they emit light when disturbed. This is important in locating school fishes at night.

biomass *See also* standing crop. 1. The total wet weight of all living organisms beneath a unit surface area of water or in a specified volume of water. 2. Total weight of a particular organism. 3. Total particulate organic matter present by unit area or volume.

biometry Use of statistical methods to solve biological problems.

biota All fauna and flora.

bivalve Mollusk with a paired shell usually connected by a hinge that permits the two valves to open or close.

boat Fishing craft of less than 5 net tons capacity.

boreal zone Subarctic zone; usually considered as waters lying north (or south) of the thermosphere (between the arctic and subtropical zones) with a water temperature range of 3° to 8° C.

box Pair of empty oyster valves. The fact they have not separated indicates the recent death of the oyster.

brackish Water that is slightly salty.

branchiostegals Bony rays supporting the branchiostegal membrane that encloses the gill chamber ventrally.

brood year Year in which all of the fish of a particular age were spawned.

brownbow Hybrid of rainbow trout, *Salmo gairdneri,* × male brown trout, *Salmo trutta.*

buffered Buffered solution contains weak acids and their salts in solution, which tends to stabilize the pH despite small additions of acid or base.

bushel U. S. standard bushel for oyster meats, etc. has a volume of 2150.4 cubic inches. Out of 17 Atlantic and Gulf coast states only five use the U. S. bushel. The other state bushels vary from 2148.4 to 5343.9 cubic inches.

byssus Horny threadlike structure in mussels and some other mollusks attaching them to the substrate.

cabelling Sinking of water caused by the horizontal mixing of two water masses of the same density but of different temperatures and salinities. Because of the nonlinear relationship between the temperature and density of seawater and the practically linear relationship between salinity and density, a mixture of the two water masses will increase the density, and the resulting mixture will sink to its own density level. This process can be of considerable magnitude in such cases as the meeting of the warm Gulf Stream with the cold Labrador Current.

caecum (pl. **caeca**) Blind sac(s) from the anterior end of the intestine; pyloric caeca.

canvass System of gathering statistics on fishery production by making interviews, usually annually.

carapace Exoskeletal fold or plate covering the head and thorax. In decapod crustaceans it is fastened along the back but the sides are free and cover the gills, which are between the body and the carapace.

carrying capacity Maximum quantity of fish that any particular body of water can support over a long period. Temporary carrying capacity may be much higher.

cascading Process in which winter-cooled water sinks and flows off the continental shelf into deeper water and is replaced by surface water of lower nutrient content.

catadromous Species spawning in the sea that make some or most of their growth in fresh water.

chela (pl. **chelae**) Pincer. An appendage, especially of Crustacea, ending in a pincer is termed a chelate appendage or a chela.

chemotrophic Organisms (chiefly bacteria) that form organic chemicals from inorganic chemicals utilizing for energy in lieu of light such substances as ammonia, nitrite, methane, hydrogen, and hydrogen sulfide.

chitin Nitrogen-containing polysaccharides. Chitin, which may be reinforced with deposits of calcium, forms most of the exoskeleton of crustaceans and other arthropods.

chlorophyll Green coloring matter in living cells necessary in photosynthesis.

circuli Fine, usually concentric, lines on a fish scale. On most scales it is the narrower spacing between circuli in winter that forms the "annulus." In clupeids the annulus usually cuts across the circuli, which are not concentric.

claspers Modified pelvic fins of male sharks, rays, and chimaeras for transfer of sperm to the females.

cline Gradient; often used to describe a gradient in a taxonomic character that is associated with a parallel gradient in some environmental variable.

cloaca Common duct or passage for reproductive and excretory products.

coccolithophore Very small, globular, unicellular, brown alga, usually with two flagella and two chromatophores; chiefly present in warm seas. The surface of the cell has buttonlike shields of calcium carbonate that contribute to *Globigerina* oozes.

compensation point Depth at which light is just sufficient for the oxygen produced by an organism in photosynthesis to balance the oxygen it utilizes in respiration.

competition 1. Interaction between organisms for food, shelter, or other survival factor that is injurious to one or both groups. Interspecific competition is between species; intraspecific competition is between individuals of the same species. 2. Effect of a unit of fishing effort in reducing the size of the catch of another unit of fishing effort.

conchiferous stage Any stage of a molluscan larva after shell formation has commenced.

confluent Meeting smoothly without a notch.

conservative elements Applied to those chemical substances in seawater that tend to bear a constant ratio to the salinity throughout the world ocean.

consumers Organisms nourished by particulate organic matter.

continental rise Gradually sloping bottom between the steep continental slope and the abyssal plain.

continental shelf Submerged edge of a continent (or island) to where it begins a steep descent. This can be as shallow as 20 m (coral shelves) or as deep as 500 m, e.g., portions of the Barents Sea. Legally, it is sometimes considered to be landward of the 200 m or the 100 fm contour.

continental slope Steep slope seaward of the edge of the continental shelf.

contranatant Applied to a return migration of an organism toward its birthplace.

convection Vertical movement of water masses.

convection cells Rolling cylinders of water that form at about a right angle to the prevailing wind. Adjacent cells rotate in opposite directions. The depth of the cells and the speed of rotation are directly related to wind speed. These rotating cells result in an upward flow between every other cell with a downward flow between each two upward flows. This mechanism produces the streaks or slicks observed on a breezy day, since the wind cannot create effective friction on a sinking surface. Slightly motile organisms such as dinoflagellates can, when the breeze is gentle, maintain their surface position against the downward current and thus become concentrated in streaks.

convergence Imaginary line along which two surface currents meet; one or both water masses may sink.

coral shelf Continental or island shelf of coral usually ending at about 20 m, the maximum depth for shelf-building corals.

coriolis force (effect) Effect on the direction of flow of water masses caused by the spinning of the earth.

corselet Band of modified scales on the anterior of the body of tunas.

cran British measure originally 37.5 Imperial gallons averaging over 1000 herrings; now 5.5 crans weigh 1 metric ton.

cryptodepression 1. Area of an inland sea or lake (or dry depression) that is below sea level. 2. Depth below sea level of the bottom of such an area.

crystalline style Gelatinous rod occurring only in oysters and other bivalves and certain snails. It is formed in a style sac and projects across the stomach cavity, pressing against the gastric shield. It is rotated continuously by cilia, thus mixing food and bringing it into contact with the stomach walls. It also releases digestive enzymes as it wears off against the gastric shield.

ctenoid scale Teleost scale with small sharp spines or ctenii on the posterior margin.

culling Discarding at sea unwanted organisms that occur in the catch. These may be unsalable because of species or small size.

cultch Shells or other material, spread over oyster grounds, on which oyster larvae can attach and develop into spat.

curvilinear relation Result when changes in a variable that are associated with changes in another variable differ significantly from a straight line.

cycloid scale Teleost scale with smooth edges.

cyclonic eddy Surface eddy (usually wind-driven) that rotates counterclockwise in the northern hemisphere and clockwise in the southern hemisphere.

deciduous Refers to scales loosely attached, especially in clupeids.

demersal Benthic; dwelling on or close to the bottom; also applied to adhesive spawn adhering to the bottom.

denatant Applied to migration of an organism away from its place of birth.

denitrification Reduction from nitrate to nitrite and further to elemental nitrogen.

density-dependent Describes predators whose abundance is largely controlled by the level of abundance of a certain species or type of prey; opposite of density-independent.

dentary Bone, usually carrying teeth, forming anterior portion of each lower jaw.

depuration (purification) Elimination or reduction of harmful quantities of pathogenic bacteria from live shellfish.

detritus Finely divided organic material from animal and plant remains.

diatom Unicellular primitive plant enclosed in a siliceous frustule. It is a principal component of the plankton.

diatom ooze Siliceous oceanic sediment derived chiefly from the shells of diatoms.

dimorphism Marked difference between the sexes of an organism in size, color, or form.

dinoflagellates Unicellular protista of the class Flagellata (or Mastigophora) with two flagella. Some are armored (usually a cellulose cuticle); others are naked. Many are autotrophic. A number of the species produce powerful toxins causing the dreaded red tides and paralytic shellfish poisoning.

divergence Imaginary line along which two surface currents flow apart. Deeper water usually rises between the two currents.

Doldrums Belt of calm and variable winds near the equator between the northeast and southeast trade winds.

drill Gastropod that feeds on oysters and other mollusks by making a hole in their shell with its radula.

ecdysis Molt in which the chitinous exoskeleton is shed.

ecology Study of the relationship of an organism to its environment.

ecosystem More or less self-sustaining biological area, e.g., a salt marsh or, in a larger sense, an estuary and the adjacent shelf with its array of adult organisms dependent on the estuary at some life history stage.

eelgrass True seed-producing bladelike marine plant.

elver Young eel that has metamorphosed; usually caught in estuaries or attempting to ascend streams.

embedded scales Completely enveloped in skin and thus without a free edge.

endemic Native to the locality.

endorheic Area or body of water in which evaporation exceeds freshwater input.

environmental limit Limit in numbers or biomass that a population can attain in a given environment.

epibenthic Benthic marine species living landward of the edge of the continental shelf.

epifauna Organisms dwelling on the surface of a firm substrate.

epilimnion Portion of a freshwater body lying above the thermocline.

epipelagic Species living close to the surface of the water column in the photic zone.

equilibrium Population is in equilibrium when births and deaths balance.

escapement Portion of a run of anadromous fish that escape capture either in the sea or the stream by fishermen while on a migration to the spawning area.

estuary Protected body of water in which the salinity departs significantly from the adjacent sea or ocean. Most estuaries have a lower salinity (positive estuary). Some have a higher salinity (negative estuary). Estuaries are characterized by a fluctuating salinity as opposed to the stable conditions in brackish seas or inland salt lakes.

ethology Study of behavior.

euryhaline Tolerant of wide changes in salinity; characteristic of most estuarine species and certain stages in the life history of many other species.

eutrophic Applied chiefly to lakes rich in nutrients, in which the hypolimnion usually becomes exhausted of oxygen during the summer.

exorheic Area or body of water in which freshwater input exceeds evaporation.

extrapolate To project a curve (function) beyond the range of the observed coordinates.

eye diameter Usually the greatest anterior-posterior diameter of the eye socket; can be diameter of the eyeball.

fecundity Reproductive potential as indicated by the size and number of mature ova in relation to the length or weight of the mature organism. It may also include the sex ratio of a population.

fetch Uninterrupted distance over which wind can blow to generate waves.

finfish Classes Cyclostomata, Elasmobranchii, and Pisces of the phylum Vertebrata; excludes other marine organisms.

finlets Small finlike structures lacking rigid supports occurring posterior to the main dorsal and anal fins in some fishes.

finnan haddie Lightly salted and lightly smoked fillets of haddock.

fjord Semienclosed body of water formed by glacial erosion in young mountains; typically deep, usually long and narrow, with deep shores and often with a sill. Although often classed as estuaries, they differ in almost all respects from the classic concept of an estuary.

flocculation Process whereby mineral and organic sediments carried into an estuary by a stream form aggregates and start to sink toward the bottom as the fresh waters of the stream mix with saline water.

fluvial Pertains to streams; also to organisms spending their entire life in moving fresh waters.

fluvial anadromous Anadromous fishes whose life histories do not normally require lakes in streams they ascend to spawn.

food chain Successive steps from the autotrophic bacteria and phytoplankton that can use inorganic nutrients (the base of the food chain or pyramid) to the zooplankton, forage fishes, and so on to the highest predators.

food web Pattern by which energy is transferred from one trophic level to another.

foot In describing mollusks, term used for the ventral surface of the body as modified for clinging, creeping, digging, or swimming (as in the cephalopods). In some bivalve mollusks the foot is present only in the larval form until after it has set.

forage fishes Small fishes that are normal prey for larger fishes.

forebay Impounded waters just above a dam.

fork length Length of a fish from the snout to the fork in the tail fin.

fouling organisms Organisms that attach to or penetrate firm substrates to the detriment of more desirable species or that interfere with the use of, or do damage to, marine equipment; may include barnacles, bryozoans, mussels, teredos, algae, etc.

fracture zones Large fissures on the ocean floor accompanied by mountains and escarpments and usually crossing midoceanic ridges at right angles.

genotype *See* phenotype.

gill arch One of the bony supports for attachment of gill rakers and gill membranes.

gill rakers Bony protuberances on anterior edge of the gill arches; normally short and sturdy in predator fishes, but long and slender in fishes subsisting chiefly on plankton.

glaciated shelf Continental shelf once occupied by glaciers; characterized by uneven bottom, moraines, and very large rubble.

Globigerina ooze Calcareous oceanic sediment derived chiefly from Foraminifera, especially *Globigerina*.

gonad Term including both ovaries and testes.

gravid fish Fish with mature gonads.

grilse Precocious salmon or anadromous trout

(usually a male) that has matured at a much smaller size, and usually at a younger age, than that of the normal adult fish.

groundfish New England term for fish living on or near the bottom and usually caught by otter trawl or longline, especially gadoids, flatfishes, and ocean perch.

gutted Fish from which the contents of the body cavity have been removed. It may or may not entail removal of the gills.

guyot Submarine mountain with a flat top rising at least 1 km above the adjacent ocean floor.

gyre Large oceanic eddy.

hermaphrodite Individual with both male and female functional organs. It may or may not be self-fertilizing.

heterocercal Upper lobe of caudal fin much larger than lower lobe and supported by the upturned end of the vertebral column.

heterotrophic Organisms requiring organic material for nourishment.

hinge Articulation between the two shells (valves) of a bivalve mollusk held together by a horny ligament.

holopelagic Pelagic species dwelling indifferently in the surface layers over both neritic and oceanic waters.

homocercal Caudal fin lobes of nearly equal or equal length and the vertebral column ending at the midbase of the caudal fin.

homoiosmotic Applied to organisms that attempt to control the concentration of their internal fluids against external differences.

hydrography Study of the physical and chemical attributes of a body of water.

hypolimnion Waters of a freshwater lake lying below the thermocline.

ichthyology Study of the classification and systematic relationships of fishes.

illicium Modified dorsal fin spine or ray forming a forward-directed whiplike structure, usually with an enlarged tip to attract prey, as in the angler fishes; it may be luminescent.

indigenous Species native to an area.

industrial fish Fish used for other than human food, such as canned or frozen pet or fur farm food, bait, or reduction.

infauna Organisms dwelling on or within a soft substrate.

intertidal Zone or area of the shore between high and low tide.

isohaline Contour of equal salinity.

isopleths Contours that delimit the values of a dependent variable plotted against two other variables as ordinate and abscissa.

isotherm Contour of equal temperature.

juvenile Immature organism that resembles an adult.

kelt Mature Atlantic salmon that has spawned and has not yet recovered its weight or silvery color; sometimes called "black" salmon.

kippered herring Herring are split open down the back without removing the head or backbone; the belly remains intact. They are brined for less than an hour and then smoked lightly. The product is highly perishable.

kokanee Small-sized freshwater race of the sockeye salmon, *Oncorhynchus nerka kennerlyi*.

krill Common name (Norwegian) for euphausiids, the principal diet of baleen whales.

kype Hooked prolongation of the upper jaw that develops in male salmon just previous to spawning.

labial palps Labial, pertaining to lips; in bivalves the palps surround the mouth and aid in sorting particles of food and detritus trapped in the train of mucus secreted by the gills.

lacustrine anadromous Anadromous fishes that normally spawn in streams containing lakes in which the young dwell.

landlocked Pertains especially to certain adfluvial and lacustrine populations of salmonids. These populations usually have access to the sea but have largely lost the anadromous habit.

larviparous *See* viviparous.

lateral line Row of modified scales, sometimes with branches, along the side and sometimes extending onto the head. The scales have pore-like openings to a sensory canal beneath.

limnic Pertains to fresh waters.

limnology Study of inland waters.

live weight Weight of entire organism, including all organs, gills, head, shell, or skeleton.

mariculture Commercial rearing of marine organisms.

maxillary Upper jawbone of fishes, comprising the whole jaw or only the posterior part; it may have teeth.

mean lethal dose (LD$_{50}$) Dose of a toxic substance that on the average kills 50% of animals in a specified time.

megalops Last larval stage in crabs.

meristic Pertains to segmentation of the body (metameres); describes such racial characters as dorsal and anal fin rays, scale rows, and vertebral numbers, which are correlated with the number of body segments. Recently term has been misused by some ichthyologists as pertaining to such enumeration characters as pyloric caeca and branchiostegal rays and even to morphologic characters.

meromictic Lake in which a layer of high-density water in the deeper portion does not take part in the annual turnover.

meroplankton Organisms occurring in the plankton during early life history stages before assuming either a free or attached benthic or nektonic existence.

mesobenthic Species living on the deeper portions of the continental shelf and down the slope to about 700 m.

microgram atom One millionth of the atomic weight of the element multiplied by grams.

micron One thousandth of a millimeter; usually designated by μ.

midoceanic ridge Ridge found in nearly all oceans approximately midway between the continents. It usually consists of two parallel mountain ranges with a rift valley between them, which appears to be the line along which the continents are drifting apart.

molt *See* ecdysis.

monsoon Strong wind that blows toward the Himalaya Mountains during the southern winter (wet season) and away from the mountains during the southern summer (dry season).

morphometric Describes racial characters based on measurement of body proportions.

mud line Maximum depth at which fine terrigenous mud forms on the sea bottom. Along exposed coasts it is usually about 100 fm (200 m).

nannoplankton Dwarf plankton; very small forms about 5 to 60 μ, such as smaller diatoms, dinoflagellates, coccolithophores, protozoans, and bacteria, that readily pass through a new No. 20 plankton net of bolting cloth with a mesh aperture of 0.076 mm. Forms smaller than 5 μ are called ultraplankton.

natural mortality Death of organisms from any causes other than fishing, usually expressed as an annual rate for a year class.

nekton Actively swimming organisms.

neritic Coastal waters, nearshore; often applied to all waters over the continental shelf.

nutrients Usually refers to dissolved nitrates, phosphates, and silicates plus trace elements necessary to the growth of phytoplankton.

oblique tow Sampling method in which a net is retrieved from the deepest point to the surface either by towing it for similar periods of time at each of regularly spaced depths or by reeling in the net at a constant speed while towing. This method has largely replaced the vertical tow through the water column with the classic Hensen net, which usually yields insufficient specimens.

oceanic Waters beyond the continental shelf.

oceanography Study of marine waters.

oligotrophic Lake with low fertility and normally a year-round oxygen sufficiency in the hypolimnion.

ooze Oceanic sediment.

opercle (operculum) flap of bone covering the gills of the higher fishes. Opercular bones are the opercle, preopercle, subopercle, and interopercle.

osmosis Passage of liquids through a semipermeable membrane. The movement is from the dilute to the more concentrated solution.

otoliths Earstones; aggregations of calcium carbonate contained in the semicircular canals on each side of the head. In teleosts there are three on each side, or six in all. The largest ones are used to determine the age of fishes, especially of those with undecipherable scales.

out-migration Describes a seasonal migration of young salmon, smelt, or other fish from a stream into a lake or sea.

overfishing Fishing with a sufficiently high intensity on all or on certain portions of a population so as to reduce the continuous annual surplus it should be capable of producing. Any fishing whatsoever reduces the number of a population, but all populations exhibit a greater or lesser degree of resistance by increased rates of growth and greater survival of young to the adult stage. Only when fishing reduces a population below the point where the forces of resistance balance fishing intensity can there be said to be overfishing.

overpopulation Level of abundance so high as to militate against future abundance or even to invite self-destruction.

oxygen minimum Stratum of water deficient in oxygen compared to the adjacent layers.

paralytic shellfish poisoning Serious condition caused by eating mollusks that have ingested toxic organisms, usually one of the dinoflagellates.

parr Young salmon and trout in fresh water before reaching the migratory stage. *See* smolt.

pelagic Species in the water column; those dwelling on or close to the bottom are benthic.

pelagic deposits Marine sediments not derived from the land; red clays and calcareous and siliceous oozes.

periostracum Horny outer exposed layer of a molluscan shell.

pH Hydrogen-ion concentration; expressed as the reciprocal of the common logarithm of the hydrogen-ion concentration in gram equivalents per liter. $pH = 7$ means that the hydrogen-ion concentration is 10^{-7}, or $1/10^{7}$, or $1/10,000,000$, or 0.0000001 normal. A pH of 7 is approximately neutral; a lower value of pH means increasing acidity and a higher value increasing alkalinity.

phenotype Morphologic aspect of an organism apart from its genetic properties. Two organisms may differ phenotypically through exposure to different environments but yet be similar genotypically.

photoperiodism Regulation of body functions in accordance with the frequency and duration of periods of light. Spawning may be hastened or induced in some species by a gradual increase or decrease in the length of exposure to light to simulate seasonal changes.

photosynthetic zone Surface waters to a depth beyond which light is insufficient for photosynthesis.

phytoplankton Producers; most of the diatoms, dinoflagellates, and other plants or protista capable of photosynthesis.

piscivorous Fish-eating; applied to predators subsisting chiefly on fishes.

plankton Very feebly swimming or floating organisms in the water column. *See* phytoplankton; zooplankton.

plasticity Ability of a species to adapt to varied habitats. Species that have been long subjected to a very stable environment may lose this ability.

pleopods Abdominal appendages in Crustacea anterior to the last appendages (which are part of the tail fan or uropods). In the caridean shrimps the fertilized ova are carried attached to the pleopods of the female.

poikilosmotic Organisms not regulating the concentration of body fluids against outside concentrations.

poikilotherm Cold-blooded vertebrate in which the temperature of the blood fluctuates widely in harmony with external temperatures. Among fishes the blood of the tuna, although fluctuating, remains much warmer than the surrounding water.

polar easterlies Winds blowing from the east close to the poles, e.g., along the coast of Antarctica.

Polar Front Boundary between subpolar and subtropical waters; also known as Arctic or Antarctic Convergence.

population Stock or race of a species that exists as a biological unit.

population pressure Condition of excessive numbers in relation to the space occupied. This often causes migration, presumably to readjust the numbers of individuals per unit of space.

predator Animal that kills and consumes other animals.

preopercle Bone on outside of operculum in front of the opercle bone.

prevailing westerlies Winds blowing from the west almost constantly, especially in the Southern Hemisphere. They originate at the Subtropical High, or Horse Latitudes, about 35° latitude in the Southern Hemisphere.

primary productivity Rate of formation of organic carbon by photosynthesis.

production *See* yield.

productivity Yield, either in the general sense of harvest of marine organisms or in the more specialized usage of the annual production of the basic food substance, plankton, in any particular body of water.

protandrous Describes change of sex in the individual organism. In some species all and in other species some or most of the younger organisms may spawn for the first time as males. Later most of them may change to females.

prototroch Ciliated band located slightly above the midline on an early larval stage of a mollusk or annelid.

pseudofeces False feces; waste material not taken into the digestive tract; applies especially to mollusks that entrap their food on a continuously exuded band of mucus.

pteropod ooze Calcareous ooze derived chiefly from the shells of pteropods (pelagic mollusks).

pumice Very porous (floating) stone ejected by volcanoes.

pycnocline Contour of equal density.

quasi-catadromous Species spawning in high salinity water, the young of which return to the lower salinity of the estuarine nursery grounds, e.g., blue crab, mullet, and menhaden.

quick-freezing Several methods have been developed to freeze tissues very rapidly so that the crystals that form in the protoplasm are too small to rupture the cell walls with the attendant loss of liquids.

race Denotes subspecific differences, often of an isolated population.

Radiolaria Large (50 μ to several millimeters) pelagic rhizopods usually with intricate siliceous skeletons. They capture diatoms and small zooplankton with their pseudopodia.

radiolarian ooze Siliceous ooze derived chiefly from the skeletons of radiolarians.

random Without choice. In random samples every individual of a group being sampled has an equal chance of being included in the sample.

recruit Young fish that has just become available (vulnerable) to the fishing gear. In long-lived species only a portion of a year class may be recruited each year until finally all are vulnerable.

recycling Refers to the breakdown of dead organisms into dissolved or particulate organic or dissolved inorganic form so that the material is again usable by living organisms.

redd Nest dug in a gravel bottom by a salmonid fish. It may contain two or more egg pits.

reduction Process whereby whole or discarded portions of marine organisms are converted into such products as meal, oil, and solubles.

relative abundance Measure or index of the size of a population in any particular year in relation to other years without reference to actual numbers or biomass.

relay To transplant shellfish from one bed to another.

relict Species or fauna that once occupied a much greater area; a remnant.

replication Repetition of each independent unit of an experiment two or more times in order to determine the experimental and random errors needed to judge the significance of the results of the test.

reproduction curve Curve of the numbers of adults in a population in successive years as the dependent variable *y* plotted against the numbers of their parents as the independent variable *x*.

reproductive potential Potential number of a species that will attain maturity from the spawning of each adult. Obviously the long-term average cannot exceed 1.0, but it varies both with environmental stress and with the size of the population itself, tending to increase as the size of the population decreases. It is this fact that permits the taking of large numbers without inevitably causing depletion.

residual salmon Sockeye salmon of the anadromous type that fail to migrate out of their nursery lake.

residual variation Amount of variation in a dependent variate unaccounted for after the variation caused by one or more independent variates has been removed.

rift valley Valley between the two parallel mountain ranges that form the midoceanic ridges.

river shelf Continental shelf off the mouth of a major river; the bottom is usually smooth.

roundfish Applied to fishes more or less round or oval in cross section as opposed to those dorsoventrally flattened. Used chiefly in reference to the benthic bank fishes.

salt wedge Layer or wedge of higher salinity water moving along the bottom toward the head of a typical estuary.

school More or less compact group of individuals acting in concert. Many species of schooling fish are rarely found alone; some form dense schools at certain seasons or periods for spawning or migration but scatter rather widely at other times.

scrod Smallest market size category of haddock or cod.

seamount Peaked-top submarine mountain rising at least 1 km above the adjacent ocean floor.

sea-run Anadromous; term may be applied to individuals in fluvial populations of which only varying portions enter the sea.

Secchi disk Disk 20 cm in diameter, usually with two white and two black quadrants. When lowered into the water, the average of the distance below the surface at which it disappears from sight and the distance at which it reappears while being hauled back is used as a rough measure of turbidity.

sediments Bottom deposits. Those derived from the land are terrigenous; the oceanic (pelagic) deposits consist of various oozes and red clay.

seiche Rhythmic vertical movement of the water surface in a confined or semiconfined body of water. It can be caused by a piling up of wind-driven water along one shore, by a very local change in barometric pressure, or by a rainstorm. A seiche is independent of tidal movement and the elapsed time between the height of a movement varies from a few minutes to several hours, according to the configuration of the basin.

selectivity Catching unequal proportions of a population considered in relation to some attribute such as length, weight, age, or sex. Gill nets are highly selective for size.

sessile Attached to the substrate, e.g., oysters or mussels, or very feebly motile, e.g., most clams.

significance Term reserved for the evaluation of a rigorous statistical test. When the probability of the occurrence of a particular event is only 1 in 20 or less ($P = 0.05$), the probability of its nonoccurrence is termed significant. When the probability is 1 in 100 or less ($P = 0.01$), it is termed highly significant. Because of the high variability in most biological data a probability of 0.05 is usually regarded with suspicion without replication.

silicoflagellate Small unicellular brown alga with one long flagellum and a latticed siliceous skeleton.

sill Shallower entrance to an enclosed body of deeper water.

siphon In bivalve mollusks the clams and cockles, which spend most of their time beneath the surface, have both an inhalant siphon to bring in water and obtain food and oxygen and an exhalant siphon to expel water and excretory products. Cockles, which spend much of their time on or near the surface, have extremely short siphons. Oysters and scallops do not have siphons. Mussels have an exhalant aperture formed by the adherent edges of the mantle. Deeply buried clams often have a long inhalant siphon usually held at or protruding from the bottom and a short exhalant siphon discharging into the substrate.

slope *See* continental slope.

smolt Young salmon or anadromous trout in which the scales have become silvery, hiding the underlying markings, in readiness for a marine existence. Young pink salmon, which go directly to the sea, have no parr marks to hide.

Southern Ocean Nondefinitive term for the portions of the Atlantic, Pacific, and Indian Oceans surrounding Antarctica; sometimes applied loosely to the Antarctic waters south of the Antarctic Convergence.

spat Young oyster that has settled on a substrate.

spent Applies to a fish that has recently spawned.

splake Hybrid of *Cristivomer namaycush* × male

Salvelinus fontinalis; called splake from lake trout and Canadian speckled trout (brook trout or eastern charr in the United States).

sponge (of Crustacea) Large mass of fertilized eggs carried by a female crustacean adhering to the abdomen and swimmerets. Females with large-sized attached eggs, e.g., lobster, are usually called "berried."

standing crop Total quantity at a given time of any species or of the total biomass in any body of water.

steelhead Anadromous rainbow trout, *Salmo gairdneri;* sometimes also applied to sea-run cutthroat trout, *S. clarki.*

stenohaline Lacking in ability to withstand wide changes in salinity.

straight-hinge larva Molluscan larva after the trochophore stage when the hinge of the early shell is straight.

stratified Applied to a lake or other water body during periods in which distinct differences in temperature or other characteristics exist between horizontal layers or strata.

substrate Materials comprising the bottom.

subtidal Waters below the low tide level; usually refers to below the mean low tide but can be used as below mean lower low water.

supersaturation Condition in which water contains over 100% of any or all atmospheric gases that it could hold at the ambient temperature and pressure while in equilibrium with the atmosphere.

swim bladder Gas bladder. Many fishes have a swim bladder in the body cavity. Some swim bladders are closed, and others have a pneumatic duct so that they can gulp air. The swim bladder serves several functions in different fishes such as a hydrostatic organ, a breathing apparatus, and a sound-producing organ.

swimmerets Pleopods; biramous appendages of abdominal segments in Crustacea.

taintor gate Row of taintor gates is often placed across the crest of the spillway of a dam. The gates are raised and lowered by an overhead traveling crane. Water leaves the forebay underneath the gate, often at a depth of 50 feet below the surface. The very sudden release of pressure as the water emerges from beneath the gate to slide down the spillway can be dangerous to young downstream migrants.

tambak Brackish water pond used for rearing herbivorous fishes and shrimps in Indonesia.

taxon (pl. **taxa**) Any of the formal groups to which living organisms are assigned, e.g., family, order, or genus.

temperature minimum stratum Stratum of water, especially prominent in the North Pacific, from about 40 to 200 m below the surface that is colder (in summer) than both the overlying and underlying layers because it lies above the depth of the winter cooling and below the depth of the summer warming.

terrigenous deposits Marine deposits derived from the land; seldom far from shore, but may slide down a submarine canyon.

territoriality Defense of a particular area against encroachment by other fish.

thermal dome Applied to areas, especially in tropical waters on the eastern boundaries of the oceans where the thermocline is shallow, in which cooler, nutrient-rich water is in the photosynthetic zone without usually being at the surface, e.g., the Costa Rica Dome in the eastern Pacific and the Guinea Dome in the eastern Atlantic.

thermocline Water layer with a rapid decrease in temperature with increasing depth; usually defined in fresh waters as a drop of $1°$ C/m.

thermohaline Shifts in water masses induced by density changes generated by variations in temperature and salinity.

thermosphere Surface lens of oceanic water that is above $8°$ C and lying between about $50°$ to $60°$ S lat. and about $40°$ to $50°$ N lat.

thigmotropic Pertains to an organism attracted to any solid body.

tidal pool Pool of entrapped water left by the receding tide.

tidal prism In any semienclosed body of water the volume of the water in the basin between high and low tide levels. It will vary somewhat with the lunar cycle.

tiger Hybrid of the brown trout, *Salmo trutta,* × male eastern charr, *Salvelinus fontinalis.*

trace elements Chemical elements necessary in trace amounts to sustain life.

trade winds Originate from the side of the Subtropical High opposite to the prevailing westerlies. They blow toward the equator from the northeast in the northern hemisphere and the southeast in the southern hemisphere.

transformation Changing of the units of measurement of data from common integers to logarithms, powers, arc sines, or some other form in order to facilitate statistical analysis.

trench Deep area close to the continental shelf, deeper than most of oceans and usually paralleling young mountains.

trochophore Early larval stage of a bivalve with a prototroch and a shell gland.

trophic levels Energy levels. Algae are in the primary trophic level. Herbivores are in the first consumer level.

turbidity current Bottom current generated by water of very high density, caused by excessive turbidity, which flows down a sloping bottom, especially down the sometimes very steep underwater canyons.

tychoplankton Forms of the littoral community occurring accidentally in the plankton, e.g., sessile diatoms broken off by turbulent water.

ultraplankton Extremely small forms at least under 5 μ in size.

umbo Usually peaked small portion of the adult bivalve shell near the hinge that represents the shell of the spat.

upwelling Slow vertical movement to the surface of deeper water, usually from between 50 and 300 m.

varve Annual layer of sediment. Such annual layers are usually detected by a seasonal difference in color, texture, or size of sediment particles or of some biological component of the sediment, e.g., seasonal deposits of pollen grains in freshwater lakes. Varves are of value in estimating the age of the sediments at various depths below the surface of the bottom.

veliger Free-swimming larval mollusk after development of the velum, a foot, and a shell.

velum Retractile bilobed rim with a preoral circlet of cilia in the veliger larvae of mollusks that is resorbed after setting.

vermiculations Wormlike, from Vermes; wavy markings usually on the dorsal surface as in mackerel or eastern charr.

vessel Fishing craft with a capacity of 5 net tons or more.

Vigneron-Dahl trawl Otter trawl rigged by connecting the wings of the trawl to the otter boards with long cables called pennants. This is done in most fish otter trawls; the long cables frighten the fish toward the net, increasing the effective width of the gear and resulting in larger catches.

viscosity Property of a liquid that presents a resistance to flow.

vital stain (dye) Stain used to color living organisms without causing harm; very useful in marking shrimp, small fishes, and other organisms in large numbers.

viviparous Live bearing. In invertebrates the fertilized ova are retained within the female and undergo growth and differentiation before they are released. In mollusks this is also called "larviparous."

vulnerable Describes the portion of a population liable to be captured by any particular type of gear. Some individuals, because of their size or mode of life, may be vulnerable (available) to one form of gear but not to another.

water column Vertical column of water extending from the surface to the bottom beneath any unit of surface area.

weir 1. In New England a herring trap in which the fish follow a barrier into an enclosure. 2. Fence or screen to obstruct fish passage in a stream so they may be counted. 3. Low dam for gauging water flow.

winterkill Killing of the fish in a shallow lake by freezing or by lack of oxygen when thick or snow-covered ice decreases photosynthesis.

year class All of the progeny of the reproduction from any particular year. In species with fluctuating spawning success the progeny of the successful spawning of one year class may dominate the population at successive ages for several years.

yield Annual harvest of desirable species from a body of water.

zoea Larval stage in some crustaceans. The eggs hatch into zoea larvae in crabs, but zoea are the third free-swimming larval stage in penaeid shrimp and in mysids.

zooplankton Faunal components of the plankton, including tintinnids, radiolarians, foraminifera; many small crustaceans such as copepods, ostracods, euphausiids, and amphipods; the jellyfishes and siphonophores; many worms; many mollusks such as pteropods and heteropods; and egg and larval stages of the majority of benthic and nektonic animals.

appendix E

Conversions

Length

1 inch = 2.54 cm = 25.4 mm
1 foot = 0.305 m = 30.5 cm = 305 mm = 0.1667 fm
1 yard = 0.914 m = 91.4 cm = 3 feet = 0.5 fm
1 mile = 1.609 km = 1609 m = 5280 feet = 0.869 nautical miles
1 nautical mile = 1.852 km = 1852 m = 6076 feet = 1.151 statute miles
1 fathom = 1.829 m = 6 feet
1 centimeter = 0.3937 inch = 10 mm
1 meter = 39.37 inch = 3.281 foot = 1.0936 yard = 100 cm = 0.5468 fm
1 kilometer = 0.6214 mile = 0.5400 nautical mile = 3281 feet = 546.8 fm

Area

1 acre = 0.4047 ha = 43,560 square feet
1 square mile = 2.59 km^2 = 259 ha = 640 acres = 0.7551 square nautical mile
1 square nautical mile = 3.4299 km^2 = 1.3243 square mile = 847.5 acres
1 hectare = 2.4711 acres = 0.00954 square mile = 10,000 m^2
1 kilometer^2 = 0.3861 square mile = 0.2916 square nautical mile

Volume

1 cubic foot = 0.0283 m^3 = 7.48 gallons = 28.316 liters
1 cubic yard = 0.7646 m^3 = 202 gallons = 764.5 liters
1 acre-foot = 43,560 cubic feet = 325,850 gallons = 2233.5 m^3
1 cubic mile = 4.1682 km^3
1 cubic nautical mile = 6.352 km^3
1,000,000 cubic feet = 22.95 acre-feet
1,000,000 gallons = 3.07 acre-feet
1 gallon = 3.78533 liters = 0.1337 cubic foot
1 meter^3 = 35.315 cubic feet = 1.3080 cubic yard
1 kilometer^3 = 0.23991 cubic mile = 0.1574 cubic nautical mile

Miscellaneous

1 acre-foot flows 0.5042 cubic feet/second for 1 day
1 cubic foot/second for 1 day requires 1.9837 acre-feet

Weight

1 pound = 0.4536 kg
1 ton = 0.9072 metric tons = 2000 pounds
1,000,000 pounds = 453.59 metric tons = 500 tons
1 metric ton = 1.1023 tons = 2204.6 pounds = 0.0022 million pounds
1 kilogram = 2.2046 pounds
1 pound/acre = 1.1209 kg/ha = 0.11209 g/m^2
1 metric ton/km^2 = 1 g/m^2 = 10 kg/ha = 2.855 tons/square mile
1 ton/acre = 2.2417 metric tons/ha

✿ Author index*

Abbott, R. T., 365
Adkins, G., 377, 380
Adler, C., 272
Ahlstrom, E. H., 240-241, 242, 246
Aldevice, D. F., 297-298
Aldrich, D. V., 63, 280
Alekin, O. A., 115
Alekseev, A. P., 168, 202
Allen, D. M., 347-348
Alverson, D. L., 53, 62, 75, 118, 120t, 344t, 345, 386, 387t, 392
Anderson, C. O., Jr., 269t
Anderson, W. W., 348
Aplin, J. A., 275
Asada, Y., 257, 264
Atkins, C. G., 152

Bader, R. G., 273, 287
Bailey, J. S., 115
Bailey, R. M., 385
Baker, R. C., 325
Baker, R. L., 272
Baltzo, C. H., 325
Banse, K., 45
Bardach, J. E., 313, 382
Barnaby, J. T., 225, 337
Barnes, H., 39
Barr, L., 348
Barraclough, W. E., 116
Bates, D. W., 297-298
Baxter, J. L., 241, 246

Baylor, E. R., 36, 39
Beam, M. G., 298
Bean, T. H., 335
Beardsley, A. J., 319
Beardsley, G. L., Jr., 362
Bell, F. H., 208-211, 392
Bell, M. C., 277
Belyanina, T. N., 264
Berg, L. S., 325
Bergman, P. K., 228, 234
Berner, L., Jr., 109, 128
Beverton, R. J. H., 246
Bieri, R., 77
Bigelow, H. B., 74-75, 78, 80-81, 208, **209**, 211, 289, 362, 386, 387t, 392
Blackburn, M., 111
Blacker, R. W., 345
Boerema, L. K., 128
Bond, L. H., 332
Borgstrom, G., 128
Bourne, N., 374
Breese, W. P., 45
Brett, J. R., 297-298
Brongersma-Sanders, M., 64
Bronikovsky, N., 64
Broom, J., 304, 313
Brown, R. P., 271
Buck, D. H., 278
Bull, H. O., 57
Bullis, H. R., Jr., 128
Butler, P. A., 55, **56**, 60, 62
Butler, T. H., 378, 380

Cable, L. E., 9
Cahn, A. R., 374

*Page numbers in boldface refer to a figure citation. Page numbers followed by a "t" refer to a table citation.

469

✿ Subject index*

---

*Page numbers in boldface refer to a figure citation. Page numbers followed by a "t" refer to a table citation.